Modern Trigonometry

Revised Edition

Modern Trigonometry

William Wooton

Edwin F. Beckenbach

O. Lexton Buchanan, Jr.

Mary P. Dolciani

Revised Edition

Editorial Adviser

Albert E. Meder, Jr.

Houghton Mifflin Company
Boston
Atlanta
Dallas
Geneva, Illinois
Hopewell, New Jersey
Palo Alto
Toronto

The Authors

William Wooton, former Professor of Mathematics, Los Angeles Pierce College. Mr. Wooton has taught mathematics at both the junior and senior high school levels. He has also been a team member of the NCTM summer writing projects.

Edwin F. Beckenbach, Professor of Mathematics, Emeritus, University of California, Los Angeles. Dr. Beckenbach has been a team member and coordinator of the NCTM summer writing projects for elementary mathematics teachers. He is currently serving as Chairman of the Committee on Publications of the Mathematical Association of America.

O. Lexton Buchanan, Jr., Resource Teacher for gifted students in the Fulton County, Georgia School System. Dr. Buchanan has been active in many areas of mathematics education, including writing projects, state mathematics organizations, and teacher training. He has taught mathematics at several high schools and universities.

Mary P. Dolciani, Professor of Mathematics, Hunter College, City University of New York. A member of the United States Commission on Mathematical Instruction, Dr. Dolciani has also been a director and teacher in National Science Foundation and New York State Education Department institutes for mathematics teachers, and Visiting Secondary School Lecturer for the Mathematical Association of America.

Editorial Adviser

Albert E. Meder, Jr., Professor of Mathematics and Dean of the University, Emeritus, Rutgers, The State University of New Jersey.

ISBN 0-395-21687-7

Contents

Chapter One   The Cosine and Sine Functions

Properties of Periodic Functions

1–1   **Periodic Functions**   1

Basic Circular Functions

1–2   **The Functions cos and sin**   5
1–3   **Values of cos x and sin x for Special Values of x**   10

Properties of Basic Circular Functions

1–4   **Addition Properties of cos**   15
1–5   **Deriving and Verifying Identities**   23
1–6   **Addition Properties of sin**   27

Graphs and Further Properties of Basic Circular Functions

1–7   **Graphs of cos and sin**   32
1–8   **Properties of cos and sin for 2x and $\dfrac{x}{2}$**   38
1–9   **Values for cos x and sin x**   40

Chapter Summary   44

Chapter Test   45

Computer Investigations   46

Chapter Two   Four More Circular Functions

The Tangent Function

2–1   **The Function tan**   49

The Reciprocal Circular Functions

2–2   **The Functions sec, csc, and cot**   56
2–3   **Graphs of sec, csc, cot**   60

Identities

2–4   **Additional Basic Identities**   64
2–5   **Working with Identities**   68

Chapter Summary 72

Chapter Test 73

Computer Investigations 74

Waves and the World We Live In 76

Chapter Three Applications of Circular Functions

Graphs

3–1 *Amplitude and Location* 79
3–2 *Periods and Phase Shifts* 83
3–3 *The Family y = a sin b(x − c) + d* 89
3–4 *Graphing by Addition of Ordinates* 92

Periodic Motion

3–5 *Uniform Circular Motion* 95
3–6 *Simple Harmonic Motion* 100

Chapter Summary 104

Chapter Test 104

Computer Investigations 105

Cumulative Review · Chapters 1–3 106

Chapter Four Inverses of Circular Functions

Principal Inverse Functions

4–1 *Inverses of cos and sin* 109
4–2 *Inverses of Other Circular Functions* 117
4–3 *Arc Lengths* 122

Solving Open Sentences

4–4 *Open Sentences Involving One Circular Function* 127
4–5 *Open Sentences Involving Two Circular Functions* 132

Chapter Summary 137

Chapter Test 138

Environmental Exploration 139

Chapter Five   Trigonometric Functions

Basic Concepts

5–1	Angle Measure	143
5–2	Trigonometric Functions	148
5–3	Trigonometric Identities	152

Values for Trigonometric Functions

5–4	Tables for Trigonometric Functions	153
5–5	Describing an Angle by Its Terminal Side	158
5–6	Trigonometric Equations and Inverse Functions	161

The Solution of Triangles

5–7	Right Triangles	164
5–8	The Law of Cosines	170
5–9	The Area of a Triangle; The Law of Sines	173
5–10	The Ambiguous Case	177
	Chapter Summary	179
	Chapter Test	180
	Computer Investigations	181

Chapter Six   Vectors

Properties of Vectors

6–1	Vectors and Their Geometric Representation	185
6–2	Basis Vectors	192
6–3	The Inner Product of Two Vectors	198

Applications

6–4	Free Vectors; Navigational Applications	204
6–5	Vector Applications to Forces	211

Polar Coordinates and Graphs

6–6	Polar Coordinates	216
6–7	Graphs of Polar Equations	224
	Chapter Summary	230
	Chapter Test	232
	Cumulative Review · Chapters 4–6	232
	World Maps	234

Chapter Seven   Complex Numbers

The Field of Complex Numbers

7–1   *Addition and Multiplication of Complex Numbers*   239
7–2   *Division and Subtraction of Complex Numbers*   242
7–3   *Complex Numbers in Standard Form*   245
7–4   *Graphical Representation of Complex Numbers*   249

Polar Representation of Complex Numbers

7–5   *Polar Form for Complex Numbers*   254
7–6   *De Moivre's Theorem*   258
7–7   *Roots of Complex Numbers*   261

Chapter Summary   265

Chapter Test   266

Exploring the Universe   267

Chapter Eight   Matrices

Operations with Matrices

8–1   *Basic Properties of 2 × 2 Matrices*   271
8–2   *Products of 2 × 2 Matrices*   277
8–3   *The Inverse of a Matrix*   282

Matrix Representation of Complex Numbers and Vectors

8–4   *Complex Numbers and Matrices*   287
8–5   *Vectors and Matrices*   291
8–6   *Rotations*   298

Chapter Summary   302

Chapter Test   303

Computer Investigations   304

Chapter Nine   Infinite Series
and Circular Functions

Fundamental Concepts

9–1   *Sequences*   307
9–2   *Infinite Series*   311

Some Important Sequences and Series

9–3	*Geometric Sequences and Series*	3
9–4	*Power Series*	319
9–5	*Binomial Series*	323

Infinite Series and Circular Functions

9–6	*Series for cos x and sin x*	328
9–7	*Hyperbolic Functions*	332
	Chapter Summary	335
	Chapter Test	337
	Cumulative Review · Chapters 7–9	338
	Synthesis and Analysis of Waves	340
	Computer Investigations	343
	Comprehensive Test	345
	Appendix A · Sets, Relations, and Functions	356
	Appendix B · Using Logarithms	369
	Appendix C · Spherical Trigonometry	382
	Appendix D · Graphs of Pure Waves	390
	Tables	391
	Summary of Formulas	409
	Glossary	414
	Index	425

List of Symbols

	ımbers	3
	's	3
	is in	3
	abscissa u and ordinate v	6
	...ction	6
sın	the sine function	6
$\angle$**ABC**	the angle **ABC**, also denoted B	10
$\triangle$**ABC**	the triangle **ABC**	10
$d(\overline{\textbf{AB}})$	the length of line segment $\overline{\textbf{AB}}$; distance from point **A** to point **B**	10
$\doteq$	is approximately equal to	12
$\overset{\frown}{\textbf{DE}}$	the arc **DE**	16
tan	the tangent function	49
sec	the secant function	56
csc	the cosecant function	56
cot	the cotangent function	57
$\overrightarrow{\textbf{OS}}$	the ray **OS**	95
ω	the rotational velocity	95
R^{-1}	the inverse relation of R	109
Cos, Sin, Tan, Cot, Sec, Csc	the principal circular functions	111, 112, 117
$\text{Cos}^{-1}, \text{Sin}^{-1},$ $\text{Tan}^{-1}, \text{Cot}^{-1},$ $\text{Sec}^{-1}, \text{Csc}^{-1}$	the principal inverse circular functions	111, 113, 117
$m^{\circ}(\alpha)$	the degree measure of angle α	144
$m^{\text{R}}(\alpha)$	the radian measure of angle α	144
x^{R}	x radians	144
θ^{C}	θ centangles	147
$1'$	1 minute; $\frac{1}{60}$ degree	153
$1''$	1 second; $\frac{1}{60}$ minute	153
m	the slope of a line	154
v, $\vec{\text{v}}$, (x, y)	vectors	186
$\|\textbf{v}\|$	the norm of vector **v**	186
0	the zero vector	187

V	the set of two-dimensional vectors	188
r	scalar	188
$\mathbf{i}, \mathbf{j}$	the unit orthogonal vectors $(1, 0)$, $(0, 1)$	193
$\mathbf{u} \cdot \mathbf{v}$	the inner product of vectors $\mathbf{u}$ and $\mathbf{v}$	198
$\mathbf{a}_u$	component of $\mathbf{a}$ parallel to $\mathbf{u}$	201
(ρ, θ)	polar coordinates of a point	216
z	complex number	240
C	the set of complex numbers	240
$\bar{z}$	the conjugate of z	244
i	the complex number $(0, 1)$; $\sqrt{-1}$	246
$|z|$	the absolute value of the complex number z	249
$\rho \operatorname{cis} \theta$	$\rho(\cos \theta + i \sin \theta)$	255
$\begin{bmatrix} a & b \\ c & d \end{bmatrix}$	2×2 matrix	272
O	the zero matrix	272
$S_{m \times n}$	the set of matrices of order $m \times n$ (m rows, n columns)	274
I	the identity matrix, $\begin{bmatrix} 1 & 0 \\ 0 & 1 \end{bmatrix}$	278
A^{-1}	the multiplicative inverse of matrix A	282
$\delta(A)$	the determinant of matrix A	283
S_R	the set of matrices of the form aI	287
J	the matrix $\begin{bmatrix} 0 & 1 \\ -1 & 0 \end{bmatrix}$	288
a_n	the nth term of a sequence	307
$\{a_n\}$	sequence	307
$\lim\limits_{n \to \infty} s_n$	the limit of sequence $\{s_n\}$	308
$\sum\limits_{i=1}^{n} a_i$	the nth term of a sequence of partial sums	312
$\sum\limits_{i=1}^{\infty} a_i$	the summation form for the series $a_1 + a_2 + a_3 + \cdots + a_n + \cdots$	312
$n!$	n factorial: $n(n - 1)(n - 2) \cdots (2)(1)$	324
e	$\lim\limits_{n \to \infty} \left(1 + \dfrac{1}{n}\right)^n \doteq 2.718$	326
cosh, sinh, tanh, coth, sech, csch	hyperbolic functions	333

Chapter One

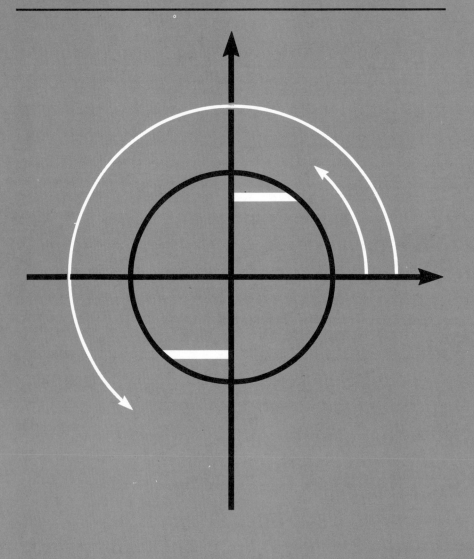

The Cosine and Sine Functions

OBJECTIVES

1. *To define the periodic functions cosine and sine.*
2. *To find exact values of cos x and sin x for some special values of x.*
3. *To derive simple reduction formulas for sine and cosine and prove simple identities involving sin x and cos x.*
4. *To graph the cosine and sine functions over specified intervals of values of x.*
5. *To derive and use simple identities involving sin 2x, cos 2x, sin $\frac{x}{2}$, and cos $\frac{x}{2}$.*

Properties of Periodic Functions

1–1 *Periodic Functions*

The continuous motion of the hands of a clock as they revolve to indicate the endlessly repeating hours of the day suggests a simple model for periodically repeating phenomena. Such phenomena may be described mathematically by *periodic functions*, some of which are defined by means of a unit circle. We begin with an example of one kind of periodic function and then give a general definition.

If you divide any integer by 5, the quotient will be an integer, and the remainder will be one of the members of the set $\{0, 1, 2, 3, 4\}$. You can use this fact to define a function f having the set of integers as domain and $\{0, 1, 2, 3, 4\}$ as range. Thus

$f = \{(x, f(x)): x \text{ is an integer and } f(x) \text{ is the remainder (nonnegative) when } x \text{ is divided by 5}\}.$

Some ordered pairs in f are tabulated and graphed below.

x	-5	-4	-3	-2	-1	0	1	2	3	4	5	6	7	8	9	10
$f(x)$	0	1	2	3	4	0	1	2	3	4	0	1	2	3	4	0

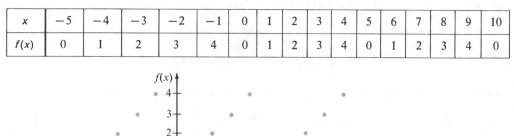

FIGURE 1–1

You can see that the elements of the range, $\{0, 1, 2, 3, 4\}$, are paired repeatedly with elements of the domain that are 5 units apart. For example,

$$f(1) = 1 \quad \text{and} \quad f(1 + 5) = f(6) = 1,$$
$$f(-2) = 3 \quad \text{and} \quad f(-2 + 5) = f(3) = 3,$$
$$f(-5) = 0 \quad \text{and} \quad f(-5 + 5) = f(0) = 0.$$

That is, for each x in the domain of f, it is true that $f(x + 5) = f(x)$.

Functions with this "repeating" property are called *periodic functions*, and the difference between any two elements of the domain corresponding to the same value of the function is called a *period* of the function. In this case, -5, 5, and 10 are all periods of the function f. The least positive period, 5, is called the *fundamental period* of f.

We define a periodic function as follows:

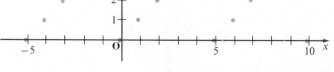

Suppose that for a nonconstant function f there is a nonzero number p such that for every number x in the domain of f, the numbers $x + p$ and $x - p$ are also in the domain of f, and

$$f(x + p) = f(x).$$

Then f is said to be a **periodic function** and the number p is said to be a **period** of f. If a periodic function f has a *least positive period* p, then p is called the **fundamental period** of f.

Example   Let g be the periodic function with domain the set of integers and with fundamental period the least period consistent with the data in the table:

x	1	2	3	4	5	6	7	8	9	10
$g(x)$	0	3	6	9	12	15	0	3	6	9

State: **(a)** the fundamental period of g
      (b) $g(20)$ **(c)** $g(-10)$

Solution   **(a)** The values repeat in the sequence 0, 3, 6, 9, 12, 15. Hence, the fundamental period of g is 6.
(b) Since the greatest multiple of 6 less than 20 is 18, we have
$$g(20) = g(2 + 18) = g(2) = 3.$$
(c) Since $-10 = 2 + (-12)$,
$$g(-10) = g(2 + (-12)) = g(2) = 3.$$

Throughout the remainder of this book, frequent use will be made of the following notation:

The set of all real numbers is denoted by the symbol $\mathfrak{R}$.

The set of all integers, $\{\ldots, -3, -2, -1, 0, 1, 2, 3, \ldots\}$, is denoted by J.

The symbol $\in$ is often used in conjunction with a variable. For example, "$k \in J$" means "k is any element of the set J," or "k is any integer."

Exercises 1–1

Each numbered row below shows values of a function f having the set of integers as domain. In each case, assume that f is periodic with fundamental period the least period that is consistent with the data and state: (a) The fundamental period a of f, (b) $f(20)$, (c) $f(-10)$.

		x	0	1	2	3	4	5	6	7	8	9	10
A	**1.**	$f(x)$	3	4	5	6	3	4	5	6	3	4	5
	2.	$f(x)$	1	3	5	7	9	1	3	5	7	9	1
	3.	$f(x)$	1	0	−1	0	1	0	−1	0	1	0	−1
	4.	$f(x)$	0	1	0	1	0	1	0	1	0	1	0
	5.	$f(x)$	−2	−1	0	1	2	1	0	−1	−2	−1	0
	6.	$f(x)$	−2	−1	3	1	−2	−1	3	1	−2	−1	3

B **7.** Given that f is a periodic function whose domain is $\mathfrak{R}$ (the set of all real numbers) and whose fundamental period is p, which of the following are *always* equal to $f(p)$? Justify each of your answers.

  (a) $f(2p)$ **(c)** $f\left(\dfrac{1}{p}\right)$ **(e)** $f(\tfrac{1}{2}p)$ **(g)** $f(-2p)$

  (b) $f(3p)$ **(d)** $f(0)$ **(f)** $f(-p)$ **(h)** $f(p^2)$

8. Given that f is a periodic function whose domain is $\mathfrak{R}$ and whose fundamental period is p, if x denotes *any* real number, which of the following are *always* equal to $f(x)$? Justify each of your answers.

  (a) $f(x + p)$ **(c)** $f(x - p)$ **(e)** $f(-p)$ **(g)** $f(x^2)$
  (b) $f(p)$ **(d)** $f(0)$ **(f)** $f(2x)$

Each of the functions in Exercises 9–12 is periodic and has domain $\mathfrak{R}$. Graph each function over the interval given. State the fundamental period.

Example $f(x) = x - k$ if $k - 1 \le x < k$, k any integer; $-3 \le x < 2$

Solution   For each integer k, you obtain an interval, $\{x: k - 1 \le x < k\}$, of the domain of f. The length of each such interval is 1. The interval* $-3 \le x < 2$ is the union of five such intervals:

$$f(x) = \begin{cases} x + 2 & \text{if } -3 \le x < -2 \text{ (for } k = -2) \\ x + 1 & \text{if } -2 \le x < -1 \text{ (for } k = -1) \\ x & \text{if } -1 \le x < 0 \text{ (for } k = 0) \\ x - 1 & \text{if } 0 \le x < 1 \text{ (for } k = 1) \\ x - 2 & \text{if } 1 \le x < 2 \text{ (for } k = 2) \end{cases}$$

The graph of f is shown in the figure, and f is periodic with fundamental period 1.

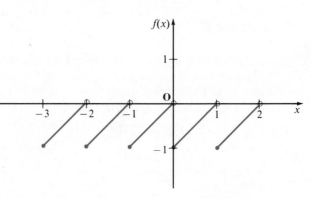

C **9.** $f(x) = k - x$ if $k - 1 \le x < k$, k any integer; $-1 \le x < 3$

10. $g(x) = x - 3k$ if $3k \le x < 3k + 3$, k any integer; $-6 \le x < 9$

---

*More precisely, $\{x: -3 \le x < 2\}$. We shall often use an abbreviated form like that shown above.

11. $h(x) = \begin{cases} x - 4k & \text{if } 4k - 1 \le x < 4k + 1 \\ x - 4k - 2 & \text{if } 4k + 1 \le x < 4k + 3, \ k \text{ any integer}; \ -5 \le x < 9 \end{cases}$

12. $g(x) = \begin{cases} (x - k)^2 & \text{if} \quad k \le x < k + 1 \\ 2 + k - x & \text{if } k + 1 \le x < k + 2, \ k \text{ any } \textit{even} \text{ integer}; \ 0 \le x < 6 \end{cases}$

Basic Circular Functions

1–2 *The Functions cos and sin*

In this book, we shall be concerned with a special class of periodic functions. Because a **unit circle**, or circle with radius 1, is used in defining these functions, they are called **circular functions**.

In a uv-plane, consider the unit circle that has its center at the origin. The equation of this circle is

$$u^2 + v^2 = 1.$$

Now imagine an x number line, with the same scale as that on the u- and v-axes, that is tangent to the circle at the point $(1, 0)$ on the circle and the point $\mathbf{O}$ on the line (Figure 1–2).

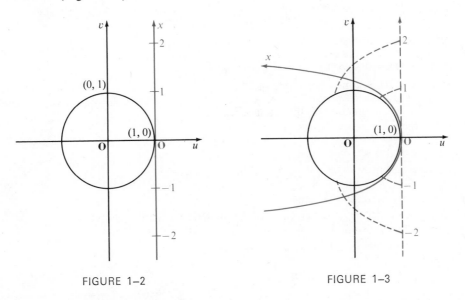

FIGURE 1–2   FIGURE 1–3

If you think of the line as being completely flexible, you can visualize the process of endlessly winding both halves of it around the circle—the positive ray going in the counterclockwise direction and the negative ray in the clockwise direction. Each number x on the number line will wind into one and only one point on the circle (Figure 1–3).

Note, however, that each time either ray completes one loop around the circle, another real number is paired with each point of the circle. Thus, each point of the circle is associated with infinitely many real numbers, some positive and some negative. Since the circumference of the unit circle is 2π, any two real numbers that differ by 2π (or by an integral multiple of 2π) will wind into the same point on the circle. Thus, if the real number x is associated with the point $\mathbf{P}(u, v)$ on the circle, then so are all the numbers

$$x + k(2\pi),$$

where $k \in J$ (Figure 1–4).

This winding process, associating real numbers x with points $\mathbf{P}(u, v)$ on the unit circle, establishes a function

$$\{(x, (u, v))\},$$

with domain the set $\mathcal{R}$ of real numbers x and range the set of real-number pairs (u, v) satisfying the equation

$$u^2 + v^2 = 1. \tag{1}$$

Further, this function is periodic, with fundamental period 2π, as noted above.

It is more convenient and useful, however, to consider u and v separately, and thus to deal with two functions:

$$\{(x, u): u \text{ is the first coordinate of } \mathbf{P}\}$$
$$\{(x, v): v \text{ is the second coordinate of } \mathbf{P}\}$$

The domain of each of these functions is the set $\mathcal{R}$ of real numbers x, and, by (1), their respective ranges are

$$\{u: u \in \mathcal{R} \text{ and } 0 \le u^2 \le 1\}, \text{ or } \{u: u \in \mathcal{R} \text{ and } |u| \le 1\},$$
$$\{v: v \in \mathcal{R} \text{ and } 0 \le v^2 \le 1\}, \text{ or } \{v: v \in \mathcal{R} \text{ and } |v| \le 1\}.$$

Thus the two ranges are actually the same set.

The first of these two functions is called the **cosine function** and is abbreviated cos (read "cosine"). Thus, $\cos = \{(x, u): u = \cos x\}$, or, using the variable y in place of u for the elements in the range of cos, we have:

$$\cos = \{(x, y): y = \cos x\}$$

The second of the two functions is called the **sine function** and is abbreviated sin (read "sine"). Thus, $\sin = \{(x, v): v = \sin x\}$, or, using the variable y in place of v for the elements in the range of sin, we have:

$$\sin = \{(x, y): y = \sin x\}$$

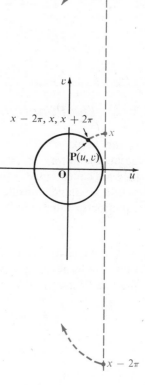

FIGURE 1–4

Note that we do not ordinarily use parentheses around the variable x in the symbols cos x and sin x, although we do so in the general function notation $f(x)$. For clarity, however, we shall use parentheses in such expressions as cos $(-x)$ and sin $(x + y)$.

Another mathematical convention we shall use is to write $\cos^2 x$ instead of $(\cos x)^2$, $\sin^3 x$ instead of $(\sin x)^3$, and so on.

Note that since cos x is, by definition, equal to the coordinate u and sin x to the coordinate v of the point **P** on the unit circle with equation

$$u^2 + v^2 = 1,$$

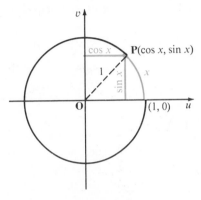

we can denote these coordinates by (cos x, sin x) instead of (u, v) and represent them by segments as shown in Figure 1–5. Hence, for every $x \in \mathfrak{R}$, we have

$$\cos^2 x + \sin^2 x = 1, \qquad (2)$$

and

$$|\cos x| \le 1 \quad \text{and} \quad |\sin x| \le 1.$$

FIGURE 1–5

The equation (2) is called a *Pythagorean identity* because the values of $|\cos x|$ and $|\sin x|$ $\left(x \ne k \cdot \dfrac{\pi}{2}, \ k \in J \right)$ are measures of the legs of a right triangle whose hypotenuse has measure 1.

We shall discuss identities further in later sections.

From Figure 1–5 it is evident that the element x in the domain denotes the arc length along the circle from the point (1, 0) to the point

$$\textbf{P}(\cos x, \sin x),$$

while cos x represents the abscissa of **P**, and sin x, the ordinate of **P**. Therefore, you know that in the first quadrant, sin x and cos x are both positive; in the second quadrant, sin x is positive and cos x is negative; in the third quadrant, both sin x and cos x are negative; and in the fourth quadrant, cos x is positive and sin x is negative. Figure 1–6 shows these facts.

QUADRANT II	QUADRANT I
cos x < 0 sin x > 0 (−, +)	cos x > 0 sin x > 0 (+, +)
QUADRANT III	QUADRANT IV
cos x < 0 sin x < 0 (−, −)	cos x > 0 sin x < 0 (+, −)

FIGURE 1–6

From the definition of cos and sin by means of the unit circle, it follows that both cos and sin are periodic functions with fundamental period 2π. For every $x \in \mathfrak{R}$:

$$\cos (x + 2k\pi) = \cos x \qquad (k \in J)$$
$$\sin (x + 2k\pi) = \sin x \qquad (k \in J)$$

If you wish to find the value of $\cos x_1$ or $\sin x_1$ for a number x_1 which is not in the interval $0 \le x < 2\pi$, you will need to express x_1 in the form $x_1 = x + 2k\pi$, where $0 \le x < 2\pi$ and k is an integer. The following example illustrates how this may be done.

Example Express each of the numbers $\dfrac{23\pi}{4}$ and $-\dfrac{3\pi}{4}$ in the form $x + 2k\pi$, where $0 \le x < 2\pi$ and $k \in J$.

Solution For $\dfrac{23\pi}{4}$, you make successive *subtractions* of 2π until you obtain a number in the interval $0 \le x < 2\pi$:

$$\frac{23\pi}{4} - 2\pi = \frac{15\pi}{4} \qquad \text{but} \qquad \frac{15\pi}{4} > 2\pi$$

$$\frac{15\pi}{4} - 2\pi = \frac{7\pi}{4} \qquad \text{and} \qquad 0 \le \frac{7\pi}{4} < 2\pi$$

Thus,

$$\frac{23\pi}{4} = \frac{7\pi}{4} + 4\pi \qquad \text{and} \qquad k = 2.$$

For $-\dfrac{3\pi}{4}$, you make successive *additions* of 2π until you obtain a number in the interval $0 \le x < 2\pi$:

$$-\frac{3\pi}{4} + 2\pi = \frac{5\pi}{4} \qquad \text{and} \qquad 0 \le \frac{5\pi}{4} < 2\pi$$

Thus,

$$-\frac{3\pi}{4} = \frac{5\pi}{4} + (-2\pi), \qquad \text{and} \qquad k = -1.$$

Exercises 1–2

Express each number in the form $x + 2k\pi$, where $0 \le x < 2\pi$ and k is an integer. In each case, state the value of k.

A 1. $\dfrac{5\pi}{2}$ 3. $-\dfrac{5\pi}{4}$ 5. $-\dfrac{9\pi}{4}$ 7. 5π 9. 2107π

2. $\dfrac{17\pi}{3}$ 4. $\dfrac{9\pi}{4}$ 6. $-\dfrac{17\pi}{3}$ 8. -3π 10. -145π

In Exercises 11–22, use the equations $\cos(x + 2k\pi) = \cos x$ and $\sin(x + 2k\pi) = \sin x$ to express each of the following as the cosine or sine of a number x, where $0 \le x < 2\pi$.

Example $\cos\left(-\dfrac{7\pi}{3}\right)$

Solution First, express $-\dfrac{7\pi}{3}$ in the form $x + 2k\pi$, where $0 \le x < 2\pi$,

and $k \in J$:

$$-\frac{7\pi}{3} = \frac{5\pi}{3} + (-4)\pi$$

Thus,

$$\cos\left(-\frac{7\pi}{3}\right) = \cos\left(\frac{5\pi}{3} + (-4)\pi\right) = \cos\frac{5\pi}{3}.$$

11. $\sin\dfrac{13\pi}{2}$ **14.** $\cos(-\pi)$ **17.** $\cos 26\pi$ **20.** $\sin 3.215\pi$

12. $\cos\dfrac{18\pi}{5}$ **15.** $\sin\left(-\dfrac{13\pi}{3}\right)$ **18.** $\cos 13\pi$ **21.** $\sin 2315\pi$

13. $\sin\left(-\dfrac{\pi}{2}\right)$ **16.** $\sin 18\pi$ **19.** $\cos 4.125\pi$ **22.** $\cos(-473\pi)$

In Exercises 23–28, use the equation $\cos^2 x + \sin^2 x = 1$ to find values for $\sin x$ when $\cos x$ and the quadrant are as given.

Example $\cos x = \dfrac{\sqrt{3}}{2}$, first quadrant

Solution By replacing $\cos x$ with $\dfrac{\sqrt{3}}{2}$ in $\cos^2 x + \sin^2 x = 1$, you have

$$\left(\frac{\sqrt{3}}{2}\right)^2 + \sin^2 x = 1$$
$$\sin^2 x = 1 - \tfrac{3}{4} = \tfrac{1}{4}$$

so that $\sin x$ is either $\tfrac{1}{2}$ or $-\tfrac{1}{2}$. Since the point $\mathbf{P}(\cos x, \sin x)$ is in the first quadrant, and since $\sin x$ is positive in the first quadrant, the required value for $\sin x$ is $\tfrac{1}{2}$.

23. $\cos x = \dfrac{\sqrt{2}}{2}$, first quadrant **26.** $\cos x = -\dfrac{\sqrt{3}}{2}$, third quadrant

24. $\cos x = \dfrac{\sqrt{2}}{2}$, fourth quadrant **27.** $\cos x = \tfrac{1}{2}$, fourth quadrant

25. $\cos x = -\dfrac{\sqrt{3}}{2}$, second quadrant **28.** $\cos x = -\tfrac{1}{2}$, second quadrant

B 29. Find the value of $\cos x$ and $\sin x$ for $x = 0, \dfrac{\pi}{2}, \pi$, and $\dfrac{3\pi}{2}$.

Determine the fundamental period of each of the specified functions. Justify your answers. Each domain is $\mathcal{R}$.

C 30. $f(x) = 4\pi + \sin x$ **32.** $f(x) = \sin x \cos x$

31. $f(x) = \sin x + \cos x$ **33.** $f(x) = \sin^2 x$

1–3 *Values of cos x and sin x for Special Values of x*

How can we determine values for cos x and sin x? For some special values of x, we can use the geometry of the unit circle. Since the circumference of the unit circle is 2π, and since the u- and v-axes in the uv-plane divide this circle into four equal arcs, we can identify values of cos x and sin x for the points on the x number line having coordinates

$$0, \frac{\pi}{2}, \pi, \text{ and } \frac{3\pi}{2}$$

quite readily, as suggested by Figure 1–7.

Because the real number 0 is associated with the ordered pair $(1, 0)$, and because the first component in the ordered pair $(1, 0)$ is cos 0 while the second component is sin 0, we have:

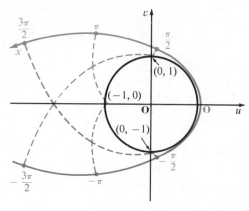

$$\cos 0 = 1$$
$$\sin 0 = 0$$

Similarly:

FIGURE 1–7

$$\cos \frac{\pi}{2} = 0 \qquad \cos \pi = -1 \qquad \cos \frac{3\pi}{2} = 0$$

$$\sin \frac{\pi}{2} = 1 \qquad \sin \pi = 0 \qquad \sin \frac{3\pi}{2} = -1$$

Also:

$$\cos 2\pi = \cos 0 = 1$$
$$\sin 2\pi = \sin 0 = 0$$

Since $\frac{\pi}{4}$ is half of $\frac{\pi}{2}$, it follows that the point **B** on

the circle* $u^2 + v^2 = 1$ into which $\frac{\pi}{4}$ is wound bisects

the quarter-circle in the first quadrant (Figure 1–8). Hence $\angle \mathbf{AOB} = 45°$. Therefore, $\triangle \mathbf{OBD}$ is a $45°$–$45°$ right triangle with legs of length

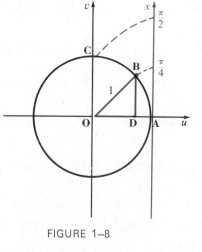

$$d(\overline{\mathbf{OD}}) = \frac{\sqrt{2}}{2} \quad \text{and} \quad d(\overline{\mathbf{BD}}) = \frac{\sqrt{2}}{2}.$$

Thus, the coordinates of **B** are $\left(\frac{\sqrt{2}}{2}, \frac{\sqrt{2}}{2}\right)$, and so

$$\cos \frac{\pi}{4} = \frac{\sqrt{2}}{2}, \qquad \sin \frac{\pi}{4} = \frac{\sqrt{2}}{2}.$$

FIGURE 1–8

*We shall often use this convenient abbreviation for "the circle with equation."

Figure 1–9 shows the points on the unit circle with which $\frac{\pi}{6}$ and $\frac{\pi}{3}$ are paired by our winding process. Since $\angle AOB = 30°$, $\triangle ODB$ is a $30°$–$60°$ right triangle and

$$d(\overline{BD}) = \frac{1}{2} \quad \text{and} \quad d(\overline{OD}) = \frac{\sqrt{3}}{2},$$

so that **B** has coordinates $\left(\frac{\sqrt{3}}{2}, \frac{1}{2}\right)$. By similar considerations, you can show that the coordinates of **C** are $\left(\frac{1}{2}, \frac{\sqrt{3}}{2}\right)$. Thus:

$$\cos \frac{\pi}{6} = \frac{\sqrt{3}}{2} \qquad \cos \frac{\pi}{3} = \frac{1}{2}$$

$$\sin \frac{\pi}{6} = \frac{1}{2} \qquad \sin \frac{\pi}{3} = \frac{\sqrt{3}}{2}$$

FIGURE 1–9

By using the fact that the unit circle is symmetric with respect to the u-axis, the v-axis, and the origin, you can identify the coordinates of all the points shown in Figure 1–10, and you can determine the values for $\sin x$ and $\cos x$ shown in the table on page 12.

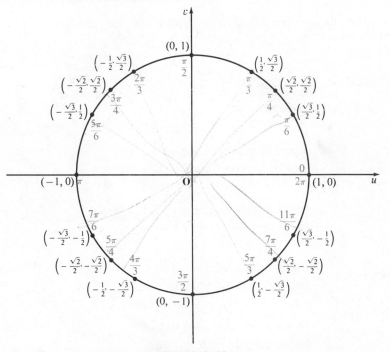

FIGURE 1–10

VALUES FOR SIN X AND COS X

x	$\cos x$	$\sin x$
	1	0
$\dfrac{\pi}{6}$	$\dfrac{\sqrt{3}}{2} \doteq 0.87$	$\dfrac{1}{2} = 0.5$
$\dfrac{\pi}{4}$	$\dfrac{\sqrt{2}}{2} \doteq 0.71$	$\dfrac{\sqrt{2}}{2} \doteq 0.71$
$\dfrac{\pi}{3}$	$\dfrac{1}{2} = 0.5$	$\dfrac{\sqrt{3}}{2} \doteq 0.87$
$\dfrac{\pi}{2}$	0	1
$\dfrac{2\pi}{3}$	$-\dfrac{1}{2} = -0.5$	$\dfrac{\sqrt{3}}{2} \doteq 0.87$
$\dfrac{3\pi}{4}$	$-\dfrac{\sqrt{2}}{2} \doteq -0.71$	$\dfrac{\sqrt{2}}{2} \doteq 0.71$
$\dfrac{5\pi}{6}$	$-\dfrac{\sqrt{3}}{2} \doteq -0.87$	$\dfrac{1}{2} = 0.5$
π	-1	0

x	$\cos x$	$\sin x$
π	-1	0
$\dfrac{7\pi}{6}$	$-\dfrac{\sqrt{3}}{2} \doteq -0.87$	$-\dfrac{1}{2} = -0.5$
$\dfrac{5\pi}{4}$	$-\dfrac{\sqrt{2}}{2} \doteq -0.71$	$-\dfrac{\sqrt{2}}{2} \doteq -0.71$
$\dfrac{4\pi}{3}$	$-\dfrac{1}{2} = -0.5$	$-\dfrac{\sqrt{3}}{2} \doteq -0.87$
$\dfrac{3\pi}{2}$	0	-1
$\dfrac{5\pi}{3}$	$\dfrac{1}{2} = 0.5$	$-\dfrac{\sqrt{3}}{2} \doteq -0.87$
$\dfrac{7\pi}{4}$	$\dfrac{\sqrt{2}}{2} \doteq 0.71$	$-\dfrac{\sqrt{2}}{2} \doteq -0.71$
$\dfrac{11\pi}{6}$	$\dfrac{\sqrt{3}}{2} \doteq 0.87$	$-\dfrac{1}{2} = -0.5$
2π	1	0

Note: The symbol $\doteq$ means "is approximately equal to." Square roots may be found in Table 4 on page 401.

If you think of a point moving counterclockwise, that is, in the direction of increasing values of x, around the unit circle starting at $(1, 0)$, then you can see that the functions cos and sin behave as follows:

In Quadrant I $\begin{cases} \cos x \text{ decreases from 1 to 0,} \\ \sin x \text{ increases from 0 to 1.} \end{cases}$

In Quadrant II $\begin{cases} \cos x \text{ decreases from 0 to } -1, \\ \sin x \text{ decreases from 1 to 0.} \end{cases}$

In Quadrant III $\begin{cases} \cos x \text{ increases from } -1 \text{ to 0,} \\ \sin x \text{ decreases from 0 to } -1. \end{cases}$

In Quadrant IV $\begin{cases} \cos x \text{ increases from 0 to 1,} \\ \sin x \text{ increases from } -1 \text{ to 0.} \end{cases}$

Exercises 1–3

A 1. Copy and complete the table of values for cos x and sin x. (You should be able to make these entries without referring to the material in the text.)

x	cos x	sin x
0	1	?
$\dfrac{\pi}{6}$	$\dfrac{\sqrt{3}}{2} \doteq 0.87$	?
$\dfrac{\pi}{4}$	?	?
$\dfrac{\pi}{3}$	?	?
$\dfrac{\pi}{2}$	?	?
π	?	?
$\dfrac{3\pi}{2}$	?	?

2. Make a table, similar to the one in Exercise 1, of the values for cos x and sin x when x is

$$\frac{\pi}{6}, \frac{5\pi}{6}, \frac{7\pi}{6}, \frac{11\pi}{6}.$$

3. Make a table of the values for cos x and sin x when x is

$$\frac{\pi}{4}, \frac{3\pi}{4}, \frac{5\pi}{4}, \frac{7\pi}{4}.$$

4. Make a table of the values for cos x and sin x when x is

$$\frac{\pi}{3}, \frac{2\pi}{3}, \frac{4\pi}{3}, \frac{5\pi}{3}.$$

Let P_1 be any point in the first quadrant on the unit circle with equation $u^2 + v^2 = 1$. Then there are points P_2, P_3, and P_4 on the unit circle which are symmetric to P_1 with respect to the v-axis, the origin, and the u-axis, respectively. Thus P_1, P_2, P_3, and P_4 are in Quadrants I, II, III, IV, respectively, and are the vertices of a rectangle inscribed in the unit circle.

In each of Exercises 5–8, you are given the coordinates of *one* of the members of such a set $\{P_1, P_2, P_3, P_4\}$ and you are to determine the coordinates of the other three members of the set; in each case draw a unit circle and locate on it the four points P_1, P_2, P_3, P_4, and beside each of these points write the value of x, $0 < x < 2\pi$, such that cos x is the first coordinate of the point and sin x is the second coordinate.

Example $P_1 = \left(\dfrac{\sqrt{3}}{2}, \dfrac{1}{2} \right)$

Solution The u- and v-coordinates and the corresponding x-values for the four points P_1, P_2, P_3, P_4 are as shown in the figure.

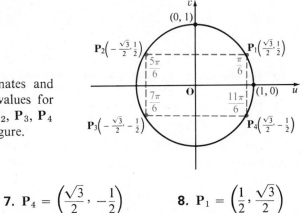

5. $P_2 = \left(-\dfrac{\sqrt{2}}{2}, \dfrac{\sqrt{2}}{2} \right)$

6. $P_3 = \left(-\dfrac{1}{2}, -\dfrac{\sqrt{3}}{2} \right)$ **7.** $P_4 = \left(\dfrac{\sqrt{3}}{2}, -\dfrac{1}{2} \right)$ **8.** $P_1 = \left(\dfrac{1}{2}, \dfrac{\sqrt{3}}{2} \right)$

Use the equations cos $(x + 2k\pi) = \cos x$, $k \in J$, and sin $(x + 2k\pi) = \sin x$, $k \in J$, together with the table on page 12, to find the value of each of the following:

9. $\sin 3\pi$

11. $\cos \dfrac{9\pi}{4}$

13. $\sin (-8\pi)$

15. $\cos \left(-\dfrac{11\pi}{2}\right)$

10. $\cos 7\pi$

12. $\sin \dfrac{71\pi}{6}$ *12*

14. $\cos (-11\pi)$

16. $\sin \left(-\dfrac{21\pi}{4}\right)$

Use the table on page 12 or the information in Figure 1–10 to find *all* values for x, $0 \le x \le 2\pi$, satisfying each of the following.

17. $\sin x = 0$

19. $\cos x = -\dfrac{\sqrt{3}}{2}$

21. $\sin x = -1$

18. $\cos x = \dfrac{1}{2}$

20. $\sin x = -\dfrac{\sqrt{2}}{2}$

22. $\cos x = 0$

Find *all* values of x shown on the unit circle in Figure 1–10, $0 \le x \le \pi$, for which each of the following is true.

B 23. $\sin x = \cos x$

25. $\sin x = \sin (x + \pi)$

27. $\sin x = \sin (\pi - x)$

24. $\sin x = -\cos x$

26. $\cos \left(\dfrac{\pi}{2} - x\right) = \sin x$

28. $\cos x = \cos (-x)$

Each of the sets in Exercises 29–32 is either an interval or the union of two or more intervals on the real number line. Using Figure 1–10 or the table on page 12, determine each set and graph it on the real number line.

Example $\{x: \cos x \ge \frac{1}{2} \text{ and } 0 \le x \le 2\pi\}$.

Solution

29. $\{x: \sin x \ge \frac{1}{2} \text{ and } 0 \le x \le 2\pi\}$

31. $\left\{x: \cos x \le \dfrac{\sqrt{3}}{2} \text{ and } 0 \le x \le 2\pi\right\}$

30. $\{x: \sin x \le 0 \text{ and } 0 \le x \le 2\pi\}$

32. $\{x: \cos x \ge 0 \text{ and } 0 \le x \le 2\pi\}$

C 33. List all values of x shown on the unit circle, Figure 1–10, $0 \le x \le 2\pi$, for which each of the following is true:

   (a) $|\sin x| = |\cos x|$ **(b)** $\sin^2 x = \cos^2 x$ **(c)** $|\sin x| = \frac{1}{2}$

34. Follow the directions given for Exercises 29–32 for each of these sets:

   (a) $\{x: \sin x \ge \cos x \text{ and } 0 \le x \le 2\pi\}$

   (b) $\{x: |\sin x| \ge |\cos x| \text{ and } 0 \le x \le 2\pi\}$

   (c) $\{x: |\cos x| \ge \sin x \text{ and } 0 \le x \le 2\pi\}$

Properties of Basic Circular Functions

1-4 *Addition Properties of cos*

A person who is familiar with the algebraic property $a(b - c) = ab - ac$, for a, b, and c any real numbers, might wonder whether or not the equation $\cos (x_2 - x_1) = \cos x_2 - \cos x_1$ is true for all real numbers x_1 and x_2. To show that it is *not* true, we need only to exhibit one pair of numbers x_1 and x_2 for which the resulting statement is false. For example,

$$\cos \left(\frac{\pi}{2} - \frac{\pi}{3} \right) = \cos \frac{\pi}{6} = \frac{\sqrt{3}}{2}, \quad \text{whereas} \quad \cos \frac{\pi}{2} - \cos \frac{\pi}{3} = 0 - \frac{1}{2} = -\frac{1}{2}.$$

There is, however, an extremely useful relationship between $\cos (x_2 - x_1)$ and values of $\cos x_1$, $\cos x_2$, $\sin x_1$, and $\sin x_2$.

To discover this relationship, let us begin by recalling that the equation $\cos^2 x + \sin^2 x = 1$ is true for all real numbers x. In particular, it is true for the real number $x = x_2 - x_1$, where x_1 and x_2 are any two real numbers. That is, for all real numbers x_1 and x_2,

$$\cos^2 (x_2 - x_1) + \sin^2 (x_2 - x_1) = 1.$$

Next, look at Figures 1–11 and 1–12, which show the unit circle and the associated x number line containing points **A, B, C,** and **D** with $d(\overline{AB}) = d(\overline{CD})$. In Figure 1–11, x_2, the coordinate of **A**, has been chosen greater than x_1, the coordinate of **B**. A similar situation results if $x_1 > x_2$ (Figure 1–12).

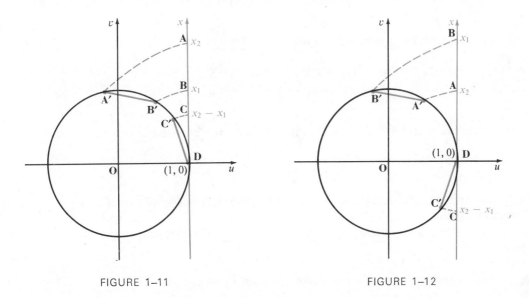

FIGURE 1–11   FIGURE 1–12

Since the segment $\overline{\textbf{AB}}$ has the same length as the segment $\overline{\textbf{CD}}$ (Figure 1–11 or Figure 1–12), it follows that, upon winding the number line onto the circle, the arc $\overset{\frown}{\textbf{A}'\textbf{B}'}$ has the same length as the arc $\overset{\frown}{\textbf{C}'\textbf{D}}$. Because arcs of a circle having equal measures have chords of equal measures, $d(\overline{\textbf{A}'\textbf{B}'}) = d(\overline{\textbf{C}'\textbf{D}})$. Notice that the coordinates of the endpoints of the segments are:

$$\textbf{A}'(\cos x_2, \sin x_2) \qquad \textbf{C}'(\cos (x_2 - x_1), \sin (x_2 - x_1))$$
$$\textbf{B}'(\cos x_1, \sin x_1) \qquad \textbf{D}(1, 0)$$

By using the distance formula

$$d = \sqrt{(u_2 - u_1)^2 + (v_2 - v_1)^2},$$

you have

$$d(\overline{\textbf{A}'\textbf{B}'}) = \sqrt{(\cos x_2 - \cos x_1)^2 + (\sin x_2 - \sin x_1)^2}$$

and

$$d(\overline{\textbf{C}'\textbf{D}}) = \sqrt{[\cos (x_2 - x_1) - 1]^2 + [\sin (x_2 - x_1) - 0]^2}.$$

Equating these two chord lengths, you can write

$$\sqrt{[\cos (x_2 - x_1) - 1]^2 + [\sin (x_2 - x_1) - 0]^2}$$
$$= \sqrt{(\cos x_2 - \cos x_1)^2 + (\sin x_2 - \sin x_1)^2}.$$

You can square both members here to obtain

$$[\cos (x_2 - x_1) - 1]^2 + [\sin (x_2 - x_1) - 0]^2 = (\cos x_2 - \cos x_1)^2 + (\sin x_2 - \sin x_1)^2,$$

which is also true for every $x_1, x_2 \in \Re$.

On expanding this latter identity, you obtain

$$\cos^2 (x_2 - x_1) - 2 \cos (x_2 - x_1) + 1 + \sin^2 (x_2 - x_1)$$
$$= \cos^2 x_2 - 2 \cos x_2 \cos x_1 + \cos^2 x_1 + \sin^2 x_2 - 2 \sin x_2 \sin x_1 + \sin^2 x_1,$$

or

$$-2 \cos (x_2 - x_1) + [\cos^2 (x_2 - x_1) + \sin^2 (x_2 - x_1)] + 1$$
$$= [\cos^2 x_2 + \sin^2 x_2] + [\cos^2 x_1 + \sin^2 x_1]$$
$$- 2 \cos x_2 \cos x_1 - 2 \sin x_2 \sin x_1.$$

Then, since you can substitute the value 1 for each of the three bracketed expressions, that is, for $\cos^2 (x_2 - x_1) + \sin^2 (x_2 - x_1)$, $\cos^2 x_2 + \sin^2 x_2$, and $\cos^2 x_1 + \sin^2 x_1$, you obtain, upon simplifying, the following important identity:

$$\cos (x_2 - x_1) = \cos x_2 \cos x_1 + \sin x_2 \sin x_1 \qquad (1)$$

Example   Find the value of $\cos x$ when x is equal to $\dfrac{\pi}{12}$.

Solution   Notice that $\dfrac{\pi}{12} = \dfrac{\pi}{3} - \dfrac{\pi}{4}$ and that we know values for $\sin x$ and $\cos x$ when x is $\dfrac{\pi}{3}$ and when x is $\dfrac{\pi}{4}$. Using (1), we have

$$\cos \frac{\pi}{12} = \cos \left(\frac{\pi}{3} - \frac{\pi}{4} \right) = \cos \frac{\pi}{3} \cos \frac{\pi}{4} + \sin \frac{\pi}{3} \sin \frac{\pi}{4}$$

$$= \left(\frac{1}{2} \right) \left(\frac{\sqrt{2}}{2} \right) + \left(\frac{\sqrt{3}}{2} \right) \left(\frac{\sqrt{2}}{2} \right) = \frac{\sqrt{2}}{4} + \frac{\sqrt{6}}{4},$$

so that

$$\cos \frac{\pi}{12} = \frac{\sqrt{2} + \sqrt{6}}{4}.$$

Using the approximations $\sqrt{2} \doteq 1.414$ and $\sqrt{6} \doteq 2.449$, we obtain the following approximation:

$$\cos \frac{\pi}{12} \doteq \frac{1.414 + 2.449}{4} \doteq 0.97$$

You can develop a number of other identities using (1). For example, if x_2 is replaced with 0 and x_1 with x, you have

$$\cos (0 - x) = \cos 0 \cos x + \sin 0 \sin x$$
$$= (1)(\cos x) + (0)(\sin x) = \cos x.$$

Thus, for every $x \in \mathfrak{R}$, we have:

▲ $\qquad \boxed{\cos (-x) = \cos x} \qquad\qquad$ (2)

The identity (2) is also evident from geometric considerations; from the symmetry of the unit circle with respect to the horizontal axis (Figure 1–13), the abscissas of the points on the circle associated with arc lengths x and $-x$ are the same. You should observe that this geometric argument is also valid for

$$x > \frac{\pi}{2}.$$

Any function f having the property that for each x in its domain, $-x$ also is in the domain and $f(-x) = f(x)$ is called an **even function**. Hence, by (2), the cosine function is even.

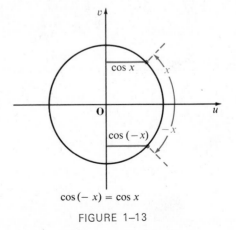

$\cos (-x) = \cos x$

FIGURE 1–13

To discover another useful identity, you can replace x_2 in (1) on page 16 with $\dfrac{\pi}{2}$, and x_1 with x, obtaining

$$\cos\left(\frac{\pi}{2} - x\right) = \cos\frac{\pi}{2}\cos x + \sin\frac{\pi}{2}\sin x$$
$$= (0)(\cos x) + (1)(\sin x)$$
$$= \sin x$$

so that for every $x \in \Re$, we have:

▲ $$\cos\left(\frac{\pi}{2} - x\right) = \sin x \qquad (3)$$

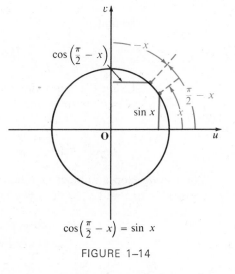

$$\cos\left(\frac{\pi}{2} - x\right)$$

$$\cos\left(\frac{\pi}{2} - x\right) = \sin\ x$$

FIGURE 1–14

Again, geometric considerations also help to make the identity (3) evident. Figure 1–14 shows that on the unit circle the abscissa of the point corresponding to

$$\frac{\pi}{2} - x$$

is equal to the ordinate of the point corresponding to x.

Another identity follows directly from (3). By replacing x with $\dfrac{\pi}{2} - x$, you find that

$$\cos\left[\frac{\pi}{2} - \left(\frac{\pi}{2} - x\right)\right] = \sin\left(\frac{\pi}{2} - x\right),$$

from which you have

$$\cos x = \sin\left(\frac{\pi}{2} - x\right).$$

Thus, for every $x \in \Re$, we have:

▲ $$\sin\left(\frac{\pi}{2} - x\right) = \cos x \qquad (4)$$

Next, if x is replaced with $-x$ in (3), the result is

$$\cos\left(\frac{\pi}{2} + x\right) = \sin(-x),$$

and since $\frac{\pi}{2} + x$ can be written as $x - \left(-\frac{\pi}{2}\right)$, you have

$$\cos\left[x - \left(-\frac{\pi}{2}\right)\right] = \sin(-x).$$

By (1) on page 16, however,

$$\cos\left[x - \left(-\frac{\pi}{2}\right)\right] = \cos x \cos\left(-\frac{\pi}{2}\right) + \sin x \sin\left(-\frac{\pi}{2}\right)$$

$$= (\cos x)(0) + (\sin x)(-1)$$

$$= -\sin x.$$

Thus, for every $x \in \mathcal{R}$, we have:

$$\sin(-x) = -\sin x \qquad (5)$$

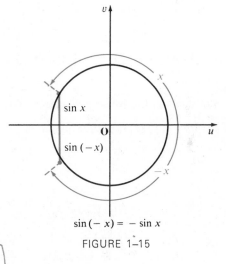

sin $(-x) = -$ sin x

FIGURE 1–15

The geometric situation corresponding to (5) is illustrated in Figure 1–15, where $\sin(-x)$ appears as the negative of $\sin x$.

Any function f having the property that for each x in its domain, $-x$ also is in the domain and

$$f(-x) = -f(x)$$

is called an **odd function**. Hence, by (5), the sine function is odd.

Then from (3) and (5) we have for every $x \in \mathcal{R}$:

$$\cos\left(\frac{\pi}{2} + x\right) = -\sin x$$

One more example of an important consequence of the identity (1) is obtained by replacing x_1 in that identity with $-x_1$. Then

$$\cos[x_2 - (-x_1)] = \cos x_2 \cos(-x_1) + \sin x_2 \sin(-x_1),$$

which, by (2) and (5), gives, for every $x \in \mathcal{R}$:

$$\cos(x_2 + x_1) = \cos x_2 \cos x_1 - \sin x_2 \sin x_1 \qquad (6)$$

Exercises 1–4

For each of the given values of x in Exercises 1–4, find the value of $\cos\left(\dfrac{\pi}{4} + x\right)$, using identity (6). Express your answers as two-place decimals. See Table 4 on page 401 for square-root approximations.

Example $x = \dfrac{\pi}{6}$

Solution
$$\cos\left(\frac{\pi}{4} + \frac{\pi}{6}\right) = \cos\frac{\pi}{4}\cos\frac{\pi}{6} - \sin\frac{\pi}{4}\sin\frac{\pi}{6}$$

$$= \frac{\sqrt{2}}{2}\cdot\frac{\sqrt{3}}{2} - \frac{\sqrt{2}}{2}\cdot\frac{1}{2} = \frac{\sqrt{6} - \sqrt{2}}{4}$$

$$\doteq \frac{2.449 - 1.414}{4} \doteq 0.26$$

Thus, since $\dfrac{\pi}{4} + \dfrac{\pi}{6} = \dfrac{5\pi}{12}$, we have shown that $\cos\left(\dfrac{5\pi}{12}\right) \doteq 0.26$.

A   **1.** $x = \dfrac{\pi}{3}$ **2.** $x = \dfrac{\pi}{2}$ **3.** $x = \dfrac{2\pi}{3}$ **4.** $x = \dfrac{5\pi}{6}$

For each of the following values of x, find the value of $\cos\left(\dfrac{\pi}{3} - x\right)$, using identity (1). Express your answers as two-place decimals.

5. $x = \dfrac{\pi}{6}$ **7.** $x = \dfrac{\pi}{2}$ **9.** $x = \dfrac{5\pi}{6}$

6. $x = \dfrac{\pi}{4}$ **8.** $x = \dfrac{2\pi}{3}$ **10.** $x = \dfrac{3\pi}{4}$

In Exercises 11–18, let $\cos x_2 = \frac{3}{5}$ and $\cos x_1 = \frac{5}{13}$. Use any identities available to find a value for the given expression. In each case, make a sketch of the unit circle, as shown in the example.

Example $\cos(x_2 - x_1),$ $0 < x_2 < \dfrac{\pi}{2},$ $\dfrac{3\pi}{2} < x_1 < 2\pi$

Solution   First, you must find $\sin x_2$ and $\sin x_1$. Since $\cos^2 x + \sin^2 x = 1$ for every $x \in \mathcal{R}$, you have

$$\left(\tfrac{3}{5}\right)^2 + \sin^2 x_2 = 1 \quad \text{and} \quad \left(\tfrac{5}{13}\right)^2 + \sin^2 x_1 = 1.$$

Hence:

$$\sin x_2 = \pm\sqrt{1 - \tfrac{9}{25}} = \pm\tfrac{4}{5}$$

and

$$\sin x_1 = \pm\sqrt{1 - \tfrac{25}{169}} = \pm\tfrac{12}{13}.$$

Since $0 < x_2 < \dfrac{\pi}{2}$ and $\dfrac{3\pi}{2} < x_1 < 2\pi$, we know that $\sin x_2$ is positive and $\sin x_1$ is negative. Thus,

$$\sin x_2 = \tfrac{4}{5} \quad \text{and} \quad \sin x_1 = -\tfrac{12}{13}.$$

Now you can use identity (1), obtaining

$$\cos (x_2 - x_1) = \cos x_2 \cos x_1 + \sin x_2 \sin x_1$$
$$= (\tfrac{3}{5})(\tfrac{5}{13}) + (\tfrac{4}{5})(-\tfrac{12}{13}) = \tfrac{15}{65} - \tfrac{48}{65} = -\tfrac{33}{65}.$$

The approximate locations on the unit circle of the points corresponding to x_2 and x_1 are shown in the figure.

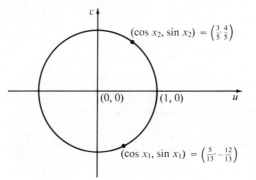

11. $\cos (x_1 - x_2),\ 0 < x_2 < \dfrac{\pi}{2},\ 0 < x_1 < \dfrac{\pi}{2}$

12. $\cos (x_2 - x_1),\ \dfrac{3\pi}{2} < x_2 < 2\pi,\ 0 < x_1 < \dfrac{\pi}{2}$

13. $\cos \left(\dfrac{\pi}{4} + x_2\right),\ 0 < x_2 < \dfrac{\pi}{2}$

14. $\cos (x_2 + x_1),\ \dfrac{3\pi}{2} < x_2 < 2\pi,\ \dfrac{3\pi}{2} < x_1 < 2\pi$

15. $\cos \left(x_2 - \dfrac{\pi}{6}\right),\ \dfrac{3\pi}{2} < x_2 < 2\pi$ **17.** $\cos \left(x_1 - \dfrac{\pi}{3}\right),\ 0 < x_1 < \dfrac{\pi}{2}$

16. $\cos \left(\dfrac{\pi}{3} - x_1\right),\ 0 < x_1 < \dfrac{\pi}{2}$ **18.** $\cos \left(x_2 - \dfrac{\pi}{4}\right),\ \dfrac{3\pi}{2} < x_2 < 2\pi$

19. Copy and complete the table at the right on the basis of the entries which have been provided for you and the identities developed in this section.

x	$\cos x$	$\sin x$
0	1	0
$\dfrac{\pi}{6}$	$\dfrac{\sqrt{3}}{2} \doteq 0.87$	$\dfrac{1}{2} = 0.50$
$\dfrac{\pi}{4}$	$\dfrac{\sqrt{2}}{2} \doteq 0.71$	?
$\dfrac{\pi}{3}$	?	?
$\dfrac{\pi}{2}$	?	?
$-\dfrac{\pi}{6}$	?	?
$-\dfrac{\pi}{4}$	?	?
$-\dfrac{\pi}{3}$	?	?
$-\dfrac{\pi}{2}$	?	?

20. For each expression in the left-hand column, determine which expression in the right-hand column is equal to it. An expression in the right-hand column may be used more than once or not at all.

(a) $\cos\dfrac{\pi}{6}\cos\dfrac{\pi}{3} + \sin\dfrac{\pi}{6}\sin\dfrac{\pi}{3}$

(b) $\cos\dfrac{\pi}{4}\cos\dfrac{\pi}{4} - \sin\dfrac{\pi}{4}\sin\dfrac{\pi}{4}$

(c) $\cos\dfrac{\pi}{4}\cos\dfrac{\pi}{2} + \sin\dfrac{\pi}{4}\sin\dfrac{\pi}{2}$

(d) $\cos\pi\cos\dfrac{\pi}{2} - \sin\pi\sin\dfrac{\pi}{2}$

(e) $\cos\dfrac{\pi}{3}\cos\pi + \sin\dfrac{\pi}{3}\sin\pi$

(f) $\cos\dfrac{\pi}{4}\cos\dfrac{\pi}{2} - \sin\dfrac{\pi}{4}\sin\dfrac{\pi}{2}$

(g) $\cos\dfrac{\pi}{4}\cos\dfrac{\pi}{3} - \sin\dfrac{\pi}{3}\sin\dfrac{\pi}{4}$

(h) $\cos\dfrac{\pi}{2}\cos\dfrac{\pi}{6} - \sin\dfrac{\pi}{2}\sin\dfrac{\pi}{6}$

(1) $\cos\left(-\dfrac{\pi}{6}\right)$

(2) $\cos 0$

(3) $\cos\dfrac{\pi}{12}$

(4) $\cos\dfrac{\pi}{4}$

(5) $\cos\dfrac{\pi}{2}$

(6) $\cos\dfrac{7\pi}{12}$

(7) $\cos\dfrac{2\pi}{3}$

(8) $\cos\dfrac{3\pi}{4}$

(9) $\cos\pi$

(10) $\cos\dfrac{3\pi}{2}$

Find *all* real numbers x, $0 \leq x \leq 2\pi$, satisfying the following equations:

B **21.** $\cos \frac{\pi}{4} \sin x - \sin \frac{\pi}{4} \cos x = 0$

22. $\cos \left(x - \frac{\pi}{3} \right) = \frac{1}{2}$ **23.** $\cos \left(\frac{\pi}{2} - x \right) + \sin \left(\frac{\pi}{2} - x \right) = 0$

Simplify each expression:

C **24.** $\cos \left(x + \frac{\pi}{3} \right) \cos \frac{\pi}{6} - \sin \left(x + \frac{\pi}{3} \right) \sin \frac{\pi}{6}$

25. $\cos \left(x + \frac{\pi}{3} \right) \cos x + \sin \left(x + \frac{\pi}{3} \right) \sin x$

26. $\cos (x - y) \cos y - \sin (x - y) \sin y$

1–5   *Deriving and Verifying Identities*

In trigonometry, as in algebra, we are frequently concerned with forming generalizations involving the set of all real numbers or some particular subset of real numbers. Such a generalization, in the form of an equation containing one or more variables, is called an **identity** if the equation is true for all *permissible* values of the variable. Use of the word *permissible* is for the purpose of excluding values of variables which cause any expression in the equation to be undefined; note, for instance, III below, in which zero is excluded.

Examples of some **algebraic identities** are as follows:

I. $a - b = -(b - a)$ for a, $b \in \mathfrak{R}$ (that is, for a and b any real numbers)

II. $(a + b)^2 = a^2 + 2ab + b^2$ for a, $b \in \mathfrak{R}$

III. $\frac{a}{a} = 1$ for $a \in \mathfrak{R}$, $a \neq 0$ (that is, for a any real number except zero)

We have already met a number of identities involving circular functions in Sections 1–2 and 1–4. In deriving and verifying such identities, we use the following:

1. the definitions of the circular functions
2. identities already known to us
3. the field properties of the real numbers (see Appendix A)
4. algebraic identities, for example, $a^2 - b^2 = (a + b)(a - b)$
5. the principle of substitution

For example, in verifying the identity

$$\cos(x_2 - x_1) = \cos x_2 \cos x_1 + \sin x_2 \sin x_1$$

in Section 1–4, we used both the fact that

$$(\cos x_2 - \cos x_1)^2 = \cos^2 x_2 - 2 \cos x_2 \cos x_1 + \cos^2 x_1,$$

which is an application of the algebraic identity

$$(a - b)^2 = a^2 - 2ab + b^2,$$

and also $\cos^2 x + \sin^2 x = 1$, which is an identity already known to us.

There are two aspects of identities with which we shall be especially concerned in this book: *deriving identities* and *verifying identities*.

To *derive* an identity means to find or discover an identity. Sometimes you proceed as in Example 1.

Example 1   Derive an identity that expresses $\cos\left(\dfrac{\pi}{4} + x\right)$ in terms of $\sin x$ or $\cos x$ or both.

Solution   We begin with the known identity

$$\cos(x_2 + x_1) = \cos x_2 \cos x_1 - \sin x_2 \sin x_1.$$

Since this is true for every real number x_2 and every real number x_1, it is true in particular for $x_2 = \dfrac{\pi}{4}$ and for $x_1 = x$, where $x \in \Re$. Therefore, we can substitute $\dfrac{\pi}{4}$ for x_2, and x for x_1, from which we have

$$\cos\left(\frac{\pi}{4} + x\right) = \cos\frac{\pi}{4}\cos x - \sin\frac{\pi}{4}\sin x.$$

Since $\cos\dfrac{\pi}{4} = \dfrac{\sqrt{2}}{2}$ and $\sin\dfrac{\pi}{4} = \dfrac{\sqrt{2}}{2}$, we can substitute these values in this latter identity to obtain

$$\cos\left(\frac{\pi}{4} + x\right) = \frac{\sqrt{2}}{2}(\cos x - \sin x),$$

which expresses $\cos\left(\dfrac{\pi}{4} + x\right)$ in terms of $\sin x$ and $\cos x$, as desired.

To *verify* an identity means to prove that a given equation is an identity. To do this, we must show that for every value of any variable or variables involved for which both members are defined, the sentence becomes a true statement. This can be accomplished by showing that the given equation can be transformed into an equivalent, known identity (as in Example 2) or by showing that the two members of the sentence can be expressed identically (as in Example 3).

Example 2   Verify that

$$\cos^2 x = 1 - \sin^2 x$$

is an identity for all $x \in \mathfrak{R}$.

Solution   By adding $\sin^2 x$ to each member of the given sentence, we obtain the equivalent sentence

$$\cos^2 x + \sin^2 x = 1.$$

Since this is a known identity, the proof is complete.

Example 3   Verify that $\sin^2 x - \cos x \cos (-x) \sin^2 x = \sin^4 x$ is an identity for all $x \in \mathfrak{R}$.

Solution   Let us focus our attention on the left-hand member only and show that it can be transformed by suitable steps into the right-hand member. Since $\cos (-x) = \cos x$ for each $x \in \mathfrak{R}$, by substitution, we have

$$\sin^2 x - \cos x \cos (-x) \sin^2 x = \sin^2 x - \cos x \cos x \sin^2 x$$
$$= \sin^2 x - \cos^2 x \sin^2 x.$$

By applying the distributive property, we obtain

$$\sin^2 x - \cos^2 x \sin^2 x = \sin^2 x (1 - \cos^2 x).$$

From $\cos^2 x + \sin^2 x = 1$, we have $\sin^2 x = 1 - \cos^2 x$, so that

$$\sin^2 x (1 - \cos^2 x) = \sin^2 x \sin^2 x = \sin^4 x.$$

Thus simplification of the left-hand member to $\sin^4 x$ gives the sentence $\sin^4 x = \sin^4 x$, which is clearly an identity and which is equivalent to the given sentence. This verifies that the given sentence is an identity for all $x \in \mathfrak{R}$.

Exercises 1–5

Derive an identity expressing each of the following in terms of cos x or sin x or both.

A **1.** $\cos\left(x - \dfrac{\pi}{2}\right)$ **3.** $\cos(x - \pi)$ **5.** $\cos(2\pi - x)$

2. $\cos(\pi + x)$ **4.** $\cos\left(x - \dfrac{\pi}{3}\right)$ **6.** $\cos\left(\dfrac{\pi}{4} + x\right)$

7. Each expression in the left-hand column below can be equated with an expression in the right-hand column to form an identity by a direct application of one of the algebraic properties:

$$\text{(i) } ab + ac = a(b + c)$$
$$\text{(ii) } a^2 - b^2 = (a - b)(a + b)$$
$$\text{(iii) } (a \pm b)^2 = a^2 \pm 2ab + b^2$$

For each expression in the left-hand column, state which expression (1)–(12) is identical to it and also state which algebraic property (i), (ii), or (iii) is used. An expression in the right-hand column may be used more than once or not at all.

(**a**) $\sin x \cos x + \sin^2 x$

(**b**) $\sin^2 x - \cos^2 x$

(**c**) $(\sin x - \cos x)^2$

(**d**) $(\sin x + \cos x)^2$

(**e**) $\sin^4 x - \cos^4 x$

(**f**) $\cos^2 x + \cos x \sin x$

(**g**) $\cos x \sin x + \sin x$

(**h**) $\sin^2 x \cos x + \cos^3 x$

(1) $\cos x (\cos x + \sin x)$

(2) $\sin x (\cos x + \sin x)$

(3) $\cos x (\sin^2 x + \cos^2 x)$

(4) $\sin^3 x + \cos x$

(5) $\sin^2 x - 2 \sin x \cos x + \cos^2 x$

(6) $\sin^2 x + 2 \sin x \cos x + \cos^2 x$

(7) $\cos(x_1 + x_2)(\sin x_1 + \sin x_2)$

(8) $\cos x (2 \sin x)$

(9) $(\sin^2 x - \cos^2 x)(\sin^2 x + \cos^2 x)$

(10) $\sin x (\cos x + 1)$

(11) $\sin^2 x + \cos^2 x$

(12) $(\sin x + \cos x)(\sin x - \cos x)$

Verify each of the following identities.

8. $\sin^2 x = 1 - \cos^2 x$

9. $2 \cos^2 x - 1 = \cos^2 x - \sin^2 x$

10. $\sin x \cos^2 x + \sin^3 x = \sin x$

11. $1 - 2 \cos^2 x = 2 \sin^2 x - 1$

12. $\cos(-x) \cos x = 1 - \sin^2 x$

13. $\sin(-x) \sin x = \cos^2 x - 1$

14. $(1 + \sin x)(1 - \sin x) = \cos^2 x$

15. $\dfrac{(\sin x + \cos x)^2 - 1}{\sin x \cos x} = 2$

B 16. $\cos\left(\dfrac{\pi}{2} - x\right)\sin x + \sin\left(\dfrac{\pi}{2} - x\right)\cos x = 1$

17. $\sin^4 x - \cos^4 x = 2\sin^2 x - 1$

18. $\cos(x - \pi) - \cos(x + \pi) = 0$

19. $\cos(x_2 - x_1)\cos(x_2 + x_1) = \cos^2 x_2 - \sin^2 x_1$

In each of the following, find the least *nonnegative* value of x for which the statement is true.

20. $\cos\dfrac{\pi}{6}\cos x + \sin\dfrac{\pi}{6}\sin x = 1$

21. $\cos\dfrac{\pi}{6}\cos x + \sin\dfrac{\pi}{6}\sin x = \dfrac{\sqrt{3}}{2}$

22. $\cos\dfrac{\pi}{3}\cos x - \sin\dfrac{\pi}{3}\sin x = \cos\dfrac{\pi}{2}$

23. $x = \cos\dfrac{2\pi}{3}\cos\left(-\dfrac{\pi}{6}\right) - \sin\dfrac{2\pi}{3}\sin\left(-\dfrac{\pi}{6}\right)$

24. $x = \sin\left(-\dfrac{\pi}{3}\right)\sin\dfrac{\pi}{2} + \cos\left(-\dfrac{\pi}{3}\right)\cos\dfrac{\pi}{2}$

1–6 *Addition Properties of sin*

The identities developed for $\cos x$ in Section 1–4 have counterparts involving $\sin x$. A fundamental relationship, valid for every $x_1, x_2 \in \mathfrak{R}$, is:

$$\sin(x_2 - x_1) = \sin x_2 \cos x_1 - \cos x_2 \sin x_1 \tag{1}$$

To verify this relationship, you can begin by replacing x with $x_2 - x_1$ in the identity $\cos\left(\dfrac{\pi}{2} - x\right) = \sin x$. You then have

$$\cos\left[\dfrac{\pi}{2} - (x_2 - x_1)\right] = \cos\left[\left(\dfrac{\pi}{2} - x_2\right) + x_1\right] = \sin(x_2 - x_1),$$

so that

$$\cos\left(\dfrac{\pi}{2} - x_2\right)\cos x_1 - \sin\left(\dfrac{\pi}{2} - x_2\right)\sin x_1 = \sin(x_2 - x_1).$$

Since $\cos\left(\dfrac{\pi}{2} - x_2\right) = \sin x_2$ and $\sin\left(\dfrac{\pi}{2} - x_2\right) = \cos x_2$, you have

$$\sin x_2 \cos x_1 - \cos x_2 \sin x_1 = \sin(x_2 - x_1),$$

which, by the symmetric law of equality, is equivalent to (1).

By replacing x_1 with $-x_1$, you can show that (1), together with (2), page 17, and (5), page 19, implies that for every $x_1, x_2 \in \mathfrak{R}$:

$$\sin(x_2 + x_1) = \sin x_2 \cos x_1 + \cos x_2 \sin x_1 \tag{2}$$

Identities (1) and (6) in Section 1–4 and (1) and (2) in this section can be written compactly as

$$\cos(x_2 \pm x_1) = \cos x_2 \cos x_1 \mp \sin x_2 \sin x_1 \qquad (3)$$

$$\sin(x_2 \pm x_1) = \sin x_2 \cos x_1 \pm \cos x_2 \sin x_1 \qquad (4)$$

where you should read either the top sign in both members or the bottom sign in both members, but not the top in one and the bottom in the other.

In particular, we also have for every $x \in \Re$:

$$\blacktriangle \qquad \sin\left(\frac{\pi}{2} + x\right) = \cos x \qquad\qquad \sin\left(x - \frac{\pi}{2}\right) = -\cos x$$

By replacing x_2 with π, and x_1 with x, in the identities

$$\cos(x_2 - x_1) = \cos x_2 \cos x_1 + \sin x_2 \sin x_1$$

and

$$\sin(x_2 - x_1) = \sin x_2 \cos x_1 - \cos x_2 \sin x_1$$

and recalling that $\cos \pi = -1$ and $\sin \pi = 0$, we find that for every real number x:

$$\blacktriangle \qquad\qquad \cos(\pi - x) = -\cos x \qquad\qquad (5)$$

$$\sin(\pi - x) = \sin x \qquad\qquad (6)$$

Figure 1–16 illustrates the geometric situation in this case.

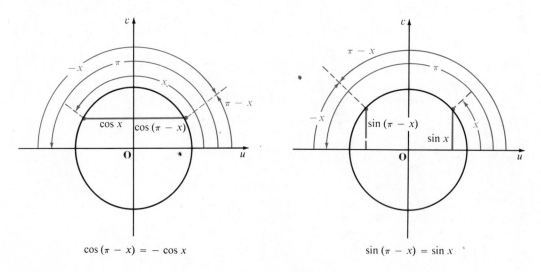

$$\cos(\pi - x) = -\cos x \qquad\qquad \sin(\pi - x) = \sin x$$

FIGURE 1–16

Next, by replacing x_2 with x and x_1 with π in the identities (3) a
recalling that $\cos \pi = -1$ and $\sin \pi = 0$, we find that for every real

▲

$$\cos (x + \pi) = -\cos x$$

$$\cos (x - \pi) = -\cos x$$

$$\sin (x + \pi) = -\sin x \qquad (9)$$

$$\sin (x - \pi) = -\sin x \qquad (10)$$

In compact form, these can be stated as:

$$\cos (x \pm \pi) = -\cos x \qquad (11)$$

$$\sin (x \pm \pi) = -\sin x \qquad (12)$$

Figure 1–17 illustrates the geometric situation for (7) and (9) for x in the first quadrant. Notice that

$$\cos (x + \pi) = \cos (x - \pi) \qquad \text{and} \qquad \sin (x + \pi) = \sin (x - \pi)$$

for all real numbers x.

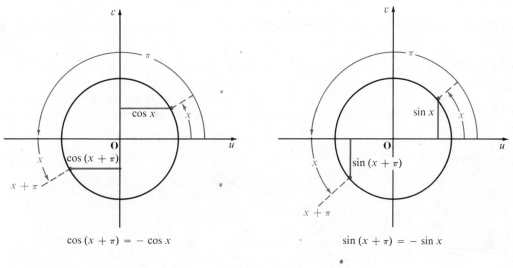

$$\cos (x + \pi) = - \cos x \qquad\qquad \sin (x + \pi) = - \sin x$$

FIGURE 1–17

We have now established enough identities to enable us to "reduce" the problem of finding values for $\cos x$ and $\sin x$ for $x < 0$ or $x > \dfrac{\pi}{2}$ to the problem of finding equivalent values for $0 \leq x \leq \dfrac{\pi}{2}$. These identities are summarized in the list given on the next page.

REDUCTION IDENTITIES

1. $\cos(x + 2k\pi) = \cos x, \quad k \in J$
2. $\cos(x \pm \pi) = -\cos x$
3. $\cos(\pi - x) = -\cos x$
4. $\cos(-x) = \cos x$

5. $\sin(x + 2k\pi) = \sin x, \quad k \in J$
6. $\sin(x \pm \pi) = -\sin x$
7. $\sin(\pi - x) = \sin x$
8. $\sin(-x) = -\sin x$

These eight identities are all special cases of the more general identities

9. $\cos(x_2 \pm x_1) = \cos x_2 \cos x_1 \mp \sin x_2 \sin x_1$
10. $\sin(x_2 \pm x_1) = \sin x_2 \cos x_1 \pm \cos x_2 \sin x_1$

Exercises 1–6

In Exercises 1–12, reduce each expression to an equivalent expression in one of the forms $\cos x$, $-\cos x$, $\sin x$, or $-\sin x$, where $0 \leq x < \dfrac{\pi}{2}$. Indicate the reduction identities 1–8 above which are used.

Example $\sin\dfrac{9\pi}{5}$ Solution $\sin\dfrac{9\pi}{5} = \sin\left(-\dfrac{\pi}{5} + 2\pi\right)$

$$= \sin\left(-\dfrac{\pi}{5}\right) \text{ by Identity 5}$$

$$= -\sin\dfrac{\pi}{5} \text{ by Identity 8}$$

A 1. $\sin\dfrac{5\pi}{6}$ 4. $\cos\dfrac{5\pi}{3}$ 7. $\sin\left(-\dfrac{5\pi}{4}\right)$ 10. $\cos\left(-\dfrac{8\pi}{3}\right)$

2. $\sin\dfrac{13\pi}{12}$ 5. $\cos\left(-\dfrac{4\pi}{3}\right)$ 8. $\sin\left(-\dfrac{2\pi}{3}\right)$ 11. $\sin\left(-\dfrac{5\pi}{4}\right)$

3. $\sin\dfrac{11\pi}{3}$ 6. $\cos\dfrac{11\pi}{2}$ 9. $\cos\dfrac{40\pi}{13}$ 12. $\cos\dfrac{7\pi}{3}$

For each of the following values of x, find first the values of $\sin x$ and $\cos x$ and then, using Identity 10 above, find the values of $\sin\left(x + \dfrac{\pi}{4}\right)$, $\sin\left(x + \dfrac{\pi}{2}\right)$, and $\sin\left(x + \dfrac{3\pi}{4}\right)$.

13. $x = \dfrac{\pi}{6}$ 14. $x = \dfrac{\pi}{3}$ 15. $x = \dfrac{3\pi}{2}$ 16. $x = \dfrac{2\pi}{3}$

If $\sin x_2 = \frac{12}{13}$, $\frac{\pi}{2} < x_2 < \pi$, and $\sin x_1 = \frac{3}{5}$, $0 < x_1 < \frac{\pi}{2}$, find the value of:

17. $\sin (x_2 + x_1)$ (In what quadrant is $x_2 + x_1$?)

18. $\sin (x_2 - x_1)$ (In what quadrant is $x_2 - x_1$?)

19. $\sin (x_2 + \pi) + \sin (x_1 + \pi)$ **21.** $\cos (-x_2) + \cos (-x_1)$

20. $\sin (-x_2) + \sin (-x_1)$ **22.** $\sin (\pi - x_2)$

If $\sin x_2 = \frac{5}{13}$, $0 < x_2 < \frac{\pi}{2}$, and $\sin x_1 = -\frac{4}{5}$, $\pi < x_1 < \frac{3\pi}{2}$, find the value of:

23. $\sin (x_2 + x_1)$ (In what quadrant is $x_2 + x_1$?)

24. $\sin (x_2 - x_1)$ (In what quadrant is $x_2 - x_1$?)

25. $\sin (x_2 + \pi) + \sin (x_1 + \pi)$.   **27.** $\cos (-x_2) - \cos (-x_1)$

26. $\sin (-x_2) - \sin (-x_1)$ **28.** $\sin (\pi - x_2)$

If $\cos x_2 = -\frac{3}{5}$, $\pi < x_2 < \frac{3\pi}{2}$, and $\cos x_1 = \frac{5}{13}$, $\frac{3\pi}{2} < x_1 < 2\pi$, find the value of:

29. $\sin (x_2 + x_1)$ (In what quadrant is $x_2 + x_1$?)

30. $\sin (x_2 - x_1)$ (In what quadrant is $x_2 - x_1$?)

31. $\sin (x_2 - \pi) + \sin (x_1 - \pi)$ **33.** $\sin (-x_2) + \sin (-x_1)$

32. $\sin (\pi - x_2) + \cos (\pi - x_2)$.   **34.** $\cos (-x_2) - \cos (-x_1)$

B 35. Prepare a table summarizing the values of $\cos x$ and of $\sin x$ for $x = \frac{\pi}{12}$ and $x = \frac{5\pi}{12}$. Show both the exact form (that is, with radicals) and two-place decimal approximations. (The square root table, Table 4, may be helpful.) Keep your table for future reference.

Find the least *nonnegative* value of a for which each statement is true.

36. $\sin (x + a) = \sin x$ **39.** $\sin (x + a) = \frac{\sqrt{2}}{2} (\sin x + \cos x)$

37. $\sin (x + a) = -\sin x$

38. $\sin (x + a) = \cos x$ **40.** $\sin (x + a) = \frac{\sqrt{2}}{2} (\sin x - \cos x)$

C 41. Show that if $x_1 + x_2 + x_3 = \pi$, then $\sin x_1 = \sin x_2 \cos x_3 + \cos x_2 \sin x_3$.

42. Explain why each of the following is an identity:

(a) $\sin (x + k\pi) = (-1)^k \sin x$ for each $k \in J$

(b) $\sin \left[x + (2k + 1) \frac{\pi}{2} \right] = (-1)^k \cos x$ for each $k \in J$

Graphs and Further Properties
of Basic Circular Functions

1–7 Graphs of cos and sin

Let us next develop the Cartesian graphs of the cos and the sin functions. This development will be made in several stages: first, their graphs over the interval $0 \leq x \leq \frac{\pi}{2}$; next, their graphs over the interval $0 \leq x \leq \pi$; then, over the interval $0 \leq x \leq 2\pi$; and finally, their graphs for *all* real numbers.

The values of cos x and sin x obtained for the special values $0, \frac{\pi}{6}, \frac{\pi}{4}, \frac{\pi}{3}$, and $\frac{\pi}{2}$ (Section 1–3) can be used to obtain certain points on the graph of cos x and sin x for the interval $0 \leq x \leq \frac{\pi}{2}$ (see Figure 1–18).

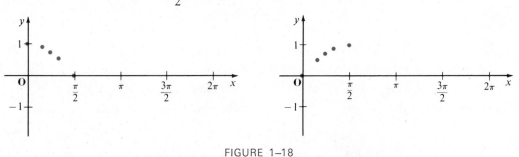

FIGURE 1–18

When we defined cos and sin by means of a number line wound onto the unit circle (Section 1–2), we noted that this winding process associates each real number x with a corresponding real number cos x and a corresponding real number sin x. From this definition, it seems reasonable to assume that the graphs of cos and sin are smooth unbroken curves. This can indeed be proved rigorously by mathematical analysis but will merely be assumed here. Connecting the points in Figure 1–18 with smooth curves thus produces the graphs shown in Figure 1–19.

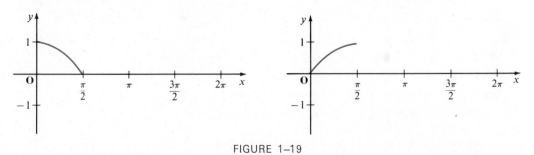

FIGURE 1–19

Next, the graphs of $y = \cos x$ and $y = \sin x$ for $0 \le x \le \pi$ can be obtained from the graphs in Figure 1–19 and the identities

$$\cos (\pi - a) = -\cos a$$

and

$$\sin (\pi - a) = \sin a.$$

Use of these identities is shown in Figure 1–20.

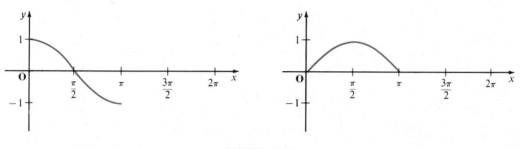

FIGURE 1–20

From the graphs in Figure 1–20 and the identities

$$\cos (a + \pi) = -\cos a$$

and

$$\sin (a + \pi) = -\sin a,$$

we obtain the graphs of $y = \cos x$ and $y = \sin x$ for $0 \le x \le 2\pi$, as shown in Figure 1–21.

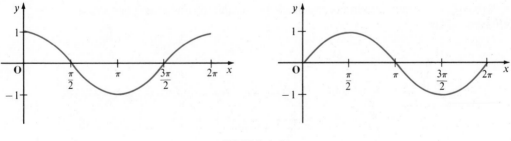

FIGURE 1–21

The periodic property of the circular functions gives their graphs a special characteristic. The fact that a function f has the property $f(x + p) = f(x)$ for all $x \in \mathcal{R}$ makes it possible for you to graph the function over an interval of length p and then to reproduce the graph indefinitely in both directions along the x-axis to obtain as much of the graph of f as is desired.

Since cos and sin are periodic with fundamental period 2π, and since we have now obtained the graphs of cos and sin over the interval $0 \leq x \leq 2\pi$, these graphs can be reproduced indefinitely in both directions along the x-axis.

One way to think of this indefinite repro-
duction is in terms of rectangular blocks.
Since the values of cos x range from -1 to 1
for $0 \leq x \leq 2\pi$, you can visualize a rectangle
with dimensions

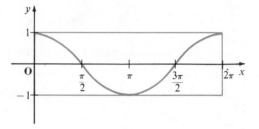

$$2\pi \text{ and } 2,$$

enclosing the graph of cos over the interval

$$0 \leq x \leq 2\pi,$$

FIGURE 1–22

as shown in Figure 1–22. Then, to obtain as
much more of the graph as you please, you can simply lay off a sequence of
these 2π-by-2 rectangles in both directions along the x-axis (Figure 1–23).

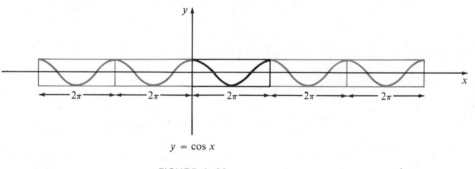

$$y = \cos x$$

FIGURE 1–23

Similarly, you can obtain as much of the graph of sin x as you please
(Figure 1–24).*

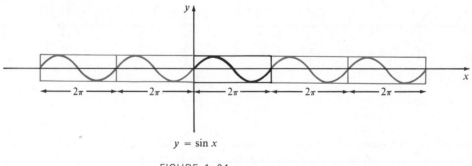

$$y = \sin x$$

FIGURE 1–24

*If you have access to an electronic computer, look at pages 46 and 47.

Another way to visualize the construction of the graphs of sin and cos is in terms of the winding process. Imagine an xy-coordinate system superimposed on a uv-coordinate system so that the origin in the xy-system is the point $(1, 0)$ in the uv-system (Figure 1–25). Now visualize the x-axis as having been "unwound" from the circle with equation $u^2 + v^2 = 1$, so that associated with each value of x is the ordered pair (u, v) (Figure 1–26).

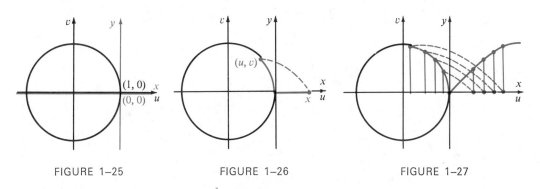

FIGURE 1–25   FIGURE 1–26   FIGURE 1–27

If, for each x, we use the ordinate v of the point on the circle associated with the arc length x as the ordinate y of the point (x, y) in the xy-plane, we obtain the graph of $y = \sin x$ (Figure 1–27).

If, on the other hand, we use the abscissa u of the point on the circle associated with the arc length x as the ordinate y of the point (x, y) in the xy-plane, we obtain the graph of $y = \cos x$ (Figure 1–28).

The graphs of cos and sin are called **wave graphs** or **sine waves**.

Any segment of such a graph over an interval on the horizontal axis with length equal to a single fundamental period of the function is called a **cycle of the wave.**

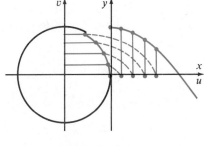

FIGURE 1–28

Alternatively, you can say that the set of number pairs $(x, \cos x)$ or $(x, \sin x)$ in the function over an interval

$$c \le x \le c + 2\pi, \qquad c \in \mathfrak{R},$$

is a **cycle of the function.**

One-half of the vertical distance between the maximum and minimum points on a sine wave is called the **amplitude of the wave.** Similarly, one-half of the difference between the maximum and minimum values of a periodic function over one fundamental period is called the **amplitude of the function.** Thus, the amplitude both of the sine function and of the cosine function is

$$\tfrac{1}{2}[1 - (-1)] = \tfrac{1}{2}(2) = 1.$$

Exercises 1–7

In Exercises 1–4, make a neat sketch of the graph of cos x or sin x for $-\pi \le x \le 2\pi$, and draw segments representing ordinates illustrating the given identity. In each case, assume a to have a value as indicated, but bear in mind that a can represent *any* real number.

Example $\sin(a - \pi) = -\sin a, \quad \dfrac{\pi}{2} < a < \pi$

Solution

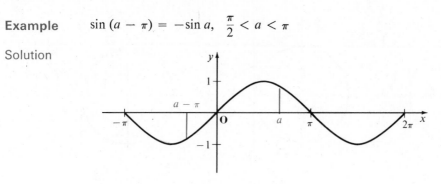

You can imagine the point a "moving" along the x-axis from 0 toward 2π and, accordingly, the point $a - \pi$ moving from $-\pi$ toward π. Notice that the two vertical line segments representing $\sin a$ and $\sin(a - \pi)$ will always have the same length and will be on opposite sides of the x-axis.

A   **1.** $\cos(a - \pi) = -\cos a, \quad \pi < a < \dfrac{3\pi}{2}$ **3.** $\sin(-a) = -\sin a, \quad 0 < a < \dfrac{\pi}{2}$

2. $\cos(-a) = \cos a, \quad 0 < a < \dfrac{\pi}{2}$ **4.** $\sin(2\pi - a) = -\sin a, \quad 0 < a < \dfrac{\pi}{2}$

5. For each of the given identities, make a neat sketch of the graphs of $\cos x$ and $\sin x$ on the same set of axes, for $0 \le x \le \dfrac{\pi}{2}$, and draw segments illustrating the identity. Assume $0 < a < \dfrac{\pi}{4}$.

   (a) $\cos\left(\dfrac{\pi}{2} - a\right) = \sin a$ **(b)** $\sin\left(\dfrac{\pi}{2} - a\right) = \cos a$

6. For each of the given identities, make a neat sketch of the graphs of $\cos x$ and $\sin x$ on the same set of axes, for $0 \le x \le \pi$, and draw segments illustrating the identity. Assume $0 < a < \dfrac{\pi}{4}$.

   (a) $\cos\left(a + \dfrac{\pi}{2}\right) = -\sin a$ **(b)** $\sin\left(a + \dfrac{\pi}{2}\right) = \cos a$

In Exercises 7–14, graph the two given sets on the same set of axes, for
$-2\pi \leq x \leq 2\pi$. Then give the coordinates of the points of intersection of
these two sets.

Example $\{(x, y): y = \sin x\}, \{(x, y): y = \frac{1}{2}\}$

Solution

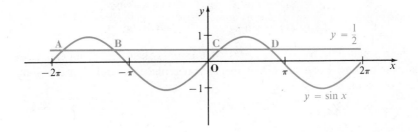

The coordinates of the points of intersection are:

$$A = \left(-\frac{11\pi}{6}, \frac{1}{2}\right) \qquad B = \left(-\frac{7\pi}{6}, \frac{1}{2}\right) \qquad C = \left(\frac{\pi}{6}, \frac{1}{2}\right) \qquad D = \left(\frac{5\pi}{6}, \frac{1}{2}\right)$$

7. $\{(x, y): y = \sin x\}, \{(x, y): y = -\frac{1}{2}\}$

8. $\{(x, y): y = \sin x\}, \left\{(x, y): y = \frac{\sqrt{3}}{2}\right\}$

9. $\{(x, y): y = \sin x\}, \{(x, y): y = 0\}$

10. $\{(x, y): y = \cos x\}, \{(x, y): y = \frac{1}{2}\}$

11. $\{(x, y): y = \cos x\}, \left\{(x, y): y = -\frac{\sqrt{3}}{2}\right\}$

12. $\{(x, y): y = \cos x\}, \{(x, y): y = 1\}$

B 13. $\{(x, y): y = \sin x\}, \{(x, y): |y| = 1\}$ **14.** $\{(x, y): y = \sin x\}, \{(x, y): y^2 = \frac{1}{4}\}$

15. Make a careful sketch of the graphs of cos and sin on the same set of
axes for $0 \leq x \leq 2\pi$, and use this sketch to determine each of the
following sets. Show your answers as graphs on a real number line.
  (a) $\{x: \sin x = \cos x\}$ **(d)** $\{x: \sin x \geq 0 \text{ and } \cos x \leq 0\}$
  (b) $\{x: \sin x \geq \cos x\}$ **(e)** $\{x: \sin x < 0 \text{ and } \cos x \geq 0\}$
  (c) $\{x: \sin x \geq 0 \text{ and } \cos x \geq 0\}$ **(f)** $\{x: \cos x < 0 \text{ and } \sin x = \frac{1}{2}\}$

16. Graph for $-4\pi \leq y \leq 4\pi$:   **(a)** $\{(x, y): x = \cos y\}$ **(b)** $\{(x, y): x = \sin y\}$

C 17. Solve for $-2\pi \leq x \leq 2\pi$:   **(a)** $|\sin x| = \frac{1}{2}$ **(b)** $\cos^2 x = \frac{1}{2}$ **(c)** $|\sin x| = |\cos x|$

18. Graph each set for $-2\pi \leq x \leq 2\pi$:
  (a) $\{(x, y): y = |\sin x|\}$ **(b)** $\{(x, y): y = \sin |x|\}$ **(c)** $\{(x, y): y = |\sin |x| |\}$

1–8   *Properties of cos and sin for 2x and $\frac{x}{2}$*

The key identities among the many you have encountered in the preceding sections are the sum and difference formulas:

$$\cos (x_2 \pm x_1) = \cos x_2 \cos x_1 \mp \sin x_2 \sin x_1 \qquad (1)$$

$$\sin (x_2 \pm x_1) = \sin x_2 \cos x_1 \pm \cos x_2 \sin x_1 \qquad (2)$$

From these you can derive all the others. Moreover, you still have not exhausted all the possibilities. For example, if in (1) you replace x_2 and x_1 with x and consider the sum,

$$\cos (x + x) = \cos x \cos x - \sin x \sin x,$$

you find that for every real number x

▲ $$\cos 2x = \cos^2 x - \sin^2 x. \qquad (3)$$

Because $\cos^2 x + \sin^2 x = 1$ for all $x \in \Re$, you can replace $\sin^2 x$ in (3) with $1 - \cos^2 x$ to obtain the alternative form

▲ $$\cos 2x = 2 \cos^2 x - 1. \qquad (4)$$

Similarly, when you replace $\cos^2 x$ with $1 - \sin^2 x$, you obtain the alternative form

▲ $$\cos 2x = 1 - 2 \sin^2 x. \qquad (5)$$

To find an expression for $\sin 2x$, replace x_2 and x_1 with x in (2). Then

$$\sin (x + x) = \sin x \cos x + \cos x \sin x,$$

from which it follows that for each real number x,

▲ $$\sin 2x = 2 \sin x \cos x. \qquad (6)$$

Identities (4) and (5) can be used to develop relationships for $\cos \frac{x}{2}$ and $\sin \frac{x}{2}$. To do this, replace x with $\frac{x}{2}$ in (4) and (5) to produce, respectively,

$$\cos 2 \left(\frac{x}{2}\right) = 2 \cos^2 \frac{x}{2} - 1, \qquad \cos 2 \left(\frac{x}{2}\right) = 1 - 2 \sin^2 \frac{x}{2},$$

from which you obtain

$$\cos x = 2 \cos^2 \frac{x}{2} - 1, \qquad \cos x = 1 - 2 \sin^2 \frac{x}{2}.$$

It then follows that

$$\cos^2\frac{x}{2} = \frac{1}{2}(1 + \cos x), \qquad \sin^2\frac{x}{2} = \frac{1}{2}(1 - \cos x),$$

and from these you obtain the formulas:

▲ $\cos\frac{x}{2} = \sqrt{\frac{1}{2}(1 + \cos x)}$ or $\cos\frac{x}{2} = -\sqrt{\frac{1}{2}(1 + \cos x)}$ (7)

$\sin\frac{x}{2} = \sqrt{\frac{1}{2}(1 - \cos x)}$ or $\sin\frac{x}{2} = -\sqrt{\frac{1}{2}(1 - \cos x)}$ (8)

where the positive or negative value is chosen according as $\cos\frac{x}{2}$ or $\sin\frac{x}{2}$, respectively, is positive or negative.

Exercises 1–8

A 1. Copy and complete the table, using identities (7) and (8). If an entry is expressed in radical form, write it also in two-place decimal form. For example,

$$\cos\frac{\pi}{12} = \cos\frac{1}{2}\left(\frac{\pi}{6}\right)$$

$$= \sqrt{\frac{1}{2}\left(1 + \frac{\sqrt{3}}{2}\right)}$$

$$\doteq \sqrt{.93} \doteq .96.$$

x	0	$\frac{\pi}{6}$	$\frac{\pi}{4}$	$\frac{3\pi}{4}$	$\frac{5\pi}{6}$	π
$\frac{x}{2}$	0	$\frac{\pi}{12}$	?	?	?	?
$\cos\frac{x}{2}$	1	$\sqrt{\frac{1}{2}\left(1+\frac{\sqrt{3}}{2}\right)}$ $\doteq .96$	?	?	?	?
$\sin\frac{x}{2}$	0	?	?	?	?	?

(A table of square roots is in Table 4, page 401.)

2. Copy and complete the table, using identities (5) and (6). Express your entries as in Exercise 1.

x	$\frac{2\pi}{3}$	$\frac{3\pi}{4}$	$\frac{5\pi}{6}$	$\frac{7\pi}{6}$	$\frac{4\pi}{3}$
$2x$	?	?	?	?	?
$\cos 2x$	?	?	?	?	?
$\sin 2x$	?	?	?	?	?

3. If $\sin x = \frac{4}{5}$ and $\frac{\pi}{2} < x < \pi$, find the value of:

(a) $\cos x$ **(b)** $\sin 2x$ **(c)** $\sin\frac{x}{2}$ **(d)** $\cos 2x$ **(e)** $\cos\frac{x}{2}$

4. If $\cos x = -\dfrac{2}{3}$ and $\pi < x < \dfrac{3\pi}{2}$, find the value of:

    (a) $\sin x$ **(b)** $\sin 2x$ **(c)** $\sin \dfrac{x}{2}$ **(d)** $\cos 2x$ **(e)** $\cos \dfrac{x}{2}$

5. If x is in the quadrant indicated, decide which quadrant or quadrants $\dfrac{x}{2}$ and $2x$ may be in and copy and complete the table at the right.

x	Quadrant			
	I	II	III	IV
$\dfrac{x}{2}$	I	?	?	?
$2x$	I or II	?	?	?

B   **6.** If $\sin x = \dfrac{1}{3}$ and $0 < x < \dfrac{\pi}{2}$:

    (a) Find $\cos x$ using the identity $\cos^2 x + \sin^2 x = 1$.

    (b) Find $\cos 2x$ and $\sin 2x$ using Identities (5) and (6).

    (c) Check your answers to part (b) by the identity $\cos^2 (2x) + \sin^2 (2x) = 1$.

Verify each of the following identities.

    7. $\cos 2x + 2 \sin^2 x = 1$ **9.** $(\sin x + \cos x)^2 = 1 + \sin 2x$

    8. $\sin 2x \cos x - \cos 2x \sin x = \sin x$ **10.** $(\sin x - \cos x)^2 = 1 - \sin 2x$

    11. $\cos^4 x - \sin^4 x = \cos 2x$

    12. $2 \sin \dfrac{x}{2} \cos \dfrac{x}{2} = \sin x$

C   **13.** $\sin 3x = 3 \sin x - 4 \sin^3 x$ (*Hint:* $3x = 2x + x$)

    14. $\cos 3x = 4 \cos^3 x - 3 \cos x$

    15. $\sin 4x = 4 \sin x \cos x - 8 \sin^3 x \cos x$

    16. $\cos 4x = 1 - 8 \sin^2 x \cos^2 x$

1–9   *Values for cos x and sin x*

In the preceding sections, you have seen how identities can be used to find values for $\sin x$ and $\cos x$ for many special values of x.

Moreover, knowing that $\sin \dfrac{\pi}{6} = \dfrac{1}{2}$ and $\cos \dfrac{\pi}{6} = \dfrac{\sqrt{3}}{2}$, you can use the identities

$$\cos \frac{x}{2} = \pm \sqrt{\frac{1}{2}(1 + \cos x)} \quad \text{and} \quad \sin \frac{x}{2} = \pm \sqrt{\frac{1}{2}(1 - \cos x)}$$

to find values for $\cos \dfrac{\pi}{12}$ and $\sin \dfrac{\pi}{12}$, $\cos \dfrac{\pi}{24}$ and $\sin \dfrac{\pi}{24}$, and so on. With the help of reduction formulas, these values can then be used to find $\cos x$ and $\sin x$ for many values of x in the other quadrants.

Because

$$\sin\left(\frac{\pi}{2} - x\right) = \cos x, \qquad \text{and} \qquad \cos\left(\frac{\pi}{2} - x\right) = \sin x,$$

it is possible to list just values for $\cos x$, say, and have a table of $\sin x$ in backward order. The abbreviated table (1) at the right has been constructed in this way, with

$$y = \frac{\pi}{2} - x.$$

(1)

x	$\cos x$	
0	1	$\dfrac{\pi}{2}$
$\dfrac{\pi}{6}$	$\dfrac{\sqrt{3}}{2}$	$\dfrac{\pi}{3}$
$\dfrac{\pi}{4}$	$\dfrac{\sqrt{2}}{2}$	$\dfrac{\pi}{4}$
$\dfrac{\pi}{3}$	$\dfrac{1}{2}$	$\dfrac{\pi}{6}$
$\dfrac{\pi}{2}$	0	0
	$\sin y$	y

(2)

x	$\cos x$	$\sin x$	
0	1	0	$\dfrac{\pi}{2}$
$\dfrac{\pi}{6}$	$\dfrac{\sqrt{3}}{2}$	$\dfrac{1}{2}$	$\dfrac{\pi}{3}$
$\dfrac{\pi}{4}$	$\dfrac{\sqrt{2}}{2}$	$\dfrac{\sqrt{2}}{2}$	$\dfrac{\pi}{4}$
$\dfrac{\pi}{3}$	$\dfrac{1}{2}$	$\dfrac{\sqrt{3}}{2}$	$\dfrac{\pi}{6}$
$\dfrac{\pi}{2}$	0	1	0
	$\sin y$	$\cos y$	y

To find $\cos x$, you locate x in the left-hand column and read $\cos x$ directly to the right in the center column.

To find $\sin y$, you locate y in the right-hand column and read $\sin y$ directly to the left in the center column.

Let us add another column to this table so that $\cos x$ and $\sin x$ can both be determined from the left-hand side, and $\cos y$ and $\sin y$ can both be determined from the right-hand side; this makes table (2).

But now we only need half table (2), that is, table (3). In this table, to find $\cos x$ (or $\cos y$), you read down the first and second columns for $0 \le x \le \dfrac{\pi}{4}$, and up the third and fourth columns for $\dfrac{\pi}{4} \le y \le \dfrac{\pi}{2}$. For $\sin x$ (or $\sin y$), you read down the first and third columns and up the second and fourth.

(3)

x	$\cos x$	$\sin x$	
0	1	0	$\dfrac{\pi}{2}$
$\dfrac{\pi}{6}$	$\dfrac{\sqrt{3}}{2}$	$\dfrac{1}{2}$	$\dfrac{\pi}{3}$
$\dfrac{\pi}{4}$	$\dfrac{\sqrt{2}}{2}$	$\dfrac{\sqrt{2}}{2}$	$\dfrac{\pi}{4}$
	$\sin y$	$\cos y$	y

Table 1 at the back of the book gives three-decimal-digit approximations of $\cos\left(m \cdot \dfrac{\pi}{2}\right)$ and $\sin\left(m \cdot \dfrac{\pi}{2}\right)$ for two-digit decimal fractions of $\dfrac{\pi}{2}$. The values of $\cos\left(m \cdot \dfrac{\pi}{2}\right)$ and $\sin\left(m \cdot \dfrac{\pi}{2}\right)$ must be approximated because, except for a very few values of m, $\cos\left(m \cdot \dfrac{\pi}{2}\right)$ and $\sin\left(m \cdot \dfrac{\pi}{2}\right)$ are irrational numbers.

At the right is an extract from Table 1. To find an approximation for $\cos \dfrac{0.23\pi}{2}$, for example, you locate 0.23 in the left-hand column and read 0.935 directly to the right under $\cos\left(m \cdot \dfrac{\pi}{2}\right)$.

Similarly, to obtain an approximation for $\sin \dfrac{0.78\pi}{2}$, you locate 0.78 in the right-hand column and read 0.941 across to the left above $\sin\left(n \cdot \dfrac{\pi}{2}\right)$.

m	$\cos\left(m \cdot \dfrac{\pi}{2}\right)$	$\sin\left(m \cdot \dfrac{\pi}{2}\right)$	
0.21	0.946	0.324	0.79
0.22	0.941	0.339	0.78
0.23	0.935	0.353	0.77
	$\sin\left(n \cdot \dfrac{\pi}{2}\right)$	$\cos\left(n \cdot \dfrac{\pi}{2}\right)$	n

To find approximate values for sin and cos between those listed in the table, it is necessary to use linear interpolation. This process will be discussed in Chapter 5, when we shall need to obtain such function values.

Exercises 1–9

In Exercises 1–12, use Table 1, page 391, to find approximations for sin x and cos x when x is as given. Use reduction formulas as required.

Example $\dfrac{2.32\pi}{2}$

Solution   Since the table covers only $0 \le x \le \dfrac{\pi}{2}$, the given value is outside the table. First, you should observe that

$$\frac{2 \cdot 32\pi}{2} = \frac{2\pi}{2} + \frac{0.32\pi}{2} = \pi + \frac{0.32\pi}{2}.$$

Thus, you can use the reduction formulas:

$$\sin(\pi + x) = -\sin x$$
$$\cos(\pi + x) = -\cos x$$

You then have:

$$\sin \frac{2.32\pi}{2} = \sin\left(\pi + 0.32 \cdot \frac{\pi}{2}\right) = -\sin\left(0.32 \cdot \frac{\pi}{2}\right)$$

Similarly for the cosine,

$$\cos \frac{2.32\pi}{2} = -\cos\left(0.32 \cdot \frac{\pi}{2}\right).$$

Using the table, you locate 0.32 in the left-hand column, and read to the right to find the values you seek:

$$-\sin\left(0.32 \cdot \frac{\pi}{2}\right) \doteq -0.482 \quad \text{and} \quad -\cos\left(0.32 \cdot \frac{\pi}{2}\right) \doteq -0.876$$

A
1. $\dfrac{0.68\pi}{2}$

2. $\dfrac{0.78\pi}{2}$

3. $\dfrac{0.28\pi}{2}$

4. $\dfrac{0.42\pi}{2}$

5. $-\dfrac{2.24\pi}{2}$

6. $-\dfrac{2.18\pi}{2}$

7. 1.23π

$\left(\textit{Hint: } 1.23\pi = \dfrac{2.46\pi}{2}\right)$

8. 0.93π

9. -1.11π

10. -3.52π

11. $\dfrac{5.76\pi}{2}$

12. $\dfrac{7.38\pi}{2}$

From Table 1, find the smallest positive approximation for *x* for which each of the given equations (Exercises 13–20) is true.

Example $\cos x = 0.412$, and $\sin x < 0$.

Solution You first locate 0.412 in one of the columns in the body of Table 1. Since it is in the second column, and you want *x* so that $\cos x = 0.412$, read across to the right-hand column and find 0.73. Note, though, that $0.73 \cdot \dfrac{\pi}{2}$ corresponds to a point in the *first* quadrant, while $\sin x < 0$ together with $\cos x > 0$ implies that the value you seek corresponds to a point in the *fourth* quadrant. Because $\cos x = \cos(-x)$, you know that $x = -0.73 \cdot \dfrac{\pi}{2}$ will satisfy the equation. You must have a positive value for *x*, however, so you use

$$\cos(x + 2\pi) = \cos x$$

to produce

$$\cos\left[-0.73\left(\frac{\pi}{2}\right) + 4\left(\frac{\pi}{2}\right)\right] = \cos\left[(-0.73 + 4)\frac{\pi}{2}\right] = \cos\frac{3.27\pi}{2}.$$

Thus $\dfrac{3.27\pi}{2}$ is the required approximation for *x*.

13. $\cos x = 0.946$, $\sin x > 0$

14. $\sin x = 0.613$, $\cos x > 0$

15. $\sin x = 0.861$, $\cos x > 0$

16. $\cos x = 0.279$, $\sin x > 0$

17. $\cos x = 0.946$, $\sin x < 0$

18. $\sin x = 0.613$, $\cos x < 0$

19. $\sin x = 0.861$, $\cos x < 0$

20. $\cos x = 0.279$, $\sin x < 0$

Chapter Summary

1. A **periodic function** f is a function having the property that for some nonzero number p and for every x in its domain, $x + p$ and $x - p$ are also in the domain and $f(x + p) = f(x)$. The number p is called a **period** of f; and if f has a least positive period, that period is called the **fundamental period** of f.

2. **Circular functions** are defined by means of the unit circle with equation $u^2 + v^2 = 1$, and an x number line that is thought of as being wound endlessly about the circle in both directions. This winding establishes a periodic function with domain the set $\Re$ of real numbers x, range the set of coordinates (u, v) of points on the unit circle, and fundamental period 2π.

3. If the coordinates of the point (u, v) corresponding to the real number x are written as $(\cos x, \sin x)$, then the basic circular functions **cosine (cos)** and **sine (sin)** are defined by

$$\cos = \{(x, y)\colon \ y = \cos x, \ x \in \Re\},$$
$$\sin = \{(x, y)\colon \ y = \sin x, \ x \in \Re\}.$$

   The range of each of these functions is $\{y\colon \ y \in \Re, \ |y| \leq 1\}$.

4. The fundamental period of cos and sin is 2π.

5. A function f is **even** if for every x in its domain, $-x$ is also in its domain and $f(-x) = f(x)$. Similarly, f is **odd** if for every x in its domain, $-x$ is also in its domain and $f(-x) = -f(x)$. The function cos is even, whereas sin is odd.

6. The periodic and other properties of the cos and sin functions are useful in drawing their graphs, and their graphs, in turn, assist us in recalling these properties. The graphs of both the cos and the sin functions are called **sine waves**.

7. Values of $\cos x$ and $\sin x$ can be determined by geometric considerations for special values of x, including $0, \dfrac{\pi}{6}, \dfrac{\pi}{4}, \dfrac{\pi}{3}$, and $\dfrac{\pi}{2}$. Prepared tables give values of $\cos x$ and $\sin x$ for these and other values of x in Quadrant I. **Reduction identities** (see page 30) can then be used to determine $\cos x$ and $\sin x$ for additional values of x.

8. To prove that a given sentence involving circular functions is an identity, you may show either that the sentence is equivalent to a known identity (or true statement) or that one member of the given sentence can be validly transformed into the other member.

Chapter Test

1–1   **1.** If f is a periodic function with fundamental period p and domain $\Re$, then state which of the following are always equal to $f(p)$:

$$f(2p), \quad f(0), \quad f(p^2), \quad f(p + 1)$$

1–2   **2.** Find the value of $\cos x$ if $\sin x = -\frac{12}{13}$ and $\pi < x < \frac{3\pi}{2}$.

1–3   **3.** Make a table of the values of $\cos x$ and $\sin x$ for

$$x = \frac{2\pi}{3}, \frac{3\pi}{4}, \frac{5\pi}{6}.$$

1–4   **4.** Simplify $\cos\dfrac{\pi}{6}\cos\dfrac{\pi}{3} - \sin\dfrac{\pi}{6}\sin\dfrac{\pi}{3}$.

1–5   **5.** Derive an identity expressing $\cos\left(\dfrac{\pi}{4} + x\right)$ in terms of $\cos x$ or $\sin x$ or both.

1–6   **6.** Verify that $\sin\left(x - \dfrac{\pi}{2}\right) = -\cos x$ is an identity.

1–7   **7.** Graph the set $\{(x, y): y = \cos x, 0 \le x \le 2\pi\}$ and draw segments representing ordinates illustrating the identity

$$\cos(2\pi - a) = \cos a$$

for $0 < a < \dfrac{\pi}{2}$.

1–8   **8.** Given that $\sin x = -\frac{2}{3}$ and $\pi < x < \dfrac{3\pi}{2}$, find the value of $\cos 2x$.

1–9   **9.** From the partial table given below, determine the least positive value z for which $\sin z = -0.941$ and $\cos z < 0$.

m	$\sin\left(m \cdot \dfrac{\pi}{2}\right)$	$\cos\left(m \cdot \dfrac{\pi}{2}\right)$	
0.22	0.339	0.941	0.78
	$\cos\left(n \cdot \dfrac{\pi}{2}\right)$	$\sin\left(n \cdot \dfrac{\pi}{2}\right)$	n

Computer Investigations

If you have access to an electronic computer that will accept BASIC, you may wish to try the following program. It will print out approximate positions of some points on the graph of

$$y = \sin x$$

for values of x from -6.6 to 6.6, as shown on page 47.

```
10    PRINT "Y = SIN X"
20    PRINT
30    LET L=20
40    LET M=L+(66-L)/2
50    PRINT "  X        Y"
60    FOR X1=-66 TO 66 STEP 2
70    LET X=.1*X1
80    LET Y=SIN(X)
90    LET Y2=10*Y+M
100   IF X1=0 THEN 210
110   IF Y2<L THEN 250
120   IF Y2>66 THEN 250
130   IF Y2<M THEN 190
140   IF Y2=M THEN 170
150   PRINT X;
151   PRINT TAB(6);Y;
152   PRINT TAB(M);"!"; TAB(Y2);"*"
160   GO TO 220
170   PRINT X;
171   PRINT TAB(6);Y;
172   PRINT TAB(Y2);"*"
180   GO TO 220
190   PRINT X;
191   PRINT TAB(6);Y;
192   PRINT TAB(Y2);"*"; TAB(M);"!"
200   GO TO 220
210   PRINT X;
211   PRINT TAB(6);Y;
212   PRINT TAB(Y2);"*"; TAB(67);"---Y"
220   NEXT X1
230   PRINT TAB(M);"X"
240   GO TO 260
250   PRINT "TOO WIDE"
260   END
```

Notice that 5 vertical line feeds make 1 unit on the X-axis, while 10 horizontal spaces make 1 unit on the Y-axis. By studying the printed coordinates and noting that the TAB function acts similarly to the INT function in counting the number of spaces, you can see why the graphs have "flat" portions.

By changing lines 10 and 80, you can also approximate portions of the graphs of the following:

$Y = COS(X)$ $Y = SIN(-X)$ $Y = COS(-X)$

$Y = SIN(2 * X)$ $Y = COS(2 * X)$ $Y = SIN(X/2)$

$Y = ABS(COS(X))$

$Y = SIN(ABS(X))$

By inserting

75 LET P1 = 3.14159

and changing lines 10 and 80, you can approximate portions of the graphs of:

$Y = COS(P1 - X)$

$Y = COS(X - P1)$

$Y = COS(X + P1)$

$Y = COS(P1/2 - X)$

$Y = COS(X - P1/2)$

$Y = COS(X + P1/2)$

$Y = SIN(P1 - X)$

$Y = SIN(X - P1)$

$Y = SIN(X + P1)$

$Y = SIN(P1/2 - X)$

$Y = SIN(X - P1/2)$

$Y = SIN(X + P1/2)$

Compare your results with graphs of:

$y = \cos x$ $y = \sin x$

$y = \cos(-x)$ $y = \sin(-x)$

RUN

Y = SIN X

X	Y
-6.6	-.311542
-6.4	-.116549
-6.2	8.30896E-02
-6	.279415
-5.8	.464603
-5.6	.631267
-5.4	.772765
-5.2	.883455
-5	.958924
-4.8	.996164
-4.6	.993691
-4.4	.951602
-4.2	.871576
-4	.756803
-3.8	.611858
-3.6	.44252
-3.4	.255541
-3.2	5.83742E-02
-3	-.14112
-2.8	-.334989
-2.6	-.515501
-2.4	-.675463
-2.2	-.808497
-2	-.909297
-1.8	-.973848
-1.6	-.999574
-1.4	-.98545
-1.2	-.932039
-1	-.841471
-.8	-.717356
-.6	-.564643
-.4	-.389418
-.2	-.198669
0	0
.2	.198669
.4	.389418
.6	.564643
.8	.717356
1	.841471
1.2	.932039
1.4	.98545
1.6	.999574
1.8	.973848
2	.909297
2.2	.808496
2.4	.675463
2.6	.515501
2.8	.334988
3	.14112
3.2	-5.83742E-02
3.4	-.255541
3.6	-.44252
3.8	-.611858
4	-.756803
4.2	-.871576
4.4	-.951602
4.6	-.993691
4.8	-.996164
5	-.958924
5.2	-.883455
5.4	-.772765
5.6	-.631267
5.8	-.464603
6	-.279415
6.2	-8.30896E-02
6.4	.116549
6.6	.311542

---Y

X

END

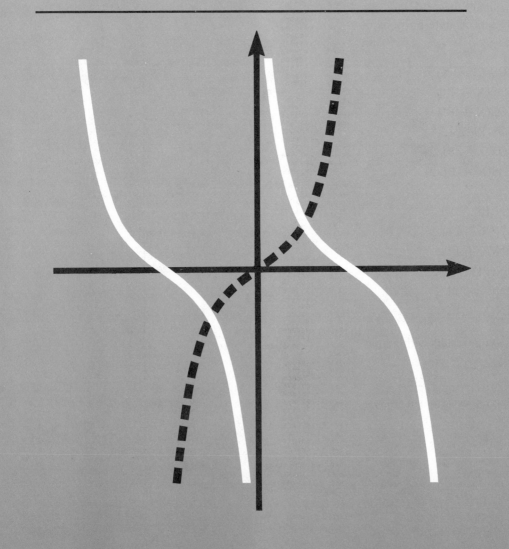

Chapter Two

Four More
Circular Functions

OBJECTIVES

1. To learn the properties of the tangent, secant, cosecant, and cotangent functions.
2. To prove identities involving tan x, sec x, csc x, cot x, and so on.

The Tangent Function

2–1 *The Function tan*

You can use the functions sin and cos to define other circular functions. In particular, the **tangent function**, abbreviated **tan**, is defined as follows:

▲   For every x for which $\cos x \neq 0$,

$$\tan = \left\{ (x, y)\colon\ y = \tan x = \frac{\sin x}{\cos x} \right\}.$$

Since $\cos x = 0$ if and only if $x = (2k + 1)\dfrac{\pi}{2}$, $k \in J$, the domain of tan is

$$\left\{ x\colon\ x \in \Re,\ x \neq (2k + 1)\frac{\pi}{2},\ k \in J \right\}.$$

The range is $\Re$, the set of all real numbers.

Because cos x and sin x can be interpreted geometrically as the abscissa and ordinate of a point on the unit circle, tan x can be interpreted as the ratio of the ordinate to the abscissa (Figure 2–1).

For example, since

$$\sin \frac{\pi}{6} = \frac{1}{2} \quad \text{and} \quad \cos \frac{\pi}{6} = \frac{\sqrt{3}}{2} \doteq \frac{1.732}{2} \doteq 0.87,$$

you have

$$\tan \frac{\pi}{6} = \frac{\frac{1}{2}}{\frac{\sqrt{3}}{2}} = \frac{1}{\sqrt{3}} = \frac{\sqrt{3}}{3} \doteq \frac{1.732}{3} \doteq 0.58.$$

By similar computations, you can find tan x for other values of x. Some of these are given in the brief table that follows.

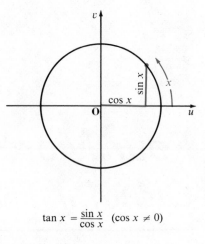

$$\tan x = \frac{\sin x}{\cos x} \quad (\cos x \neq 0)$$

FIGURE 2–1

VALUES FOR TAN X

x	$\cos x$	$\sin x$	$\tan x = \dfrac{\sin x}{\cos x}$
0	1	0	0
$\dfrac{\pi}{12}$	$\dfrac{\sqrt{6}+\sqrt{2}}{4} \doteq 0.97$	$\dfrac{\sqrt{6}-\sqrt{2}}{4} \doteq 0.26$	$2-\sqrt{3} \doteq 0.27$
$\dfrac{\pi}{6}$	$\dfrac{\sqrt{3}}{2} \doteq 0.87$	$\dfrac{1}{2} = 0.5$	$\dfrac{1}{\sqrt{3}} \doteq 0.58$
$\dfrac{\pi}{4}$	$\dfrac{\sqrt{2}}{2} \doteq 0.71$	$\dfrac{\sqrt{2}}{2} \doteq 0.71$	1
$\dfrac{\pi}{3}$	$\dfrac{1}{2} = 0.5$	$\dfrac{\sqrt{3}}{2} \doteq 0.87$	$\sqrt{3} \doteq 1.73$
$\dfrac{5\pi}{12}$	$\dfrac{\sqrt{6}-\sqrt{2}}{4} \doteq 0.26$	$\dfrac{\sqrt{6}+\sqrt{2}}{4} \doteq 0.97$	$\dfrac{1}{2-\sqrt{3}} \doteq 3.73$
$\dfrac{\pi}{2}$	0	1	Undefined

Because sin is an odd function and cos is an even function, it follows that tan is an odd function, since

$$\tan(-x) = \frac{\sin(-x)}{\cos(-x)} = \frac{-\sin x}{\cos x} = -\frac{\sin x}{\cos x} = -\tan x \qquad (1)$$

for all x in the domain of tan.

A Cartesian graph of the tangent function can now be drawn. First we plot the points corresponding to

$$x = 0, \quad \frac{\pi}{12}, \quad \frac{\pi}{6}, \quad \frac{\pi}{4}, \quad \frac{\pi}{3}, \quad \text{and} \quad \frac{5\pi}{12}$$

from the preceding table (Figure 2–2).

To complete the graph of tan x for $0 \leq x < \frac{\pi}{2}$, we note that as x increases from 0 toward $\frac{\pi}{2}$, sin x increases from 0 toward 1, while cos x decreases from 1 toward 0; accordingly, the numbers

$$\tan x = \frac{\sin x}{\cos x}$$

must increase over the same interval, becoming very large for values of x close to $\frac{\pi}{2}$. Indeed, by choosing x less than but sufficiently close to $\frac{\pi}{2}$, you can obtain a value for tan x as large as you please; this is expressed by saying that the graph of $y = \tan x$ is **asymptotic** from the left to the line with equation $x = \frac{\pi}{2}$. The graph of $y = \tan x$ in the interval $0 \leq x < \frac{\pi}{2}$ is shown in Figure 2–3. There is, of course, no point on the graph with x-coordinate $\frac{\pi}{2}$.

From the graph in Figure 2–3 and the fact that tan is an odd function, the portion of the graph of tan x for $-\frac{\pi}{2} < x \leq 0$ can be drawn. That is, for every point $(a, \tan a)$, $0 \leq a < \frac{\pi}{2}$, there is a point $(-a, -\tan a)$, $-\frac{\pi}{2} < -a \leq 0$, on the graph of tan. Thus, in Figure 2–4, we have the graph of tan in the interval $-\frac{\pi}{2} < x \leq 0$, and Figures 2–3 and 2–4 illustrate the property $\tan(-x) = -\tan x$.

Since the graph of tan x for $0 \leq x < \frac{\pi}{2}$ is *asymptotic from the left* to the line with equation $x = \frac{\pi}{2}$, the graph of tan x for $-\frac{\pi}{2} < x \leq 0$ is *asymptotic from the right* to the line with equation $x = -\frac{\pi}{2}$.

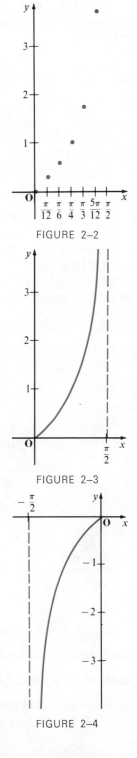

FIGURE 2–2

FIGURE 2–3

FIGURE 2–4

Unlike cos and sin, for which the fundamental period is 2π, tan has fundamental period π. You can verify this by first observing that for all x in the domain of tan,

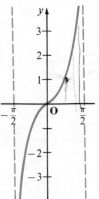

▲ $\quad \tan(x + \pi) = \dfrac{\sin(x + \pi)}{\cos(x + \pi)} = \dfrac{-\sin x}{-\cos x} = \dfrac{\sin x}{\cos x} = \tan x. \quad$ (2)

Thus, tan is periodic with period π.

To show that π *is the fundamental period of tan*, it is necessary to show that π is the least positive period of tan. That this is true is evident from Figure 2–5, since tan is one-to-one in the interval

$$-\frac{\pi}{2} < x < \frac{\pi}{2}$$

FIGURE 2–5

and the length of this interval is π.

Since tan has fundamental period π, you can obtain as much as you please of its graph by reproducing in either direction along the x-axis the portion of the

graph over the interval $-\dfrac{\pi}{2} < x < \dfrac{\pi}{2}$, as illustrated in Figure 2–6.

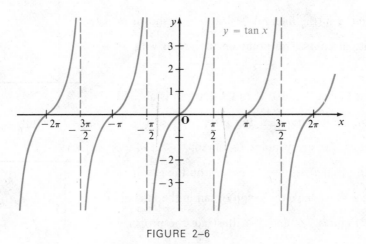

FIGURE 2–6

To find values of $\tan x$ where $x < 0$ or $x > \dfrac{\pi}{2}$, we can use the facts that tan is an odd function and that its fundamental period is π to express $\tan x$ in terms of $\tan x_1$, where $0 \le x_1 < \dfrac{\pi}{2}$. Then $\tan x_1 = \dfrac{\sin x_1}{\cos x_1}$ can be determined from our previous knowledge concerning the sin and cos functions.

Example   Evaluate:

(a) $\tan \dfrac{13\pi}{4}$ (b) $\tan \left(-\dfrac{5\pi}{3} \right)$ (c) $\tan \dfrac{15\pi}{4}$

Solution   (a) $\tan \dfrac{13\pi}{4} = \tan \left(\dfrac{\pi}{4} + 3\pi \right) = \tan \dfrac{\pi}{4}$

$$= \dfrac{\sin \dfrac{\pi}{4}}{\cos \dfrac{\pi}{4}} = \dfrac{\dfrac{\sqrt{2}}{2}}{\dfrac{\sqrt{2}}{2}} = 1$$

(b) $\tan \left(-\dfrac{5\pi}{3} \right) = \tan \left[\dfrac{\pi}{3} + (-2\pi) \right] = \tan \dfrac{\pi}{3}$

$$= \dfrac{\sin \dfrac{\pi}{3}}{\cos \dfrac{\pi}{3}} = \dfrac{\dfrac{\sqrt{3}}{2}}{\dfrac{1}{2}} = \sqrt{3}$$

(c) $\tan \dfrac{15\pi}{4} = \tan \left(-\dfrac{\pi}{4} + 4\pi \right) = \tan \left(-\dfrac{\pi}{4} \right) = -\tan \dfrac{\pi}{4}$

$$= -\dfrac{\sin \dfrac{\pi}{4}}{\cos \dfrac{\pi}{4}} = -\dfrac{\dfrac{\sqrt{2}}{2}}{\dfrac{\sqrt{2}}{2}} = -1$$

Exercises 2–1

Using the facts that tan is an odd function and that its fundamental period is π, find each of the following:

A 1. $\tan \dfrac{5\pi}{4}$ 3. $\tan \left(-\dfrac{\pi}{3} \right)$ 5. $\tan \dfrac{2\pi}{3}$ 7. $\tan \left(-\dfrac{7\pi}{4} \right)$

   2. $\tan \dfrac{10\pi}{3}$ 4. $\tan \left(-\dfrac{10\pi}{3} \right)$ 6. $\tan \dfrac{22\pi}{3}$ 8. $\tan \dfrac{5\pi}{6}$

In Exercises 9–12, find all possible values for tan x in each situation, in which x represents one or more numbers in the interval $0 \le x \le 2\pi$, $x \ne \dfrac{\pi}{2}$, $x \ne \dfrac{3\pi}{2}$. State in which quadrants the points corresponding to x are located.

Example $\sin x = \frac{3}{5}$

Solution   You can first use $\cos^2 x + \sin^2 x = 1$ to find the possible values for $\cos x$. Thus:

$$\cos^2 x + (\tfrac{3}{5})^2 = 1$$
$$\cos^2 x = 1 - \tfrac{9}{25} = \tfrac{16}{25}$$
$$\cos x = \tfrac{4}{5} \quad \text{or} \quad -\tfrac{4}{5}$$

By definition, $\tan x = \dfrac{\sin x}{\cos x}$.

For $\sin x = \frac{3}{5}$ and $\cos x = \frac{4}{5}$ ($\sin x > 0$ and $\cos x > 0$), the point corresponding to x is in the first quadrant, and

$$\tan x = \frac{\frac{3}{5}}{\frac{4}{5}} = \frac{3}{4}.$$

For $\sin x = \frac{3}{5}$ and $\cos x = -\frac{4}{5}$ ($\sin x > 0$ and $\cos x < 0$), the point corresponding to x is in the second quadrant, and

$$\tan x = \frac{\frac{3}{5}}{-\frac{4}{5}} = -\frac{3}{4}.$$

9. $\sin x = \frac{5}{13}$ **10.** $\cos x = \frac{4}{5}$ **11.** $\cos x = -\frac{12}{13}$ **12.** $\sin x = -\frac{1}{2}$

In Exercises 13–16, make a neat sketch of the graph of tan x for the given values of x and draw segments representing ordinates illustrating the given identity. Assume a to be any number in the interval stated. (See Figures in Section 1–7 for similar drawings involving the cosine and sine functions.)

13. $\tan(-x) = -\tan x$, $-\dfrac{\pi}{2} < x < \dfrac{\pi}{2}$, $0 < a < \dfrac{\pi}{2}$

14. $\tan(x + \pi) = \tan x$, $-\dfrac{\pi}{2} < x < \dfrac{3\pi}{2}$, $0 < a < \dfrac{\pi}{2}$

15. $\tan(x + \pi) = \tan x$, $-\dfrac{\pi}{2} < x < \dfrac{3\pi}{2}$, $-\dfrac{\pi}{2} < a < 0$

16. $\tan(\pi - x) = -\tan x$, $0 \le x \le \pi$, $x \ne \dfrac{\pi}{2}$, $0 < a < \dfrac{\pi}{2}$

17. Show how the identities $\tan(-x) = -\tan x$ and $\tan(x + \pi) = \tan x$ can be used to prove the identity $\tan(\pi - x) = -\tan x$, $x \neq \frac{\pi}{2} + k\pi$.

In Exercises 18–20, graph the two given sets on the same set of axes, for $-\frac{\pi}{2} < x < \frac{\pi}{2}$. Then give the coordinates of the points of intersection of these two sets.

18. $\{(x, y): y = \tan x\}$, $\{(x, y): y = \sqrt{3}\}$

19. $\{(x, y): y = \tan x\}$, $\{(x, y): y = -1\}$

20. $\{(x, y): y = \tan x\}$, $\left\{(x, y): y = -\frac{\sqrt{3}}{3}\right\}$

21. If $-\frac{\pi}{2} < x < \frac{\pi}{2}$, find $\sin x$ and $\cos x$, given that:

    (a) $\tan x = 1$ **(b)** $\tan x = -1$ **(c)** $\tan x = \sqrt{3}$ **(d)** $\tan x = -\frac{\sqrt{3}}{3}$

B 22. If $\tan x = 2$, find $\cos x$ and $\sin x$, given that:

    (a) $0 < x < \frac{\pi}{2}$ **(b)** $\pi < x < \frac{3\pi}{2}$

23. Solve each equation for $-\frac{\pi}{2} < x < 2\pi$.

    (a) $\tan x = \sqrt{3}$ **(c)** $|\tan x| = \sqrt{3}$ **(e)** $\tan 2x = 1$

    (b) $\tan x = -\sqrt{3}$ **(d)** $\tan^2 x = 3$ **(f)** $\tan^2 x - 1 = 0$

Graph each set on a real number line, for $-\pi \leq x \leq 2\pi$.

24. $\{x: \tan x \geq 0 \text{ and } \sin x \geq 0\}$

25. $\{x: \tan x \geq 0 \text{ and } \cos x < 0\}$

26. $\{x: \tan x < 0 \text{ and } \sin x < 0\}$

C 27. Graph the set $\left\{(x, y): x = \tan y, \ -\frac{\pi}{2} < y < \frac{3\pi}{2}, \ y \neq \frac{\pi}{2}\right\}$.

28. Graph the sets: **(a)** $\left\{(x, y): y = |\tan x|, \ -\frac{\pi}{2} < x < \frac{\pi}{2}\right\}$

                         (b) $\left\{(x, y): y = \tan |x|, \ -\frac{\pi}{2} < x < \frac{\pi}{2}\right\}$

29. Show that for $0 < x < \frac{\pi}{2}$, $\frac{\sin x}{\cos x} > \sin x$ and hence that $\tan x > \sin x$.

The Reciprocal Circular Functions

2–2 *The Functions sec, csc, and cot*

There are three additional circular functions in common use. We shall now define these three functions and specify certain of their basic properties.

The **secant** function, denoted by **sec**, is defined as follows:

▲   For every x for which $\cos x \neq 0$,

$$\sec = \left\{(x, y):\ y = \sec x = \frac{1}{\cos x}\right\}.$$

The *domain* of sec is

$$\left\{x:\ x \in \mathcal{R},\quad x \neq (2k + 1)\frac{\pi}{2},\quad k \in J\right\}.$$

The *range* of sec is

$$\{y:\ y \in \mathcal{R},\quad |y| \geq 1\},$$

because for all $x \in \mathcal{R}$, $|\cos x| \leq 1$, and $\sec x = \dfrac{1}{\cos x}$.

The fundamental period of sec is the same as that of cos, namely 2π. Furthermore, sec is an even function because cos is an even function.

The **cosecant** function, denoted by **csc**, is defined as follows:

▲   For every x for which $\sin x \neq 0$,

$$\csc = \left\{(x, y):\ y = \csc x = \frac{1}{\sin x}\right\}.$$

The *domain* of csc is

$$\{x:\ x \in \mathcal{R},\quad x \neq k\pi,\ k \in J\}.$$

The *range* of csc is

$$\{y:\ y \in \mathcal{R},\quad |y| \geq 1\},$$

since for all $x \in \mathcal{R}$, $|\sin x| \leq 1$, and $\csc x = \dfrac{1}{\sin x}$. Note that the range of csc is the same as that of sec.

As with the function sin, the function csc has fundamental period 2π and is an odd function.

The **cotangent** function, denoted by **cot**, is defined as follows:

▲   For every x for which $\sin x \neq 0$,

$$\cot = \left\{(x, y): y = \cot x = \frac{\cos x}{\sin x}\right\}.$$

The *domain* of cot is

$$\{x: x \in \mathcal{R}, \ \ x \neq k\pi, \ k \in J\}.$$

The *range* of cot is $\mathcal{R}$, which is also the range of tan.
  Since

$$\cot x = \frac{1}{\tan x} \ \left[\text{for } x \neq k\pi \text{ and } x \neq (2k + 1)\frac{\pi}{2}, \ k \in J\right],$$

the fundamental period of cot is the same as that of tan, namely π. Further-more, cot is an odd function, because tan is an odd function. These two prop-erties of cot are justified as follows:

$$\cot (x + \pi) = \frac{1}{\tan (x + \pi)}$$

$$= \frac{1}{\tan x} = \cot x$$

and

$$\cot (-x) = \frac{1}{\tan (-x)}$$

$$= \frac{1}{-\tan x}$$

$$= -\frac{1}{\tan x} = -\cot x$$

for all x in the domain of cot and tan.

  Since the circular functions tan, sec, csc, and cot are defined in terms of the cos and sin functions, the values for these four new functions can be determined by reference to the properties of the cos and sin functions. Of particular im-portance are the identities summarized in Section 1–6, together with the values of $\cos x$ and $\sin x$ for special values of x in the interval $0 \leq x \leq \frac{\pi}{2}$, derived in Section 1–3.

Example   Find the value of:

(a) $\sec \dfrac{13\pi}{3}$ (b) $\cot\left(-\dfrac{4\pi}{3}\right)$

Solution   (a) $\sec \dfrac{13\pi}{3} = \dfrac{1}{\cos \dfrac{13\pi}{3}} = \dfrac{1}{\cos\left(\dfrac{\pi}{3} + 4\pi\right)}$

$$= \dfrac{1}{\cos \dfrac{\pi}{3}} = \dfrac{1}{\dfrac{1}{2}} = 2$$

(b) $\cot\left(-\dfrac{4\pi}{3}\right) = \dfrac{\cos\left(-\dfrac{4\pi}{3}\right)}{\sin\left(-\dfrac{4\pi}{3}\right)} = \dfrac{\cos\left(-\dfrac{\pi}{3} - \pi\right)}{\sin\left(-\dfrac{\pi}{3} - \pi\right)}$

$$= \dfrac{-\cos\left(-\dfrac{\pi}{3}\right)}{-\sin\left(-\dfrac{\pi}{3}\right)} = \dfrac{-\cos \dfrac{\pi}{3}}{\sin \dfrac{\pi}{3}} = \dfrac{-\dfrac{1}{2}}{\dfrac{\sqrt{3}}{2}}$$

$$= -\dfrac{1}{\sqrt{3}} = -\dfrac{\sqrt{3}}{3}$$

or

$$\cot\left(-\dfrac{4\pi}{3}\right) = \dfrac{1}{\tan\left(-\dfrac{4\pi}{3}\right)} = \dfrac{1}{-\tan\left(\dfrac{4\pi}{3}\right)}$$

$$= \dfrac{1}{-\tan\left(\dfrac{\pi}{3} + \pi\right)} = \dfrac{1}{-\tan \dfrac{\pi}{3}}$$

$$= -\dfrac{1}{\dfrac{\sin \dfrac{\pi}{3}}{\cos \dfrac{\pi}{3}}} = -\dfrac{\cos \dfrac{\pi}{3}}{\sin \dfrac{\pi}{3}}$$

$$= -\dfrac{\dfrac{1}{2}}{\dfrac{\sqrt{3}}{2}} = -\dfrac{1}{\sqrt{3}} = -\dfrac{\sqrt{3}}{3}$$

Exercises 2–2

A **1.** Using the definitions of sec, csc, and cot, make a table of exact values of

sec x, csc x, and cot x for $x = 0, \dfrac{\pi}{6}, \dfrac{\pi}{4}, \dfrac{\pi}{3}, \dfrac{\pi}{2}$.

Find the value of each of the following.

2. sec 6π **4.** csc $\left(-\dfrac{\pi}{6}\right)$ **6.** cot $\dfrac{8\pi}{3}$ **8.** sec $\dfrac{5\pi}{6}$ **10.** csc $\left(-\dfrac{5\pi}{4}\right)$

3. sec $\dfrac{4\pi}{3}$ **5.** csc $\dfrac{19\pi}{2}$ **7.** cot $\left(-\dfrac{2\pi}{3}\right)$ **9.** sec $\left(-\dfrac{4\pi}{3}\right)$ **11.** csc $\left(\dfrac{\pi}{2}\right)$

12. Prepare a table comparing the domain and the range of the six circular functions, as follows: In Column 1, list the *names of the functions* in the order:

$$\cos x, \quad \sec x = \frac{1}{\cos x}, \quad \sin x, \quad \csc x = \frac{1}{\sin x}, \quad \tan x, \quad \cot x = \frac{1}{\tan x}$$

In Column 2, graph on a horizontal number line the *domain* of each function. In Column 3, graph on a horizontal number line the *range* of each function.

The first two rows of this table are shown:

Function	Domain	Range
cos x		
sec $x = \dfrac{1}{\cos x}$		

Verify (prove) each of the following identities.

13. sec $(x + \pi) = -\sec x$ **18.** cot $(\pi - x) = -\cot x$

14. sec $(\pi - x) = -\sec x$ **19.** sec $(-x) = \sec x$

15. csc $(x + \pi) = -\csc x$ **20.** csc $(-x) = -\csc x$

16. csc $(\pi - x) = \csc x$ **21.** cot $(-x) = -\cot x$

17. cot $(x + \pi) = \cot x$ **22.** sec $x \cot x = \csc x$

B **23.** $\sec^2 x + \csc^2 x = \sec^2 x \csc^2 x$

Solve each equation for $-\pi \le x \le 2\pi$.

24. $\sec x = 2$ **27.** $\csc x = 1$

25. $\sec x = -\sqrt{2}$ **28.** $\cot x = -1$

26. $\csc x = \dfrac{\sqrt{2}}{3}$ **29.** $\cot x = \sqrt{3}$

C **30.** Show how the identity $\sin^2 x + \cos^2 x = 1$ can be used to obtain the identities

$$\tan^2 x + 1 = \sec^2 x \quad \text{and} \quad 1 + \cot^2 x = \csc^2 x.$$

2–3   *Graphs of sec, csc, cot*

The graph of the sec function can easily be derived by referring to the graph of the cos function and noting that for every real number x except those of the form $(2k + 1)\dfrac{\pi}{2}$, $k \in J$, the value of sec x is the *reciprocal* of the corresponding value of cos x.

To illustrate this notion, let A_1, A_2, A_3, and A_4 denote the points on the graph of $y = \cos x$ corresponding to

$$x = 0, \ \frac{\pi}{6}, \ \frac{\pi}{4}, \ \frac{\pi}{3},$$

and let B_1, B_2, B_3, B_4 denote the points on the graph of $y = \sec x$ corresponding to these same values of x (see Figure 2–7). Then the y-coordinates of A_1, A_2, A_3, A_4 are, respectively,

$$1, \quad \frac{\sqrt{3}}{2} \doteq 0.87, \quad \frac{\sqrt{2}}{2} \doteq 0.71, \quad \frac{1}{2} = 0.5,$$

while the y-coordinates of B_1, B_2, B_3, B_4 are

$$1, \quad \frac{2}{\sqrt{3}} \doteq 1.15, \quad \frac{2}{\sqrt{2}} \doteq 1.41, \quad 2.$$

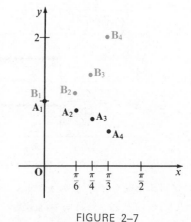

FIGURE 2–7

Now that we have graphed four special points on the graphs of $y = \cos x$ and $y = \sec x$, let us consider the graphs of these two functions for all real

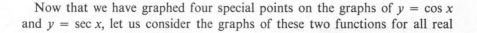

numbers in the interval $0 \leq x < \frac{\pi}{2}$. As we choose numbers x along the x-axis from 0 toward $\frac{\pi}{2}$, the corresponding values of cos x decrease from 1 toward 0, and the corresponding reciprocals of cos x increase from 1 through larger and larger positive numbers. This means that in the interval $0 \leq x < \frac{\pi}{2}$, the graph of $y = \sec x$ increases and is asymptotic from the left to the line with equation $x = \frac{\pi}{2}$.

The portions of the graph of the sec function for $-\frac{\pi}{2} < x < 0$ and for $\frac{\pi}{2} < x < \frac{3\pi}{2}$ can be obtained by similar reasoning (Figure 2–8). Specifically, as we choose numbers x along the x-axis from π toward $\frac{\pi}{2}$ (this time from right to left instead of from left to right), the corresponding numbers cos x increase from -1 toward 0 and the corresponding reciprocals of cos x decrease from -1 through negative numbers that are larger and larger in absolute value. Thus the graph of $y = \sec x$ is asymptotic from the right to the line with equation $x = \frac{\pi}{2}$.

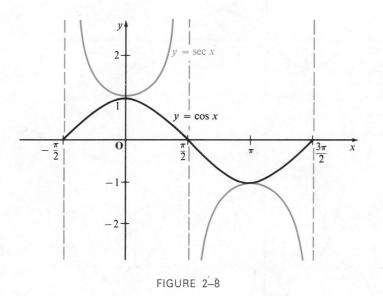

FIGURE 2–8

Since sec has fundamental period 2π, you can obtain as much as you please of its graph by reproducing in either direction along the x-axis the portion of the graph in Figure 2–8, as shown in Figure 2–9 on the next page.

Figure 2–9 displays the portion of the graph of sec over the interval $-\dfrac{5\pi}{2} < x < \dfrac{5\pi}{2}$.

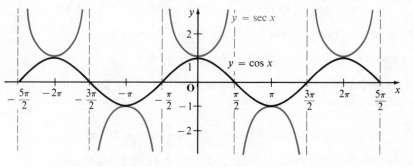

FIGURE 2–9

Just as we related the graph of the sec function to its reciprocal function, the cos function, we can relate the graphs of the csc and the cot functions to their reciprocal functions, the sin and the tan functions, respectively. These relationships are shown in Figures 2–10 and 2–11.

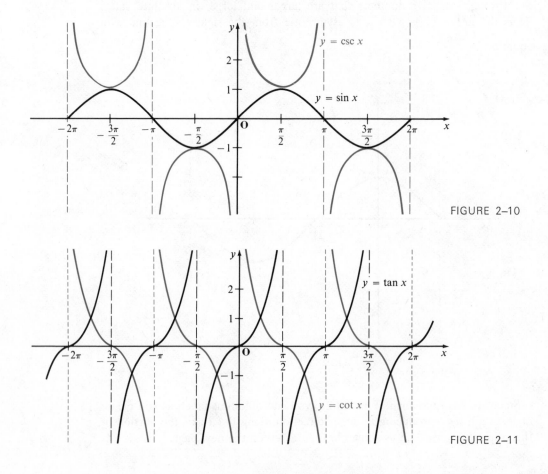

FIGURE 2–10

FIGURE 2–11

Thus, for every real number x except $k\pi$, $k \in J$, the ordinate of a point on the graph of csc is the reciprocal of the ordinate of the corresponding point on the graph of sin. Similarly, for every real number x except $k \cdot \dfrac{\pi}{2}$, $k \in J$, the ordinate of a point on the graph of cot is the reciprocal of the ordinate of the corresponding point on the graph of tan, and for $x = (2k + 1)\dfrac{\pi}{2}$, $\cot x = 0$.

Exercises 2–3

A **1.** Graph the sets $\{(x, y): y = \cos x\}$ and $\{(x, y): y = \sec x\}$ on the same set of axes for $-2\pi \leq x \leq 4\pi$.

What are the equations of the asymptotes of each of the following, in the interval $0 \leq x \leq 2\pi$?

2. $\{(x, y): y = \sec x\}$ **4.** $\{(x, y): y = \tan x\}$

3. $\{(x, y): y = \csc x\}$ **5.** $\{(x, y): y = \cot x\}$

6. Prepare a detailed sketch of the graph of $y = \tan x$, for $0 \leq x \leq \pi$, clearly indicating the y-values (to two decimal places) corresponding to $x = \dfrac{\pi}{6}, \dfrac{\pi}{4}, \dfrac{\pi}{3}, \dfrac{2\pi}{3}, \dfrac{3\pi}{4}, \dfrac{5\pi}{6}$, and π. Then, on the same set of axes, sketch the graph of $y = \cot x$ for $0 < x < \pi$.

7. Prepare a detailed sketch of the graph of $y = \sin x$, for $0 \leq x \leq \pi$, clearly indicating the y-values (to two decimal places) corresponding to $x = 0, \dfrac{\pi}{6}, \dfrac{\pi}{4}, \dfrac{\pi}{3}, \dfrac{\pi}{2}, \dfrac{2\pi}{3}, \dfrac{3\pi}{4}, \dfrac{5\pi}{6}$, and π. Then, on the same set of axes, sketch the graph of $y = \csc x = \dfrac{1}{\sin x}$ for $0 < x < \pi$.

Graph each of the following sets for $0 \leq x \leq 2\pi$.

B **8.** $\{(x, y): y = |\cot x|\}$

9. $\{(x, y): y = |\csc x|\}$

10. $\{(x, y): y = |\sec x|\}$

11. For what real numbers x is each of the following true?

(**a**) $\sin x = \dfrac{1}{\csc x}$ (**b**) $\tan x = \dfrac{1}{\cot x}$

Identities

2–4   *Additional Basic Identities*

You can obtain identities involving $\tan x$ by using the identities you have already developed for $\sin x$ and $\cos x$, together with the definition for the tangent function. For example, to discover an identity for $\tan (x_2 + x_1)$ in terms of $\tan x_2$ and $\tan x_1$, you can begin with

$$\tan (x_2 + x_1) = \frac{\sin (x_2 + x_1)}{\cos (x_2 + x_1)} \, .$$

Since $\sin (x_2 + x_1) = \sin x_2 \cos x_1 + \cos x_2 \sin x_1$, and $\cos (x_2 + x_1) = \cos x_2 \cos x_1 - \sin x_2 \sin x_1$, you have

$$\tan (x_2 + x_1) = \frac{\sin x_2 \cos x_1 + \cos x_2 \sin x_1}{\cos x_2 \cos x_1 - \sin x_2 \sin x_1} \, .$$

Now, to express the right-hand member in terms of tan, you divide the numerator and denominator of the expression on the right by $\cos x_2 \cos x_1$, obtaining

$$\tan (x_2 + x_1) = \frac{\dfrac{\sin x_2 \cos x_1}{\cos x_2 \cos x_1} + \dfrac{\cos x_2 \sin x_1}{\cos x_2 \cos x_1}}{\dfrac{\cos x_2 \cos x_1}{\cos x_2 \cos x_1} - \dfrac{\sin x_2 \sin x_1}{\cos x_2 \cos x_1}} \, ,$$

from which you obtain:

▲
$$\tan (x_2 + x_1) = \frac{\tan x_2 + \tan x_1}{1 - \tan x_2 \tan x_1} \, , \tag{1}$$

where $x_1, x_2, x_2 + x_1 \neq (2k + 1) \dfrac{\pi}{2}, \ k \in J$.

You must be careful in developing identities of this kind to exclude from the domain of the function any number for which a denominator equals zero. For example, in the foregoing derivation, $x_2 + x_1$ must be so restricted that the values $(2k + 1) \dfrac{\pi}{2}, \ k \in J$, are excluded from its domain because $\cos (x_2 + x_1)$ is equal to 0 for these values. Moreover, since you divided at one stage by $\cos x_2 \cos x_1$, neither of these factors can be permitted to equal 0. Thus, you also have to include the restriction $\cos x_2 \neq 0$ and $\cos x_1 \neq 0$, or

$x_1, x_2 \neq (2k + 1)\frac{\pi}{2}$, $k \in J$. What this amounts to is saying that the identity (1) is valid for all values of the variables for which both members are defined.

By replacing x_1 with $-x_1$ in the sum formula (1) and then using (1) on page 50, you obtain the difference formula:

▲
$$\tan (x_2 - x_1) = \frac{\tan x_2 - \tan x_1}{1 + \tan x_2 \tan x_1} \cdot \qquad (2)$$

These sum and difference relationships can then be used to obtain the reduction formulas,

▲
$$\tan (\pi + x) = \tan x, \qquad (3)$$
$$\tan (\pi - x) = -\tan x, \qquad (4)$$

where $x \neq (2k + 1)\frac{\pi}{2}$, $k \in J$, in each case.

The sum formula (1), when x_2 and x_1 are set equal to x, yields the following relationship:

▲
$$\tan 2x = \frac{2 \tan x}{1 - \tan^2 x}, \qquad (5)$$

where $\cos 2x \neq 0$, $\cos x \neq 0$.

Finally, you can prove that

▲
$$\tan \frac{x}{2} = \frac{\sin x}{1 + \cos x}, \qquad (6)$$

where $\cos \frac{x}{2} \neq 0$ and therefore $\cos x \neq -1$ $[x \neq (2k + 1)\pi, k \in J]$ as follows:

$$\tan \frac{x}{2} = \frac{\sin \frac{x}{2}}{\cos \frac{x}{2}} = \frac{2 \sin \frac{x}{2} \cos \frac{x}{2}}{2 \cos^2 \frac{x}{2}} = \frac{\sin 2 \left(\frac{x}{2}\right)}{1 + \cos 2 \left(\frac{x}{2}\right)} = \frac{\sin x}{1 + \cos x} \cdot$$

An important point has now been reached in your study of periodic functions. All six of the circular functions have been defined and a number of basic identities have been developed. A list of these identities is presented on page 66.

BASIC IDENTITIES

For each $x \in \mathfrak{R}$ for which both members are defined:

A   From the definitions of the circular functions:

$$\tan x = \frac{\sin x}{\cos x} \qquad\qquad \cot x = \frac{\cos x}{\sin x} = \frac{1}{\tan x}$$

$$\sec x = \frac{1}{\cos x} \qquad\qquad \csc x = \frac{1}{\sin x}$$

B   By referring to the identity $\cos^2 x + \sin^2 x = 1$, we can derive the two identities:

$$1 + \tan^2 x = \sec^2 x \qquad\qquad \cot^2 x + 1 = \csc^2 x$$

C $\cos\left(\dfrac{\pi}{2} - x\right) = \sin x \qquad\qquad \sin\left(\dfrac{\pi}{2} - x\right) = \cos x$

D
$$\cos(-x) = \cos x \qquad\qquad \sec(-x) = \sec x$$
$$\sin(-x) = -\sin x \qquad\qquad \csc(-x) = -\csc x$$
$$\tan(-x) = -\tan x \qquad\qquad \cot(-x) = -\cot x$$

E
$$\cos(x_2 \pm x_1) = \cos x_2 \cos x_1 \mp \sin x_2 \sin x_1$$
$$\sin(x_2 \pm x_1) = \sin x_2 \cos x_1 \pm \cos x_2 \sin x_1$$
$$\tan(x_2 \pm x_1) = \frac{\tan x_2 \pm \tan x_1}{1 \mp \tan x_2 \tan x_1}$$

F
$$\cos(x \pm \pi) = -\cos x \qquad\qquad \cos(\pi - x) = -\cos x$$
$$\sin(x \pm \pi) = -\sin x \qquad\qquad \sin(\pi - x) = \sin x$$
$$\tan(x \pm \pi) = \tan x \qquad\qquad \tan(\pi - x) = -\tan x$$

G   From the identities in Group E, for $x_2 = x_1 = x$ and for $+$:

$$\cos 2x = \cos^2 x - \sin^2 x = 2\cos^2 x - 1 = 1 - 2\sin^2 x$$
$$\sin 2x = 2\sin x \cos x$$
$$\tan 2x = \frac{2\tan x}{1 - \tan^2 x}$$

H $\cos\dfrac{x}{2} = \pm\sqrt{\tfrac{1}{2}(1 + \cos x)} \qquad \sin\dfrac{x}{2} = \pm\sqrt{\tfrac{1}{2}(1 - \cos x)} \qquad \tan\dfrac{x}{2} = \dfrac{\sin x}{1 + \cos x}$

For convenience in consulting and remembering these identities, the list on page 66 is presented in groups. Notice that in Groups E, F, G, and H, identities are shown for the cos, sin, and tan functions only. Corresponding identities can be devised, whenever needed, for the sec, csc, and cot functions, by referring to the identities in Groups E, F, G, and H and the definitions of sec, csc, and cot (in Group A).

For example,

$$\sec (x_2 - x_1) = \frac{1}{\cos (x_2 - x_1)}$$

$$= \frac{1}{\cos x_2 \cos x_1 + \sin x_2 \sin x_1} \cdot$$

Exercises 2–4

Verify (prove) each identity. State all necessary restrictions on the variables.

A **1.** $\tan (x - \pi) = \tan x$

2. $\tan \dfrac{x}{2} = \dfrac{1 - \cos x}{\sin x}$

3. $\tan \left(x + \dfrac{\pi}{4} \right) = \dfrac{1 + \tan x}{1 - \tan x}$

4. $\cot \left(\dfrac{\pi}{2} - x \right) = \tan x$

5. $\sec (x - \pi) = -\sec x$

6. $\sec \left(\dfrac{\pi}{2} - x \right) = \csc x$

7. $\csc \left(\dfrac{\pi}{2} - x \right) = \sec x$

8. $\sec x \csc x = 2 \csc 2x$

9. $\sin^2 x \cot^2 x + \cos^2 x \tan^2 x = 1$

10. $\dfrac{\sec x}{\tan x + \cot x} = \sin x$

B **11.** $\tan x = \dfrac{1 - \cos 2x}{\sin 2x}$

12. $1 - \tan x_1 \tan x_2 = \dfrac{\cos (x_1 + x_2)}{\cos x_1 \cos x_2}$

13. $\cot (x_2 + x_1) = \dfrac{\cot x_2 \cot x_1 - 1}{\cot x_2 + \cot x_1}$

14. $\tan 2x = \dfrac{2}{\cot x - \tan x}$

15. $\cot 2x = \dfrac{\cot^2 x - 1}{2 \cot x}$

16. $\sec (x_2 - x_1) = \dfrac{\sec x_2 \sec x_1}{1 + \tan x_2 \tan x_1}$

C **17.** $|\sec x - \tan x| = \sqrt{\dfrac{1 - \sin x}{1 + \sin x}}$

18. In the figure at the right, $\overline{AB}$ and $\overline{DC}$ are both perpendicular to $\overline{OA}$, and the length of $\overparen{AC}$ is x.

(a) Show that $d(\overline{AB}) = \tan x$.

(b) Show that $d(\overline{AB}) > d(\overline{DC})$ and hence that

$$\tan x > \sin x$$

for $0 < x < \dfrac{\pi}{2}$.

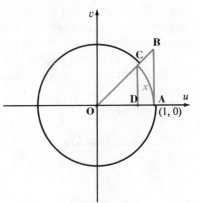

19. Show that in the figure at the right, with $d(\overline{OA}) = 1$,

$$d(\overline{OD}) = \cot x,$$

$$d(\overline{OB}) = \sec x,$$

and

$$d(\overline{OE}) = \csc x.$$

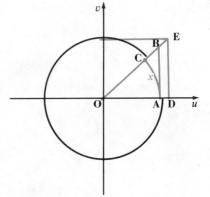

20. Prove that if $x_1 + x_2 + x_3 = \pi$, then

$$\tan x_1 + \tan x_2 + \tan x_3$$
$$= \tan x_1 \tan x_2 \tan x_3.$$

2–5 *Working with Identities*

The identities with which we have been working throughout this chapter and the preceding chapter express the most important and useful relationships among the various circular functions. Many more such relationships relating all six of the circular functions can be obtained. The exercises following this section will provide you with an opportunity to explore some of them.

Care must be exercised in making substitutions in identities when any of the circular functions involved have restricted domains, or when radicals are employed.

For example, although

$$\cos x = \frac{\sin x}{\tan x}$$

for those values of x for which both members are defined, the replacement of

$\dfrac{\sin x}{\tan x}$ with cos x in an identity is valid only so long as x is not equal to $k \cdot \dfrac{\pi}{2}$, since for even k, tan $x = 0$, while for odd k, tan x is not defined, and such a substitution would not result in an equivalent sentence.

Also, while

$$\sin x = \sqrt{1 - \cos^2 x}$$

in Quadrants I and II,

$$\sin x = -\sqrt{1 - \cos^2 x}$$

in Quadrants III and IV; thus, substitutions involving radicals such as these should be avoided where possible, since again the result in general is not an equivalent sentence.

In Section 1–5, some suggestions for deriving and verifying identities were given. The following example illustrates the method of transforming one member into the other.

Example 1   Show that for each $x \in \mathfrak{R}$ for which both members are defined,

$$\frac{1 - \sin x}{\cos x} = \frac{\cos x}{1 + \sin x}.$$

Solution   Since $1 + \sin x \neq 0$ whenever cos $x \neq 0$, we can multiply numerator and denominator of the left-hand member by $1 + \sin x$ to obtain the equivalent sentence

$$\frac{(1 + \sin x)(1 - \sin x)}{(1 + \sin x)\cos x} = \frac{\cos x}{1 + \sin x},$$

or

$$\frac{1 - \sin^2 x}{(1 + \sin x)\cos x} = \frac{\cos x}{1 + \sin x}.$$

Since $1 - \sin^2 x = \cos^2 x$ for all $x \in \mathfrak{R}$, we have

$$\frac{\cos^2 x}{(1 + \sin x)\cos x} = \frac{\cos x}{1 + \sin x}. \tag{1}$$

Now, observing that cos $x \neq 0$, we can reduce the left-hand member of (1) to obtain

$$\frac{\cos x}{1 + \sin x} = \frac{\cos x}{1 + \sin x},$$

which is true for all x for which cos $x \neq 0$. This completes the demonstration.

In verifying (proving) some identities, it is more efficient to transform both members of the given equation rather than to operate on only one member.

Example 2   Show that for each $x \in \mathfrak{R}$ for which both members are defined,

$$\tan x + \cot x = \sec x \csc x.$$

Solution   One good way to begin the proof is to express each given function value in terms of $\sin x$ and $\cos x$ only. We have

$$\frac{\sin x}{\cos x} + \frac{\cos x}{\sin x} = \frac{1}{\cos x} \cdot \frac{1}{\sin x}.$$

Since each member here is defined if and only if

$$\sin x \cdot \cos x \neq 0,$$

we can multiply each member by $\sin x \cdot \cos x$ to obtain

$$\sin x \cos x \cdot \frac{\sin x}{\cos x} + \sin x \cos x \cdot \frac{\cos x}{\sin x} = \sin x \cos x \left(\frac{1}{\cos x} \cdot \frac{1}{\sin x} \right),$$

which reduces to

$$\sin^2 x + \cos^2 x = 1.$$

Since this is a known identity and is equivalent to the given identity, we have completed our demonstration.

In verifying identities, it is helpful to keep the following possibilities in mind.

1. Try to simplify the more complicated member.

2. Look for pertinent applications of field properties.

3. Itemize restrictions on variables and make certain no new ones are introduced or old ones removed.

4. If no other approach suggests itself, express all function values in terms of sin and cos.

5. Introduce radicals only when absolutely essential.

Exercises 2–5

Verify (prove) each identity. State all necessary restrictions on the variables involved.

A **1.** $\sin x + \cos x \cot x = \csc x$

2. $\cos x \csc x = \cot x$

3. $\tan x (\sin x + \cot x \cos x) = \sec x$

4. $2 \cos^2 x - \sin^2 x + 1 = 3 \cos^2 x$

5. $\sin x \tan x + \cos x = \sec x$

6. $\sin x (\sec x - \csc x) = \tan x - 1$

7. $\cos x (\csc x - \sec x) = \cot x - 1$

8. $\dfrac{1}{1 + \sin x} + \dfrac{1}{1 - \sin x} = 2 \sec^2 x$

9. $\dfrac{1 + \sin x}{\cos x} - \dfrac{\cos x}{1 - \sin x} = 0$

10. $\dfrac{\sin^2 x}{1 + \cos x} + \cos x = 1$

11. $\dfrac{\sin x \cot x + \cos x}{\sin x} = 2 \cot x$

12. $\dfrac{1 + 2 \sin x \cos x}{\sin x + \cos x} = \sin x + \cos x$

13. Each of the expressions below may be equated with one of the four expressions

$$\sin x, \quad \cos x, \quad \tan x, \quad 1$$

to form an identity. Determine which of these four expressions matches each expression below.

(a) $\dfrac{1}{\sec^2 x} + \dfrac{1}{\csc^2 x}$

(b) $\dfrac{\sec x}{\tan x + \cot x}$

(c) $\dfrac{\csc^2 x - 1}{\cot^2 x}$

(d) $(1 + \tan^2 x)(1 - \sin^2 x)$

(e) $\sec x - \sin x \tan x$

(f) $\sin x \cos x \tan x \cot x \sec x \csc x$

(g) $\dfrac{\sin x + \tan x}{\tan x(\csc x + \cot x)}$

(h) $\dfrac{1 + \tan x}{1 + \cot x}$

(i) $\dfrac{\sin 2x}{2 \sin x}$

(j) $\sin x \sec x$

(k) $\sec^2 x(1 - \sin^2 x)$

(l) $\csc^2 x(1 - \cos^2 x)$

(m) $\sec x - \sin x \tan x$

Verify (prove) each identity. State all necessary restrictions on the variables.

B **14.** $\dfrac{\sin x \cos x}{1 - 2 \sin^2 x} = \dfrac{1}{\cot x - \tan x}$

15. $\dfrac{1 + \tan^2 x}{\tan^2 x} = \csc^2 x$

16. $\cos^4 x - \sin^4 x = \cos^2 x - \sin^2 x$

17. $\dfrac{1 - \tan x}{1 + \tan x} = \dfrac{\cot x - 1}{\cot x + 1}$

18. $\dfrac{1 - \sin^2 x}{1 - \cos^2 x} = \cot^2 x$

19. $\dfrac{\sin (x - y)}{\sin (x + y)} = \dfrac{\tan x - \tan y}{\tan x + \tan y}$

20. $\dfrac{\cos (x - y)}{\cos (x + y)} = \dfrac{\cot x + \tan y}{\cot x - \tan y}$

21. $\sin (x + y) \sin (x - y) = \sin^2 x - \sin^2 y$

22. $\sin 2x = \dfrac{2 \tan x}{1 + \tan^2 x}$

23. $\sec 2x + \tan 2x = \dfrac{\cos x + \sin x}{\cos x - \sin x}$

Verify (prove) each identity. State all necessary restrictions on the variables.

C **24.** $\cos(x_2 + x_1) + \cos(x_2 - x_1) = 2\cos x_2 \cos x_1$

25. $\cos(x_2 + x_1) - \cos(x_2 - x_1) = -2\sin x_2 \sin x_1$

26. $\sin(x_2 + x_1) + \sin(x_2 - x_1) = 2\sin x_2 \cos x_1$

27. $\cos x + \cos y = 2\cos\dfrac{x+y}{2}\cos\dfrac{x-y}{2}$

(*Hint:* Let $x = x_2 + x_1$ and $y = x_2 - x_1$ in Exercise 24.)

28. $\cos x - \cos y = -2\sin\dfrac{x+y}{2}\sin\dfrac{x-y}{2}$

29. $\sin x + \sin y = 2\sin\dfrac{x+y}{2}\cos\dfrac{x-y}{2}$

30. $\dfrac{\sin 2x}{1 + \cos 2x} = \dfrac{1 - \cos 2x}{\sin 2x}$

31. $\sin 3x + \sin x = 2\sin 2x \cos x$

32. $\tan 3x = \dfrac{3\tan x - \tan^3 x}{1 - 3\tan^2 x}$

33. $\sin(x + y)\sin(x - y) = \sin^2 x - \sin^2 y$

34. $\cos^4\left(\dfrac{x}{2}\right) - \sin^4\left(\dfrac{x}{2}\right) = \cos x$

Chapter Summary

1. Additional circular functions are **tangent (tan)**, **secant (sec)**, **cosecant (csc)**, and **cotangent (cot)**. They are defined by:

$$\tan = \left\{(x, y)\colon y = \frac{\sin x}{\cos x},\ x \in \mathfrak{R},\ x \neq (2k + 1)\frac{\pi}{2},\ k \in J\right\}$$

$$\sec = \left\{(x, y)\colon y = \frac{1}{\cos x},\ x \in \mathfrak{R},\ x \neq (2k + 1)\frac{\pi}{2},\ k \in J\right\}$$

$$\csc = \left\{(x, y)\colon y = \frac{1}{\sin x},\ x \in \mathfrak{R},\ x \neq k\pi,\ k \in J\right\}$$

$$\cot = \left\{(x, y)\colon y = \frac{\cos x}{\sin x},\ x \in \mathfrak{R},\ x \neq k\pi,\ k \in J\right\}$$

The range of each of the functions tan and cot is $\mathfrak{R}$, and that of sec and of csc is $\{y\colon y \in \mathfrak{R},\ |y| \geq 1\}$.

2. The fundamental period of sec and csc is 2π, but for tan and cot it is π.

3. The function sec is an even function, whereas the functions tan, csc, and cot are odd.

4. Values for tan, sec, csc, and cot can be determined from the definitions of these functions, which are in terms of cos and sin.

5. The periodic and other properties of the tan function are useful in drawing its graph. The graphs of the sec, csc, and cot functions can be drawn by reference to their respective reciprocal functions, namely cos, sin, and tan.

6. A summary of basic identities, developed in this chapter and the preceding chapter, is presented on page 66. Most of these identities are for the cos, sin, and tan functions only, since corresponding identities can be devised, whenever needed, for their reciprocals, the sec, csc, and cot functions.

7. Techniques for deriving and verifying identities were introduced in the preceding chapter and were developed more extensively in this chapter.

Chapter Test

2–1   **1.** Given that $\cos x = -\frac{3}{5}$ and $\frac{\pi}{2} < x < \pi$, find $\tan x$.

2–2   **2.** Find the value of:

    (a) $\sec \dfrac{5\pi}{4}$ **(b)** $\cot\left(-\dfrac{\pi}{6}\right)$

2–3   **3.** On the same set of axes, graph the sets

$$\{(x, y)\colon y = \sin x\} \quad \text{and} \quad \{(x, y)\colon y = \csc x\}$$

for $-2\pi \le x \le 4\pi$.

2–4   **4.** Verify the identity $\tan(2\pi - x) = -\tan x$.

2–5   **5.** Simplify the expression $\dfrac{2 \sin x}{\sin x \cot x + \cos x}$.

Computer Investigations

If you have access to an electronic computer that will accept BASIC, you may wish to try the following projects.

You can use the program given on page 46 to print out approximate positions of some points on one section of the graph of

$$y = \tan x$$

by making the following changes:

   10 PRINT "Y = TAN X"
   60 FOR X1 = −10 TO 10 STEP 2
   80 LET Y = TAN(X)

RUN

Y = TAN X

X	Y
−1	−1•55741
−•8	−1•02964
−•6	−•684137
−•4	−•422793
−•2	−•20271
0	0
•2	•20271
•4	•422793
•6	•684137
•8	1•02964
1	1•55741

END

You can obtain a similar portion of

$$y = \cot x$$

by using:

   10 PRINT "Y = COT X"
   60 FOR X1 = 6 TO 26 STEP 2
   80 LET Y = 1/TAN(X)

Compare these graphs with the graphs you obtained for $y = \cos x$ and $y = \sin x$ on page 47, and notice where the domains used for these graphs occur in the values for x used for cos and sin. Notice where $\cos x$ and $\sin x$ are zero.

If you wish, try to print out other sections of the graphs of tan and cot.

The following program will print out a portion of the graphs of

$$y = \cos x \quad \text{and} \quad y = \sec x$$

on the same set of axes.

```
10    PRINT "Y = COS X    ***    Y = SEC X    ..."
20    PRINT
30    LET L=6
40    LET M=L+(66-L)/2
50    PRINT "  X"
60    FOR X1=-12 TO 12 STEP 2
70    LET X=.1*X1
80    LET Y=COS(X)
90    LET Z=1/COS(X)
100   LET Y2=10*Y+M
110   IF X1=0 THEN 190
120   LET Z2=10*Z+M
130   IF Y2<L THEN 230
140   IF Z2<L THEN 230
150   IF Y2>66 THEN 230
160   IF Z2>66 THEN 230
170   PRINT X; TAB(M); "!"; TAB(Y2); "*"; TAB(Z2); "."
180   GO TO 200
190   PRINT X; TAB(M); "!"; TAB(Y2); "*"; TAB(67); "---Y"
200   NEXT X1
210   PRINT TAB(M); "X"
220   GO TO 240
230   PRINT "TOO WIDE"
240   END
```

```
Y = COS X    ***    Y = SEC X   ...

   X
 -1.2                         ! *            .
 -1                           !  *         .
 -.8                          !   *       .
 -.6                          !    *     .
 -.4                          !    **
 -.2                          !    **
  0                           !    *           ---Y
  .2                          !    **
  .4                          !    **
  .6                          !    *
  .8                          !   *       .
  1                           !  *         .
 1.2                          ! *            .
                              X
```

The following changes will print out the negative portions.

```
60 FOR X1 = 20 TO 42 STEP 2
170 PRINT X; TAB(Z2);".";TAB(Y2);"*";TAB(M);"!"
```

```
Y = COS X    ***    Y = SEC X   ...

   X
 2            .                      *    !
 2.2               .               *      !
 2.4                 .            *       !
 2.6                   .        *         !
 2.8                    .*                !
 3                      .*                !
 3.2                    .*                !
 3.4                    .*                !
 3.6                   .        *         !
 3.8                 .            *       !
 4               .               *        !
 4.2         .                      *     !
                                          X
```

You may also delete lines

110, 180, and 190.

Compare these graphs with your graph of $y = \cos x$.

Study your graph of $y = \sin x$ and modify the preceding program to print out portions of the graphs of $y = \sin x$ and $y = \csc x$.

Applications of Trigonometry

Waves and the World We Live In

You have seen that the circular functions sine and cosine are periodic and that their graphs have a wave-like appearance. You would naturally expect, then, that these functions are quite useful in studying periodic, or wave, phenomena; and this is in fact the case.

It would be difficult to imagine what the world would be like without wave phenomena. Actually, we could not imagine, or think at all, without creating electrical brain waves!

Our friends' voices are transmitted through the air to our ears as sound waves. When a violin string is bowed, a standing wave is set up in the string, and this produces a sound wave in the air. A stove produces radiant heat waves. Water waves furnish locomotion to surfers.

Light, carrying energy from the sun, travels as electromagnetic waves. In fact, electromagnetic waves occur over a wide, continuous range of wavelengths. The longest, called radio waves, can be well over a mile in length, although the ones used in ordinary radio broadcasting measure only about 500 meters. Radar waves are a few centimeters in length. Farther down the scale, infrared waves occur at about 10^{-4} to 7.5×10^{-7} meters, followed by visible light, ultraviolet rays, X-rays, gamma rays, and so on. Actually, there are no sharp divisions between the ranges of electromagnetic wavelengths, and the names reflect general properties and applications.

If you are a hi-fi enthusiast or a ham radio operator, if you plan to devote your life to the design of ingenious computer devices or television equipment, or if you plan to work as a theoretical or experimental physical scientist of almost any sort, you need a considerable understanding of wave theory and therefore of the circular functions.

In any case, you cannot avoid waves, for you live in a veritable sea of them.

This communications satellite, INTELSAT III, is one of a series of satellites owned by the International Telecommunications Satellite Consortium, an organization of almost 70 nations. This series of satellites rings the earth and provides telephone, television, and data transmission for these nations all over the world.

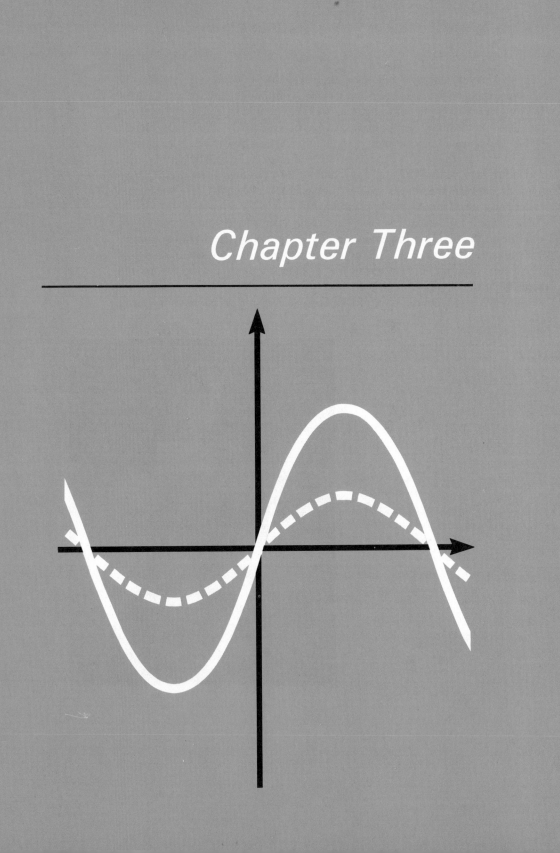

Chapter Three

Applications of Circular Functions

OBJECTIVES

1. To use the concepts of amplitude, period, cycle, and phase shift to graph circular functions.
2. To graph by using addition of ordinates.
3. To apply circular functions to solve problems involving uniform circular motion and simple harmonic motion.

Graphs

3–1 *Amplitude and Location*

Recall from Chapter 1 that the graphs of both the sine and the cosine functions are called *sine waves*. As you will see in this chapter, the more general functions $\{(x, y): y = a \sin b(x - c) + d\}$ and $\{(x, y): y = a \cos b(x - c) + d\}$, where a, b, c, and d are given constants with a and $b \neq 0$, have wave graphs which are modifications of (or, possibly, the same as) the basic sine waves. The graphs of these more general functions are also called sine waves.

Any portion of one of these wave graphs over an interval on the horizontal axis of length p, where p is the fundamental period of the function, is called a **cycle of the wave.** Similarly, the set of number pairs $(x, f(x))$ in the function over an interval $c \leq x \leq c + p$, where $c \in \Re$, is a **cycle of the function.** One-half the vertical distance between the maximum and minimum points of a sine wave is called the **amplitude of the wave,** and one-half the difference between the maximum and minimum values of a sine-wave function over one fundamental period is called the **amplitude of the function.**

In the first three sections of this chapter, we shall develop techniques for graphing functions with equations of the form $y = a \sin b(x - c) + d$. We shall consider the significance of the constants a and d in this section and that of the constants b and c in Section 3–2. In Section 3–3, we shall consolidate the ideas developed in Sections 3–1 and 3–2.

The techniques which will be developed for graphing equations of the form $y = a \sin b(x - c) + d$ can also be used to graph equations of the form $y = a \cos b(x - c) + d$ and equations of similar form for tan, cot, sec, and csc.

Figure 3–1 shows portions of the graphs of $y = 2 \sin x$, $y = \sin x$, and $y = \frac{1}{2} \sin x$ on the same set of axes. Note that the ordinate of each point on the graph of $y = 2 \sin x$ is twice the ordinate of the corresponding point on the

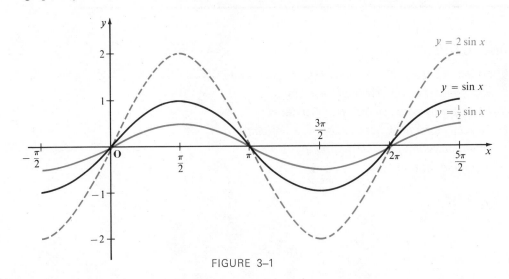

FIGURE 3–1

graph of $y = \sin x$, and that the ordinate of each point on the graph of $y = \frac{1}{2} \sin x$ is half the ordinate of the corresponding point on the graph of $y = \sin x$.

For every real number a, except 0, there exists a sine-wave function defined by $y = a \sin x$. The set of all such functions is called the *family* of functions defined by equations of the form $y = a \sin x$. The function defined by $y = \sin x$ is the member of this family for which $a = 1$.

The following generalizations can be made regarding the significance of the constant a:

1. For each real number x, the ordinate of a point on the graph of $y = a \sin x$ is a times the ordinate of the corresponding point on the graph of $y = \sin x$.
2. The amplitude of the graph of $y = a \sin x$ is $|a|$.
3. If $a < 0$, the graph of $y = a \sin x$ is a reflection in the x-axis of the graph of $y = |a| \sin x$.

As shown in Figure 3–2, the graph of $y = -2 \sin x$ can easily be obtained by first sketching the graph of $y = 2 \sin x$ and then reflecting this graph in the x-axis.

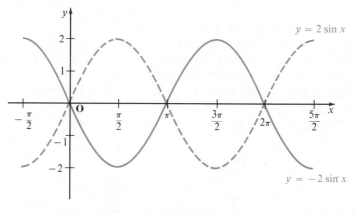

FIGURE 3–2

The addition of a constant to the right-hand member of the equation $y = \sin x$ produces an equation of the form $y = \sin x + d$. Like the equation $y = a \sin x$, the equation $y = \sin x + d$ defines a family of functions.

▲ The graph of $y = \sin x + d$ is identical with that of $y = \sin x$ except that the entire curve is shifted $|d|$ units up or down with respect to the x-axis, depending on whether $d > 0$ or $d < 0$.

Figure 3–3 shows the graphs of $y = \sin x + 2$, $y = \sin x$, and $y = \sin x - 2$ on the same set of axes.

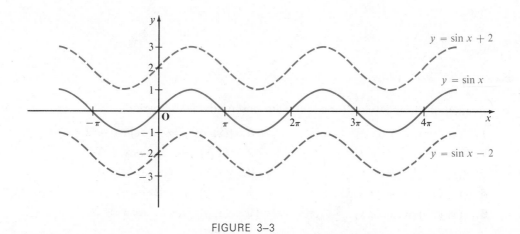

FIGURE 3–3

If we unite the two families of functions defined by $y = a \sin x$ and $y = \sin x + d$, we obtain the family of functions defined by $y = a \sin x + d$. To graph a member of this family, it is usually preferable to consider first the effect of the constant a and second the effect of the constant d.

Example   Sketch the graph of $\{(x, y): y = -3 \sin x + 1\}$.

Solution   As shown below, we sketch two preliminary graphs, those of $y = 3 \sin x$ and $y = -3 \sin x$ (in that order). Then, by shifting the graph of $y = -3 \sin x$ upward 1 unit, we obtain the graph of $y = -3 \sin x + 1$.

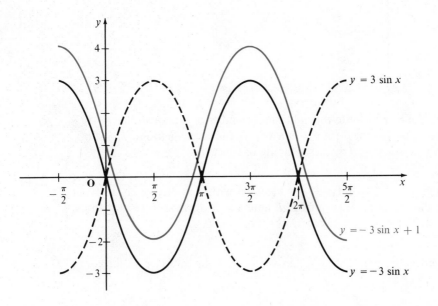

Exercises 3–1

Graph each of the following functions over one fundamental period.

A **1.** $\{(x, y): y = 4 \sin x\}$

2. $\{(x, y): y = \frac{1}{3} \cos x\}$

3. $\{(x, y): y = \frac{1}{3} \sec x\}$

4. $\{(x, y): y = -2 \tan x\}$

5. $\{(x, y): y = 3 \cot x\}$

6. $\{(x, y): y = -2 \sin x + 2\}$

7. $\{(x, y): y = 3 \cos x + 1\}$

8. $\{(x, y): y = \frac{1}{4} \tan x - 4\}$

9. $\{(x, y): y = 2 - \cot x\}$

10. $\{(x, y): y = -\sec x + 2\}$

Find the range of each of the following functions. You need not graph the functions.

B **11.** $\{(x, y): y = -2 \sin x + 3, \ 0 \leq x \leq 2\pi\}$

12. $\left\{(x, y): y = 4 \cos x - 4, \ -\dfrac{\pi}{2} \leq x \leq \dfrac{3\pi}{2}\right\}$

13. $\left\{(x, y): y = \dfrac{1}{2} \cos x + \dfrac{3}{2}, \ -\dfrac{\pi}{2} \leq x \leq \dfrac{3\pi}{2}\right\}$

14. $\left\{(x, y): y = \tan x - 5, \ -\dfrac{\pi}{2} < x < \dfrac{\pi}{2}\right\}$

15. $\left\{(x, y): y = 3 \cot x + 2, \ -\dfrac{\pi}{2} < x < \dfrac{3\pi}{2}, \ x \neq \dfrac{\pi}{2}\right\}$

16. $\left\{(x, y): y = \sec x - 2, \ -\dfrac{\pi}{2} < x < \dfrac{3\pi}{2}, \ x \neq \dfrac{\pi}{2}\right\}$

Find the value of the constant d in each of the following.

17. $\{(x, y): y = \sin x + d, 0 \leq x \leq 2\pi, 2 \leq y \leq 4\}$

18. $\{(x, y): y = -3 \sin x + d, 0 \leq x \leq 2\pi, -6 \leq y \leq 0\}$

19. $\left\{(x, y): y = -\cos x + d, \ -\dfrac{\pi}{2} \leq x \leq \dfrac{3\pi}{2}, -6 \leq y \leq -4\right\}$

20. $\left\{(x, y): y = \tan x + d, \ -\dfrac{\pi}{4} \leq x \leq \dfrac{\pi}{4}, -3 \leq y \leq -1\right\}$

In Exercises 21 and 22, graph the two given sets on the same set of axes over the given interval.

C **21.** $\{(x, y): y = 2 \sin x\}, \ \{(x, y): y = |2 \sin x|\}, \ 0 \leq x \leq 2\pi$

22. $\{(x, y): y = \cos x - 2\}, \ \{(x, y): y = |\cos x - 2|\}, \ -\dfrac{\pi}{2} \leq x \leq \dfrac{3\pi}{2}$

3–2 *Periods and Phase Shifts*

By replacing the variable x in the equation $y = \sin x$ with expressions of the form bx, where b is a real number different from zero, we obtain various members of the family of functions defined by $y = \sin bx$. Note that the function defined by $y = \sin x$ is the member of this family for which $b = 1$.

For $b = 2$, we have the equation $y = \sin 2x$, and we note that for every real number x in the interval $0 \leq x \leq \pi$, the corresponding numbers $2x$ are in the interval $0 \leq 2x \leq 2\pi$. Comparing some of the values of $\sin x, 0 \leq x \leq 2\pi$, and sin $2x$, $0 \leq x \leq \pi$, we note that

$$\sin x = 0 \text{ for } x = 0, \pi, 2\pi, \text{ whereas } \sin 2x = 0 \text{ for } x = 0, \frac{\pi}{2}, \pi.$$

$$\sin x = 1 \text{ for } x = \frac{\pi}{2}, \text{ whereas } \sin 2x = 1 \text{ for } x = \frac{\pi}{4}.$$

$$\sin x = -1 \text{ for } x = \frac{3\pi}{2}, \text{ whereas } \sin 2x = -1 \text{ for } x = \frac{3\pi}{4}.$$

We can show that the function defined by $f(x) = \sin 2x$, $x \in \Re$, is periodic, with fundamental period π, as follows: We want to show that for every real number $x, f(x + \pi) = f(x)$. We have

$$f(x + \pi) = \sin 2(x + \pi) = \sin (2x + 2\pi).$$

Since sin has fundamental period 2π,

$$\sin (2x + 2\pi) = \sin 2x = f(x).$$

Thus, $f(x + \pi) = f(x)$ for every real number x, as required.

In similar fashion, we can show that the function defined by $y = \sin \frac{1}{2}x$ is periodic, with fundamental period 4π.

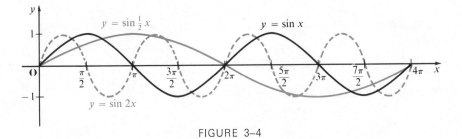

FIGURE 3–4

Figure 3–4 shows the graphs of the functions defined by $y = \sin 2x$, $y = \sin x$, and $y = \sin \frac{1}{2}x$. Notice that each of these graphs makes a complete cycle as follows: $\sin 2x$ in the interval $0 \leq x \leq \pi$, $\sin x$ in the interval $0 \leq x \leq 2\pi$, and $\sin \frac{1}{2}x$ in the interval $0 \leq x \leq 4\pi$.

To generalize:

▲   The function defined by $y = \sin bx$, $b \neq 0$, is periodic, with fundamental period $\dfrac{2\pi}{|b|}$. Its graph is cyclic, with one complete cycle occurring in the interval $0 \leq x \leq \dfrac{2\pi}{|b|}$.

For $b < 0$, the graphs of $y = \sin bx$ and $y = \sin |b|x$ are symmetric with respect to the x-axis, as shown in Figure 3–5.

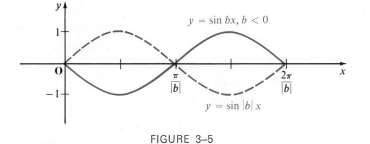

FIGURE 3–5

Next, let us investigate the family of functions defined by equations of the form $y = \sin(x - c)$, where c is any real number. If x is a number in the interval $c \leq x \leq c + 2\pi$, then $0 \leq x - c \leq 2\pi$. This means that as x increases from c to $c + 2\pi$, the corresponding numbers $x - c$ increase from 0 to 2π, and it follows that the numbers $\sin(x - c)$ vary from 0 to 1 to 0 to -1 to 0.

For example, let $c = \dfrac{\pi}{3}$. As x increases from $\dfrac{\pi}{3}$ to $\dfrac{\pi}{3} + 2\pi$, or $\dfrac{7\pi}{3}$, the corresponding numbers $x - \dfrac{\pi}{3}$ vary from 0 to 2π, and the numbers $\sin\left(x - \dfrac{\pi}{3}\right)$ vary from 0 to 1 to 0 to -1 to 0. The table below lists values of $x - \dfrac{\pi}{3}$ and $\sin\left(x - \dfrac{\pi}{3}\right)$ for selected values of x in the interval $\dfrac{\pi}{3} \leq x \leq \dfrac{7\pi}{3}$.

x	$\dfrac{\pi}{3}$	$\dfrac{7\pi}{12}$	$\dfrac{5\pi}{6}$	$\dfrac{13\pi}{12}$	$\dfrac{4\pi}{3}$	$\dfrac{19\pi}{12}$	$\dfrac{11\pi}{6}$	$\dfrac{25\pi}{12}$	$\dfrac{7\pi}{3}$
$x - \dfrac{\pi}{3}$	0	$\dfrac{\pi}{4}$	$\dfrac{\pi}{2}$	$\dfrac{3\pi}{4}$	π	$\dfrac{5\pi}{4}$	$\dfrac{3\pi}{2}$	$\dfrac{7\pi}{4}$	2π
$\sin\left(x - \dfrac{\pi}{3}\right)$	0	$\dfrac{\sqrt{2}}{2}$	1	$\dfrac{\sqrt{2}}{2}$	0	$-\dfrac{\sqrt{2}}{2}$	-1	$-\dfrac{\sqrt{2}}{2}$	0

The function defined by $f(x) = \sin\left(x - \dfrac{\pi}{3}\right)$ is periodic, with fundamental period 2π, since

$$f(x + 2\pi) = \sin\left[(x + 2\pi) - \frac{\pi}{3}\right] = \sin\left[\left(x - \frac{\pi}{3}\right) + 2\pi\right]$$

$$= \sin\left(x - \frac{\pi}{3}\right) = f(x).$$

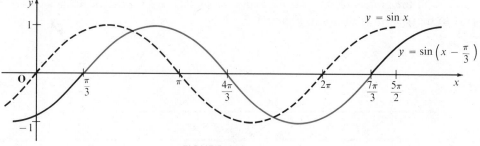

FIGURE 3–6

The graph of $f(x) = \sin\left(x - \frac{\pi}{3}\right)$, $x \in \Re$, is shown in Figure 3–6. The portion of the graph in the interval $\frac{\pi}{3} \le x \le \frac{7\pi}{3}$ is shown in color. Notice that the graph of $y = \sin\left(x - \frac{\pi}{3}\right)$ is congruent to the graph of $y = \sin x$ and can be obtained by shifting, or *translating*, the graph of $y = \sin x$ to the right $\frac{\pi}{3}$ units. In general:

▲ The graph of any function defined by an equation of the form $y = \sin(x - c)$ is congruent to the graph of $y = \sin x$ and can be obtained by translating the graph of $y = \sin x$ to the left or to the right with respect to the y-axis. The translation is to the right c units if $c > 0$ and to the left $|c|$ units if $c < 0$.

For example, given the equation $y = \sin\left(x + \frac{\pi}{4}\right)$, you can write $x + \frac{\pi}{4}$ as $x - \left(-\frac{\pi}{4}\right)$, so that $c = -\frac{\pi}{4}$. Thus the graph of $y = \sin\left(x + \frac{\pi}{4}\right)$ can be obtained by translating the graph of $y = \sin x$ to the left $\frac{\pi}{4}$ units, as shown in Figure 3–7.

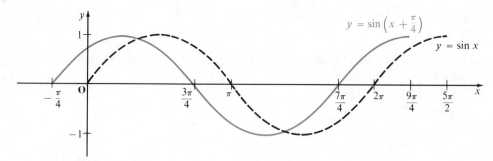

FIGURE 3–7

The preceding discussion has concerned the significance of the constants b and c in the families of functions defined by $y = \sin bx$ and $y = \sin(x - c)$. If we now unite these two families, the result is the family of functions defined by equations of the form $y = \sin b(x - c)$. To graph a member of this family, it is usually preferable to consider first the effect of the constant b and second the effect of the constant c.

Example   Graph two cycles of $y = \sin\left(2x - \dfrac{\pi}{3}\right)$.

Solution   Writing the defining equation in the form $y = \sin 2\left(x - \dfrac{\pi}{6}\right)$ indicates that we should first graph $y = \sin 2x$ and then translate that graph to the right $\dfrac{\pi}{6}$ units.

Since the fundamental period of $y = \sin 2x$ is $\dfrac{2\pi}{|2|} = \pi$, we graph one cycle of $y = \sin 2x$ over the interval $0 \le x \le \pi$. Translating this cycle to the right $\dfrac{\pi}{6}$ units gives one cycle of $y = \sin 2\left(x - \dfrac{\pi}{6}\right)$ over the interval $\dfrac{\pi}{6} \le x \le \dfrac{7\pi}{6}$. Repetition of this cycle produces two cycles of $y = \sin 2\left(x - \dfrac{\pi}{6}\right)$ over the interval $\dfrac{\pi}{6} \le x \le \dfrac{13\pi}{6}$, as shown.

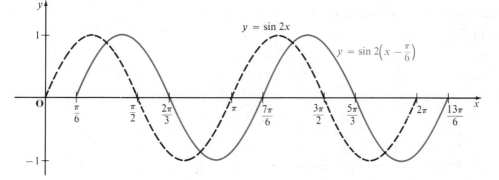

As a check, we solve the inequality $0 \le 2x - \dfrac{\pi}{3} \le 2\pi$, obtaining $\dfrac{\pi}{3} \le 2x \le \dfrac{7\pi}{3}$ and then $\dfrac{\pi}{6} \le x \le \dfrac{7\pi}{6}$. Thus one cycle of the graph of $y = \sin\left(2x - \dfrac{\pi}{3}\right)$ should occur in the interval $\dfrac{\pi}{6} \le x \le \dfrac{7\pi}{6}$, and this agrees with our solution.

The graph of $y = \sin (x - c)$ is said to **lead** (that is, to come before, as we view it from left to right) the graph of $y = \sin x$ if $c < 0$ and to **lag** (come after) the graph of $y = \sin x$ if $c > 0$. In each case, the constant c is called the **phase shift**.

The ideas developed in this section for the sine function can be applied similarly to the graphs of the five remaining circular functions.

Exercises 3–2

Graph each of the following over one fundamental period.

A 1. $\{(x, y): y = \sin 4x\}$

    2. $\{(x, y): y = \cos \frac{1}{3}x\}$

    3. $\{(x, y): y = \tan 2x\}$

    4. $\{(x, y): y = \cos 2x\}$

    5. $\left\{(x, y): y = \sin \left(x + \frac{\pi}{3}\right)\right\}$

    6. $\left\{(x, y): y = \cos \left(x - \frac{\pi}{2}\right)\right\}$

    7. $\left\{(x, y): y = \tan \left(x - \frac{\pi}{2}\right)\right\}$

    8. $\left\{(x, y): y = \sin 2 \left(x - \frac{\pi}{4}\right)\right\}$

    9. $\{(x, y): y = \sin \frac{1}{4}(x + \pi)\}$

   10. $\left\{(x, y): y = \cos 3 \left(x - \frac{\pi}{2}\right)\right\}$

   11. $\left\{(x, y): y = \tan \frac{1}{2} \left(x + \frac{\pi}{4}\right)\right\}$

   12. $\left\{(x, y): y = \sec 4 \left(x - \frac{\pi}{2}\right)\right\}$

Graph each of the following over the interval $-2\pi \leq x \leq 2\pi$.

B 13. $\{(x, y): y = \sin (-x)\}$

  14. $\{(x, y): y = \sin (2\pi - x)\}$

  15. $\{(x, y): y = \cos (-x)\}$

  16. $\{(x, y): y = \cos (\pi - x)\}$

  17. $\{(x, y): y = \tan (-x)\}$

  18. $\{(x, y): y = \tan (\pi - x)\}$

  19. $\{(x, y): y = \sin (\pi x)\}$

  20. $\{(x, y): y = \tan (\pi x)\}$

  21. Find a value for c such that the graph of $y = \sin (x - c)$ contains the point $(0, -1)$.

  22. Find a value for c such that the graph of $y = 2 \tan (x - c)$ contains the point $\left(\frac{\pi}{6}, 2\sqrt{3}\right)$.

C 23. Prove that the graph of $y = -\cos x$ has phase shift of amount π from the graph of $y = \cos x$.

  24. Determine a phase shift for cos that makes its graph coincide with that of sin. Prove your assertion by means of a suitable identity. Is more than one phase shift possible?

3-3   *The Family y* $= a \sin b(x - c) + d$

In Section 3–1, we developed techniques for graphing members of the family of functions defined by $y = a \sin x + d$. In Section 3–2, we discussed the family defined by $y = \sin b(x - c)$. By uniting these two families of functions, we obtain the family of functions defined by equations of the form $y = a \sin b(x - c) + d$.

To graph a member of this family, each of the four constants a, b, c, and d should be considered separately. Generally it is preferable to consider these constants in one of the orders a, b, c, d, or b, c, a, d. Note that in either case b is considered before c, and d is considered last.

Example 1   Sketch the graph of $\{(x, y): y = 3 \sin \frac{1}{2}(x - \pi) - 1\}$ over one fundamental period.

Solution   We shall first graph one cycle of each of three preliminary graphs, those of $y = \sin \frac{1}{2}x$, $y = \sin \frac{1}{2}(x - \pi)$, and $y = 3 \sin \frac{1}{2}(x - \pi)$, in the order listed.

The graph of $y = \sin \frac{1}{2}x$ makes one cycle in the interval $0 \leq x \leq 4\pi$. Translating this graph to the right π units gives a cycle of $y = \sin \frac{1}{2}(x - \pi)$ in the interval $\pi \leq x \leq 5\pi$. Multiplying the ordinate of each point on the graph of $y = \sin \frac{1}{2}(x - \pi)$ by 3 gives a cycle of $y = 3 \sin \frac{1}{2}(x - \pi)$ in the interval $\pi \leq x \leq 5\pi$.

Since $d = -1$, we lower the preceding graph by 1 unit, to produce the graph of $y = 3 \sin \frac{1}{2}(x - \pi) - 1$ shown below.

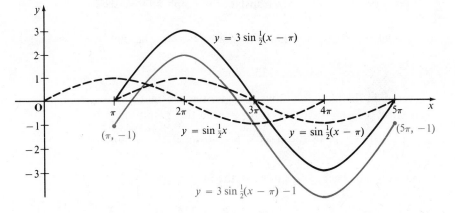

Applying the ideas of graphing that we have discussed to circular functions other than the sine function should now be relatively easy for you. To illustrate, in the next example we graph a member of the family of functions $\{(x, y): y = a \sec b(x - c) + d\}$.

Example 2   Sketch the graph of $\left\{(x, y): y = -\sec\left(2x + \dfrac{\pi}{3}\right)\right\}$ over two fundamental periods.

Solution   Writing the defining equation in the form

$$y = -\sec 2\left[x - \left(-\frac{\pi}{6}\right)\right]$$

identifies the function as a member of the family

$$y = a \sec b(x - c) + d,$$

with $a = -1$, $b = 2$, $c = -\dfrac{\pi}{6}$, and $d = 0$.

Recall that the interval $-\dfrac{3\pi}{2} < x < \dfrac{5\pi}{2}$ is convenient for graphing $y = \sec x$ over two fundamental periods. Since the fundamental period of $y = \sec 2x$ is $\dfrac{2\pi}{|2|}$, or π, we shorten the interval $-\dfrac{3\pi}{2} < x < \dfrac{5\pi}{2}$ by a factor of 2. Thus we graph $y = \sec 2x$ over $-\dfrac{3\pi}{4} < x < \dfrac{5\pi}{4}$, as shown in black at the top of page 91.

Next, since $c = -\dfrac{\pi}{6}$, we translate the graph of $y = \sec 2x$ to the left $\dfrac{\pi}{6}$ units, so that the graph lies in the interval $-\dfrac{11\pi}{12} < x < \dfrac{13\pi}{12}$, as shown in color.

To obtain the final graph, we consider the constant $a = -1$. The effect of this constant is to reflect the graph of $y = \sec 2\left[x - \left(-\dfrac{\pi}{6}\right)\right]$ in the x-axis, as shown at the bottom of page 91.

As a partial check, you can solve the inequality

$$-\frac{3\pi}{2} < 2x + \frac{\pi}{3} < \frac{5\pi}{2}, \quad \text{obtaining} \quad -\frac{11\pi}{12} < x < \frac{13\pi}{12}.$$

Thus the graph should lie in the interval $-\dfrac{11\pi}{12} < x < \dfrac{13\pi}{12}$, which it does.

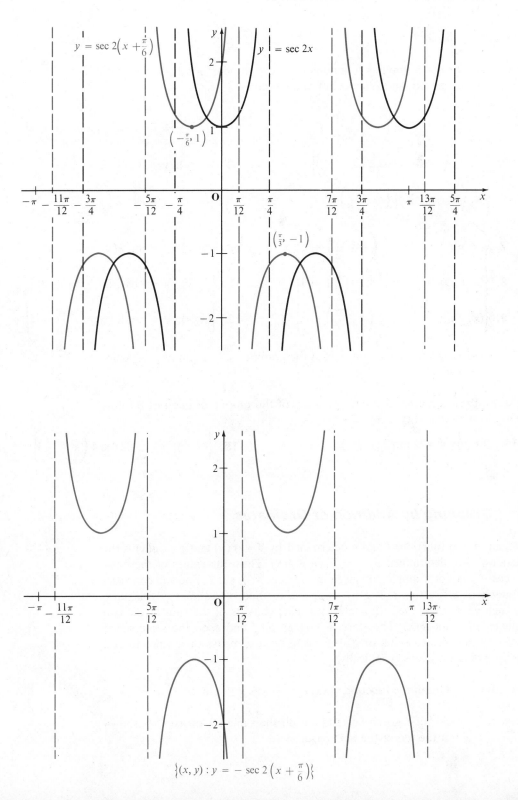

$y = \sec 2\left(x + \frac{\pi}{6}\right)$

$y = \sec 2x$

$\left(-\frac{\pi}{6}, 1\right)$

$\left(\frac{\pi}{3}, -1\right)$

$\{(x, y) : y = -\sec 2\left(x + \frac{\pi}{6}\right)\}$

Exercises 3–3

Graph each of the following functions over one fundamental period. State
the amplitude, period, and phase shift of each curve.

A 1. $\{(x, y): y = 2 \sin\left(x + \frac{\pi}{4}\right)\}$

2. $\{(x, y): y = -5 \cos 2\left(x - \frac{\pi}{6}\right)\}$

3. $\{(x, y): y = \sin 4\left(x - \frac{\pi}{8}\right) - 2\}$

4. $\{(x, y): y = -\cos\frac{1}{2}(x + \pi) + 3\}$

5. $\{(x, y): y = \tan\left(3x - \frac{\pi}{2}\right) - 1\}$

6. $\{(x, y): y = \sec 2\left(x + \frac{\pi}{3}\right) - 2\}$

B 7. $\{(x, y): y = 2 \sec\frac{1}{4}\left(x + \frac{\pi}{2}\right) + 1\}$

8. $\{(x, y): y = -\cos\left(4x + \frac{\pi}{2}\right) + 1\}$

9. $\{(x, y): y = -\cot 2\left(x + \frac{\pi}{6}\right) + 2\}$

10. $\{(x, y): y = \sin \pi(x - 3) - 4\}$

11. $\{(x, y): y = \cos\frac{\pi}{2}(x + 1) + 2\}$

12. $\{(x, y): y = \sec 8\left(x - \frac{\pi}{16}\right) - 4\}$

C 13. Find values for a and c such that the graph of $y = a \tan(x - c)$ coincides with the graph of $y = \cot x$.

What are the equations of the asymptotes of the graphs of each of the following in the interval $0 \le x \le 2\pi$?

14. $\{(x, y): y = 2 \tan 2x\}$

15. $\{(x, y): y = -2 \sec 4\left(x - \frac{\pi}{8}\right)\}$

3–4 Graphing by Addition of Ordinates

The **sum** of two functions f and g determined by $y = f(x)$ and $y = g(x)$ is the function $f + g$ determined by $y = f(x) + g(x)$. Thus, the values of the function $\cos + \sin$, for example, are given by $y = \cos x + \sin x$. You can construct the graph of a function $f + g$ by using the method of *addition of ordinates*. For each value of x, the ordinate $f(x) + g(x)$ consists of the sum of the two ordinates $f(x)$ and $g(x)$. Therefore, if you graph f and g on the same set of axes, you can locate points on $f + g$ by using a compass or a ruler to add corresponding ordinates graphically.

Example Graph the function $\{(x, y): y = \cos x + \sin x\}$.

Solution We first graph cos and sin on the same set of axes, as shown at the top of the next page.

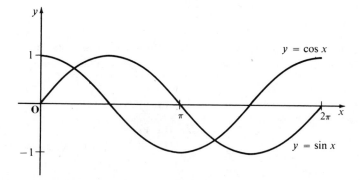

Next, we locate points on the graph of cos + sin by selecting values of x, measuring off the ordinate of one of the curves at these values, and graphically adding this ordinate to the other to obtain the ordinate of the graph we are constructing. The figure below shows $\cos x + \sin x$ for selected values of x. Ordinates of points below the x-axis are, of course, negative, and all sums of ordinates must be treated graphically as sums of *directed* distances.

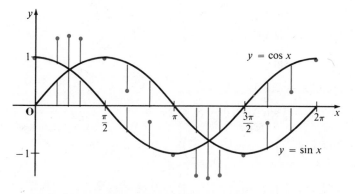

The completed graph appears as follows.

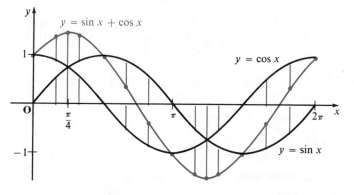

Exercises 3–4

Graph each of the following functions over the interval $0 \leq x \leq 2\pi$ by graphically adding ordinates, and then sketch one additional cycle at each end of this interval.

A 1. $\{(x, y): y = \frac{1}{2} \sin x + \frac{1}{2} \cos x\}$

2. $\{(x, y): y = \frac{3}{2}(\sin x + \cos x)\}$

3. $\{(x, y): y = \sin x - \cos x\}$
(*Hint:* Graph $\{(x, y): y = \sin x\}$ and $\{(x, y): y = -\cos x\}$ and *add* ordinates.)

4. $\{(x, y): y = \cos x - \sin x\}$

5. $\{(x, y): y = \sin x + 2 \cos x\}$

6. $\{(x, y): y = 3 \sin x + \cos x\}$

7. $\{(x, y): y = \sin(-x) + 2 \cos(-x)\}$
(*Hint:* Recall that $\sin(-x) = -\sin x$ and $\cos(-x) = \cos x$.)

8. $\{(x, y): y = 3 \sin(-x) + \frac{1}{2} \cos(-x)\}$

9. $\{(x, y): y = 2 \sin(-x) - 3 \cos(-x)\}$

10. $\{(x, y): y = \frac{1}{2} \sin(-x) - 2 \cos(-x)\}$

Graph each of the following functions over the indicated interval.

B 11. $\{(x, y): y = \sin 2x + \cos x\}$, $0 \leq x \leq 2\pi$

12. $\{(x, y): y = \cos 2x + \sin x\}$, $0 \leq x \leq 2\pi$

13. $\{(x, y): y = \cos \frac{1}{2}x + \sin x\}$, $0 \leq x \leq 4\pi$

14. $\{(x, y): y = \cos 2x + \sin \frac{1}{2}x\}$, $0 \leq x \leq 4\pi$

15. $\{(x, y): y = 2 \sin 2x - \cos 3x\}$, $0 \leq x \leq 2\pi$

16. $\{(x, y): y = \cos 2x - \frac{1}{2} \sin 3x\}$, $0 \leq x \leq 2\pi$

17. $\left\{(x, y): y = \sin\left(x - \frac{\pi}{4}\right) + \cos\left(x - \frac{\pi}{3}\right)\right\}$, $0 \leq x \leq 2\pi$

18. $\left\{(x, y): y = \sin\left(x + \frac{\pi}{3}\right) + \cos\left(x + \frac{\pi}{6}\right)\right\}$, $0 \leq x \leq 2\pi$

C 19. Show that the graph of the equation $y = \cos x + \sin x$ is the same as the graph of the equation $y = \sqrt{2} \cos\left(x - \frac{\pi}{4}\right)$.

20. Find values for a and c so that the graph of $y = \cos 2x + \sin 2x$ will be the same as the graph of $y = a \cos(2x - c)$.
(*Hint:* Expand the expression $a \cos(2x - c)$.)

21. Find values for a and c so that the graph of $y = 4 \cos x + 3 \sin x$ will be the same as the graph of $y = a \cos(x - c)$.
(*Hint:* Expand the expression $a \cos(x - c)$.)

Periodic Motion

3–5 *Uniform Circular Motion*

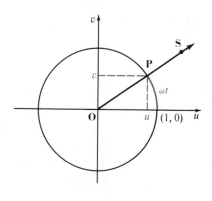

FIGURE 3–8

Figure 3–8 shows a unit circle with center at the origin **O** in the uv-plane and a ray $\overrightarrow{OS}$ intersecting the circle at the point **P**. If the ray $\overrightarrow{OS}$ rotates in a counterclockwise direction about the origin in such a way that **P** maintains a constant speed around the circle, that is, if **P** travels with **uniform circular motion**, then we can express the position of **P** as a function of time. Thus, by expressing arc length in terms of time, we can express the coordinates, cos and sin, of **P** as functions of time rather than directly as functions of arc length.

Let T be the number of units of time required for **P** to complete one revolution of the unit circle, that is, to travel an arc of length 2π. Since **P** is traveling with uniform circular motion, its speed can be expressed as the ratio of the distance traveled to the time elapsed, $\dfrac{2\pi}{T}$. We call the ratio of the arc length traveled on a unit circle to the time elapsed the **rotational velocity** of the ray $\overrightarrow{OS}$ or of the point **P**, and denote it by the Greek letter ω (omega). Thus the rotational velocity of **P** is

▲
$$\omega = \frac{2\pi}{T}.$$

Of course, it then follows that given a constant rotational velocity ω, the time T required to complete one revolution is just

▲
$$T = \frac{2\pi}{\omega}.$$

Now, the arc length traveled by **P** in t units of time is $\left(\dfrac{2\pi}{T}\right) t$, or ωt. Hence, from Figure 3–8 you can see that if **P** is at the point $(1, 0)$ when $t = 0$, then the coordinates of **P** at time t will be

$$u = \cos \omega t, \qquad v = \sin \omega t.$$

If, however, **P** is already at a length b from the point $(1, 0)$ on the circle when $t = 0$ (see Figure 3–9), so that its coordinates are $(\cos b, \sin b)$ when

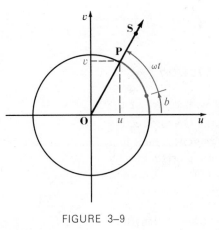

FIGURE 3–9

$t = 0$, then at time t it will be at a length $\omega t + b$ from $(1, 0)$ on the circle, and its coordinates will then be

$$u = \cos (\omega t + b), \qquad v = \sin (\omega t + b).$$

Example 1   Let **P** move with constant speed in a counterclockwise direction around the unit circle starting at the point $(1, 0)$, and let **P** complete $\frac{5}{2}$ revolutions per second.

(a) Find the value of ω.
(b) Find the coordinates of **P** after 3 seconds.

Solution   (a) Since $\omega = \dfrac{2\pi}{T}$, and since one revolution is completed in $\frac{2}{5}$ second, you have

$$\omega = \frac{2\pi}{\frac{2}{5}} = 5\pi.$$

(b) At time t, the coordinates of **P** will be $(\cos 5\pi t, \sin 5\pi t)$, so that when $t = 3$, **P** will have coordinates $(\cos 15\pi, \sin 15\pi)$. Since $(\cos 15\pi, \sin 15\pi) = (\cos \pi, \sin \pi) = (-1, 0)$, **P** has coordinates $(-1, 0)$ after 3 seconds.

In Figure 3–8, page 95, all points on the ray $\overrightarrow{OS}$ will, of course, complete one revolution about the origin in the same amount of time. Since this is so, points located on $\overrightarrow{OS}$ at different distances from the origin will have different speeds *along their respective circles;* the farther a point is from the origin, the greater the circumference of the circle it travels and, consequently, the greater its speed.

Figure 3–10 shows two circles: C_1, a unit circle, and C_2, a circle of radius a ($a > 1$), both with center at the origin in the uv-plane. The ray $\overrightarrow{OS}$ intersects the circles C_1 and C_2 at points P_1 and P_2, respectively. If $\overrightarrow{OS}$ is rotating with uniform rotational velocity ω in a counterclockwise direction, then at time t the length of arc $\widehat{A_1P_1}$ will be ωt. Since P_2 will traverse its circumference length, $2\pi a$, in the same amount of time that P_1 traverses 2π, the speed of P_2 along its circle is $\dfrac{2\pi a}{T}$, or ωa, and the length of the arc $\widehat{A_2P_2}$ is $a\omega t$. Notice that the speed of a point along a circle is equal to its rotational velocity if and only if the circle is a unit circle.

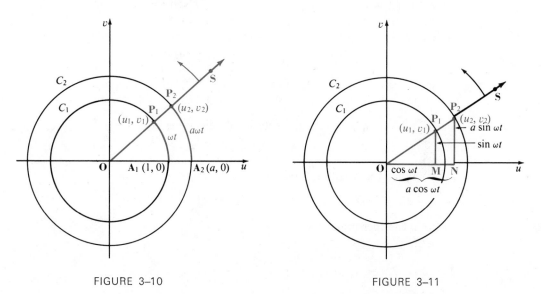

FIGURE 3–10   FIGURE 3–11

In Figure 3–11, the same situation is shown, this time with perpendiculars dropped from P_1 and P_2 to the u-axis. From a consideration of similar triangles, you can see that when P_1 has coordinates ($\cos \omega t$, $\sin \omega t$), P_2 will have coordinates ($a \cos \omega t$, $a \sin \omega t$). That is, in similar triangles OP_1M and OP_2N, it is true that

$$\frac{v_1}{d(\overline{OP_1})} = \frac{v_2}{d(\overline{OP_2})}, \quad \text{or} \quad \frac{\sin \omega t}{1} = \frac{v_2}{a},$$

so that $v_2 = a \sin \omega t$. Similarly, because

$$\frac{u_1}{d(\overline{OP_1})} = \frac{u_2}{d(\overline{OP_2})}, \quad \text{you have} \quad \frac{\cos \omega t}{1} = \frac{u_2}{a},$$

and $u_2 = a \cos \omega t$.

Thus far we have been concerned with points traveling with constant speed around a circle in a counterclockwise direction. The discussion in this section can also be applied, however, to situations in which the point is traveling in a clockwise direction, except that we assign a negative rotational velocity to a clockwise rotation. In solving problems, if it is not specified whether the rotation is clockwise or counterclockwise, you should assume that the rotational velocity is positive.

Example 2   A phonograph record of radius 6 inches spins on a turntable at a rate of $33\frac{1}{3}$ revolutions per minute.

(a) What is the rotational velocity of any given ray from the center of the record?

(b) With what speed are points on the record passing beneath the needle when the needle is 2 inches from the center?

Solution   (a) Since the record is turning at $33\frac{1}{3}$, or $\frac{100}{3}$, revolutions per unit of time (that is, per minute), it turns 1 revolution in $\frac{3}{100}$ minute, so that the rotational velocity ω equals $\dfrac{2\pi}{\frac{3}{100}}$, or $\dfrac{200\pi}{3}$.

(b) When the needle is 2 inches from the center, points on the record pass beneath it at a speed of $2\left(\dfrac{200\pi}{3}\right)$, or $\dfrac{400\pi}{3}$, inches per minute.

Exercises 3–5

In Exercises 1–6, a point is moving along a circle of radius r at a constant rotational velocity ω in a counterclockwise direction. Find the length of arc traversed in t units of time under the given conditions.

A   **1.** $\omega = \dfrac{\pi}{6}$; $r = 3$; $t = 2$ **3.** $\omega = \dfrac{2\pi}{3}$; $r = 9$; $t = \dfrac{1}{2}$ **5.** $\omega = \dfrac{5\pi}{4}$; $r = \dfrac{4}{3}$; $t = 2$

2. $\omega = \dfrac{3\pi}{2}$; $r = 4$; $t = 3$ **4.** $\omega = \dfrac{7\pi}{12}$; $r = 6$; $t = \dfrac{1}{3}$ **6.** $\omega = \dfrac{11\pi}{12}$; $r = \dfrac{6}{5}$; $t = 5$

7. A point moving with constant speed counterclockwise around a circle of radius 5 inches completes 3 revolutions in 2 seconds. What is its rotational velocity? What is its speed along the circle?

8. A wheel of diameter 12 inches turns at a constant rate of 120 revolutions per minute (rpm). What is the rotational velocity of the wheel? If the wheel rolls along the ground without slipping, how far will it roll in 3 minutes?

9. If the minute hand of a clock is 2 inches long, how far does the tip of the hand move in 15 minutes? What is the rotational velocity of the minute hand? (*Note:* A clockwise rotation is assigned a negative rotational velocity.)

10. A wheel 6 inches in diameter is driven with a belt by a wheel 8 inches in diameter. If the 8-inch wheel revolves at 120 revolutions per minute, and there is no slippage, how fast is a point on the belt moving? What is the rotational velocity of the 6-inch wheel?

B 11. A point **P** moves with constant rotational velocity $\frac{5\pi}{6}$ in a counterclockwise direction around a circle with center at the origin and with radius 6 units. If **P** is located at $(6, 0)$ when t is 0, what are the coordinates of **P**

(a) 3 units of time after 0 time?
(b) 3 units of time prior to 0 time?

12. Points P_1 and P_2 move with constant rotational velocity in a counterclockwise direction around a circle with center at the origin and with radius 3 inches. If the rotational velocity of P_1 is $\frac{5\pi}{6}$ and that of P_2 is $\frac{\pi}{3}$, and if P_1 and P_2 are both located at $(3, 0)$ when $t = 0$, how many units of time will pass before P_1 and P_2 again coincide? What will the coordinates of P_1 be then? (*Hint:* When P_1 and P_2 next meet, P_1 will have made one revolution more than P_2.)

13. In Exercise 12, let the rotational velocities of P_1 and P_2 be $\frac{4\pi}{3}$ and $\frac{\pi}{2}$, respectively, and answer the same questions.

14. In Exercise 12, let the rotational velocities of P_1 and P_2 be $-\frac{\pi}{8}$ and $\frac{\pi}{4}$, respectively, and answer the same questions.

C 15. A point P_1 is located at $(3, 0)$ when P_2 is at $\left(\frac{3\sqrt{3}}{2}, \frac{3}{2}\right)$ on a circle of radius 3. P_1 is moving with rotational velocity $\omega_1 = \frac{\pi}{3}$ and P_2 is moving with rotational velocity $\omega_2 = \frac{\pi}{4}$. How many units of time will elapse before P_1 and P_2 occupy the same point **P**? What will be the coordinates of **P**? How far will P_1 have traveled in moving from $(3, 0)$ to **P**?

16. In Exercise 15, let $\omega_1 = -\frac{\pi}{3}$ and $\omega_2 = -\frac{\pi}{4}$, and answer the same questions.

17. If P_1 is located at point $\left(\dfrac{5\sqrt{3}}{2}, \dfrac{5}{2}\right)$ when $t = 0$, and if P_1 is moving with constant rotational velocity ω around a circle with center at the origin, write expressions for the coordinates of P_1 at any time t.

18. In Exercise 17, find expressions for the coordinates of P_1 at any time t if P_1 is located at the point $\left(\dfrac{2}{\sqrt{2}}, \dfrac{2}{\sqrt{2}}\right)$ when $t = 0$.

3–6 *Simple Harmonic Motion*

Any particle that moves back and forth between the endpoints of a line segment and whose position on the segment at any time t can be determined by means of an equation of the form

$$y = a \cos(\omega t + b) \quad \text{or} \quad y = a \sin(\omega t + b)$$

where a, ω, and b are constants, is said to be in **simple harmonic motion**. Some examples of close approximations to such motion are a point on a prong of a tuning fork, a buoy bobbing up and down in water, a piston in an internal-combustion engine, and a particle of air during the passage of a simple sound wave.

Simple harmonic motion can be described completely by means of a mathematical model involving uniform circular motion. To see how the two motions are related, look at Figure 3–12, which shows a point P on a circle of radius a.

If you think of P as moving counterclockwise around the circle with rotational velocity ω, then as P moves, so does M, the projection of P on the u-axis. As P travels a distance $2\pi a$ beginning at $(a, 0)$, M travels along the u-axis from $(a, 0)$ to $(-a, 0)$ and back again to $(a, 0)$. Because the coordinate of M on the u-axis is equal to the abscissa of P, the motion of M is described by the equation

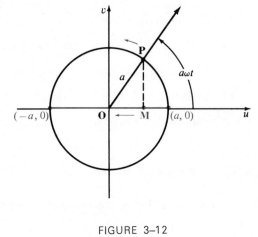

FIGURE 3–12

$$u_M = a \cos \omega t,$$

and, by definition, M is in simple harmonic motion. The number u_M is called the **displacement** of M at time t, and it represents the directed distance of M from the midpoint of its path.

In the simple harmonic motion described by

$$y = a \cos (\omega t + b), \tag{1}$$

the time period is $T = \dfrac{2\pi}{\omega}$. The number of cycles completed in a unit of time is called the **frequency** of the motion. Since one cycle is completed in T units of time, the number of cycles completed in one unit of time is $\dfrac{1}{T}$. Thus the frequency f is the reciprocal of the period T; that is, f is given by

$$f = \frac{1}{T} = \frac{\omega}{2\pi}.$$

Example 1   The voltage E in an electric circuit carrying alternating current can, under idealized conditions, be described by

$$E = E_{\max} \sin (\omega t + b),$$

where E is the voltage at time t and $E_{\max}$ is the maximum voltage attained in one cycle.

(a) If the circuit is carrying a 60-cycle-per-second current, find ω.

(b) If $b = 0$, and if the maximum voltage is 120 volts, what is the voltage in the circuit at $t = \frac{1}{180}$?

Solution   (a) Since the frequency of the current is 60 cycles per second, we have

$$f = \frac{\omega}{2\pi} = 60, \quad \text{and} \quad \omega = 120\pi.$$

(b) Since $E_{\max}$ is given as 120, and b as 0, and since $\omega = 120\pi$, the equation for the voltage in this case is

$$E = 120 \sin 120\pi t.$$

Substituting $\frac{1}{180}$ for t, we have

$$E = 120 \sin 120\pi \left(\frac{1}{180} \right) = 120 \sin \frac{2\pi}{3}.$$

Replacing $\sin \dfrac{2\pi}{3}$ with its value, $\dfrac{\sqrt{3}}{2}$, we find

$$E = 120 \left(\frac{\sqrt{3}}{2} \right) = 60\sqrt{3} \doteq 103.92,$$

so that the voltage in the circuit at $\frac{1}{180}$ second after $t = 0$ is about 104 volts.

The constant b in the equation $y = a \cos (\omega t + b)$ determines the phase shift of the wave graph defined by this equation. Since

$$y = a \cos (\omega t + b) = a \cos \left[\omega \left(t + \frac{b}{\omega} \right) \right],$$

you can see by inspection that the phase shift of the graph is $-\dfrac{b}{\omega}$. Figure 3–13

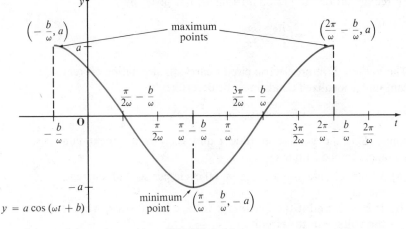

FIGURE 3–13

shows a graph of one cycle of $y = a \cos (\omega t + b)$, for $b > 0$, with some important characteristics identified. For example, the period is $\dfrac{2\pi}{\omega}$, and because each point on the graph of $y = a \cos (\omega t + b)$ occurs $\dfrac{b}{\omega}$ units to the left of the corresponding point on the graph of $y = a \cos \omega t$, the former wave graph leads the latter by $\dfrac{b}{\omega}$.

Example 2 Prove that the graph of $y = a \cos \omega t$ leads the graph of $y = a \sin \omega t$ by $\dfrac{\pi}{2\omega}$.

Solution Since $\sin \left(x + \dfrac{\pi}{2} \right) = \cos x$ (page 28), we have

$$a \cos \omega t = a \sin \left(\omega t + \frac{\pi}{2} \right)$$

$$= a \sin \omega \left(t + \frac{\pi}{2\omega} \right).$$

Since the phase shift of the graph of $y = a \sin \omega \left(t + \dfrac{\pi}{2\omega} \right)$ from the graph of $y = a \sin \omega t$ is $-\dfrac{\pi}{2\omega}$, the graph of $y = a \cos \omega t$ leads the graph of $y = a \sin \omega t$ by $\dfrac{\pi}{2\omega}$.

Exercises 3–6

A   **1.** A 60-cycle-per-second generator produces a voltage in accordance with the relationship

$$E = E_{\max} \sin (\omega t + b), \quad -\frac{\pi}{2} \le b \le \frac{\pi}{2}.$$

If $E = E_{\max}$ when $t = \frac{1}{4}$, and $E_{\max} = 120$ volts, what is the voltage when $t = \frac{1}{120}$?

2. In Exercise 1, what is the voltage when $t = \frac{1}{360}$?

3. Let $E = E_{\max} \sin \omega t$ describe the voltage in a circuit operating at 50 cycles per second and producing a maximum voltage of 115 volts. Find E when $t = \frac{1}{200}$.

4. In Exercise 3, find E when $t = \frac{1}{50}$.

B   **5.** A particle is in simple harmonic motion, passing back and forth through the origin an equal distance in each direction. Its period is 2π, and when $t = 0$ it is located at its maximum distance from the origin, 3 units. Find an equation describing its distance y from the origin in terms of t.

6. In Exercise 5, let $y = 1$ when $t = 0$, and assume the maximum value attained by y is 2. Find an equation for y in terms of t.

C   **7.** It is shown in the calculus that if $y = a \sin (\omega t + b)$ describes the location of a point in simple harmonic motion, then the velocity of the point at any time t is given by $v = a\omega \cos (\omega t + b)$. What is the velocity of the particle when $y = 0$? When $y = a$? For what values of t (in terms of b and ω) is the velocity a maximum? A minimum? Zero?

8. If a particle is moving in simple harmonic motion in accordance with the equation $y = \sqrt{2} \sin 3t$, what is the velocity of the particle when $t = \dfrac{\pi}{12}$? What is the maximum velocity of the particle?

Chapter Summary

1. The graphs of both the sine and the cosine functions, as well as the graphs of the more general functions $\{(x, y): y = a \sin b(x - c) + d\}$ and $\{(x, y): y = a \cos b(x - c) + d\}$ are called **sine waves**. The portion of the graph of such a function over any interval along the horizontal axis with length equal to a single fundamental period of the function is a **cycle** of the wave. One-half the vertical distance between the maximum and minimum points on a sine wave is called the **amplitude** of the wave.

2. The graphs of the functions defined by $y = a \sin b(x - c) + d$ and $y = a \cos b(x - c) + d$ have **amplitude** $|a|$, **period** $\dfrac{2\pi}{|b|}$, and **phase shift** c. They are shifted up or down with respect to the x-axis by $|d|$, up if $d > 0$, down if $d < 0$. The graphs of the other circular functions are affected in a similar way by corresponding constants.

3. To graph the sum $f + g$ of functions f and g, you can add the ordinates of corresponding points on the graphs of f and g.

4. If a point **P** moves around the circumference of a circle at a constant speed, it is traveling with **uniform circular motion**. Its rotational velocity is given by $\omega = \dfrac{2\pi}{T}$, where T is the time required to complete one revolution.

5. Any particle moving back and forth between the endpoints of a line segment in accordance with an equation of the form

$$y = a \cos (\omega t + b) \quad \text{or} \quad y = a \sin (\omega t + b)$$

is in **simple harmonic motion**. Its distance y from the midpoint of the segment at any time t is called its **displacement** at time t.

Chapter Test

Sketch the graph of the given function over one fundamental period.

3–1   **1.** $\{(x, y): y = -2 \cos x + 4\}$

3–2   **2.** $\left\{(x, y): y = \sin 2\left(x - \dfrac{\pi}{4}\right)\right\}$

3–3   **3.** $\{(x, y): y = 3 \sin \frac{1}{4}(x + \pi)\}$

   4. $\{(x, y): y = 1 - 3 \tan 2x\}$

3–4   **5.** Sketch the graph of $\{(x, y): y = \cos x + 2 \sin x\}$ using graphical addition of ordinates.

3–5   **6.** A point is moving on a circle of radius r at a constant rotational velocity ω. If $\omega = \dfrac{5\pi}{6}$ and $r = 4$, what is the length of the arc traversed in 3 units of time?

3–6   **7.** What are two general forms for an equation that expresses the position y at time t of a particle moving in simple harmonic motion?

Computer Investigations

If you have access to an electronic computer that will accept BASIC, you may wish to try the following experiments. Use the program given on page 46.

By changing lines 10 and 80, you can print approximations of some points on the graphs of:

$y = 2 \sin x$	$y = \sin x + 1$	$y = \sin x + \cos x$
$y = 2 \cos 2x$	$y = \cos 2x - 1$	$y = \sin x - \cos x$

Try also

$$y = \sin 2x + \cos x \qquad y = \sin 2x - \cos 3x$$

and so on.

You can obtain a greater width for your print-outs by making the following changes in the program:

```
30  LET L = 6
50  PRINT "X"
151
171
191
211
```

Now you can try such examples as:

$y = 3 \sin x$	$y = -2 \cos 3x + 1$	$y = 2 \sin 3x + \cos 2x$
$y = 2.5 \cos x$	$y = 3 \sin 2x$	$y = 3 \sin x + \sin 3x$

Cumulative Review · Chapters 1–3

Chapter 1

1. Find the value of $\cos x$ if $\sin x = -\frac{1}{6}$ and $\pi < x < \frac{3\pi}{2}$.

Simplify:

2. $\sin^2 x \cos x + \cos^3 x$

3. $\cos \frac{2\pi}{3} \cos \frac{\pi}{6} + \sin \frac{2\pi}{3} \sin \frac{\pi}{6}$

4. $\cos \pi \sin \left(-\frac{\pi}{3}\right) - \sin \pi \cos \left(-\frac{\pi}{3}\right)$

5. If $\cos x_1 = \frac{3}{4}$, $\sin x_2 = \frac{1}{2}$, $0 < x_1 < \frac{\pi}{2}$, and $\frac{\pi}{2} < x_2 < \pi$, find $\sin (x_1 + x_2)$.

Prove that the given equation is an identity.

6. $\cos^2 x - \sin^2 x + 1 = 2 \cos^2 x$

7. $\cos 2x + 2 \sin^2 x = 1$

8. Sketch the graph of $y = \sin x$, $0 \le x \le 2\pi$, and draw ordinates illustrating the identity $\sin (a + \pi) = -\sin a$, for $0 < a < \pi$.

Graph each set over $0 \le x \le 2\pi$.

9. $\{(x, y): y = \sin x\} \cap \left\{(x, y): y = \frac{\sqrt{3}}{2}\right\}$

10. $\{(x, y): y = \cos x\} \cap \{(x, y): y = -\frac{1}{2}\}$

Chapter 2

11. Find $\tan x$ when $\sin x = -\frac{4}{5}$ and $\cos x > 0$.

12. Evaluate: **(a)** $\tan \frac{23\pi}{3}$, **(b)** $\cot \left(-\frac{5\pi}{6}\right)$, **(c)** $\sec \frac{17\pi}{4}$.

13. Given that $\csc x = \frac{5}{4}$ and $\frac{\pi}{2} < x < \pi$, find $\cos x$, $\sin x$, $\tan x$, $\sec x$, and $\cot x$.

Simplify each expression.

14. $\sin x \sec x$

15. $\sin x + \cos x \cot x$

16. $\csc^2 x(1 - \cos^2 x)$

17. $\sin x \tan x + \cos x$

Prove that each equation is an identity.

18. $\sec x - \cos x = \sin x \tan x$

19. $\dfrac{\sin x}{\sin x \cot x + \cos x} = \dfrac{1}{2} \tan x$

20. $\dfrac{\cot x}{\sin x + \cot x \cos x} = \cos x$

Chapter 3

Graph each function over one fundamental period.

21. $\{(x, y): y = \sin \tfrac{1}{3}x\}$

23. $\left\{(x, y): y = \sin 2 \left(x + \dfrac{\pi}{3}\right)\right\}$

22. $\{(x, y): y = \tfrac{5}{3} \cos x\}$

24. $\left\{(x, y): y = 2 \cos \tfrac{1}{2} \left(x - \dfrac{\pi}{3}\right)\right\}$

25. Graph $\{(x, y): y = 2 \cos x + \sin x\}$ over the interval $0 \le x \le 2\pi$.

26. Graph $\{(x, y): y = 2x - \sin x\}$ over the interval $0 \le x \le 2\pi$.

Find the length of arc traversed by a point moving along a circle of radius r at a constant rotational velocity ω in a counterclockwise direction if:

27. $\omega = \dfrac{2\pi}{3}$, $r = 3$, and $t = 4$.

28. $\omega = \dfrac{\pi}{3}$, $r = 10$, and $t = \tfrac{9}{2}$.

29. A circular wheel of diameter 6 inches is revolving in a counterclockwise direction, completing 4 revolutions in 3 seconds. What is the rotational velocity of a point on the rim of the wheel?

30. In Exercise 29, what is the speed of the point along the rim of the wheel?

Chapter Four

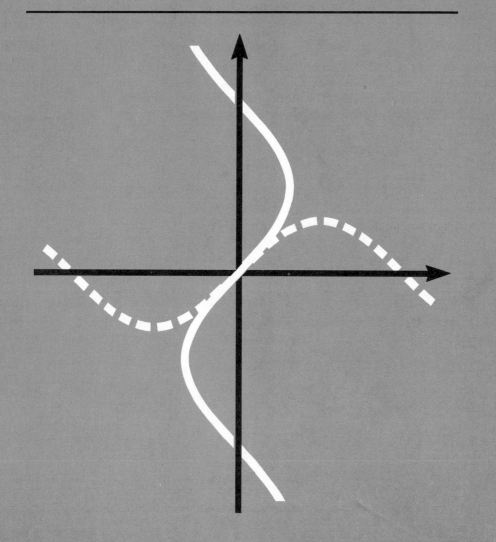

Inverses of
Circular Functions

OBJECTIVES

1. To learn the basic properties of the inverse circular functions and their graphs.
2. To find general and particular solutions for equations involving circular functions and their inverses.

Principal Inverse Functions

4–1 *Inverses of cos and sin*

You should recall from earlier courses in mathematics that each relation R has an inverse relation R^{-1} which consists of all the ordered pairs obtained by interchanging the components of the ordered pairs in R. Moreover, if $y = R(x)$ defines a relation R, then $x = R(y)$ defines the inverse relation R^{-1}. Thus, if we exchange the variables in the defining equation of the cosine function,

$$\cos = \{(x, y): y = \cos x\},$$

we obtain the equation for the inverse of the cosine function, $x = \cos y$, which defines the relation

$$\{(x, y): x = \cos y\}.$$

The inverse relation of cos is denoted by $\cos^{-1}$ (read "the inverse cosine"). Thus we have

$$\cos^{-1} = \{(x, y): x = \cos y\}.$$

To obtain the graph of $\cos^{-1}$, recall that the graphs of any two relations R and R^{-1} are the reflections of each other in the line $y = x$. When such a reflection is made of the graph of cos, we obtain the graph of $\cos^{-1}$, as shown in Figure 4–1, below. It is clear from the figure that the relation $\cos^{-1}$ is not a function because, by definition, a function associates with each number x in the domain only one number in the range. The relation $\cos^{-1}$ pairs each number x in the domain with infinitely many numbers y in the range. For example, the number 0 is paired with all numbers y of the form $\dfrac{\pi}{2} + k\pi$, $k \in J$. Thus

$$\left(0, \frac{\pi}{2}\right), \left(0, -\frac{\pi}{2}\right), \left(0, \frac{3\pi}{2}\right), \left(0, -\frac{19\pi}{2}\right), \text{ and } \left(0, \frac{203\pi}{2}\right) \text{ are all in } \cos^{-1}.$$

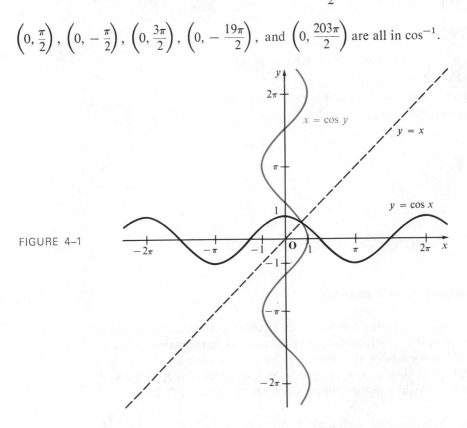

FIGURE 4–1

By placing suitable restrictions on the domain of cos, however, we can obtain a function whose inverse is also a function. We shall denote this restricted function by Cos (read "principal cosine"). To define Cos, we restrict the domain of cos to an interval in which the function is one-to-one (that is, an interval in which each element in the domain corresponds to a different element in the range). The most convenient such interval is $0 \leq x \leq \pi$. Thus

$$\text{Cos} = \{(x, y): y = \cos x, \ 0 \leq x \leq \pi\}.$$

Note that the *domain* of Cos is $\{x: 0 \leq x \leq \pi\}$ and the *range* is $\{y: -1 \leq y \leq 1\}$. The graph of Cos is shown in color in Figure 4–2.

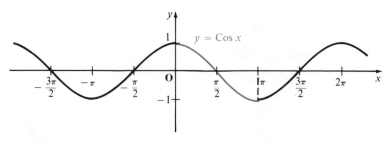

FIGURE 4–2

By exchanging the variables in the defining equation of Cos, we obtain the equation of the inverse of Cos, namely Cos^{-1}, where

$$\text{Cos}^{-1} = \{(x, y): x = \cos y, \ 0 \leq y \leq \pi\}.$$

The symbol Cos^{-1}, written with a capital C, therefore denotes the function defined by $x = \cos y$ with *domain* $\{x: -1 \leq x \leq 1\}$ and *range* $\{y: 0 \leq y \leq \pi\}$. The notation Cos^{-1} is read "principal inverse cosine," and we write

$$\text{Cos}^{-1} = \{(x, y): y = \text{Cos}^{-1} x, \ -1 \leq x \leq 1\}.$$

In Figure 4–3, the graphs of

$$y = \text{Cos } x$$
and
$$y = \text{Cos}^{-1} x$$

are shown on the same set of axes. As observed on page 110, the graphs of these two sets are reflections of each other in the line $y = x$.

Notice also that the domain of Cos is the same set as the range of Cos^{-1} and that the range of Cos is the same set as the domain of Cos^{-1}.

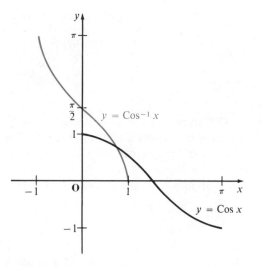

FIGURE 4–3

Example 1   Find each of the following:

(a) $\mathrm{Cos}^{-1}\dfrac{\sqrt{3}}{2}$ (b) $\mathrm{Cos}^{-1}\left(-\tfrac{1}{2}\right)$ (c) $\mathrm{Cos}^{-1}\,0.309$

Solution   (a) Let $y = \mathrm{Cos}^{-1}\dfrac{\sqrt{3}}{2}$. Then our problem is to find the number y in the range of Cos^{-1} which corresponds to the number $\dfrac{\sqrt{3}}{2}$ in the domain of Cos^{-1}. In other words, we want to find the number y in the interval $0 \le y \le \pi$ such that $\cos y = \dfrac{\sqrt{3}}{2}$. Since $\cos\dfrac{\pi}{6} = \dfrac{\sqrt{3}}{2}$, and $\dfrac{\pi}{6}$ is in the interval $0 \le y \le \pi$,

$$\mathrm{Cos}^{-1}\frac{\sqrt{3}}{2} = \frac{\pi}{6}.$$

(b) Letting $y = \mathrm{Cos}^{-1}\left(-\tfrac{1}{2}\right)$, we are to find the number y in the interval $0 \le y \le \pi$ such that $\cos y = -\tfrac{1}{2}$. Since $\cos\dfrac{2\pi}{3} = -\dfrac{1}{2}$, and $\dfrac{2\pi}{3}$ is in the interval $0 \le y \le \pi$,

$$\mathrm{Cos}^{-1}\left(-\frac{1}{2}\right) = \frac{2\pi}{3}.$$

(c) Using Table 1, page 391, we can locate 0.309 in the body of the table. Then, reading to the right, we find the corresponding number to be $0.80 \cdot \dfrac{\pi}{2}$, or 0.40π. Thus $\cos 0.40\pi \doteq 0.309$, so that

$$\mathrm{Cos}^{-1}\,0.309 \doteq 0.40\pi.$$

The inverse of the sine function, like that of the cosine function, is not a function but simply a relation. However, by placing suitable restrictions on the domain of sin, we can obtain a function, Sin (read "principal sine"), whose inverse is also a function. To define Sin, we restrict the domain of sin to an interval in which sin is one-to-one. The most convenient such interval is $-\dfrac{\pi}{2} \le x \le \dfrac{\pi}{2}$. Thus:

$$\mathrm{Sin} = \left\{(x, y)\colon y = \sin x, \ -\frac{\pi}{2} \le x \le \frac{\pi}{2}\right\}$$

The *domain* of Sin is $\left\{x: -\frac{\pi}{2} \le x \le \frac{\pi}{2}\right\}$; the *range* is $\{y: -1 \le y \le 1\}$.
The graph of Sin is shown in color in Figure 4–4 below.

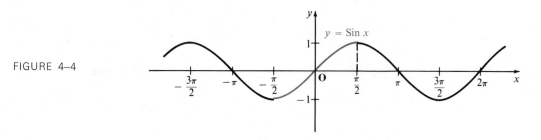

FIGURE 4–4

Then we define the function Sin^{-1} (read "the principal inverse sine") as follows:

▲
$$\text{Sin}^{-1} = \left\{(x, y): x = \sin y, -\frac{\pi}{2} \le y \le \frac{\pi}{2}\right\}$$

We also write

▲
$$\text{Sin}^{-1} = \{(x, y): y = \text{Sin}^{-1} x, -1 \le x \le 1\}.$$

The *domain* of Sin^{-1} is $\{x: -1 \le x \le 1\}$ and the *range* is $\left\{y: -\frac{\pi}{2} \le y \le \frac{\pi}{2}\right\}$.

In Figure 4–5, the graphs of $y = \text{Sin } x$ and $y = \text{Sin}^{-1} x$ are shown on the same set of axes. Note that the domain of Sin is the same set as the range of Sin^{-1} and that the range of Sin is the same set as the domain of Sin^{-1}.

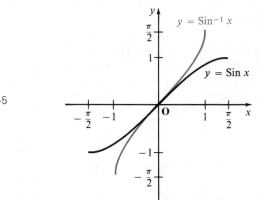

FIGURE 4–5

Comparing the graphs in Figures 4–3 and 4–5, you can see that the functions Cos^{-1} and Sin^{-1} have *the same domain*, namely, $\{x: -1 \le x \le 1\}$, but *different ranges*.

Example 2   Find **(a)** $\text{Sin}^{-1}\left(-\dfrac{\sqrt{3}}{2}\right)$, **(b)** $\text{Sin}^{-1} 1$, and **(c)** $\text{Sin}^{-1}(-0.562)$.

Solution   **(a)** Let $y = \text{Sin}^{-1}\left(-\dfrac{\sqrt{3}}{2}\right)$. Then our problem is to find the number y in the range of Sin^{-1} which corresponds to the number $-\dfrac{\sqrt{3}}{2}$ in the domain of Sin^{-1}. Thus we want to find the number y in the interval $-\dfrac{\pi}{2} \le y \le \dfrac{\pi}{2}$ such that $\sin y = -\dfrac{\sqrt{3}}{2}$. Since $\sin\left(-\dfrac{\pi}{3}\right) = -\dfrac{\sqrt{3}}{2}$, and $-\dfrac{\pi}{3}$ is within the required interval,

$$\text{Sin}^{-1}\left(-\frac{\sqrt{3}}{2}\right) = -\frac{\pi}{3}.$$

(b) Letting $y = \text{Sin}^{-1} 1$, we are to find the number y in the interval $-\dfrac{\pi}{2} \le y \le \dfrac{\pi}{2}$ such that $\sin y = 1$. Since $\sin\dfrac{\pi}{2} = 1$, and $\dfrac{\pi}{2}$ is in the interval $-\dfrac{\pi}{2} \le y \le \dfrac{\pi}{2}$,

$$\text{Sin}^{-1} 1 = \frac{\pi}{2}.$$

(c) Using Table 1, page 391, we can locate 0.562 in the body of the table. Reading across to the left, we find the corresponding number to be $0.38 \cdot \dfrac{\pi}{2}$, or 0.19π. Thus $\sin 0.19\pi \doteq 0.562$. Since $\sin(-x) = -\sin x$, it follows that $\sin(-0.19\pi) \doteq -0.562$, so that

$$\text{Sin}^{-1}(-0.562) \doteq -0.19\pi.$$

The notation $\sin(\text{Sin}^{-1} x)$, for a number x in the interval $-1 \le x \le 1$, is explained in the following example.

Example 3   Find $\sin(\text{Sin}^{-1} \tfrac{1}{2})$.

Solution   Starting within the parentheses, we find that $\text{Sin}^{-1}\dfrac{1}{2} = \dfrac{\pi}{6}$, since $\sin\dfrac{\pi}{6} = \dfrac{1}{2}$, and $\dfrac{\pi}{6}$ is in the interval $-\dfrac{\pi}{2} \le y \le \dfrac{\pi}{2}$. Then

$$\sin\left(\text{Sin}^{-1}\frac{1}{2}\right) = \sin\frac{\pi}{6} = \frac{1}{2}.$$

Exercises 4–1

Solve each equation for y over the interval $0 \le y \le \pi$.

A **1.** $\cos y = 1$ **2.** $\cos y = -\dfrac{\sqrt{3}}{2}$ **3.** $\cos y = \dfrac{\sqrt{2}}{2}$ **4.** $\cos y = 0$

Solve each equation for y over the interval $-\dfrac{\pi}{2} \le y \le \dfrac{\pi}{2}$.

  5. $\sin y = \dfrac{\sqrt{3}}{2}$ **6.** $\sin y = -\dfrac{\sqrt{2}}{2}$ **7.** $\sin y = \frac{1}{2}$ **8.** $\sin y = -1$

Find the value of each of the following. Use Table 1, page 391, if necessary.

  9. $\mathrm{Cos}^{-1}\,\frac{1}{2}$

  10. $\mathrm{Cos}^{-1}\,(-1)$

  11. $\mathrm{Sin}^{-1}\,\dfrac{\sqrt{3}}{2}$

  12. $\mathrm{Sin}^{-1}\,(-\frac{1}{2})$

  13. $\mathrm{Cos}^{-1}\,0.853$

  14. $\mathrm{Cos}^{-1}\,(-0.924)$

  15. $\mathrm{Sin}^{-1}\,0.800$

  16. $\mathrm{Sin}^{-1}\,(-0.203)$

  17. $\cos\,(\mathrm{Cos}^{-1}\,0.800)$

  18. $\cos\,(\mathrm{Cos}^{-1}\,\frac{3}{5})$

  19. $\sin\left(\mathrm{Sin}^{-1}\,\dfrac{\sqrt{2}}{2}\right)$

  20. $\sin\,[\mathrm{Sin}^{-1}\,(-\frac{3}{5})]$

  21. $\mathrm{Cos}^{-1}\left(\cos\dfrac{\pi}{6}\right)$

  22. $\cos\,[\mathrm{Cos}^{-1}\,(-0.426)]$

B **23.** Make a copy of the following table and fill in the missing entries. Keep your copy for use in subsequent exercises in this section.

x	$\mathrm{Cos}^{-1} x$	$\cos\,(\mathrm{Cos}^{-1} x)$	$\mathrm{Sin}^{-1} x$	$\sin\,(\mathrm{Sin}^{-1} x)$
-1	π	-1	$-\dfrac{\pi}{2}$	-1
$-\dfrac{\sqrt{3}}{2}$	?	?	?	?
$-\dfrac{1}{2}$	?	?	?	?
0	$\dfrac{\pi}{2}$	0	0	0
$\dfrac{1}{2}$	?	?	?	?
$\dfrac{\sqrt{3}}{2}$	?	?	?	?
1	?	?	?	?

24. On the basis of the entries which you made in the table in Exercise 23, what generalization can be made regarding the value of:

(a) $\cos (\text{Cos}^{-1} x)$ for $-1 \le x \le 1$?
(b) $\sin (\text{Sin}^{-1} x)$ for $-1 \le x \le 1$?

25. Find the value of the expression $\text{Cos}^{-1} x + \text{Sin}^{-1} x$ for each of the following values of x:

$$-1, \ -\frac{\sqrt{3}}{2}, \ -\tfrac{1}{2}, \ 0, \ \tfrac{1}{2}, \ \frac{\sqrt{3}}{2}, \ \text{and } 1.$$

The columns labeled x, $\text{Cos}^{-1} x$, and $\text{Sin}^{-1} x$ in the table in Exercise 23 will be helpful in making these calculations. What generalization can be made regarding the value of $\text{Cos}^{-1} x + \text{Sin}^{-1} x$ for $-1 \le x \le 1$?

C 26. (a) Make a copy of the following table and fill in the missing entries. (*Hint:* Use a sketch of the Cos^{-1} function to help you determine the entries.)

x	$\cos x$	$\text{Cos}^{-1} (\cos x)$
0	?	?
$\dfrac{\pi}{2}$	?	?
π	-1	π
$\dfrac{3\pi}{2}$	?	?
2π	?	?
$\dfrac{5\pi}{2}$	0	$\dfrac{\pi}{2}$
3π	?	?
$\dfrac{7\pi}{2}$	?	?
4π	?	?

(b) Using the results of Part (a), graph the function

$$\{(x, y): y = \text{Cos}^{-1} (\cos x), \ 0 \le x \le 4\pi\}.$$

(c) Let f be the function $\{(x, y): y = \text{Cos}^{-1} (\cos x), \ x \in \mathfrak{R}\}$. Is f periodic? If so, what is its fundamental period?
(d) For what values of x is $\text{Cos}^{-1} (\cos x) = x$?
(e) For what values of x is $\text{Cos}^{-1} (\text{Cos } x)$ defined? For what values of x is $\text{Cos}^{-1} (\text{Cos } x) = x$?

27. (a) Determine the values of sin x and Sin^{-1} (sin x) for $x = -\dfrac{\pi}{2}$, 0, $\dfrac{\pi}{2}$, π, $\dfrac{3\pi}{2}$, 2π, $\dfrac{5\pi}{2}$, 3π, and $\dfrac{7\pi}{2}$. Display your answers in a table similar to the one in Exercise 26, with columns labeled x, sin x, and Sin^{-1} (sin x).

(b) Using the results of Part (a), graph the function

$$\left\{(x, y): y = \text{Sin}^{-1} (\sin x),\ -\frac{\pi}{2} \le x \le \frac{7\pi}{2}\right\}.$$

(c) Let f be the function $\{(x, y): y = \text{Sin}^{-1} (\sin x),\ x \in \Re\}$. Is f periodic? If so, what is its fundamental period?

(d) For what values of x is Sin^{-1} (sin x) $= x$?

(e) For what values of x is Sin^{-1} (Sin x) defined? For what values of x is Sin^{-1} (Sin x) $= x$?

4–2 Inverses of Other Circular Functions

In a manner similar to that used in defining Cos^{-1} and Sin^{-1}, we can define functions Tan^{-1}, Cot^{-1}, Sec^{-1}, and Csc^{-1}. First, we place suitable restrictions on the domains of tan, cot, sec, and csc, obtaining functions, denoted by Tan, Cot, Sec, and Csc, whose inverses are functions.

Thus we have:

▲
$$\text{Tan} = \left\{(x, y): y = \tan x,\ -\frac{\pi}{2} < x < \frac{\pi}{2}\right\} \tag{1}$$

$$\text{Cot} = \{(x, y): y = \cot x,\ 0 < x < \pi\} \tag{2}$$

$$\text{Sec} = \left\{(x, y): y = \sec x,\ 0 \le x \le \pi,\ x \ne \frac{\pi}{2}\right\} \tag{3}$$

$$\text{Csc} = \left\{(x, y): y = \csc x,\ -\frac{\pi}{2} \le x \le \frac{\pi}{2},\ x \ne 0\right\} \tag{4}$$

By exchanging the variables in the defining equations of these functions, we obtain their inverses:

▲
$$\text{Tan}^{-1} = \left\{(x, y): x = \tan y,\ -\frac{\pi}{2} < y < \frac{\pi}{2}\right\} \tag{5}$$

$$\text{Cot}^{-1} = \{(x, y): x = \cot y,\ 0 < y < \pi\} \tag{6}$$

$$\text{Sec}^{-1} = \left\{(x, y): x = \sec y,\ 0 \le y \le \pi,\ y \ne \frac{\pi}{2}\right\} \tag{7}$$

$$\text{Csc}^{-1} = \left\{(x, y): x = \csc y,\ -\frac{\pi}{2} \le y \le \frac{\pi}{2},\ y \ne 0\right\} \tag{8}$$

Graphs of these functions are shown in Figures 4–6, 4–7, 4–8, and 4–9. Note that Tan^{-1} and Cot^{-1} both have domain $\mathcal{R}$, but their ranges are different. Similarly, Sec^{-1} and Csc^{-1} both have $\{x: |x| \geq 1\}$ as domain, but their ranges are different.

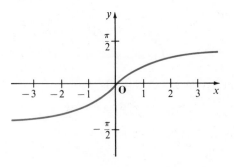

$$\{(x, y): y = \text{Tan}^{-1} x\}$$

Domain $= \mathcal{R}$

Range $= \left\{y: -\dfrac{\pi}{2} < y < \dfrac{\pi}{2}\right\}$

FIGURE 4–6

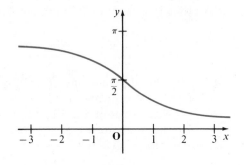

$$\{(x, y): y = \text{Cot}^{-1} x\}$$

Domain $= \mathcal{R}$

Range $= \{y: 0 < y < \pi\}$

FIGURE 4–7

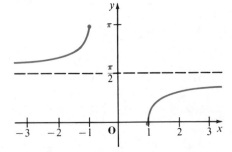

$$\{(x, y): y = \text{Sec}^{-1} x\}$$

Domain $= \{x: |x| \geq 1\}$

Range $= \left\{y: 0 \leq y \leq \pi, y \neq \dfrac{\pi}{2}\right\}$

FIGURE 4–8

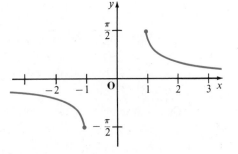

$$\{(x, y): y = \text{Csc}^{-1} x\}$$

Domain $= \{x: |x| \geq 1\}$

Range $= \left\{y: -\dfrac{\pi}{2} \leq y \leq \dfrac{\pi}{2}, y \neq 0\right\}$

FIGURE 4–9

Example   Find **(a)** $\text{Cot}^{-1} \sqrt{3}$ and **(b)** $\text{Sec}^{-1} 2$.

Solution   **(a)** Let $\text{Cot}^{-1} \sqrt{3} = y$. Then we want to find the number y in the range of Cot^{-1} which corresponds to the number $\sqrt{3}$ in the domain of Cot^{-1}; that is, we want to find the number y in the interval $0 < y < \pi$ such that $\cot y = \sqrt{3}$.

Since $\cot \dfrac{\pi}{6} = \sqrt{3}$, and $0 < \dfrac{\pi}{6} < \pi$,

$$\text{Cot}^{-1} \sqrt{3} = \frac{\pi}{6}.$$

(b) Letting $y = \text{Sec}^{-1} 2$, we are to find the number y $\left(y \neq \dfrac{\pi}{2} \right)$ in the interval $0 \leq y \leq \pi$ such that $\sec y = 2$.

Since $\sec \dfrac{\pi}{3} = 2$, and $0 \leq \dfrac{\pi}{3} \leq \pi$,

$$\text{Sec}^{-1} 2 = \frac{\pi}{3}.$$

Since secant and cosine are *reciprocal functions,* we should expect some close relationship between their principal inverses. This relationship takes the form:

▲
$$\text{Sec}^{-1} x = \text{Cos}^{-1} \frac{1}{x} \qquad \text{for } |x| \geq 1. \tag{9}$$

Similarly, we also have:

▲
$$\text{Csc}^{-1} x = \text{Sin}^{-1} \frac{1}{x} \qquad \text{for } |x| \geq 1 \tag{10}$$

$$\text{Cot}^{-1} x = \begin{cases} \text{Tan}^{-1} \dfrac{1}{x} + \pi & \text{for } x < 0 \\[2mm] \text{Tan}^{-1} \dfrac{1}{x} & \text{for } x > 0 \end{cases} \tag{11}$$

In working with the exercises of Section 4–1, you may have been led to discover the following relationships between the Cos and Cos^{-1} functions and the Sin and Sin^{-1} functions:

▲
$$\text{Cos} (\text{Cos}^{-1} x) = x \qquad \text{for} \qquad |x| \leq 1 \tag{12}$$

$$\text{Sin} (\text{Sin}^{-1} x) = x \qquad \text{for} \qquad |x| \leq 1 \tag{13}$$

Moreover:

▲ $$\text{Cos}^{-1}(\text{Cos } x) = x \quad \text{for} \quad 0 \le x \le \pi \tag{14}$$

$$\text{Sin}^{-1}(\text{Sin } x) = x \quad \text{for} \quad -\frac{\pi}{2} \le x \le \frac{\pi}{2} \tag{15}$$

Actually, we can make the following generalization about all pairs of inverse functions:

▲ If f and g are any two functions which are inverses of each other, then the domain of f is the range of g and the range of f is the domain of g, and we have

$$f[g(x)] = x \text{ for all } x \text{ in the domain of } g \tag{16}$$

and

$$g[f(x)] = x \text{ for all } x \text{ in the domain of } f. \tag{17}$$

For example, let f be the function Tan and g the function Tan^{-1}. Then, applying the general statements (16) and (17), we have

$$\text{Tan}(\text{Tan}^{-1} x) = x \quad \text{for} \quad x \in \Re$$

and

$$\text{Tan}^{-1}(\text{Tan } x) = x \quad \text{for} \quad -\frac{\pi}{2} < x < \frac{\pi}{2}.$$

Corresponding statements can be made for the other principal circular functions.

Exercises 4–2

Solve each equation for y over the stated interval.

A 1. $\tan y = \sqrt{3},\ -\frac{\pi}{2} < y < \frac{\pi}{2}$

2. $\cot y = -1,\ 0 < y < \pi$

3. $\sec y = -2,\ 0 \le y \le \pi,\ y \ne \frac{\pi}{2}$

4. $\sec y = \sqrt{2},\ 0 \le y \le \pi,\ y \ne \frac{\pi}{2}$

5. $\csc y = 1,\ -\frac{\pi}{2} \le y \le \frac{\pi}{2},\ y \ne 0$

6. $\tan y = -\frac{1}{\sqrt{3}},\ -\frac{\pi}{2} < y < \frac{\pi}{2}$

Find the value of each of the following.

7. $\text{Tan}^{-1} 1$

8. $\text{Sec}^{-1} 2$

9. $\text{Sec}^{-1} \sqrt{2}$

10. $\text{Cot}^{-1} (-\sqrt{3})$

11. $\text{Csc}^{-1} \left(-\dfrac{2}{\sqrt{3}}\right)$

12. $\text{Tan}^{-1} 0$

13. $\text{Csc}^{-1} 2$

14. $\text{Csc}^{-1} (-\sqrt{2})$

15. $\tan (\text{Tan}^{-1} 1)$

16. $\sec \left(\text{Sec}^{-1} \dfrac{2}{\sqrt{3}}\right)$

17. $\sec (\text{Sec}^{-1} 1)$

18. $\cot [\text{Cot}^{-1} (-1)]$

19. $\tan \left(\text{Cot}^{-1} \dfrac{1}{\sqrt{3}}\right)$

20. $\cot [\text{Tan}^{-1} (-\sqrt{3})]$

21. $\sin \left(\text{Csc}^{-1} \dfrac{2}{\sqrt{3}}\right)$

B 22. **(a)** Copy the table and fill in the missing entries.

x	$-\sqrt{3}$	-1	$-\dfrac{1}{\sqrt{3}}$	0	$\dfrac{1}{\sqrt{3}}$	1	$\sqrt{3}$
(i) $\text{Tan}^{-1} x$	$-\dfrac{\pi}{3}$	$-\dfrac{\pi}{4}$	$-\dfrac{\pi}{6}$	0	$\dfrac{\pi}{6}$	$\dfrac{\pi}{4}$	$\dfrac{\pi}{3}$
(ii) $\text{Cot}^{-1} x$	$\dfrac{5\pi}{6}$	?	?	?	?	?	?
(iii) $\text{Tan}^{-1} x + \text{Cot}^{-1} x$	$\dfrac{\pi}{2}$	?	?	?	?	?	?
(iv) $\text{Tan}^{-1} \dfrac{1}{x}$	$-\dfrac{\pi}{6}$	?	?	?	?	?	?
(v) $\text{Tan}^{-1} x + \text{Tan}^{-1} \dfrac{1}{x}$	$-\dfrac{\pi}{2}$	?	?	?	?	?	?

(b) On the basis of your entries in the table in Part (a), what generalization can be made regarding $\text{Tan}^{-1} x + \text{Cot}^{-1} x$, $x \in \mathcal{R}$?

23. Check your entries in Rows (ii) and (iv) of the table in Exercise 22 by the formula

$$\text{Cot}^{-1} x = \begin{cases} \text{Tan}^{-1} \dfrac{1}{x} + \pi & \text{for } x < 0 \\[2mm] \text{Tan}^{-1} \dfrac{1}{x} & \text{for } x > 0 \end{cases}$$

C 24. From the table in Exercise 22, form a generalization regarding

$$\text{Tan}^{-1} x + \text{Tan}^{-1} \dfrac{1}{x}, \quad x \in \mathcal{R}, \; x \neq 0.$$

Use this generalization to find (to three decimal places) the value of $\text{Tan}^{-1} \frac{1}{6}$ given that $\text{Tan}^{-1} 6 = 1.406$. Also, find $\text{Tan}^{-1} (-7)$ given that $\text{Tan}^{-1} (-\frac{1}{7}) = -0.1435$.

25. State generalizations similar to (12) and (14), pages 119 and 120, for each of the following pairs of functions, being sure to state the values of x for which the statements are true:

$$\text{Cot and Cot}^{-1}, \text{ Sec and Sec}^{-1}, \text{ Csc and Csc}^{-1}.$$

26. Using the identity for tan $(x_2 + x_1)$, evaluate tan $(\text{Tan}^{-1} \frac{1}{2} + \text{Tan}^{-1} \frac{1}{3})$. What conclusion can be made about the value of $\text{Tan}^{-1} \frac{1}{2} + \text{Tan}^{-1} \frac{1}{3}$?

27. Graph the function

$$\left\{ (x, y): y = \text{Tan}^{-1} (\tan x),\ -\frac{\pi}{2} < x < \frac{3\pi}{2},\ x \neq \frac{\pi}{2} \right\}.$$

Is the function

$$\left\{ (x, y): y = \text{Tan}^{-1} (\tan x),\ x \in \Re,\ x \neq (2k + 1)\frac{\pi}{2},\ k \in J \right\}$$

periodic? If so, what is its fundamental period?

4–3   Arc Lengths

Geometrically, you can interpret $\text{Cos}^{-1} x$ and $\text{Sin}^{-1} x$ as arc lengths on the unit circle. As indicated in Figure 4–10, the length of the arc from the point $(1, 0)$ to the point (u, v) on the unit circle in the uv-plane can be interpreted as

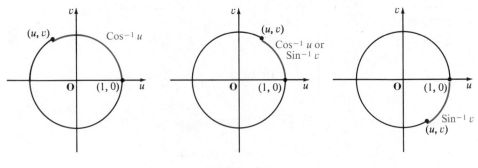

FIGURE 4–10

$\text{Cos}^{-1} u$ if (u, v) is in the first or second quadrants, or as $\text{Sin}^{-1} v$ if (u, v) is in the first or fourth quadrants.

Since $\mathrm{Cos}^{-1}\,x$ and $\mathrm{Sin}^{-1}\,x$ can be represented as arc lengths, these expressions are sometimes denoted by Arccos x (read "Arc cosine of x") and Arcsin x (read "Arc sine of x"), respectively. The expressions $\mathrm{Tan}^{-1}\,x$, $\mathrm{Cot}^{-1}\,x$, $\mathrm{Sec}^{-1}\,x$, and $\mathrm{Csc}^{-1}\,x$ are also written in "arc" notation, as Arctan x, Arccot x, Arcsec x, and Arccsc x.

It should be noted, in passing, that some authors use small letters c, s, and a, for example, writing $\cos^{-1}$, $\sin^{-1}$, arccos, arcsin, and so forth, leaving it to the reader to determine from the context that it is the function rather than the relation that is intended. Nevertheless, in this book we shall continue using the capital letters to emphasize the restricted ranges of the functions.

We can now evaluate combinations (or compositions) of various expressions involving circular functions and their principal inverses, such as

$$\cos(\mathrm{Sin}^{-1}\,x), \qquad \sin(\mathrm{Cos}^{-1}\,x), \qquad \mathrm{Tan}^{-1}(\sin x).$$

First, recall from page 119 that $\mathrm{Sin}\,(\mathrm{Sin}^{-1}\,x) = x$ for all x such that $|x| \le 1$. Actually, since the range of $\mathrm{Sin}^{-1}\,x$ is $\left\{y:\ -\dfrac{\pi}{2} \le y \le \dfrac{\pi}{2}\right\}$, and since we have

$\sin y = \mathrm{Sin}\,y$ for $\left\{y:\ -\dfrac{\pi}{2} \le y \le \dfrac{\pi}{2}\right\}$, it is also true that

$$\sin(\mathrm{Sin}^{-1}\,x) = x \qquad \text{for } |x| \le 1.$$

For example, as you saw in Example 3, page 114, $\sin(\mathrm{Sin}^{-1}\,\tfrac{1}{2}) = \tfrac{1}{2}$. Similarly, you have

$$\cos(\mathrm{Cos}^{-1}\,x) = x \qquad \text{for } |x| \le 1.$$

In Figure 4–11, the length of the arc from the point $(1, 0)$ to the point $\left(\dfrac{\sqrt{3}}{2}, \dfrac{1}{2}\right)$ in the first quadrant can

be denoted by either $\mathrm{Cos}^{-1}\,\dfrac{\sqrt{3}}{2}$ or

$\mathrm{Sin}^{-1}\,\tfrac{1}{2}$. To verify that this is true,

note that $\cos\dfrac{\pi}{6} = \dfrac{\sqrt{3}}{2}$ and that

$\sin\dfrac{\pi}{6} = \dfrac{1}{2}$. It follows that

$$\sin(\mathrm{Sin}^{-1}\,\tfrac{1}{2}) = \tfrac{1}{2}$$

and that

$$\cos\left(\mathrm{Cos}^{-1}\,\dfrac{\sqrt{3}}{2}\right) = \dfrac{\sqrt{3}}{2}.$$

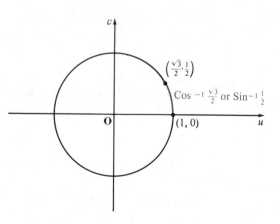

FIGURE 4–11

Moreover, it *appears* that

$$\sin\left(\text{Cos}^{-1}\frac{\sqrt{3}}{2}\right) = \frac{1}{2} \quad \text{and} \quad \cos\left(\text{Sin}^{-1}\tfrac{1}{2}\right) = \frac{\sqrt{3}}{2}.$$

Example 1 shows that this latter statement is true.

Example 1   Find $\cos\left(\text{Sin}^{-1}\tfrac{1}{2}\right)$.

Solution   Since $\text{Sin}^{-1}\dfrac{1}{2} = \dfrac{\pi}{6}$, we have

$$\cos\left(\text{Sin}^{-1}\tfrac{1}{2}\right) = \cos\frac{\pi}{6}$$

$$= \frac{\sqrt{3}}{2}.$$

Example 2   Find an algebraic expression for $\cos\left(\text{Sin}^{-1}x\right)$, where x is any number in the interval $-1 \le x \le 1$.

Solution   Let x be any number in the interval $-1 \le x \le 1$. Then $-\dfrac{\pi}{2} \le \text{Sin}^{-1}x \le \dfrac{\pi}{2}$. Hence $\text{Sin}^{-1}x$ is the length of the arc from the point $(1, 0)$ to the point (u, v) in the first or the fourth quadrants, where

$$u = \cos\left(\text{Sin}^{-1}x\right) \quad \text{and} \quad v = \sin\left(\text{Sin}^{-1}x\right).$$

Since $u = \cos\left(\text{Sin}^{-1}x\right)$, we want to find an expression for u in terms of x.

Because $u^2 + v^2 = 1$, $u = \pm\sqrt{1 - v^2}$, and we take only the nonnegative square root since $u \ge 0$ in the first and fourth quadrants. Thus

$$u = \sqrt{1 - v^2}.$$

Moreover, $v = \sin\left(\text{Sin}^{-1}x\right) = x.$

Substituting $v = x$ in the equation $u = \sqrt{1 - v^2}$ gives

$$u = \sqrt{1 - x^2}.$$

Therefore, we can conclude from Example 2 that

▲ $$\cos (\text{Sin}^{-1} x) = \sqrt{1 - x^2} \quad \text{for } -1 \le x \le 1. \tag{1}$$

Similarly, it can be shown that

▲ $$\sin (\text{Cos}^{-1} x) = \sqrt{1 - x^2} \quad \text{for } -1 \le x \le 1. \tag{2}$$

In working with inverse circular functions, you may need to use the identities for $\sin (x_1 \pm x_2)$, $\cos (x_1 \pm x_2)$, or $\tan (x_1 \pm x_2)$, as illustrated in the next example.

Example 3 Find the value of $\sin (\text{Arcsin } \frac{1}{4} + \text{Arccos } \frac{1}{2})$.

Solution Let $x_1 = \text{Arcsin } \frac{1}{4}$ and $x_2 = \text{Arccos } \frac{1}{2}$. Then we are looking for $\sin (x_1 + x_2)$.
Since

$$\sin (x_1 + x_2) = \sin x_1 \cos x_2 + \cos x_1 \sin x_2,$$

we want the value of

$$\sin (\text{Arcsin } \tfrac{1}{4}) \cos (\text{Arccos } \tfrac{1}{2}) + \cos (\text{Arcsin } \tfrac{1}{4}) \sin (\text{Arccos } \tfrac{1}{2}). \quad (*)$$

From (1) and (2) above, we know that

$$\cos (\text{Arcsin } \tfrac{1}{4}) = \sqrt{1 - (\tfrac{1}{4})^2} = \frac{\sqrt{15}}{4}$$

and

$$\sin (\text{Arccos } \tfrac{1}{2}) = \sqrt{1 - (\tfrac{1}{2})^2} = \frac{\sqrt{3}}{2}.$$

Also, we have

$$\sin (\text{Arcsin } \tfrac{1}{4}) = \tfrac{1}{4} \quad \text{and} \quad \cos (\text{Arccos } \tfrac{1}{2}) = \tfrac{1}{2}.$$

Substituting these values in the expression $(*)$ yields

$$\left(\frac{1}{4}\right)\left(\frac{1}{2}\right) + \left(\frac{\sqrt{15}}{4}\right)\left(\frac{\sqrt{3}}{2}\right) = \frac{1}{8} + \frac{3\sqrt{5}}{8} = \frac{1 + 3\sqrt{5}}{8}$$

$$\doteq \frac{1 + 3(2.236)}{8} \doteq 0.96.$$

Exercises 4–3

Find the value of each of the following.

A 1. $\sin (\text{Cos}^{-1} \tfrac{1}{3})$

8. $\text{Cos}^{-1} \left(-\dfrac{\sqrt{3}}{2}\right) + \text{Cos}^{-1} (-\tfrac{1}{2})$

2. $\cos (\text{Sin}^{-1} \tfrac{2}{3})$

9. $\tan (\text{Sin}^{-1} \tfrac{1}{2})$

3. $\sin [\text{Arccos} (-\tfrac{1}{2})]$

$\left(Hint:\ \tan x = \dfrac{\sin x}{\cos x}. \right)$

4. $\cos [\text{Arcsin} (-\tfrac{1}{4})]$

10. $\cot [\text{Cos}^{-1} (-\tfrac{1}{2})]$

5. $\text{Arcsin } 1 + \text{Arcsin } 0$

11. $\csc \left(\text{Sin}^{-1} \dfrac{\sqrt{3}}{2} \right)$

6. $\text{Arcsin } \dfrac{\sqrt{2}}{2} + \text{Arcsin } \dfrac{\sqrt{3}}{2}$

12. $\tan (\text{Cos}^{-1} \tfrac{1}{3})$

7. $\text{Sin}^{-1} \tfrac{1}{2} + \text{Sin}^{-1} \dfrac{\sqrt{3}}{2}$

13. $\sec (\text{Cos}^{-1} \tfrac{3}{5})$

Arrange the elements of each set in increasing order of value, from least to greatest.

14. $\left\{ \text{Arccos} \left(-\dfrac{\sqrt{3}}{2}\right),\ \text{Arccos } 0,\ \text{Arccos } \tfrac{1}{2} \right\}$

15. $\left\{ \text{Arcsin} \left(-\dfrac{\sqrt{3}}{2}\right),\ \text{Arcsin } 0,\ \text{Arcsin } \tfrac{1}{2} \right\}$

16. $\{\text{Arctan} (-\sqrt{3}),\ \text{Arctan } 0,\ \text{Arctan } 1\}$

17. $\{\text{Arcsin } 1,\ \text{Arccos } 1,\ \text{Arctan } 1\}$

18. $\{\text{Arcsin} (-1),\ \text{Arccos} (-1),\ \text{Arctan} (-1)\}$

Find the value of each expression.

19. $\sin \left(\text{Arcsin} \dfrac{1}{2} + \text{Arccos} \dfrac{\sqrt{3}}{2} \right)$

20. $\cos \left(\text{Arcsin} \dfrac{1}{2} + \text{Arccos} \dfrac{\sqrt{3}}{2} \right)$

21. $\sin \left(\text{Arccos} \dfrac{1}{2} + \text{Arccos} \dfrac{\sqrt{2}}{2} \right)$

B 22. $\sin (\text{Arcsin} \tfrac{2}{5} + \text{Arcsin} \tfrac{3}{5})$

25. $\tan (\text{Tan}^{-1} \sqrt{3} + \text{Tan}^{-1} 1)$

23. $\sin (2 \text{ Arcsin} \tfrac{4}{5})$

26. $\tan \left(\text{Tan}^{-1} \dfrac{1}{4} + \dfrac{\pi}{3} \right)$

24 $\cos (2 \text{ Arcsin} \tfrac{1}{5})$

27. $\tan (\text{Tan}^{-1} \tfrac{1}{2} + \text{Tan}^{-1} \tfrac{1}{3})$

28. If $0 < x_1 < x_2 < 1$, which of the following statements are true:

(a) $\sin (\text{Sin}^{-1} x_1) < \sin (\text{Sin}^{-1} x_2)$ (d) $\cos (\text{Sin}^{-1} x_1) < \cos (\text{Sin}^{-1} x_2)$

(b) $\cos (\text{Cos}^{-1} x_1) < \cos (\text{Cos}^{-1} x_2)$ (e) $\text{Tan}^{-1} x_1 < \text{Tan}^{-1} x_2$

(c) $\sin (\text{Cos}^{-1} x_1) < \sin (\text{Cos}^{-1} x_2)$

C **29.** Find a value of x such that **(a)** $\text{Sin}^{-1}(\sin x) = x$ and **(b)** $\text{Sin}^{-1}(\sin x) \neq x$.

30. Find a value of x such that **(a)** $\text{Cos}^{-1}(\cos x) = x$ and **(b)** $\text{Cos}^{-1}(\cos x) \neq x$.

31. Show that $\sin(\text{Arcsin } x + \text{Arccos } x) = 1$ for $|x| \leq 1$.

32. Show that $\text{Arcsin } x + \text{Arccos } x = \dfrac{\pi}{2}$ for $|x| \leq 1$.

33. Graph $\{(x, y): y = \sqrt{1 - x^2}, |x| \leq 1\}$

34. Prove that $\sin(\text{Cos}^{-1} x) = \sqrt{1 - x^2}$ for $|x| \leq 1$.

35. Express **(a)** $\sin(\frac{1}{2} \text{Cos}^{-1} x)$ and **(b)** $\cos(\frac{1}{2} \text{Sin}^{-1} x)$ as an algebraic expression in x.

Solving Open Sentences

4–4 *Open Sentences Involving One Circular Function*

In algebra, you learned how to solve equations of the form $ax + c = 0$ and $ax^2 + bx + c = 0$, where a, b, and c are constants. In this section, we shall be concerned with equations of the form $az + c = 0$ and $az^2 + bz + c = 0$, where a, b, and c are constants and z represents an expression involving a circular function. Examples of such equations are

$$2 \sin x + 1 = 0 \qquad \text{and} \qquad \tan^2 x + 4 \tan x - 4 = 0.$$

To solve equations involving circular functions, you may use the properties of real numbers, algebraic techniques (such as factoring), the properties of the circular functions and their inverses, and the identities discussed in Chapters 1 and 2. Because of the periodic properties of the circular functions, the solution sets for such equations will often have infinitely many members. For example, the equation

$$\sin x = 1$$

has $\left\{x: x = \dfrac{\pi}{2} + 2k\pi, \ k \in J\right\}$, which is an infinite set, as its solution set. The

solution $\dfrac{\pi}{2} + 2k\pi$, $k \in J$, is called the **general solution** of the equation. Any

solution that can be obtained by assigning a particular value to k in this expres-

sion is called a **particular solution**. For example, $\dfrac{\pi}{2}, \dfrac{5\pi}{2}$, and $-\dfrac{3\pi}{2}$ are particular
solutions.

Example 1   Find the general solution set and the set of particular solutions over the interval $0 \le x < 2\pi$ for each of the following equations.

(a) $2 \cos x + \sqrt{3} = 0$ **(b)** $2 \sin 3x - 1 = 0$

Solution   **(a)** Notice that the given equation,

$$2 \cos x + \sqrt{3} = 0,$$

is of the form

$$2z + \sqrt{3} = 0,$$

with $z = \cos x$. Therefore, we can solve it for $\cos x$ by the same method that we would use to solve the equation $2z + \sqrt{3} = 0$ for z. Thus, adding $-\sqrt{3}$ to both members of the given equation and then multiplying both members by $\frac{1}{2}$, we have

$$\cos x = -\frac{\sqrt{3}}{2}.$$

The particular solutions of this equation in the interval $0 \le x < 2\pi$ are $\frac{5\pi}{6}$ and $\frac{7\pi}{6}$. Since cos has period 2π, the general solution set is

$$\left\{ x\colon x = \frac{5\pi}{6} + 2k\pi \text{ or } x = \frac{7\pi}{6} + 2k\pi, k \in J \right\}.$$

(b) The given equation is of the form $2z - 1 = 0$ with $z = \sin 3x$. Adding 1 to both members of this equation and then multiplying both members by $\frac{1}{2}$, we have

$$\sin 3x = \tfrac{1}{2}.$$

Solving this equation for $3x$ over the interval from 0 to 2π, we have

$$3x = \frac{\pi}{6} \quad \text{or} \quad 3x = \frac{5\pi}{6}.$$

Thus the general solution for $3x$ is

$$3x = \frac{\pi}{6} + 2k\pi \quad \text{or} \quad 3x = \frac{5\pi}{6} + 2k\pi.$$

Consequently the general solution set for x is

$$\left\{x: x = \frac{\pi}{18} + \frac{2}{3}k\pi \text{ or } x = \frac{5\pi}{18} + \frac{2}{3}k\pi, \ k \in J\right\}.$$

For appropriate values of k, we obtain the particular solution set over $0 \leq x < 2\pi$ as follows:

$$\text{For } k = 0, \ x = \frac{\pi}{18} \text{ or } \frac{5\pi}{18}.$$

$$\text{For } k = 1, \ x = \frac{13\pi}{18} \text{ or } \frac{17\pi}{18}.$$

$$\text{For } k = 2, \ x = \frac{25\pi}{18} \text{ or } \frac{29\pi}{18}.$$

Thus the particular solution set over $0 \leq x < 2\pi$ is

$$\left\{\frac{\pi}{18}, \frac{5\pi}{18}, \frac{13\pi}{18}, \frac{17\pi}{18}, \frac{25\pi}{18}, \frac{29\pi}{18}\right\}.$$

Sometimes the procedures used in solving certain equations may introduce solutions which are not members of the solution set of the *original* equation. (For instance, the squaring process used in Example 2 of Section 4–5 introduces the numbers $x = \dfrac{3\pi}{2} + 2k\pi$, which must, upon checking, be rejected.) Therefore, it is generally wise to verify (that is, to "check") that each solution you have obtained is actually a solution of the original equation.

For the general solution obtained in Example 1(b), this check would appear as follows:

For $x = \dfrac{\pi}{18} + \dfrac{2}{3}k\pi$, $k \in J$, we have

$$2 \sin 3\left(\frac{\pi}{18} + \frac{2}{3}k\pi\right) - 1 = 2 \sin\left(\frac{\pi}{6} + 2k\pi\right) - 1$$

$$= 2 \sin \frac{\pi}{6} - 1 = 2(\tfrac{1}{2}) - 1 = 0.$$

For $x = \dfrac{5\pi}{18} + \dfrac{2}{3}k\pi$, $k \in J$, we have

$$2 \sin 3\left(\frac{5\pi}{18} + \frac{2}{3}k\pi\right) - 1 = 2 \sin\left(\frac{5\pi}{6} + 2k\pi\right) - 1$$

$$= 2 \sin \frac{5\pi}{6} - 1 = 2(\tfrac{1}{2}) - 1 = 0,$$

as desired.

Example 2   Find the general solution set and the set of particular solutions over the interval $0 \le x < 2\pi$ for each of the following equations:

(a) $2 \cos^2 x - \cos x = 1$ (b) $\tan^2 x - 3 = 0$

Solution   (a) The equation $2 \cos^2 x - \cos x = 1$, or

$$2(\cos x)^2 - (\cos x) - 1 = 0,$$

is of the form $2z^2 - z - 1 = 0$, with $z = \cos x$. Therefore we can solve it for $\cos x$ by the same method that we would use to solve the equation $2z^2 - z - 1 = 0$ for z. Thus, factoring the left-hand member of

$$2 \cos^2 x - \cos x - 1 = 0,$$

we have

$$(2 \cos x + 1)(\cos x - 1) = 0.$$

Then

$$2 \cos x + 1 = 0 \quad \text{or} \quad \cos x - 1 = 0,$$

$$\cos x = -\tfrac{1}{2} \quad \text{or} \quad \cos x = 1.$$

Hence the general solution set of $2 \cos^2 x - \cos x = 1$ is the union of the solution sets of $\cos x = -\tfrac{1}{2}$ and $\cos x = 1$, namely,

$$\left\{ x: x = \frac{2\pi}{3} + 2k\pi \text{ or } x = \frac{4\pi}{3} + 2k\pi, k \in J \right\} \cup \{x: x = 2k\pi, k \in J\}.$$

The particular solution set over $0 \le x < 2\pi$ is $\left\{ 0, \dfrac{2\pi}{3}, \dfrac{4\pi}{3} \right\}$, which can be obtained from the general solution set by setting $k = 0$.

(b) Solving the given equation for $\tan x$, we have

$$\tan^2 x = 3,$$

$$\tan x = \sqrt{3} \quad \text{or} \quad \tan x = -\sqrt{3}.$$

Then the general solution set of $\tan^2 x - 3 = 0$ is the union of the solution sets of $\tan x = \sqrt{3}$ and $\tan x = -\sqrt{3}$, namely,

$$\left\{ x: x = \frac{\pi}{3} + k\pi, k \in J \right\} \cup \left\{ x: x = \frac{2\pi}{3} + k\pi, k \in J \right\}.$$

The particular solution set over $0 \le x < 2\pi$ is

$$\left\{ \frac{\pi}{3}, \frac{2\pi}{3}, \frac{4\pi}{3}, \frac{5\pi}{3} \right\},$$

which can be obtained from the general solution set by letting $k = 0$ and 1.

Checking that the solution sets obtained in Examples 2(a) and 2(b) actually are the solution sets of the original equations is left as an exercise (Exercise 22, below).

Exercises 4–4

Find the solution set of each of the following over the interval $0 \le x < 2\pi$.

A **1.** $\sin x - 1 = 0$

2. $\sqrt{2} \cos x + 1 = 0$

3. $2 + \sec x = 0$

4. $4 \sin^2 x - 1 = 0$

5. $\tan^2 x - 1 = 0$

6. $\cot^2 x - \sqrt{3} \cot x = 0$

7. $\sin^2 3x = 0$

8. $\sin^2 x - 2 \sin x + 1 = 0$

9. $2 \cos^2 x + 3 \cos x + 1 = 0$

10. $\tan x(1 - \tan x) = 0$

11. $\cot^2 x + 2 \cot x + 1 = 0$

12. $2 \sec^2 x = 2 - 3 \sec x$

13. $3 \tan^2 x - 1 = 0$

14. $2 \cos^2 x = 1 + \cos^2 x$

15. $2 \cot^2 x + 2 \cot x = 0$

16. $\tan^2 x - \sqrt{3} \tan x = 0$

B **17.** $\cos^2 4x + \cos 4x = 0$

18. $\tan^2 6x = 1$

19. $\cos^2 \frac{x}{2} = \frac{1}{4}$

20. $\sin^2 (x + 4) = 1$

21. $\left(1 + \sin \frac{x}{2} \right) \left(\sin \frac{x}{2} \right) = 0$

22. Verify that the general solution sets obtained in Examples 2(a) and 2(b) on page 130 are correct.

Find the general solution set of each of the following.

C **23.** $4 \cos^3 x - \cos x = 0$

24. $\sin^2 \left| x - \frac{\pi}{3} \right| = \frac{1}{4}$

25. $\left| \sin \frac{x}{\pi} \right| = 1$

4–5 *Open Sentences Involving Two Circular Functions*

An open sentence involving two or more circular functions can often be transformed into an equivalent open sentence which involves only one circular function and which can thus be solved by the methods discussed in Section 4–4. In some cases, the resulting open sentence may *not* be equivalent to the original open sentence for certain values of the variable, and these values must be carefully noted. Example 1 illustrates some ways in which such transformations can be accomplished.

Example 1   For each open sentence, obtain an open sentence which involves only one circular function and which is equivalent to the original open sentence except, possibly, for certain specified real numbers.

(a) $\cos 2x \sec x + 1 = 0$
(b) $\sec^2 x = 3 - \tan x$
(c) $\cos (2x - \pi) = \sin x$

Solution   (a) Replacing $\cos 2x$ with $2 \cos^2 x - 1$ and $\sec x$ with $\dfrac{1}{\cos x}$, we obtain the equation

$$(2 \cos^2 x - 1) \left(\frac{1}{\cos x} \right) + 1 = 0,$$

or, multiplying both members by $\cos x$,

$$2 \cos^2 x - 1 + \cos x = 0.$$

This equation is equivalent to the original equation except for values of x for which $\sec x$ is not defined, that is, for which $\cos x = 0$. These values are of the form $\dfrac{\pi}{2} + 2k\pi$ or $\dfrac{3\pi}{2} + 2k\pi$, $k \in J$.

(b) Replacing $\sec^2 x$ with $\tan^2 x + 1$, we obtain the equation

$$\tan^2 x + 1 = 3 - \tan x,$$

which is equivalent to

$$\tan^2 x + \tan x - 2 = 0.$$

Since $\sec^2 x$ and $\tan^2 x + 1$ are both undefined for values of x for which $\cos x = 0$, the equations $\sec^2 x = 3 - \tan x$ and $\tan^2 x + \tan x - 2$ are equivalent.

(c) Using the formula

$$\cos (x_2 - x_1) = \cos x_2 \cos x_1 + \sin x_2 \sin x_1,$$

we have

$$\cos (2x - \pi) = -\cos 2x,$$

and from page 38 we have

$$-\cos 2x = -(1 - 2 \sin^2 x)$$
$$= 2 \sin^2 x - 1.$$

Therefore, replacing the left-hand member of

$$\cos (2x - \pi) = \sin x$$

with $2 \sin^2 x - 1$ yields the equivalent equation

$$2 \sin^2 x - 1 = \sin x.$$

No restrictions need be specified for the variable since all expressions involved are defined for all real numbers.

Several additional procedures for finding solution sets are illustrated in the remaining examples.

Example 2   Find the general solution set of

$$\sin x + \cos x = 1.$$

Solution   We proceed as follows:

$$\sin x + \cos x = 1$$
$$\sin x = 1 - \cos x$$
$$\sin^2 x = (1 - \cos x)^2$$
$$= 1 - 2 \cos x + \cos^2 x$$
$$1 - \cos^2 x = 1 - 2 \cos x + \cos^2 x$$
$$-2 \cos^2 x + 2 \cos x = 0$$
$$-2 \cos x(\cos x - 1) = 0$$
$$\cos x = 0 \quad \text{or} \quad \cos x = 1$$

(Solution continued)

The solution set for this sentence is

$$\left\{x\colon x = \frac{\pi}{2} + 2k\pi \text{ or } x = \frac{3\pi}{2} + 2k\pi, \, k \in J\right\} \cup \{x\colon x = 2k\pi, \, k \in J\}.$$

Checking in the original equation, we find

$$\sin\left(\frac{\pi}{2} + 2k\pi\right) + \cos\left(\frac{\pi}{2} + 2k\pi\right) = 1 + 0 = 1,$$

$$\sin\left(\frac{3\pi}{2} + 2k\pi\right) + \cos\left(\frac{3\pi}{2} + 2k\pi\right) = -1 + 0 \neq 1,$$

$$\sin 2k\pi + \cos 2k\pi = 0 + 1 = 1.$$

Hence we must reject the values $x = \dfrac{3\pi}{2} + 2k\pi$, which actually were introduced in the squaring process, and the solution set is

$$\left\{x\colon x = \frac{\pi}{2} + 2k\pi, \, k \in J\right\} \cup \{x\colon x = 2k\pi, \, k \in J\}.$$

Example 3   Find the general solution set of

$$\sin x = \cos x.$$

Solution   If both members of the given equation are divided by $\cos x$, then for values of x for which $\cos x \neq 0$, the result is the equivalent equation

$$\frac{\sin x}{\cos x} = 1.$$

Since, for $\cos x \neq 0$, $\dfrac{\sin x}{\cos x} = \tan x$, we have

$$\tan x = 1,$$

and

$$x = \frac{\pi}{4} + k\pi.$$

If $\cos x = 0$, then $\sin x = \pm 1 \neq \cos x$. Thus the general solution set is

$$\left\{x\colon x = \frac{\pi}{4} + k\pi, \, k \in J\right\}.$$

Check   For k even, we have

$$\sin\left(\frac{\pi}{4} + k\pi\right) = \frac{\sqrt{2}}{2} = \cos\left(\frac{\pi}{4} + k\pi\right).$$

For k odd, we have

$$\sin\left(\frac{\pi}{4} + k\pi\right) = -\frac{\sqrt{2}}{2} = \cos\left(\frac{\pi}{4} + k\pi\right).$$

Example 4   Find the particular solution set of

$$\sin 2x = 5 \cos x$$

over $0 \le x < 2\pi$.

Solution   Replacing $\sin 2x$ with $2 \sin x \cos x$ gives

$$2 \sin x \cos x = 5 \cos x,$$

or

$$2 \sin x \cos x - 5 \cos x = 0.$$

Factoring, we have

$$\cos x(2 \sin x - 5) = 0,$$

$$\cos x = 0 \quad \text{or} \quad 2 \sin x - 5 = 0.$$

These conditions simplify to

$$\cos x = 0 \quad \text{or} \quad \sin x = \tfrac{5}{2}.$$

  Since $|\sin x| \le 1$ for all x, the solution set of $\sin x = \tfrac{5}{2}$ is the empty set. Thus the equations

$$\sin 2x = 5 \cos x$$

and

$$\cos x = 0$$

have the same particular solution set over the interval $0 \le x < 2\pi$, namely,

$$\left\{\frac{\pi}{2}, \frac{3\pi}{2}\right\}.$$

(Solution continued)

Check   For $x = \dfrac{\pi}{2}$,

$$\sin 2x = \sin \pi = 0 \quad \text{and} \quad 5 \cos x = 5 \cos \frac{\pi}{2} = 5(0) = 0.$$

For $x = \dfrac{3\pi}{2}$,

$$\sin 2x = \sin 3\pi = 0 \quad \text{and} \quad 5 \cos x = 5 \cos \frac{3\pi}{2} = 5(0) = 0.$$

Exercises 4–5

Find the solution set of each of the following over the interval $0 \le x < 2\pi$.

A   **1.** $\sin 2x = \sin x$

2. $\sin 2x = \cos x$

3. $\cos 2x + \sin x - 1 = 0$

4. $\sin x - \sqrt{3} \cos x = 1$

5. $\sin 2x + \cos 2x - 1 = 0$

6. $\sqrt{3} \cos x + \sin x = -1$

7. $\sin 2x + \cos x + 2 \sin x = -1$

8. $2 \sin x \sec x = \sec x$

9. $3 \csc x - \sin x = 2$

10. $3 \tan \dfrac{x}{2} = \cot \dfrac{x}{2}$

11. $\frac{1}{2} \tan 2x = \cos x$

12. $\sec^2 2x = 1 - \tan 2x$

13. $\tan^2 x = \sin 2x$

14. $\sin x + \cos x \sin x = 2$

15. $\cos 2x = \cos^2 x - 1$

16. $1 - \sin^2 x = \cos 2x$

Solve each of the following.

B **17.** $\text{Arctan } x = \dfrac{\pi}{6}$ **18.** $\text{Arctan } \sqrt{x} = \dfrac{\pi}{3}$ **19.** $\text{Arctan } (x - 1) = -\dfrac{\pi}{4}$

Find the general solution of each of the following. Use Table 1, page 391, if necessary.

20. $\sin (\pi - 2x) = \cos x$

21. $\sin \left(2x + \dfrac{2\pi}{3}\right) + \sin \left(2x - \dfrac{2\pi}{3}\right) = \dfrac{\sqrt{2}}{2}$

22. $\sin 2x \tan^2 2x - \tan 2x = \sin 2x$

23. $\sin^4 x - \cos^4 x = 1$

C **24.** $2 \tan x + \sec x = 1$

25. $3 \cot x + 5 \csc x = 4$

26. $\sin x \cos x = 0$

27. $\sin 2x - \sin 4x = 2 \sin x$

28. $\cos 3x + \cos x = \cos 2x$

Chapter Summary

1. By restricting the domain of a circular function, you can obtain a function whose inverse is also a function. The **principal inverse circular functions** are defined as follows:

$$\text{Cos}^{-1} = \{(x, y) \colon x = \cos y, |x| \le 1, 0 \le y \le \pi\}$$

$$\text{Sin}^{-1} = \left\{(x, y) \colon x = \sin y, |x| \le 1, |y| \le \frac{\pi}{2}\right\}$$

$$\text{Tan}^{-1} = \left\{(x, y) \colon x = \tan y, x \in \Re, |y| < \frac{\pi}{2}\right\}$$

$$\text{Cot}^{-1} = \{(x, y) \colon x = \cot y, x \in \Re, 0 < y < \pi\}$$

$$\text{Sec}^{-1} = \left\{(x, y) \colon x = \sec y, |x| \ge 1, 0 \le y \le \pi, y \ne \frac{\pi}{2}\right\}$$

$$\text{Csc}^{-1} = \left\{(x, y) \colon x = \csc y, |x| \ge 1, 0 < |y| \le \frac{\pi}{2}\right\}$$

2. The principal inverse functions Cot^{-1}, Sec^{-1}, and Csc^{-1} are related as follows to the other inverse circular functions:

$$\text{Cot}^{-1} x = \begin{cases} \text{Tan}^{-1} \dfrac{1}{x} + \pi & \text{for } x < 0 \\[2mm] \text{Tan}^{-1} \dfrac{1}{x} & \text{for } x > 0 \end{cases}$$

$$\text{Sec}^{-1} x = \text{Cos}^{-1} \frac{1}{x} \qquad \text{for } |x| \ge 1$$

$$\text{Csc}^{-1} x = \text{Sin}^{-1} \frac{1}{x} \qquad \text{for } |x| \ge 1$$

3. For any real number x such that $|x| \le 1$:

$$\cos (\text{Sin}^{-1} x) = \sqrt{1 - x^2}$$
$$\sin (\text{Cos}^{-1} x) = \sqrt{1 - x^2}$$

4. You can use the identities developed in Chapters 1 and 2 and the properties of inverse circular functions, together with algebraic techniques and the properties of real numbers, to solve equations involving circular functions and their inverses.

Chapter Test

4–1   **1.** Solve the equation $\sin y = -\frac{1}{2}$ over the interval $-\frac{\pi}{2} \le y \le \frac{\pi}{2}$.

Find the value of each of the following.

2. $\text{Cos}^{-1} \dfrac{\sqrt{3}}{2}$ **3.** $\cos (\text{Cos}^{-1} 1)$

4–2   **4.** $\text{Tan}^{-1} (\sin \pi)$ **5.** $\text{Sec}^{-1} (-2)$

6. $\text{Tan}^{-1} \dfrac{\sqrt{3}}{2} + \text{Cot}^{-1} \dfrac{\sqrt{3}}{2}$

4–3   **7.** $\cos (\text{Sin}^{-1} \frac{3}{5})$

Find the general solution set for each of the following.

4–4   **8.** $4 \sin^2 x = 3$ **9.** $\tan^2 x - \tan x = 0$

Find the set of particular solutions over the interval $0 \le x < 2\pi$.

4–5   **10.** $\cos 2x = \sin x$

11. $3 \sin^2 x = 1 - \frac{5}{2} \cos x$

12. $\tan x = \frac{1}{2} \sec x$

Applications of Trigonometry

Environmental Exploration

Scientific technology permits us to "see" the world about us in many different ways. Trigonometry provides a method for solving many theoretical and practical problems in the physical, social, and life sciences.

Optical and radio telescopes reveal objects and activities at a *distance* of up to eight or nine billion light years. Of course, what these instruments reveal happened that long ago in *time*, too. Thus we can observe events that transpired not long after the "big bang" of some ten billion years ago when the universe as we know it is supposed to have had its origin.

The twin radio telescope shown here is used to study planets and other large celestial bodies, and to pinpoint the location of radio sources outside our galaxy. Located in a California valley, the telescope consists of twin 90-foot parabolic antennas mounted on a 1600-foot track.

This photograph, showing the surface of the earth under a heavy cloud cover, was taken from the lunar surface during the Apollo 16 mission. Mexico and much of the southwestern United States are clearly visible through the clouds. Shots such as this greatly increase our knowledge of the earth's atmosphere and its weather patterns.

Nearer home, tree rings—for example, of bristlecone pines, living and dead —also permit us to look backward in time. They reveal climatic conditions during the last eight thousand years.

Moreover, carbon dating helps fix the time of ancient archaeological and geological events.

Optical microscopes magnify the apparent size of an object by about a thousand diameters, and now electron microscopes give a magnification of over a million diameters! Thus we can observe not only enormous galaxies and quasars but also tiny bacteria, viruses, and even molecules and some atoms.

Artificial satellites, through photography, are giving us a better understanding of atmospheric dynamics and are furnishing data for improved weather forecasting. They have proved to be valuable in map making and in precisely locating objects on or near the surface of the earth. Thus they are a great aid to air pilots and mariners. Potentially they are the best means of controlling air traffic

The stars near the center of the Milky Way Galaxy are shown in this photograph, which was taken during the Apollo 16 mission using an ultraviolet camera with hydrogen light filtered out. Only the very hot, blue stars are recorded in this photograph, which is streaked because of the moon's rotation during its 30-minute exposure. The bright object at the lower left is the planet Jupiter.

since they could be made capable of following the locations of individual aircraft accurately in three dimensions to within a few hundred feet.

Sophisticated radar, infrared, and other instruments in satellites, airplanes, and helicopters can spot icebergs; discover mineral deposits and sources of fresh water; make global agricultural surveys; detect volcanic activity, possible sources of geothermal power, forest fires, and diseased crops; and study the migration patterns of birds and animals.

Ships and submarines use side-looking radar and light-amplifying television tubes to map and examine the ocean floor and to locate and study schools of fish.

Thus, through environmental exploration, we are developing a deeper understanding of the interdependence of geological processes, and a more complete and accurate catalogue of the limited resources of the earth.

Chapter Five

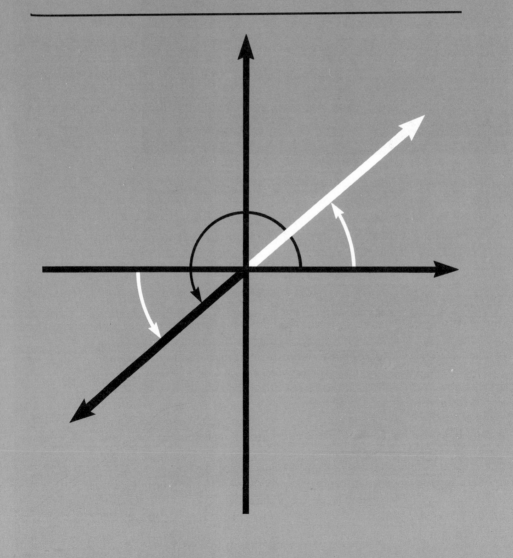

Trigonometric Functions

OBJECTIVES

1. To apply principles of angle measure.
2. To learn the relationship of trigonometric functions to circular functions.
3. To use tables of values of trigonometric functions, and to apply these functions to solve right triangles.
4. To apply the Laws of Sines and Cosines to solve problems involving oblique triangles.

Basic Concepts

5–1 *Angle Measure*

The branch of mathematics called *trigonometry*, from the Greek words for "triangle measurement," concerns the relationships between the measures of the sides and the measures of the angles in plane and spherical triangles. Originally developed to calculate the positions of the stars and planets, trigonometry dealt mainly with spherical triangles. Today, however, we are primarily interested in the plane trigonometry which we shall study in this chapter.

In studying geometry, you learned that an **angle** can be defined as the union of two rays having a common endpoint. Furthermore, a measure can be assigned to an angle by using a circle as a ruler. Such rulers are called **protractors**.

If a unit circle is superimposed upon an angle, with the center of the circle at the vertex of the angle, then an assignment of either degree measure or radian measure can be made to the angle. If the unit circle is divided into 360 congruent arcs, then the *degree* measure of the angle is the number of those congruent arcs in the arc contained in the union of the angle and its interior. (See Figure 5–1.) If, instead, the unit of arc-length measure is the radius of the unit circle (the number 1), then the measure of the angle is called its *radian* measure.

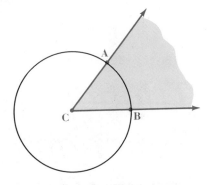

The degree measure of an angle α (alpha) is denoted by $m^{\circ}(\alpha)$ and the radian measure of α is denoted by $m^{R}(\alpha)$.

Since the circumference of a unit circle is 2π, a unit circle can be divided into 2π arcs, each of length 1. Thus, for an angle α, you have the ratio

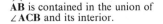

$\overarc{AB}$ is contained in the union of $\angle ACB$ and its interior.

FIGURE 5–1

▲ $$\frac{m^{\circ}(\alpha)}{m^{R}(\alpha)} = \frac{360}{2\pi} = \frac{180}{\pi}.$$

For example, if $m^{\circ}(\alpha) = 180$, then $m^{R}(\alpha) = \pi$; if $m^{R}(\alpha) = \dfrac{\pi}{2}$, then $m^{\circ}(\alpha) = 90$; and so on. We shall follow the usual convention of writing

▲ $$180^{\circ} = \pi^{R} \tag{1}$$

to mean that if $m^{\circ}(\alpha) = 180$, then $m^{R}(\alpha) = \pi$, and conversely.

Example 1   Express 15° in radians.

Solution   Since $1^{\circ} = \dfrac{\pi^{R}}{180}$, $15^{\circ} = 15 \cdot \dfrac{\pi^{R}}{180} = \dfrac{\pi^{R}}{12}$.

Example 2   Express $\dfrac{\pi^{R}}{6}$ in degrees.

Solution   Since $\pi^{R} = 180^{\circ}$, $\dfrac{\pi^{R}}{6} = \dfrac{180^{\circ}}{6} = 30^{\circ}$.

It is customary in geometry courses to consider only angles of measure between 0° and 180°. In trigonometry, however, it is necessary to consider angles of all degree measures.

Given two rays with a common endpoint, we shall designate one of these rays as the **initial side** of the angle and the other ray as the **terminal side**. The terminal side will be regarded as having been rotated a certain amount from the position occupied by the initial side. This rotation may be *counterclockwise* (in a *positive* direction) or it may be *clockwise* (in a *negative* direction). The rotation may be less than, equal to, or greater than a complete revolution.

For example, various angles may be formed using the two rays $\overrightarrow{OP_1}$ and $\overrightarrow{OP_2}$ in Figure 5-2. By designating $\overrightarrow{OP_1}$ as the initial side, we obtain the following angles:

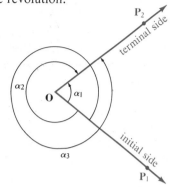

α_1 (read "alpha sub one"), formed by rotating $\overrightarrow{OP_2}$ counterclockwise (in a positive direction) less than one complete revolution.

α_2, formed by rotating $\overrightarrow{OP_2}$ clockwise (in a negative direction) less than one complete revolution.

α_3, formed by rotating $\overrightarrow{OP_2}$ counterclockwise more than one, but less than two, complete revolutions.

FIGURE 5-2

By rotating $\overrightarrow{OP_2}$ more than two complete revolutions, either counterclockwise or clockwise, other angles may be formed having $\overrightarrow{OP_1}$ as initial side and $\overrightarrow{OP_2}$ as terminal side. Similarly, other angles may be formed by designating $\overrightarrow{OP_2}$ as the initial side and $\overrightarrow{OP_1}$ as the terminal side, as shown in Figure 5-3.

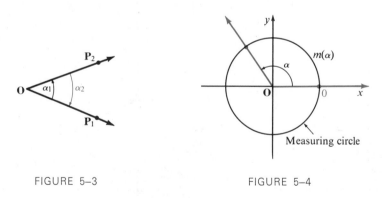

FIGURE 5-3   FIGURE 5-4

When an *xy*-coordinate system is established in the plane containing an angle, with the origin at the vertex of the angle and with the positive ray of the *x*-axis coincident with the initial side of the angle, the angle is said to be in **standard position**.

As shown in Figure 5-4, we measure an angle in standard position by assigning the number 0 to a point on the initial side and then proceeding counterclockwise or clockwise along the **measuring circle**, as indicated by the arc showing the amount of rotation for the angle, until we arrive finally at a point on the terminal side. Taking proper account of the amount of rotation involved, we then read off the unique real number that gives the measure of the angle in the chosen units, either radians or degrees.

The **sum** $\alpha + \beta$ of two angles can be thought of as the angle formed by putting the vertex of β at the vertex of α, and the initial side of β in coincidence with the terminal side of α. The angle whose initial side is the initial side of α, whose terminal side is the terminal side of β, and whose rotation is obtained by adjoining the rotation for β to that for α, is then the sum $\alpha + \beta$, as illustrated in Figure 5–5.

The **negative** of the angle α, $-\alpha$, is the angle whose initial side is the terminal side of α, whose terminal side is the initial side of α, and whose rotation is obtained by just reversing the rotation for α. Thus, in Figure 5–3 on page 145, α_2 is the negative of α_1,

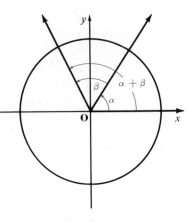

FIGURE 5–5

$$\alpha_2 = -\alpha_1.$$

The **difference** $\alpha - \beta$ of angles α and β is simply the sum $\alpha + (-\beta)$. (See Figure 5–6.)

FIGURE 5–6

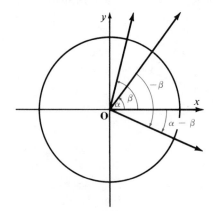

In accordance with these definitions, we have:

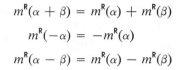

$$m^R(\alpha + \beta) = m^R(\alpha) + m^R(\beta)$$

$$m^R(-\alpha) = -m^R(\alpha)$$

$$m^R(\alpha - \beta) = m^R(\alpha) - m^R(\beta)$$

and similar expressions for $m°$ or any other angle-measure function. We shall continue to use the symbols α and $m(\alpha)$ interchangeably when the intent is clear from the context.

For an angle θ (theta) in standard position, with measure as indicated, the terminal side of θ is located in the quadrant shown in the table below.

θ	Quadrant of Terminal Side of θ
$0° < \theta < 90°$ $90° < \theta < 180°$ $180° < \theta < 270°$ $270° < \theta < 360°$	I II III IV
$-90° < \theta < 0°$ $-180° < \theta < -90°$ $-270° < \theta < -180°$ $-360° < \theta < -270°$	IV III II I

The terminal side of $\theta + n360°$, $n \in J$, coincides with that of θ. This fact can be used in conjunction with the table above to locate the quadrant of the terminal side of an angle greater than 360° or less than $-360°$. If the terminal side lies on one of the axes, the angle is said to be a **quadrantal angle**.

Exercises 5–1

State the degree measure of the angle whose radian measure is as given.

A **1.** $\dfrac{\pi}{4}^R$ **3.** $\dfrac{2\pi}{3}^R$ **5.** $4\pi^R$ **7.** $\dfrac{18\pi}{5}^R$

2. $\dfrac{7\pi}{8}^R$ **4.** $\dfrac{5\pi}{6}^R$ **6.** $-\dfrac{3\pi}{2}^R$ **8.** $-\dfrac{5\pi}{3}^R$

State the radian measure of the angle whose degree measure is as given.

9. $45°$ **11.** $120°$ **13.** $210°$ **15.** $-150°$

10. $80°$ **12.** $150°$ **14.** $-30°$ **16.** $420°$

Suppose a circle is divided into 100 congruent arcs. We shall refer to the measure of a central angle subtended by one of these arcs as one *centangle*, denoted m^C. In Exercises 17–20, find the measure in centangles of an angle whose measure is as given.

B **17.** $\dfrac{\pi}{2}^R$ **18.** $\dfrac{\pi}{5}^R$ **19.** $32°$ **20.** $-298°$

In Exercises 21–24, using the definition of centangle given in the directions for Exercises 17–20, find (a) the degree measure and (b) the radian measure of an angle whose centangle measure is as given.

21. 45^C **22.** 130^C **23.** 260^C **24.** -120^C

5–2 *Trigonometric Functions*

In Chapters 1 and 2 we studied circular functions, whose domains and ranges are sets of real numbers, and in Sections 3–5 and 3–6 we investigated some physical applications of these functions. Let us next define some closely related functions, called **trigonometric functions**, whose domains are sets of *angles* and whose ranges are sets of real numbers. Then we shall see how these functions can be applied to the solution of physical problems.

The trigonometric functions are given the same names as their closely related circular functions; only the domains are different. Namely:

▲　　If θ is an angle whose radian measure is x, then by definition

$$\cos \theta = \cos x, \qquad \sec \theta = \sec x,$$
$$\sin \theta = \sin x, \qquad \csc \theta = \csc x,$$
$$\tan \theta = \tan x, \qquad \cot \theta = \cot x.$$

Because every angle in standard position has a radian measure, and because every angle can be considered to be in standard position relative to suitably placed coordinate axes, with every angle θ there are associated the six real numbers $\cos \theta$, $\sin \theta$, $\tan \theta$, $\sec \theta$, $\csc \theta$, and $\cot \theta$.

The reduction identities for the circular functions presented in Section 1–6 are equally applicable to the trigonometric functions. The following list of reduction formulas, for θ measured in degrees, is particularly useful as an aid in determining the trigonometric values of angles greater than 90° or less than 0°.

REDUCTION FORMULAS

1. $\cos (\theta \pm 360°) = \cos \theta$
2. $\cos (180° + \theta) = -\cos \theta$
3. $\cos (180° - \theta) = -\cos \theta$
4. $\cos (-\theta) = \cos \theta$

5. $\sin (\theta \pm 360°) = \sin \theta$
6. $\sin (180° + \theta) = -\sin \theta$
7. $\sin (180° - \theta) = \sin \theta$
8. $\sin (-\theta) = -\sin \theta$

9. $\tan (\theta \pm 360°) = \tan \theta$
10. $\tan (180° + \theta) = \tan \theta$
11. $\tan (180° - \theta) = -\tan \theta$
12. $\tan (-\theta) = -\tan \theta$

Using these reduction formulas, you can reduce the problem of finding function values for angles with terminal sides in Quadrants II, III, and IV to the problem of finding values for angles with terminal sides in Quadrant I.

Figures 5–7, 5–8, and 5–9 show angles θ_2, θ_3, and θ_4, with terminal sides in Quadrants II, III, and IV, respectively. For each of these angles, we shall denote by α the positive angle in the first quadrant whose trigonometric values are equal to the absolute values of the corresponding trigonometric values of θ_2, θ_3, and θ_4. The statements made in Figures 5–7, 5–8, and 5–9 involve the cosine function; similar statements can be made relative to the other trigonometric functions. Keep in mind that in discussing the cosine values for θ_2, θ_3, and θ_4, we shall be making frequent references to the preceding list of reduction identities.

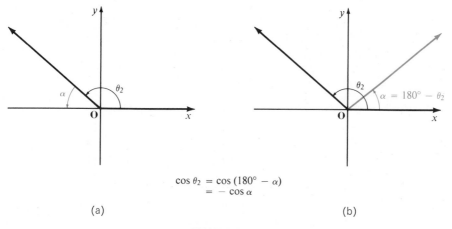

$$\cos \theta_2 = \cos (180° - \alpha)$$
$$= -\cos \alpha$$

(a)   (b)

FIGURE 5–7

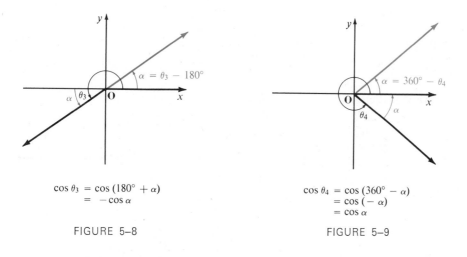

$$\cos \theta_3 = \cos (180° + \alpha)$$
$$= -\cos \alpha$$

FIGURE 5–8

$$\cos \theta_4 = \cos (360° - \alpha)$$
$$= \cos (-\alpha)$$
$$= \cos \alpha$$

FIGURE 5–9

Notice that in Figures 5–7, 5–8, and 5–9, the angle α is the positive acute angle between the x-axis and the terminal side of θ_2, θ_3, and θ_4. In each case we call α the **reference angle**.

Thus $\cos \theta_2 = -\cos \alpha$, $\cos \theta_3 = -\cos \alpha$, and $\cos \theta_4 = \cos \alpha$. Whether the plus or minus sign is attached to $\cos \alpha$ (or to any other trigonometric function) can be determined in one of several ways:

(a) Application of appropriate reduction identities listed on page 148.
(b) Reference to the unit circle to recall in which quadrants the function has positive values and in which quadrants it has negative values. Keeping in mind a drawing such as that shown in Figure 5–10 can be helpful.
(c) Reference to quick sketches of the graph of the function. Figure 5–11 helps determine the sign for the cosine function.

As you become more familiar with sketches such as those presented in Figures 5–10 and 5–11, you will often be able to visualize them mentally without actually having to draw them on paper.

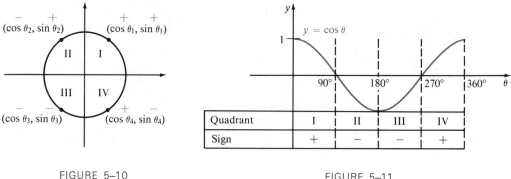

FIGURE 5–10   FIGURE 5–11

Example 1   Express each of the following in terms of a reference angle.

(**a**) $\cos 150°$ (**b**) $\cos 205°$ (**c**) $\cos 315°$

Solution   (**a**) We sketch an angle measuring $150° = 180° - 30°$. Here the reference angle, α, is $30°$. Thus,

$$\cos 150° = \cos (180° - 30°)$$
$$= -\cos 30°$$

by Identity 3.

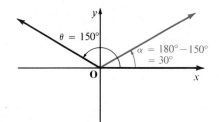

(**b**) $\cos 205° = \cos (180° + 25°)$
$= -\cos 25°$
    by Identity 2.

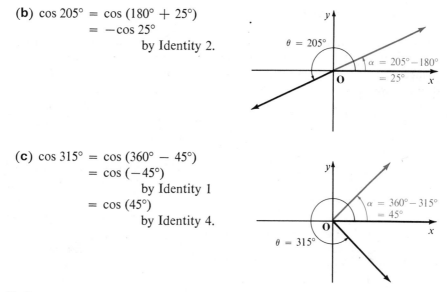

(**c**) $\cos 315° = \cos (360° - 45°)$
$= \cos (-45°)$
    by Identity 1
$= \cos (45°)$
    by Identity 4.

Exercises 5–2

A 1. Continue the following table, showing rows of entries for

$$m^R(\theta) = 0, \frac{\pi}{6}, \frac{\pi}{4}, \frac{\pi}{3}, \frac{\pi}{2}, \frac{2\pi}{3}, \frac{3\pi}{4}, \frac{5\pi}{6}.$$

$m^R(\theta)$	$m°(\theta)$	$\cos \theta$	$\sin \theta$	$\tan \theta$
0	0	1	0	0
$\dfrac{\pi}{6}$	30	$\dfrac{\sqrt{3}}{2}$	$\dfrac{1}{2}$	$\dfrac{1}{\sqrt{3}}$

Using the reduction formulas on page 148, express each of the following in terms of its reference angle.

2. $\cos 450°$ **6.** $\tan 620°$ **10.** $\sin (-65°)$

3. $\tan 510°$ **7.** $\sin 225°$ **11.** $\cos (-120°)$

4. $\sin 920°$ **8.** $\cos (-1200°)$

5. $\cos 1000°$ **9.** $\tan (-420°)$

Find the value of each of the following, using the table in Exercise 1.

12. $\sin 390°$ **15.** $\sin (-60°)$ **18.** $\sin 330°$

13. $\cos 210°$ **16.** $\tan 240°$ **19.** $\cos 510°$

14. $\cos (-210°)$ **17.** $\tan (-150°)$ **20.** $\cos (-300°)$

5–3 *Trigonometric Identities*

The circular-function identities with which you worked in Chapters 1 and 2 retain their validity when the variables involved denote angles rather than real numbers, that is, when you are dealing with trigonometric functions. This is a direct consequence of the definition of trigonometric functions.

Accordingly, the list of Basic Identities on page 66 holds true for x replaced by θ, x_1 replaced by θ_1, and x_2 by θ_2. It is recommended that you review this list of identities which you will be using in this text and in your future work in more advanced mathematics.

Some of these fundamental relationships of trigonometric functions bear titles involving the word "angle." For example, the identities in Part G on page 66 are concerned with function values of an angle of twice the measure of a given angle and hence are called **double-angle formulas**. Similarly, the identities in Part H are called **half-angle formulas**.

By methods similar to those used in Chapters 1 and 2 you can use these Basic Identities to prove additional identities.

Example   Prove the identity $\tan \dfrac{\theta}{2} = \pm\sqrt{\dfrac{1 - \cos \theta}{1 + \cos \theta}}$.

Solution   Since $\tan \dfrac{\theta}{2} = \dfrac{\sin \dfrac{\theta}{2}}{\cos \dfrac{\theta}{2}} = \dfrac{\pm\sqrt{\frac{1}{2}(1 - \cos \theta)}}{\pm\sqrt{\frac{1}{2}(1 + \cos \theta)}}$, we have

$$\tan \dfrac{\theta}{2} = \pm\sqrt{\dfrac{1 - \cos \theta}{1 + \cos \theta}} .$$

Exercises 5–3

Prove each identity.

A **1.** $\cot \theta = \dfrac{\csc \theta}{\sec \theta}$

2. $\tan \theta = \dfrac{\sec \theta}{\csc \theta}$

3. $\cos^2 \theta(1 + \tan^2 \theta) = 1$

4. $\sin^2 \theta(1 + \cot^2 \theta) = 1$

5. $(\sec \theta - \tan \theta)(\sec \theta + \tan \theta) = 1$

6. $(\csc \theta - \cot \theta)(\csc \theta + \cot \theta) = 1$

7. $\dfrac{\sin \theta \cos \theta}{1 - 2 \cos^2 \theta} = \dfrac{1}{\tan \theta - \cot \theta}$

8. $\dfrac{1 - \tan^2 \theta}{1 + \tan^2 \theta} = 1 - 2 \sin^2 \theta$

9. $\tan \theta = \dfrac{1 - \cos 2\theta}{\sin 2\theta}$

10. $\cot \theta = \dfrac{\sin 2\theta}{1 - \cos 2\theta}$

11. $\csc^2 \dfrac{\theta}{2} = \dfrac{2 \sec \theta}{\sec \theta - 1}$

12. $2 \cos^2 \dfrac{\theta}{2} = \dfrac{1 + \sec \theta}{\sec \theta}$

13. $\cos^3 \theta - \sin^3 \theta = (\cos \theta - \sin \theta)(1 + \frac{1}{2} \sin 2\theta)$

14. $\cot^2 \theta - \cos^2 \theta = \cot^2 \theta \cos^2 \theta$

B 15. $\sin (\theta_2 + \theta_1) + \sin (\theta_2 - \theta_1) = 2 \sin \theta_2 \cos \theta_1$

16. $\sin (\theta_2 + \theta_1) - \sin (\theta_2 - \theta_1) = 2 \cos \theta_2 \sin \theta_1$

17. $\cos (\theta_2 + \theta_1) + \cos (\theta_2 - \theta_1) = 2 \cos \theta_2 \cos \theta_1$

18. $\cos (\theta_2 + \theta_1) - \cos (\theta_2 - \theta_1) = -2 \sin \theta_2 \sin \theta_1$

19. $\dfrac{\sin \theta_1 - \sin \theta_2}{\cos \theta_1 + \cos \theta_2} = \tan \left(\dfrac{\theta_1 - \theta_2}{2} \right)$

20. $\dfrac{\sin \theta_1 + \sin \theta_2}{\cos \theta_1 + \cos \theta_2} = \tan \left(\dfrac{\theta_1 + \theta_2}{2} \right)$

Values for Trigonometric Functions

5–4 *Tables for Trigonometric Functions*

To obtain finer units of angle measurement, a degree is commonly subdivided into 60 equal parts, each of which is called one **minute**. A minute is denoted by the superscript ′. Similarly, a minute is subdivided into 60 **seconds**. A second is denoted by the superscript ″. Thus, we read 48°11′15″ as "forty-eight degrees, eleven minutes, and fifteen seconds."

Approximate values for the trigonometric functions in degree and minute measure can be found from Table 2, page 392. In the left-hand column of this table, reading from top to bottom, measures of angles from 0°00′ to 45°00′ are listed at intervals of 10′. In the right-hand column, reading from bottom to top, measures of angles from 45°00′ to 90°00′ are listed at similar intervals. The remaining columns in the table contain approximations to four significant digits for the corresponding values of the six trigonometric functions.

To find an approximate value for a trigonometric function of an angle with measure given in degrees and minutes:

1. Locate the measure of the angle in either the left-hand or right-hand column.

2. Read horizontally across the table from the angle measure to the appropriate column, which can be identified from the top row if the angle measure is listed in the left-hand column, and from the bottom row if the angle measure is listed in the right-hand column.

Example 1   Find sec 61°20′.

Solution   We find 61°20′ listed in the right-hand column of Table 2. Reading horizontally across, we find, in the column labeled *sec* at the bottom, the required value, 2.085. Therefore,

$$\sec 61°20′ \doteq 2.085.$$

In the event the measure of an angle falls between two tabular entries, you can use *linear interpolation* to approximate a function value. Figure 5–12 shows a schematic depiction of the graph of a trigonometric function f, where θ_1 and θ_2 denote two different tabular values of θ. To find $f(\theta_k)$, where θ_k has a degree measure between θ_1 and θ_2, you must find the point $(\theta_k, f(\theta_k))$ on the graph of f and read the value of $f(\theta_k)$ from the vertical axis. Because the straight line

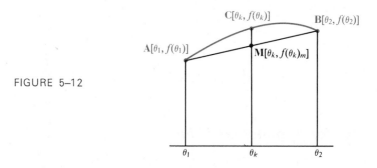

FIGURE 5–12

joining points **A** and **B** can be assumed to be reasonably close to the curve joining these points (the scale in Figure 5–12 is distorted to make a clearer picture), the second coordinate of point **M** on line $\overline{\mathbf{AB}}$, $f(\theta_k)_m$, is a very good approximation to $f(\theta_k)$. Moreover, you can compute $f(\theta_k)_m$ very easily by using the slope of $\overline{\mathbf{AB}}$. You should first recall, from your earlier study of algebra, that if (x_1, y_1) and (x_2, y_2) are any two points on a line not parallel to the y-axis, then the slope m of the line is given by

$$m = \frac{y_2 - y_1}{x_2 - x_1}.$$

Then, since

$$\text{slope of } \overline{\mathbf{AM}} = \text{slope of } \overline{\mathbf{AB}},$$

you know that

$$\frac{f(\theta_k)_m - f(\theta_1)}{\theta_k - \theta_1} = \frac{f(\theta_2) - f(\theta_1)}{\theta_2 - \theta_1}. \tag{1}$$

Being given θ_1, θ_2, and θ_k, you find $f(\theta_1)$ and $f(\theta_2)$ in the table, and then solve Equation (1) for $f(\theta_k)_m$ to obtain the desired approximation to $f(\theta_k)$.

Example 2   Find an approximation to sin 15°23′.

Solution   Note that in Table 2 we can find values for sin θ when θ has degree measure 15°20′ or 15°30′. Therefore, we know the coordinates of **A** and **B**. What we wish to find is the second

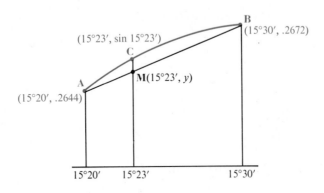

coordinate y for point **M** to use as an approximation to the second coordinate of point **C**. We have

$$\text{slope of } \overline{\mathbf{AM}} = \text{slope of } \overline{\mathbf{AB}},$$

$$\frac{y - 0.2644}{15°23′ - 15°20′} = \frac{0.2672 - 0.2644}{15°30′ - 15°20′}$$

$$\frac{y - 0.2644}{3′} = \frac{0.0028}{10′}$$

$$y = \tfrac{3}{10}(0.0028) + 0.2644$$

$$y = 0.00084 + 0.2644 \doteq 0.2652.$$

Hence, sin 15°23′ ≐ 0.2652.

This process can be shortened by arranging the values of θ and $f(\theta)$ in convenient tabular form as shown in Example 3.

Example 3   Find an approximation to sec 76°47′.

Solution   Arrange the facts as shown.

$$10' \left[7' \begin{bmatrix} \begin{array}{c|c} \theta & \sec \theta \\ \hline 76°40′ & 4.336 \\ 76°47′ & y \\ 76°50′ & 4.390 \end{array} \end{bmatrix} d \right] 0.054$$

Then $d = \tfrac{7}{10}(0.054) \doteq 0.0378$. We now add $d \doteq 0.0378$ to sec 76°40′ ≐ 4.336 to obtain

$$\text{sec } 76°47′ \doteq 0.0378 + 4.336 \doteq 4.374.$$

In most cases, interpolation such as is shown in the preceding example can be accomplished mentally. If interpolation is used to find an approximation to a value of a decreasing function, then the difference $[f(\theta_2) - f(\theta_1)]$ will be negative, and hence d will be negative. Notice that the value of y always lies between the given trigonometric values.

Example 4   Find an approximation to csc 34°22'.

Solution   Arrange the facts as shown.

$$
\begin{array}{c|c}
\theta & \csc \theta \\
\hline
10'\left[\,2'\begin{bmatrix}34°20' \\ 34°22' \\ 34°30'\end{bmatrix}\right. & \left.\begin{bmatrix}1.773 \\ y \\ 1.766\end{bmatrix}d\right]-0.007
\end{array}
$$

Then $d = \frac{2}{10}(-0.007) = -0.0014$.

Therefore, csc 34°22' $\doteq (-0.0014) + 1.773 \doteq 1.772$.

Of course, you can also use linear interpolation to find a degree measure for θ when given a value $f(\theta)$.

Example 5   Find an approximate measure, between 0° and 90°, for an angle θ for which $\tan \theta = 1.379$.

Solution   We first look for 1.379 in the tangent column of Table 2. We find that it is not listed, but that it lies between two entries, 1.376 and 1.385. We can arrange the facts in the usual tabular form.

$$
\begin{array}{c|c}
\theta & \tan \theta \\
\hline
10'\left[\,k\begin{bmatrix}54°00' \\ x \\ 54°10'\end{bmatrix}\right. & \left.\begin{bmatrix}1.376 \\ 1.379\end{bmatrix}0.003\atop 1.385\right]0.009
\end{array}
$$

Then $k = \dfrac{0.003}{0.009}(10') = \frac{1}{3}(10') \doteq 03'$.

Therefore, $\theta = 54° + k \doteq 54°03'$.

Table 3 on page 397 can be used to find values for trigonometric functions when the unit of angle measure is the radian. Values are shown at intervals of 0.01^R. Notice that, unlike Table 2, this table can *not* be read from both sides. This is because $\dfrac{\pi}{2}^R$ does not correspond to an integral multiple of 0.01^R.

Example 6 Find an approximation to csc 1.447^R.

Solution We have

$$0.010 \left[0.007 \begin{bmatrix} 1.440 \\ 1.447 \\ 1.450 \end{bmatrix} \begin{array}{|c} \csc \theta \\ \hline 1.009 \\ y \\ 1.007 \end{array} \, d \right] -0.002$$

$$\theta \qquad \csc \theta$$

Then $d = \dfrac{0.007}{0.010}\,(-0.002) \doteq -0.0014$.

Therefore, csc $1.447^R \doteq -0.0014 + 1.009 \doteq 1.008$.

Example 7 Find an approximate radian measure for an angle θ for which $\sin \theta = 0.6939$.

Solution We have:

$$\theta \qquad \sin \theta$$

$$0.010^R \left[k \begin{bmatrix} 0.760 \\ x \\ 0.770 \end{bmatrix} \begin{array}{|c} 0.6889 \\ 0.6939 \\ 0.6961 \end{array} -0.0050 \right] -0.0072$$

Then $k = \dfrac{-0.0050}{-0.0072}\,(0.010^R) \doteq 0.007^R$.

Therefore, $\theta \doteq 0.767^R$.

Exercises 5–4

Find a four-significant-digit approximation to each of the following.

A
1. cos 58°40′	**5.** csc 74°30′	**9.** cot 0.88^R	**13.** sec 1.003^R
2. tan 62°50′	**6.** sin 69°47′	**10.** sin 1.14^R	**14.** cos 1.502^R
3. sec 23°30′	**7.** cos 24°14′	**11.** tan 0.742^R	**15.** tan 1.323^R
4. cot 84°10′	**8.** sin 55°12′	**12.** cos 1.333^R	**16.** sin 1.068^R

Find $m°(\theta)$ to the nearest minute, if the function value for θ is as given.

17. $\cos \theta = 0.8056$ **21.** $\csc \theta = 1.832$

18. $\sin \theta = 0.3118$ **22.** $\sec \theta = 1.420$

19. $\tan \theta = 3.224$ **23.** $\sin \theta = 0.30987$

20. $\cot \theta = 3.500$ **24.** $\cos \theta = 0.38088$

25–32. Find $m^R(\theta)$ to the nearest hundredth for each angle θ in Exercises 17–24.

Find each of the following, using Table 2 as needed.

33. $\sin 195°$ **35.** $\tan 572°$ **37.** $\sec (-123°)$

34. $\cos 275°$ **36.** $\cot 602°$ **38.** $\cos (-211°)$

B **39.** When linear interpolation is used to find an approximate value for $\sin \theta$, where $0° < \theta < 90°$, would you expect the approximation to be greater than or less than the actual value of $\sin \theta$? Why?

40. When linear interpolation is used to find an approximate value for θ, where $0 < \sin \theta < 1$ and θ is an angle with terminal side in Quadrant I, would you expect the approximation to be greater than or less than the actual value of θ? Why?

C **41.** When linear interpolation is used to find an approximate value for $\sin \theta$, where would you expect to obtain the closer approximation: when θ is close to $0°$ or when θ is close to $90°$? Why?

42. Answer the questions in Exercise 39 when $\sin \theta$ is replaced with $\tan \theta$.

43. Answer the questions in Exercise 40 when $\sin \theta$ is replaced with $\tan \theta$.

44. Answer the questions in Exercise 41 when $\sin \theta$ is replaced with $\tan \theta$.

5–5   *Describing an Angle by Its Terminal Side*

In preceding sections of this chapter, we were concerned with determining one or more trigonometric values of an angle θ whose measure, in either degrees or radians, was known to us; and, conversely, with determining the measure of θ given one of its trigonometric values.

Instead of being given either the measure of an angle or one of its trigonometric values, you may be given other information about θ which will enable you to find either its measure or its trigonometric values.

Suppose θ is an angle in standard position in an *xy*-coordinate plane, with vertex at the center of the unit circle $x^2 + y^2 = 1$. Recall that the terminal side of θ intersects the unit circle at a point **A** with coordinates $(\cos \theta, \sin \theta)$. If $\mathbf{A}'(x, y)$ is *any* point (other than the origin) on the terminal side of θ and r is the distance from point $\mathbf{A}'(x, y)$ to point $(0, 0)$, then $\triangle\mathbf{ABO}$ is similar to $\triangle\mathbf{A'B'O}$, as shown in Figure 5–13.

FIGURE 5–13

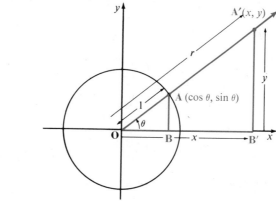

Then by the properties of similar triangles,

$$\frac{\mathbf{OB'}}{\mathbf{OA'}} = \frac{\mathbf{OB}}{\mathbf{OA}}, \quad \text{or} \quad \frac{x}{r} = \frac{\cos \theta}{1}.$$

Similarly,

$$\frac{\mathbf{B'A'}}{\mathbf{OA'}} = \frac{\mathbf{BA}}{\mathbf{OA}}, \quad \text{or} \quad \frac{y}{r} = \frac{\sin \theta}{1}.$$

By the Pythagorean theorem you know that

$$r = \sqrt{x^2 + y^2}.$$

Therefore:

$$\cos \theta = \frac{x}{r} = \frac{x}{\sqrt{x^2 + y^2}}; \quad x = r \cos \theta \qquad (1)$$

and

$$\sin \theta = \frac{y}{r} = \frac{y}{\sqrt{x^2 + y^2}}; \quad y = r \sin \theta \qquad (2)$$

Example   If the terminal side of θ contains the point $(-3, -4)$, find:
(a) $\cos \theta$ (b) $\tan \theta$ (c) the degree measure of θ

Solution   (a) Here $x = -3$ and $y = -4$, so that

$$\cos \theta = \frac{x}{\sqrt{x^2 + y^2}} = \frac{-3}{\sqrt{9 + 16}} = -\frac{3}{5}.$$

(b) Using the fact that

$$\sin \theta = \frac{y}{\sqrt{x^2 + y^2}} = \frac{-4}{\sqrt{9 + 16}} = -\frac{4}{5}$$

and the fact that $\cos \theta = -\frac{3}{5}$ (as determined in part (a)), we have

$$\tan \theta = \frac{\sin \theta}{\cos \theta} = \frac{-\frac{4}{5}}{-\frac{3}{5}} = \frac{4}{3}.$$

(c) To find the degree measure of θ, we can use any of the facts

$$\cos \theta = -\frac{3}{5} = -0.6000, \qquad \sin \theta = -\frac{4}{5} = -0.8000,$$

$$\tan \theta = \frac{4}{3} \doteq 1.333,$$

together with the reference-angle concept and the fact that the point $(-3, -4)$ on the terminal side of θ lies in Quadrant III. Arranging the values from Table 2 in tabular form, we have

θ	$\sin \theta$
53°00′	0.7986
α	0.8000
53°10′	0.8004

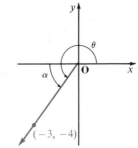

from which we obtain

$$\alpha \doteq \tfrac{14}{18}(10') + 53°00' \doteq 53°08'$$

and $\theta \doteq 180° + \alpha \doteq 180° + 53°08' = 233°08'$.

Of course, it follows from (1) and (2) on page 159 that

$$\tan \theta = \frac{y}{x},$$

so that part (b) of the Example could be accomplished directly using this equation. Similarly, you can show that

▲ $$\cot \theta = \frac{x}{y}, \qquad \sec \theta = \frac{\sqrt{x^2 + y^2}}{x}, \qquad \text{and} \qquad \csc \theta = \frac{\sqrt{x^2 + y^2}}{y}.$$

Exercises 5–5

Determine $\cos \theta$, $\sin \theta$, $\tan \theta$, and the degree measure of θ, where $0° \le \theta < 360°$ and θ is in standard position with its terminal side containing the given point.

A **1.** $(-1, 1)$ **4.** $(8, -15)$ **7.** $(1, -3)$

2. $(-2, 2\sqrt{3})$ **5.** $(2, 0)$ **8.** $(2, 3)$

3. $(6, 8)$ **6.** $(0, -3)$ **9.** $(1, -\sqrt{3})$

For each given value of r and θ (in standard position) find the xy-coordinates of the point of intersection of the terminal side of θ and the circle $x^2 + y^2 = r^2$.

10. $r = 1$, $\theta = 60°$ **14.** $r = 10$, $\theta = -420°$

11. $r = 2$, $\theta = 120°$ **15.** $r = 5$, $\theta = 810°$

12. $r = 4$, $\theta = 45°$ **16.** $r = 10$, $\theta = 22°$

13. $r = 4$, $\theta = -150°$ **17.** $r = 3$, $\theta = -40°$

Determine $\cos \theta$ and $\sin \theta$ if θ is an angle in standard position having the graph of the given relation as terminal side.

B **18.** $\{(x, y): x + y = 0, x \ge 0\}$ **21.** $\{(x, y): x = 0, y \ge 0\}$

19. $\{(x, y): x - y = 0, x \le 0\}$ **22.** $\{(x, y): y = 0, x \le 0\}$

20. $\{(x, y): x - 2y = 0, y \le 0\}$ **23.** $\{(x, y): \sqrt{3}\,x - y = 0, x \ge 0\}$

5–6 *Trigonometric Equations and Inverse Functions*

In Section 4–1, we found that the circular function cos had a principal inverse function Cos^{-1}, or Arccos, with domain $\{x: |x| \le 1\}$ and range $\{y: 0 \le y \le \pi\}$.

Similarly, a principal inverse function Cos^{-1}, or Arccos, can be defined for the trigonometric function cos. This function has the same domain, $\{x: |x| \le 1\}$, but its range is $\{\theta: 0° \le \theta \le 180°\}$, or $\{\theta: 0^R \le \theta \le \pi^R\}$. Thus

▲ $$\text{Cos}^{-1} = \{(x, \theta): x = \cos \theta, 0° \le \theta \le 180°\}.$$

In fact, you can define a principal inverse function for each of the six trigonometric functions exactly as in Sections 4–1 and 4–2 for circular functions. You can determine bounds for the range in each case by considering the real-number bounds for the range of the corresponding circular function to be the measure in radians of an angle θ, and then converting from radian measure to degree measure. The properties of inverse trigonometric functions parallel those of their circular counterparts.

The notation $\text{Cos}^{-1} x$ can be read, "the angle (in the interval $0° \leq \theta \leq 180°$) whose cosine is x."

Example 1   Find $\tan [\text{Cos}^{-1} (-\frac{3}{5})]$.

Solution

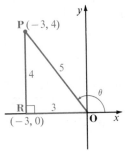

Because the range of Cos^{-1} encompasses only the angles θ in the interval $0° \leq \theta \leq 180°$, $\text{Cos}^{-1} (-\frac{3}{5})$ must have terminal side in the second quadrant, as shown. In right $\triangle POR$, $d(\overline{OR}) = 3$, $d(\overline{OP}) = 5$, and by the Pythagorean theorem, $d(\overline{RP}) = 4$.

Therefore, $(-3, 4)$ is one particular point on the terminal side of θ, so that, by the methods of Section 5–5, $\tan \theta = \dfrac{4}{-3} = -\frac{4}{3}$. That is,

$\tan [\text{Cos}^{-1} (-\frac{3}{5})] = -\frac{4}{3}$.

By referring to the figure in Example 1 and using the results of Section 5–5, you will note that we have a situation in which $x = -3$, $y = 4$, and $r = 5$. You can deduce immediately that

$$\sin \left[\text{Cos}^{-1}\left(-\frac{3}{5}\right)\right] = \frac{y}{r} = \frac{4}{5},$$

$$\cos \left[\text{Cos}^{-1}\left(-\frac{3}{5}\right)\right] = \frac{x}{r} = -\frac{3}{5},$$

$$\cot \left[\text{Cos}^{-1}\left(-\frac{3}{5}\right)\right] = \frac{x}{y} = -\frac{3}{4},$$

$$\sec \left[\text{Cos}^{-1}\left(-\frac{3}{5}\right)\right] = \frac{r}{x} = -\frac{5}{3},$$

$$\csc \left[\text{Cos}^{-1}\left(-\frac{3}{5}\right)\right] = \frac{r}{y} = \frac{5}{4}.$$

Example 2   Find all angles θ, $0° \leq \theta < 360°$, for which

$$2 \sec^2 \theta - 5 \sec \theta + 2 = 0.$$

Solution   If the left-hand member of this equation is factored, we have

$$(2 \sec \theta - 1)(\sec \theta - 2) = 0,$$

which is true for all values of θ in the replacement set of the given equation. Then either

$$2 \sec \theta - 1 = 0 \quad \text{or} \quad \sec \theta - 2 = 0.$$

Solving these equations for θ, we find, respectively,

$$\sec \theta = \tfrac{1}{2}, \quad \text{or} \quad \sec \theta = 2.$$

Since $\cos \theta = \dfrac{1}{\sec \theta}$, the general solution set is

$$\{\theta : \cos \theta = 2\} \cup \{\theta : \cos \theta = \tfrac{1}{2}\}.$$

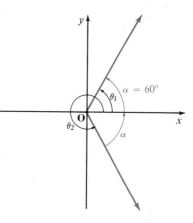

Because $|\cos \theta| \le 1$ for all angles θ, $\{\theta : \cos \theta = 2\} = \emptyset$, so that the general solution set is $\{\theta : \cos \theta = \tfrac{1}{2}\}$.

For a reference angle, we use $\alpha = 60°$, since $\cos 60° = \tfrac{1}{2}$. Because $\cos \theta$ is positive in the first and fourth quadrants, we have the situation shown in the sketch, in which

$$\theta_1 = 0° + 60° = 60°$$
and
$$\theta_2 = 360° - 60° = 300°.$$

Therefore, $\{60°, 300°\}$ is the desired solution set.

Exercises 5–6

State the domain and range for each of the given inverse trigonometric functions.

A **1.** Sin^{-1} **3.** Tan^{-1} **5.** Csc^{-1}
   2. Cos^{-1} **4.** Cot^{-1} **6.** Sec^{-1}

Find the value of each of the following.

   7. $\mathrm{Cot}^{-1}(\csc 90°)$ **9.** $\sin (\mathrm{Tan}^{-1} \sqrt{3})$ **11.** $\mathrm{Sin}^{-1} (\tan 45°)$
   8. $\mathrm{Sin}^{-1} (\cos 30°)$ **10.** $\cos (\mathrm{Sin}^{-1} 1)$ **12.** $\mathrm{Cos}^{-1} (\cot 45°)$

Solve each of the following for all angles θ, $0° \leq \theta < 360°$.

13. $\tan^2 \theta + \sqrt{3} \tan \theta = 0$

14. $\cos^2 \theta = \cos \theta$

15. $\cot^2 \theta - 3 \csc \theta + 3 = 0$

16. $\tan 2\theta = \cot \theta$

17. $\cot \theta = \tan (2\theta - 270°)$

18. $\sin \theta = \sin (2\theta - 180°)$

B **19.** $2 \cos^2 \theta \sin^2 \theta - \cos \theta \sin \theta = 0$

20. $\sec^2 2\theta + \tan 2\theta = 1$

Find the cos, sin, and tan values of each of the following angles.

21. $\text{Sec}^{-1} 2$

22. $\text{Cos}^{-1} \frac{2}{3}$

23. $\text{Sin}^{-1} \frac{1}{2}$

24. $\text{Sin}^{-1} \left(-\frac{2}{5}\right)$

Evaluate each of the following expressions.

C **25.** $\tan \left(180° + \text{Arcsin} \dfrac{\sqrt{2}}{2}\right)$

26. $\cos [\text{Arcsin} (-\frac{1}{2}) + \text{Arccos} \frac{5}{13}]$

27. $\cos (\frac{1}{2} \text{Arctan} \frac{3}{4})$

28. $\sin (\frac{1}{2} \text{Arctan} \frac{3}{5})$

The Solution of Triangles

5–7 *Right Triangles*

As remarked in Section 5–1, the study of the trigonometric functions originated in connection with geometrical problems involving triangles. Right triangles

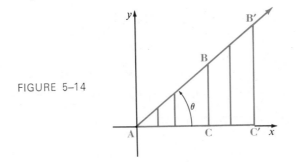

FIGURE 5–14

have properties that can be related directly to these functions. Figure 5–14 shows a family of similar right triangles, all members of which have the acute angle θ in common. The lengths of the corresponding sides of these triangles must be proportional; in particular, the following proportions hold:

$$\frac{d(\overline{\mathbf{AC}})}{d(\overline{\mathbf{AB}})} = \frac{d(\overline{\mathbf{AC'}})}{d(\overline{\mathbf{AB'}})}, \tag{1}$$

$$\frac{d(\overline{\mathbf{CB}})}{d(\overline{\mathbf{AB}})} = \frac{d(\overline{\mathbf{C'B'}})}{d(\overline{\mathbf{AB'}})}. \tag{2}$$

If you refer back to Figure 5–13 of Section 5–5, you will observe that each of the ratios in (1), above, is equal to the ratio $\dfrac{x}{r}$, and each of those in (2) is equal to $\dfrac{y}{r}$. By Equations (1) and (2), page 159, however,

$$\frac{x}{r} = \cos\theta, \qquad \frac{y}{r} = \sin\theta.$$

Thus, for θ an acute angle of any right triangle, you have:

▲
$$\cos\theta = \frac{\text{length of side adjacent to }\theta}{\text{length of hypotenuse}} \tag{3}$$

$$\sin\theta = \frac{\text{length of side opposite }\theta}{\text{length of hypotenuse}} \tag{4}$$

Similarly, for θ an acute angle in any right triangle, you have:

▲
$$\tan\theta = \frac{\text{length of side opposite }\theta}{\text{length of side adjacent to }\theta} \tag{5}$$

$$\cot\theta = \frac{\text{length of side adjacent to }\theta}{\text{length of side opposite }\theta} \tag{6}$$

$$\csc\theta = \frac{\text{length of hypotenuse}}{\text{length of side opposite }\theta} \tag{7}$$

$$\sec\theta = \frac{\text{length of hypotenuse}}{\text{length of side adjacent to }\theta} \tag{8}$$

You can use these relationships to "solve right triangles." That is, you can find values for all the sides and angles of a right triangle, provided you know the lengths of two sides or the length of one side and the measure of an angle other than the right angle.

Example 1   Solve the given right triangle.

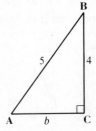

Solution   Since we know the lengths of two sides of △**ABC**, we can use the Pythagorean theorem to find the length of the remaining side. Thus,

$$b = \sqrt{5^2 - 4^2} = \sqrt{25 - 16} = \sqrt{9} = 3.$$

Then, from any of the relationships (3)–(8), we can find an approximation for *A* or *B*. Using (4), we have

$$\sin A = \tfrac{4}{5} = 0.8000.$$

Using Table 2, we find that $A \doteq 53°08'$. Since angles *A* and *B* are complementary,

$$B = 90° - A,$$
$$B \doteq 90° - 53°08' = 36°52'.$$

Hence, the missing parts of the triangle are

$$b = 3, \quad A \doteq 53°08', \quad \text{and} \quad B \doteq 36°52'.$$

(The angle *C*, of course, is a known angle measuring 90°.)

Example 2   Solve the given right triangle.

Solution   From relationship (7),

$$\csc 25°30' = \frac{c}{8},$$

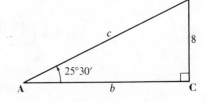

so that

$$c = 8(\csc 25°30').$$

From Table 2, $\csc 25°30' \doteq 2.323$, so

$$c \doteq 8(2.323) = 18.584.$$

We could now find an approximation for *b* by means of the Pythagorean theorem, but it is perhaps easier to use relationship (6), from which we have

$$\cot 25°30' = \frac{b}{8},$$

so that

$$b = 8 \cot 25°30'.$$

Again, from Table 2, cot $25°30' \doteq 2.097$, so

$$b \doteq 8(2.097) = 16.776.$$

Since $B = 90° - A$, we find

$$B = 90° - 25°30' = 64°30'.$$

Thus the parts of $\triangle ABC$ that were not given are (to the nearest hundredth of a unit of length and the nearest minute of angle measure)

$$c \doteq 18.58, \qquad b \doteq 16.78, \qquad \text{and} \qquad B = 64°30'.$$

When solving right triangles, it is a good idea to check that your results are correct within the range of accuracy of the computation. You can use the Pythagorean theorem and the theorem that the sum of the measures of the angles in any triangle equals 180° to do this.

When the trigonometric functions of the angles of a right triangle are considered in conjunction with the unit circle (Figure 5–15, below), interesting geometric representations of the trigonometric functions become evident. For example, from right triangles **OAB** and **OCD** you can verify that

$$d(\overline{BA}) = \sin\theta, \qquad d(\overline{DC}) = \tan\theta,$$
$$d(\overline{OB}) = \cos\theta, \qquad d(\overline{OC}) = \sec\theta.$$

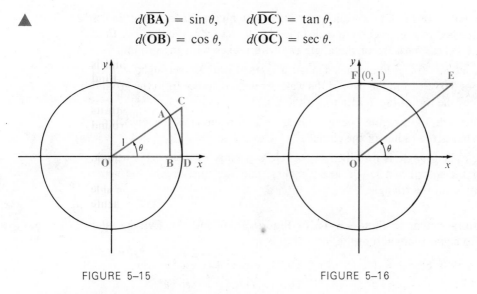

FIGURE 5–15   FIGURE 5–16

The remaining two trigonometric functions, $\cot\theta$ and $\csc\theta$, can be represented geometrically as lengths of line segments, as shown in Figure 5–16. The side $\overline{FE}$ of $\triangle OFE$ is tangent to the unit circle at $F(0, 1)$. Since $m°(E) = m°(\theta)$, you have

$$d(\overline{FE}) = \cot\theta, \qquad d(\overline{OE}) = \csc\theta.$$

When solving triangles we shall assume the given data are exact and, unless otherwise stated, shall find answers to the nearest hundredth of a unit for lengths and the nearest minute for angle measures. In the exercises in the remainder of this chapter, we shall specify how answers should be stated.

Exercises 5–7

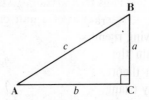

In Exercises 1–8, solve the right triangle when given the following parts. Find answers to the nearest hundredth or the nearest minute. Assume the data are exact.

A 1. $b = 12$, $c = 13$ **5.** $c = 20$, $B = 64°15'$

 2. $a = 9$, $b = 12$ **6.** $b = 10$, $B = 80°25'$

 3. $c = 13$, $A = 36°$ **7.** $c = 20$, $a = 10$

 4. $b = 6$, $A = 53°10'$ **8.** $c = 20$, $b = 15$

Find answers to the nearest unit or the nearest degree.

9. A guy wire holding a radio-transmitter antenna is 70 feet long and is attached to the antenna at a distance of 50 feet from the ground. Find the degree measure of the angle the wire makes with the ground.

10. A ladder 30 feet long leans against a vertical wall 30 feet high, with its foot 5.0 feet from the base of the wall. At what distance from the ground does the top of the ladder touch the wall?

11. One side of a regular octagon inscribed in a circle is 8 inches long. What is the radius of the circle?

12. A right triangle is inscribed in a circle of radius 10 inches. If one side of the inscribed triangle is 8.0 inches, find the measure of the acute angles of the triangle.

Use a figure similar to Figure 5–15 or Figure 5–16 and the Pythagorean theorem to show that each of the following is true.

13. $\sin^2 \theta + \cos^2 \theta = 1$ **15.** $1 + \cot^2 \theta = \csc^2 \theta$

14. $\sin^2 \theta = 1 - \cos^2 \theta$ **16.** $1 + \tan^2 \theta = \sec^2 \theta$

Use a sketch of a right triangle to help you do Exercises 17–22 for a first-quadrant angle θ.

Example   If $\sin \theta = x$, find an expression for $\sec \theta$ in terms of x.

Solution

If you let the hypotenuse of the right triangle be of length 1, you have the figure shown at the right. By the Pythagorean theorem, then, the remaining side must measure $\sqrt{1 - x^2}$. From the triangle and relationship (8), you therefore have

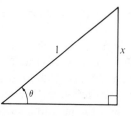

$$\sec \theta = \frac{1}{\sqrt{1 - x^2}} \cdot$$

B **17.** If $\cos \theta = x$, find an expression for $\csc \theta$ in terms of x.

18. If $\sec \theta = x$, find an expression for $\sin \theta$ in terms of x.

19. If $\sin \theta = x$, find an expression for $\cot \theta$ in terms of x.

20. If $\cos \theta = x$, find an expression for $\tan \theta$ in terms of x.

21. If $\cot \theta = \sqrt{1 - x^2}$, $x > 0$, find an expression for $\sin \theta$ in terms of x.

22. If $\sin \theta = \sqrt{1 - x^2}$, $x > 0$, find an expression for $\tan \theta$ in terms of x.

Unless otherwise stated, find answers to the nearest foot.

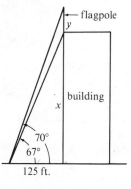

C **23.** A flagpole stands atop a tall building (which is located on level ground). From a point 125 ft. away from the base of the building, the **angles of elevation** of the top and bottom of the flagpole measure 70° and 67°, respectively. How tall is the building? How long is the flagpole?

24. From a point on the ground, the angle of elevation (see Exercise 23) of the top of a 25-foot flagpole on the roof of a building (located on level ground) is 47°, and the angle of elevation of the bottom of the pole is 45°. How tall is the building?

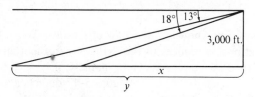

25. From the top of a mountain 3000 feet above sea level, the **angles of depression** of two ships lying in a vertical plane with the mountain top measure 18° and 13°, respectively. To the nearest 10 ft., find the distance between the ships.

26. From the top of building A, the angle of elevation of the top of building B 100 feet away is 38° and the angle of depression of the foot of B is 50°. How tall is building B?

5–8   *The Law of Cosines*

The Pythagorean theorem relates the lengths of the three sides of a right triangle. You can use the distance formula, together with Equations (1) and (2) on page 159, to find a more general relationship involving the lengths of the sides and the measures of the angles of *any* triangle.

In Figure 5–17, a triangle has been oriented so that angle θ has vertex at the origin, and side $\overline{\text{CB}}$ lies on the positive x-axis. From Equations (1) and (2), page 159, it is evident that the coordinates of point **A** must be $(b \cos \theta, b \sin \theta)$. By the distance formula, then,

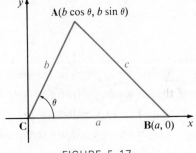

FIGURE 5–17

$$c = \sqrt{(b \cos \theta - a)^2 + (b \sin \theta - 0)^2},$$

or

$$c^2 = (b \cos \theta - a)^2 + (b \sin \theta - 0)^2.$$

Expanding the terms in the right-hand member, you obtain

$$c^2 = b^2 \cos^2 \theta - 2ab \cos \theta + a^2 + b^2 \sin^2 \theta$$
$$= a^2 + b^2 (\cos^2 \theta + \sin^2 \theta) - 2ab \cos \theta.$$

Since $\sin^2 \theta + \cos^2 \theta = 1$ for every value of θ, you therefore have

$$c^2 = a^2 + b^2 - 2ab \cos \theta.$$

Observe that, if you designate the angle θ by its vertex C, you could write this equivalently as:

▲ $$c^2 = a^2 + b^2 - 2ab \cos C \qquad (1)$$

This relationship is known as the **Law of Cosines**. When $C = 90°$, $\cos C = 0$, and this relationship reduces to the Pythagorean theorem. It also expresses the converse of the Pythagorean theorem, namely, if $c^2 = a^2 + b^2$, then $C = 90°$.

Although the triangle shown in Figure 5–17 depicts θ as an angle with terminal side in the first quadrant, the argument is perfectly general and applies to any θ, $0° < \theta < 180°$. By simply reorienting the triangle, you have the corresponding relationships:

▲ $$a^2 = b^2 + c^2 - 2bc \cos A \qquad (2)$$

$$b^2 = a^2 + c^2 - 2ac \cos B \qquad (3)$$

Example   Solve the given triangle.

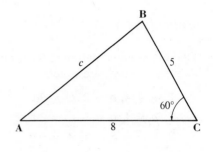

Solution   Using (1), we have

$$c^2 = 5^2 + 8^2 - 2(5)(8) \cos 60°$$
$$= 25 + 64 - 80(\tfrac{1}{2})$$
$$= 89 - 40 = 49,$$
$$c = \sqrt{49} = 7.$$

Then, to find A, we can use (2):

$$5^2 = 8^2 + 7^2 - 2(8)(7) \cos A,$$
$$25 = 64 + 49 - 16(7) \cos A.$$

Solving for $\cos A$, we find

$$\cos A = \frac{-88}{-16(7)} = \frac{11}{14} \doteq 0.7857,$$

and therefore, using Table 2,

$$A \doteq 38°13'.$$

Since

$$B = 180° - (A + C),$$
$$B \doteq 180° - (38°13' + 60°)$$
$$= 180° - 98°13' = 81°47',$$

and the missing parts of the triangle are

$$c = 7,$$
$$A \doteq 38°13',$$
$$B \doteq 81°47'.$$

In Section 5–9 you will find a way to shorten the procedure used in this example to find A. Note, however, that the Law of Cosines provides a means of completely solving *any* triangle whenever you know either two sides and the included angle or three sides.

In solving a triangle that is not a right triangle, you can check your results for the measures of the angles using $A + B + C = 180°$. You can check your results for the lengths of the sides by substituting in an equation not used in the computation or by comparing your results with a fairly accurate sketch of the given triangle.

Exercises 5–8

Find the required part of △**ABC** either to the nearest tenth or the nearest 10'.
Assume the data are exact.

A 1. $a = 4, b = 2, C = 30°, c = $ __?__   **6.** $a = 3, b = 5, c = 6, A = $ __?__

   2. $a = 1, b = 3, C = 30°, c = $ __?__   **7.** $a = 5, b = 6, c = 8, C = $ __?__

   3. $c = 6, b = 4, A = 60°, a = $ __?__   **8.** $a = 5, b = 5, c = 9, C = $ __?__

   4. $c = 3, b = 4, A = 30°, a = $ __?__   **9.** $a = 6, b = 8, C = 53°, A = $ __?__

   5. $b = 7, c = 2, A = 135°, a = $ __?__   **10.** $a = 7, b = 8, C = 10°, A = $ __?__

Find answers to the nearest tenth or the nearest 10'.

11. Two submarines starting from the same point cruise for two hours, one
covering 30 miles per hour and the other 40 miles per hour. If their courses
diverge by 40°00', how far apart are they at the end of the two hours?

12. As a pilot flying from city A to city B, a distance of 200 miles, is leaving
A, he flies 20°00' off course for 50.0 miles. How far is he then from city B?
By how much must he change his course to correct his error?

13. A parallelogram has adjacent sides of length 11 centimeters and 8
centimeters, and the measure of an included angle is 42°. Find the length
of each diagonal of the parallelogram.

14. Two points, **A** and **B**, are on opposite sides of a pond.
A third point, **C**, is located on land 86 meters from
A and 61 meters from **B**, and the triangle formed by
points **A**, **B**, and **C** is such that $C = 76°$. How far
apart are **A** and **B**?

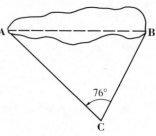

15. Two sides of a triangular plot of land measure 250 meters and 310
meters, respectively, and the angle between these sides measures 52°00'.
What is the perimeter of the plot of land?

16. A navigator locates his position, **C**, on a map.
He finds that he is 52 miles due east of Port **A**,
43 miles from Port **B**, and the distance between
the two ports is 22 miles. Find the degree
measure of C.

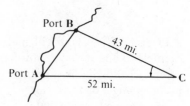

B 17. Show that $1 + \cos A = \dfrac{(b + c + a)(b + c - a)}{2bc}$.

     (*Hint:* Use the fact that $a^2 = b^2 + c^2 - 2bc \cos A$.)

   18. Show that $1 - \cos A = \dfrac{(a - b + c)(a + b - c)}{2bc}$.

19. Show that the length of the diagonal in the parallelogram **ABCD** is $\sqrt{a^2 + b^2 + 2ab \cos A}$.

20. Show that in any triangle, $a^2 + b^2 + c^2 = 2(bc \cos A + ac \cos B + ab \cos C)$.

C 21. Use the results of Exercises 17 and 18 to prove the **Half-Angle Law**:

$$\tan \frac{A}{2} = \sqrt{\frac{(a + b - c)(a - b + c)}{(b + c + a)(b + c - a)}}.$$

22. Use the results of Exercise 21 to show that if $s = \dfrac{a + b + c}{2}$ and

$r = \sqrt{\dfrac{(s - a)(s - b)(s - c)}{s}}$, then $\tan \dfrac{A}{2} = \dfrac{r}{s - a}$.

5–9   *The Area of a Triangle; The Law of Sines*

Since the area of a triangle is equal to one-half the product of the lengths of its base and its altitude, you can use Figure 5–18 to discover a means of

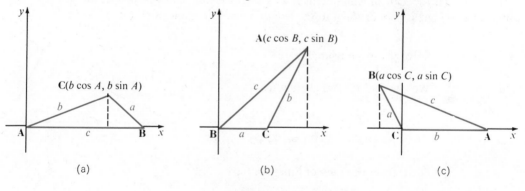

(a)   (b)   (c)

FIGURE 5–18

expressing the area of any triangle in terms of two of its sides and the sine of their included angle. In Figure 5–18, $\triangle$**ABC** is shown in three positions. In Figure 5–18(a) the base of the triangle has length c, and the length of the altitude is given by $b \sin A$; in 5–18(b), the length of the base is a and the length of the altitude is $c \sin B$; and in 5–18(c), the length of the base is b and that of the altitude is $a \sin C$. Therefore, the area of $\triangle$**ABC** is given by any one of

$$\text{Area} = \tfrac{1}{2}bc \sin A, \tag{1}$$

$$\text{Area} = \tfrac{1}{2}ac \sin B, \tag{2}$$

$$\text{Area} = \tfrac{1}{2}ab \sin C. \tag{3}$$

In general, then, the area of a triangle is equal to one-half the product of the lengths of two sides and the sine of their included angle.

Example 1   Find the area of a triangle having $a = 11$, $b = 6$, and $C = 30°$.

Solution   Using (3), we have

$$\text{Area} = \tfrac{1}{2}(11)(6) \sin 30°$$
$$= \tfrac{1}{2}(11)(6)(\tfrac{1}{2}),$$
$$\text{Area} = \tfrac{33}{2}.$$

Since (1), (2), and (3) all express the area of the same triangle, it follows that

$$\tfrac{1}{2}bc \sin A = \tfrac{1}{2}ac \sin B = \tfrac{1}{2}ab \sin C.$$

If each expression in this chain of equalities is multiplied by $\dfrac{2}{abc}$, you have

$$\frac{\sin A}{a} = \frac{\sin B}{b} = \frac{\sin C}{c} \tag{4}$$

which is called the **Law of Sines**. This law is the assertion that the sine of an angle in a triangle is proportional to the length of the side opposite it.

Example 2   Solve the given triangle.

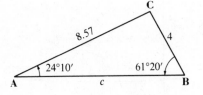

Solution   We can find C immediately from

$$C = 180° - 24°10' - 61°20'$$
$$= 180° - 85°30' = 94°30'$$

Next, from the Law of Sines we have

$$\frac{\sin 24°10'}{4} = \frac{\sin 61°20'}{8.57} = \frac{\sin 94°30'}{c},$$

which, in turn, can be solved for c by pairing either the first and third expressions or the second and third, to yield, respectively,

$$c = \frac{4 \sin 94°30'}{\sin 24°10'}$$

or

$$c = \frac{8.57 \sin 94°30'}{\sin 61°20'}.$$

Since the first of these involves 4 as a factor, in contrast to 8.57 in the second, we choose the first as simpler. From Table 2, using 85°30′ as a reference angle for 94°30′, we have

$$c = \frac{4(0.9969)}{0.4094} \doteq 9.74.$$

Computations such as those involved in this example can be somewhat simplified by using logarithms, although recently the use of electric calculators or electronic computers is replacing logarithms for this purpose.

The Law of Sines provides a means of completely solving any triangle when you know two angles and any side. It also provides a solution—insofar as there is a solution—when two sides and the angle opposite one of them are known, as will be shown in the next section.

Exercises 5–9

To the nearest tenth, find the area of the triangle with measurements as given. Assume the data are exact.

A **1.** $a = 12$, $b = 20$, $C = 30°$ **4.** $a = 25$, $c = 30$, $B = 42°$

  2. $a = 6$, $b = 15$, $C = 60°$ **5.** $a = 35$, $b = 25$, $C = 150°$

  3. $b = 18$, $c = 40$, $A = 28°$ **6.** $a = 40$, $b = 46$, $C = 135°$

Find the required part of $\triangle$**ABC** either to the nearest tenth or the nearest 10′. Assume the data are exact.

  7. $A = 60°$, $B = 45°$, $a = 6$, $b = \underline{\ ?\ }$ **10.** $C = 135°$, $a = 8$, $c = 16$, $A = \underline{\ ?\ }$

  8. $A = 45°$, $B = 30°$, $b = 30$, $a = \underline{\ ?\ }$ **11.** $\sin B = \frac{1}{4}$, $a = 12$, $b = 28$, $A = \underline{\ ?\ }$

  9. $A = 30°$, $a = 25$, $b = 20$, $B = \underline{\ ?\ }$ **12.** $\sin A = \frac{4}{5}$, $a = 18$, $b = 6$, $B = \underline{\ ?\ }$

Find answers to the nearest tenth.

  13. Two lighthouses **D** and **E** are located 12.0 miles apart. A ship is observed between the two at point **F**, and an observer at lighthouse **D** notes that $\angle$**FDE** measures 70°30′. An observer in lighthouse **E** notes that $\angle$**FED** measures 23°50′. How far is the ship from each lighthouse?

  14. An isosceles triangle has base of length 24.0. If the vertex angle measures 54°00′, what is the perimeter of the triangle?

  15. A tree grows vertically on the side of a hill that slopes upward from the horizontal by 8°00′. When the angle of elevation of the sun measures 20°00′, the shadow of the tree falls 42.0 ft. down the hill. How tall is the tree?

16. A surveyor observes that the angle of elevation (from the horizontal) from a point on a hill to the top of a tower on top of the hill measures 48°00′, and from the same point the angle of elevation to the bottom of the tower measures 37°00′. If the tower is 300 meters tall, how far is the surveyor from the bottom of the tower?

B 17. Show that the area of a triangle can be given by

$$\text{Area} = \frac{b^2 \sin A \sin C}{2 \sin B}.$$

(*Hint:* Begin with Area $= \frac{1}{2}bc \sin A$.)

18. Show that in $\triangle ABC$, $\dfrac{a - b}{b} = \dfrac{\sin A - \sin B}{\sin B}$.

$\left(\textit{Hint: Start with } \dfrac{a}{b} = \dfrac{\sin A}{\sin B}.\right)$

19. Show that in $\triangle ABC$, $\dfrac{a + b}{b} = \dfrac{\sin A + \sin B}{\sin B}$.

20. Show that in $\triangle ABC$, $\dfrac{a - b}{a + b} = \dfrac{\sin A - \sin B}{\sin A + \sin B}$.

21. Show that in $\triangle ABC$, $\dfrac{a - b}{a + b} = \dfrac{\tan\left(\dfrac{A - B}{2}\right)}{\tan\left(\dfrac{A + B}{2}\right)}$.

This relationship is known as the **Law of Tangents.** (*Hint:* Use the results of Exercise 20, above, and Exercises 20 and 21, page 153.)

C 22. Show that the area of a triangle **ABC** can be given by

$$\text{Area} = bc \sin \frac{A}{2} \cos \frac{A}{2}.$$

23. Use the results of Exercise 22, the half-angle formulas, and the results of Exercises 17 and 18 on page 172 to prove that for any triangle **ABC**,

$$(\text{Area})^2 = \frac{(a + b + c)(b + c - a)(a + b - c)(a - b + c)}{16}.$$

24. Use the results of Exercise 23 to prove **Heron's Formula** for the area of a triangle **ABC**: Area $= \sqrt{s(s - a)(s - b)(s - c)}$, where $s = \dfrac{a + b + c}{2}$.

5–10 *The Ambiguous Case*

If all that you know about a triangle is the length of two of its sides and the measure of an angle opposite one of them, you may be able to find one triangle, two triangles, or no triangle having the given specifications. For this reason the situation is called the **ambiguous case**. Figures 5–19 and 5–20 show the various possibilities.

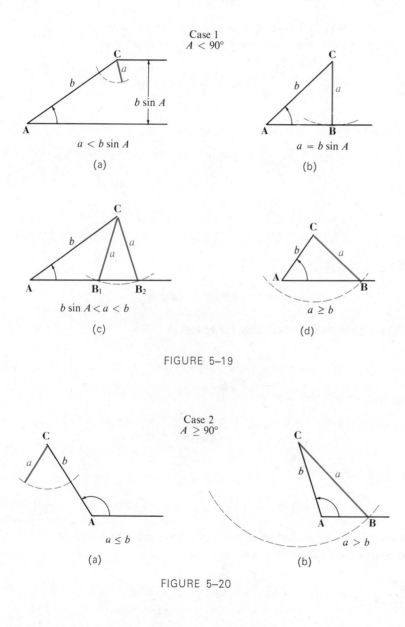

Case 1
$A < 90°$

$a < b \sin A$

(a)

$a = b \sin A$

(b)

$b \sin A < a < b$

(c)

$a \geq b$

(d)

FIGURE 5–19

Case 2
$A \geq 90°$

$a \leq b$

(a)

$a > b$

(b)

FIGURE 5–20

Example   Solve the triangle with parts as given:

$$a = 14, \qquad b = 18, \qquad A = 38°10'.$$

Solution   From Table 2, $\sin 38°10' = 0.6180$, so that

$$b \sin A = 18(0.6180) = 11.124.$$

Since $A < 90°$, and $b \sin A < a < b$, we can see from Figure 5–19(c) that two solutions exist. First, we can find $\sin B$,

$$\sin B = \frac{b \sin A}{a} = \frac{11.124}{14} = 0.7946,$$

so that either

$$B \doteq 52°37' \qquad \text{or} \qquad B \doteq 180° - 52°37' = 127°23'.$$

If $B \doteq 52°37'$, then

$$C = 180° - A - B \doteq 180° - 90°47'$$
$$= 89°13';$$

but if $B \doteq 127°23'$, then

$$C \doteq 180° - 165°33' = 14°27'.$$

Taking $C \doteq 89°13'$, and using the equation

$$\frac{\sin A}{a} = \frac{\sin C}{c},$$

we find

$$c = \frac{a \sin C}{\sin A} \doteq \frac{14(0.999)}{0.6180} \doteq 22.65.$$

Taking $C \doteq 14°27'$, we obtain

$$c \doteq \frac{14(0.2495)}{0.6180} \doteq 5.65.$$

Hence, two triangles meet the specifications given. These triangles have the following measurements:

(1) $B \doteq 52°37'$, $C \doteq 89°13'$, $c \doteq 22.65$.

(2) $B \doteq 127°23'$, $C \doteq 14°27'$, and $c \doteq 5.65$.

Exercises 5–10

In Exercises 1–6, find all triangles meeting the specifications given. Find answers to the nearest hundredth or the nearest minute. Assume the given data are exact.

A **1.** $b = 7, c = 8, C = 42°$ **4.** $b = 27, c = 24, C = 101°$

  2. $a = 6, b = 8, A = 135°$ **5.** $a = 15, b = 13, A = 87°$

  3. $b = 7, c = 9, B = 35°$ **6.** $a = 16, c = 26, C = 127°$

7. If the Earth (**E**) and Venus (**V**) are located approximately 9.3×10^7 and 6.7×10^7 miles from the Sun (**S**), respectively, and if the angle from the Sun to Earth to Venus ($\angle$**SEV**) measures 28°, find possible distances from Earth to Venus.

8. The figure at the right shows a car moving due east which is approaching the range of a radio transmitter. The effective range of the transmitter is 120 miles. To the nearest mile, for what distance $\overline{UV}$ will the car be within range of the transmitter at **T** if, when the car is at **S**, the angle **RST** measures 47°, and the distance from **S** to **T** is 152 miles?

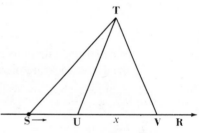

B **9.** Use the relationship $\dfrac{\sin A}{a} = \dfrac{\sin B}{b}$ to show that if $a < b \sin A$, then there can exist no triangle with corresponding measures.

10. Given $A \ (0° \leq A < 90°)$, a, and b, show that if $a \geq b$, then there is exactly one triangle with corresponding measures.

Chapter Summary

1. An **angle** is the union of two rays with a common endpoint, formed by a specific rotation from one ray to the other. Angles are assigned a measure using a unit circle as a frame of reference. The two units of angle measure in common use are the **degree** and the **radian.**

2. A **trigonometric function** has a set of angles as domain and a set of real numbers as range. Trigonometric functions are related to circular functions through the radian measure of angles.

3. Identities valid for circular functions are valid for the corresponding trigonometric functions, and conversely.

4. Trigonometric tables can be used to find approximate values for trigonometric functions.

5. If (x, y) is a point on the terminal side of an angle θ in standard position, then

$$\cos \theta = \frac{x}{\sqrt{x^2 + y_2}} \quad \text{and} \quad \sin \theta = \frac{y}{\sqrt{x^2 + y^2}}.$$

6. Inverse trigonometric functions can be used to solve trigonometric equations.

7. The **Law of Cosines** or the **Law of Sines** can be used to "solve" a triangle when the measures of three parts, including one side, are known.

Chapter Test

5–1   **1.** State **(a)** the radian measure of an angle α if $m°(\alpha) = 432$, and **(b)** the degree measure of an angle β if $m^R(\beta) = -\frac{5}{36}\pi$.

5–2   **2.** Express each of the following in terms of its reference angle:
      (a) sin 172°   **(b)** cos 305°

      3. State the value of:
      (a) sin 750°   **(b)** csc $(-1020°)$

5–3   **4.** Prove that

$$\csc \theta - \cos \theta \cot \theta = \sin \theta$$

      is an identity.

5–4   **5.** Given that cos 32°10′ = 0.8465 and cos 32°20′ = 0.8450, find an approximation (to 4 decimal digits) to cos 32°17′.

5–5   **6.** Determine $\cos \theta$ and $\sin \theta$ if $(3, -7)$ is a point on the terminal side of the angle θ in standard position.

5–6   **7.** Solve $\cos 2\theta = 1 - \sin^2 \theta$ for all angles θ for which $\theta \le m°(\theta) < 360$.

5–7   **8.** The hypotenuse of a right triangle measures 9 inches, and one acute angle measures 35°. Express the length of the longer leg in terms of a trigonometric function of 35°.

5–8   **9.** In triangle **ABC**, $b = 7$, $c = 8$, $A = 120°$. Find a to the nearest unit.

5–9   **10.** In triangle **ABC**, $A = 30°$, $B = 45°$, and $a = 6$ feet. Find b to the nearest foot.

5–10   **11.** Given a, b, and A, how many possible triangles **ABC** are there if
      (a) $A < 90°$, $a < b \sin A$?   **(b)** $A < 90°$, $b \sin A < a < b$?
      (c) $A \ge 90°$, $a \le b$?

Computer Investigations

If you have access to an electronic computer that will accept BASIC, you may wish to try using it to solve triangles.

A triangle may be considered to have 6 "parts" — 3 angles and 3 sides. A triangle is determined if we know:

(1) the measures of a side and any 2 angles

(2) the measures of 2 sides and the included angle

(3) the measures of 3 sides

If we know

(4) the measures of 2 sides and an angle that is not included,

a triangle is sometimes determined. This is called the ambiguous case.

(1) Two Angles and the Included Side

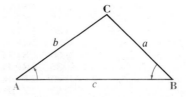

If any two angles of a triangle are given, the third angle can easily be found, and so we only give the program for "2 angles and the included side."

In this program the computation uses the Law of Sines.

Notice that measures of angles in degrees must be changed to radians.

Also, a rounding function has been introduced in line 75. This will round the results to 2 decimal places.

What restrictions must be put on the measures of the angles?

```
5    PRINT "TWO ANGLES AND THE INCLUDED SIDE"
6    PRINT
10   PRINT "ANGLE A (DEGREES):";
15   INPUT A1
20   PRINT "ANGLE B (DEGREES):";
25   INPUT B1
30   PRINT "SIDE C:";
35   INPUT C
40   LET P1=3.14159
45   LET C1=180-A1-B1
50   LET A2=A1*P1/180
55   LET B2=B1*P1/180
60   LET C2=C1*P1/180
65   LET A=C*SIN(A2)/SIN(C2)
70   LET B=C*SIN(B2)/SIN(C2)
75   DEF FNR(X)=INT(100*X+.5)/100
80   PRINT "ANGLE C:"; FNR(C1);" DEGREES"
85   PRINT "SIDE A:"; FNR(A);"    SIDE B:"; FNR(B)
90   END
```

Try using this program to solve some of the exercises in Section 5–9.

(2) Two Sides and the Included Angle

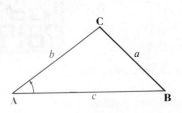

The BASIC language gives an inverse function only for tangent. This program uses the Law of Cosines to find *a*, and the Law of Sines and the Law of Cosines to find tan (*B*).

```
5   PRINT "TWO SIDES AND THE INCLUDED ANGLE"
6   PRINT
10  PRINT "SIDE B (CHOOSE B<=C):";
15  INPUT B
20  PRINT "SIDE C:";
25  INPUT C
30  PRINT "ANGLE A (DEGREES):";
35  INPUT A1
40  LET P1=3.14159
45  LET A2=A1*P1/180
47  REM: S=A*A
50  LET S=B*B+C*C-2*B*C*COS(A2)
52  REM: T=TAN(B2)
55  LET T=2*B*C*SIN(A2)/(S+C*C-B*B)
60  LET B2=ATN(T)
65  LET B1=B2*180/P1
70  LET C1=180-A1-B1
75  LET A=SQR(S)
80  DEF FNR(X)=INT(100*X+.5)/100
85  PRINT "SIDE A:";FNR(A)
90  PRINT "ANGLE B:";FNR(B1);" DEGREES";
95  PRINT "   ANGLE C:";FNR(C1);" DEGREES"
100 END
```

Try using this program to solve some of the exercises in Section 5–9.

(3) Three Sides

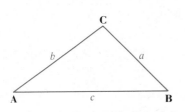

This program uses the formula

$$\tan\frac{A}{2} = \sqrt{\frac{(s-b)(s-c)}{s(s-a)}}$$

where

$$s = (a + b + c)/2.$$

This formula can be derived from the material in Exercises 17–22 on pages 172–173.

```
5   PRINT "THREE SIDES"
6   PRINT
10  PRINT "SIDE A:";
15  INPUT A
20  PRINT "SIDE B:";
25  INPUT B
30  PRINT "SIDE C:";
35  INPUT C
40  IF A+B <= C THEN 125
45  IF B+C <= A THEN 125
50  IF C+A <= B THEN 125
55  LET S=(A+B+C)/2
57  REM: A3 = TAN(A2/2)
60  LET A3=SQR((S-B)*(S-C)/(S*(S-A)))
65  LET A2=2*ATN(A3)
67  REM: B3 = TAN(B2/2)
70  LET B3=SQR((S-A)*(S-C)/(S*(S-B)))
75  LET B2=2*ATN(B3)
80  LET P1=3.14159
85  LET A1=A2*180/P1
90  LET B1=B2*180/P1
95  LET C1=180-A1-B1
100 DEF FNR(X)=INT(100*X+.5)/100
105 PRINT "ANGLE A:";FNR(A1);" DEGREES";
110 PRINT "   ANGLE B:";FNR(B1);" DEGREES";
115 PRINT "   ANGLE C:";FNR(C1);" DEGREES"
120 STOP
125 PRINT "NO TRIANGLE"
130 END
```

Try using this program to solve some of the exercises in Section 5–8.

(4) Two Sides, Angle Not Included

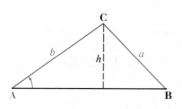

Because of rounding problems, it is unlikely that h will come out exactly equal to a. Therefore, this program assumes that the triangle is a right triangle if

$$.999999 < \frac{h}{a} < 1.00001.$$

Try using this program to solve some of the exercises in Section 5–10.

```
5    PRINT "TWO SIDES, ANGLE NOT INCLUDED"
6    PRINT
10   PRINT "ANGLE A (DEGREES)";
15   INPUT A1
20   PRINT "SIDE A:";
25   INPUT A
30   PRINT "SIDE B:";
35   INPUT B
40   LET P1=3.14159
45   LET A2=A1*P1/180
50   LET H=B*SIN(A2)
55   IF H/A>1.00001 THEN 250
60   IF H/A>.999999 THEN 120
62   REM: S=SIN(B2)
65   LET S=H/A
67   REM: T=TAN(B2)
70   LET T=S/SQR(1-S*S)
75   LET B2=ATN(T)
80   LET B1=B2*180/P1
85   DEF FNR(X)=INT(100*X+.5)/100
90   GOSUB 200
95   IF A >= B THEN 255
100  LET B1=180-B1
105  PRINT "SECOND CASE"
110  GOSUB 200
115  STOP
120  PRINT "ANGLE B: 90 DEGREES";
125  PRINT "   ANGLE C:";90-A1;" DEGREES"
130  PRINT "SIDE C:";FNR(A/TAN(A2))
135  STOP
200  LET C1=180-A1-B1
205  LET C2=C1*P1/180
210  LET C=A*SIN(C2)/SIN(A2)
215  PRINT "ANGLE B:";FNR(B1);" DEGREES";
220  PRINT "   ANGLE C:";FNR(C1);" DEGREES"
225  PRINT "SIDE C:";FNR(C)
230  RETURN
250  PRINT "NO TRIANGLE"
255  END
```

1. Change lines 5–35 in program (1) to give fixed values for angle A and side c. Then let angle B take on measures from $10°$ to $170° - A$. Compare the results.

2. Change lines 5–35 in program (2) to give fixed values for sides b and c. Then let angle A take on measures from $10°$ to $170°$. Compare the results.

3. Change lines 5–35 in program (3) to give fixed values for sides a and b (choose values > 1). Then let side c take on measures from 1 to $a + b - 1$ and compare the results.

4. Change lines 5–35 in program (4) to give fixed values for sides a and b. Then let angle A take on measures from $10°$ to $170°$. Compare the results. (Take $a > b$.)

Chapter Six

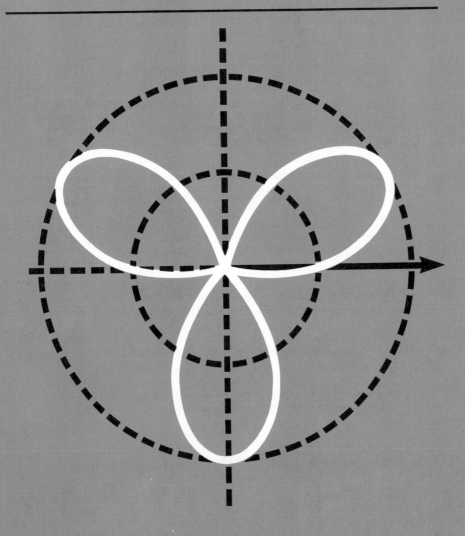

Vectors

OBJECTIVES

1. To learn the properties of vectors and the binary operations involving vectors.
2. To apply vectors to real-life problems involving navigation and forces.
3. To use polar coordinates and relate them to Cartesian coordinates.
4. To graph polar equations.

Properties of Vectors

6–1 *Vectors and Their Geometric Representation*

In the physical sciences, one of the most widely used mathematical concepts is that of a vector. Many physical properties can be measured as real-number multiples of a unit on a linear scale. For this reason, they are called scalar quantities, or **scalars**. The description of other kinds of physical properties, such as the motion of a rocket, involves two specifications: a magnitude (a scalar) and a direction (given by one or more reference angles, depending on the number of dimensions involved). Quantities having both magnitude and direction are called *vectors*. In this chapter, we shall examine some of the basic properties of two-dimensional vectors, and shall see how trigonometric functions can be used to illustrate these properties.

A two-dimensional **vector** is an ordered pair (x, y) of real numbers. In this book, we shall use a special heavy typeface to identify a vector; for example, **v, u, i,** and **j** will designate vectors. In your own work with vectors, you will probably find it best to represent a vector by drawing a small arrow above the symbol you use to name the vector; for example, you would write $\vec{v}, \vec{u}, \vec{i}$, and $\vec{j}$.

Since vectors are ordered pairs of real numbers, we could specify some binary operations on vectors and treat the set of vectors with the given operations as an abstract mathematical system, without considering what geometric interpretation vectors might have. Because vectors have a particularly useful geometric representation, however, we shall introduce this representation here and shall study vectors and their geometric counterparts together.

By the term **geometric vector** corresponding to the vector $\mathbf{v} = (x, y)$, we shall mean the directed line segment, depicted by an arrow (Figure 6–1), whose **initial point** is the origin and whose **terminal point** is (x, y). Such a geometric vector is said to be in **standard position**, or to be a **bound vector** (since its initial point is "bound" to the origin). Unless otherwise stated, geometric vectors will

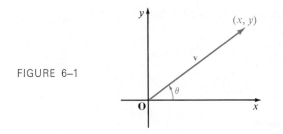

FIGURE 6–1

always be understood to be in standard position. As is customary, we shall use the same symbol **v** to denote both the vector and the geometric vector; the context should always make it clear which is meant.

If $\mathbf{v} = (x, y)$, then the **norm** of **v** is designated by $\|\mathbf{v}\|$, and is defined by

$$\|\mathbf{v}\| = \sqrt{x^2 + y^2}. \tag{1}$$

The length of the geometric vector corresponding to $\mathbf{v} = (x, y)$ is called the **magnitude** of the vector. From the distance formula, we know that the magnitude of the geometric vector **v** is $\sqrt{x^2 + y^2}$; hence the norm of **v** and the magnitude of the geometric vector **v** are equal.

For $\|\mathbf{v}\| \neq 0$, the **direction angle** θ of **v** is given by

$$\cos \theta = \frac{x}{\|\mathbf{v}\|}, \qquad \sin \theta = \frac{y}{\|\mathbf{v}\|}, \qquad 0° \leq \theta < 360°. \tag{2}$$

The angle that the geometric vector **v** forms with the positive x-axis is called the **direction** of the vector, and its measure is equal to the direction angle of **v**.

Example 1   Find the vector with norm 4 and direction angle 300°.

Solution   From the equations in (2), page 186, we have $\cos 300° = \dfrac{x}{4}$ and $\sin 300° = \dfrac{y}{4}$.

Then

$$x = 4(\cos 300°) = 4(\tfrac{1}{2}) = 2,$$

and

$$y = 4(\sin 300°) = 4\left(-\frac{\sqrt{3}}{2}\right) = -2\sqrt{3}.$$

Thus, the required vector is $(2, -2\sqrt{3})$.

Two vectors $\mathbf{u} = (x_1, y_1)$ and $\mathbf{v} = (x_2, y_2)$ are said to be **equal** if and only if $x_1 = x_2$ and $y_1 = y_2$. Geometrically, vectors are equal if and only if they have the same magnitude and direction, that is, if and only if they are coincident when in standard position.

Two geometric vectors which lie on the same line are said to be **collinear**. In Figure 6–2, $\mathbf{u}$, $\mathbf{v}$, and $\mathbf{w}$ are collinear.

If $\mathbf{v} = (x, y)$, then $-\mathbf{v}$, the **negative of v**, is defined by

$$-\mathbf{v} = (-x, -y).$$

For example, if $\mathbf{v} = (3, -1)$, then $-\mathbf{v} = (-3, 1)$. Since $\sqrt{x^2 + y^2} = \sqrt{(-x)^2 + (-y)^2}$, you can see that $\mathbf{v}$ and $-\mathbf{v}$ have the same norm, but since their direction angles differ by 180°, they are of **opposite direction** (Figure 6–3).

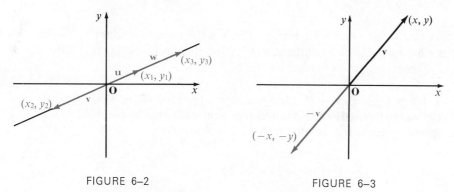

FIGURE 6–2   FIGURE 6–3

The vector $(0, 0)$ is called the **zero vector** and is denoted by $\mathbf{0}$. The norm of $\mathbf{0}$ is 0. The formulas in (2) cannot now be applied, so $\mathbf{0}$ *may be assigned* any convenient direction. The geometric counterpart of $\mathbf{0}$ is just a single point at the origin.

Two basic operations in the set V of vectors (x, y) are (a) vector addition and (b) multiplication of a vector by a scalar, defined respectively as follows:

If $\mathbf{u}, \mathbf{v} \in V$, $\mathbf{u} = (x_1, y_1)$, and $\mathbf{v} = (x_2, y_2)$, then

▲ $$\mathbf{u} + \mathbf{v} = (x_1, y_1) + (x_2, y_2) = (x_1 + x_2, y_1 + y_2).$$

If $\mathbf{v} \in V$, $\mathbf{v} = (x, y)$, and $r \in \mathfrak{R}$, then

▲ $$r\mathbf{v} = (rx, ry).$$

These operations may be represented by geometric vectors as follows:

1. The sum, or **resultant**, of two geometric vectors $\mathbf{u}$ and $\mathbf{v}$ is the geometric vector $\mathbf{u} + \mathbf{v}$ which extends from the origin to the opposite side of the parallelogram having two sides coincident with the given geometric vectors (Figure 6–4).

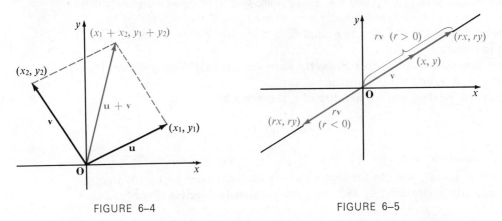

FIGURE 6–4   FIGURE 6–5

2. The product $r\mathbf{v}$ of a scalar r and a geometric vector $\mathbf{v}$ is the geometric vector collinear with $\mathbf{v}$ having the same direction as $\mathbf{v}$ if $r > 0$ and opposite direction if $r < 0$, and of magnitude $|r|\,\|\mathbf{v}\|$ (Figure 6–5).

Example 2   Let $\mathbf{u} = (-4, 3)$, $\mathbf{v} = (6, 2)$, $r = 2$, $s = -\frac{1}{2}$. Find **(a)** $\mathbf{u} + \mathbf{v}$, **(b)** $r\mathbf{u}$, **(c)** $s\mathbf{v}$, **(d)** $r\mathbf{u} + s\mathbf{v}$, and represent each by the corresponding geometric vector.

Solution   **(a)** $\mathbf{u} + \mathbf{v} = (-4, 3) + (6, 2) = (2, 5)$.

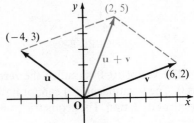

(b) $r\mathbf{u} = 2(-4, 3) = (-8, 6)$, as shown on the left, below.

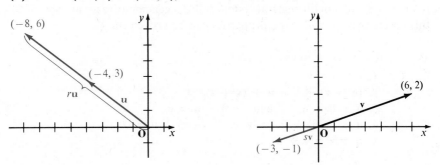

(c) $s\mathbf{v} = -\frac{1}{2}(6, 2) = (-3, -1)$, as shown on the right, above.

(d) $r\mathbf{u} + s\mathbf{v} = 2(-4, 3) + (-\frac{1}{2})(6, 2)$
$$= (-8, 6) + (-3, -1)$$
$$= (-11, 5)$$

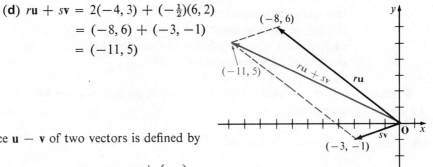

The difference $\mathbf{u} - \mathbf{v}$ of two vectors is defined by

$$\mathbf{u} - \mathbf{v} = \mathbf{u} + (-\mathbf{v}),$$

or, in terms of the components of $\mathbf{u}$ and $\mathbf{v}$,

▲ $\mathbf{u} - \mathbf{v} = (x_1, y_1) + (-x_2, -y_2) = (x_1 - x_2, y_1 - y_2).$

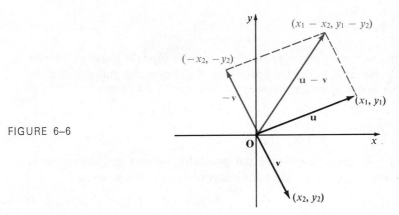

FIGURE 6–6

Graphically, the geometric vector corresponding to $\mathbf{u} - \mathbf{v}$ is the resultant $\mathbf{u} + (-\mathbf{v})$ [Figure 6–6].

The set V of two-dimensional vectors, under the operation of vector addition, is an example of a mathematical system called a **commutative group**. Specifically, this means that the following properties can be proved for V.

 If **u, v, s** $\in V$, then:

1. $\mathbf{u} + \mathbf{v} \in V$
2. $(\mathbf{u} + \mathbf{v}) + \mathbf{s} = \mathbf{u} + (\mathbf{v} + \mathbf{s})$
3. $\mathbf{u} + \mathbf{0} = \mathbf{u}$,   and $\mathbf{0} + \mathbf{u} = \mathbf{u}$
4. $\mathbf{u} + (-\mathbf{u}) = \mathbf{0}$,   and $(-\mathbf{u}) + \mathbf{u} = \mathbf{0}$
5. $\mathbf{u} + \mathbf{v} = \mathbf{v} + \mathbf{u}$

These five properties express the following facts, respectively, regarding the operation of addition:

> V is **closed**,
> the operation is **associative**,
> there is an **additive identity element 0**,
> each element **v** has an **additive inverse element** $-\mathbf{v}$,
> the operation is **commutative**.

Furthermore, it can be shown that the following properties of multiplication by a scalar also hold in V.

 If **u, v** $\in V$, and $r, s \in \mathcal{R}$, then:

6. $r\mathbf{u} \in V$
7. $r(s\mathbf{u}) = (rs)\mathbf{u}$
8. $(r + s)\mathbf{u} = r\mathbf{u} + s\mathbf{u}$
9. $r(\mathbf{u} + \mathbf{v}) = r\mathbf{u} + r\mathbf{v}$
10. $1\mathbf{u} = \mathbf{u}$
11. $-1\mathbf{u} = -\mathbf{u}$
12. $0\mathbf{u} = \mathbf{0}$
13. $r\mathbf{0} = \mathbf{0}$

Any commutative group which possesses properties (6)–(13) is called a **vector space**. Hence, the set V, under the operations of addition and multiplication by a real-number scalar, is a vector space.

Exercises 6–1

In Exercises 1–6, show graphically the geometric vectors corresponding to the vectors **u**, **v**, and **u + v**. State the norm of each of these vectors.

A **1.** $\mathbf{u} = (1, 3)$, $\mathbf{v} = (6, 2)$ **4.** $\mathbf{u} = (\sqrt{2}, \sqrt{2})$, $\mathbf{v} = (-3\sqrt{2}, 0)$

  2. $\mathbf{u} = (-2, 3)$, $\mathbf{v} = (4, -2)$ **5.** $\mathbf{u} = (-4, 1)$, $\mathbf{v} = (1, 4)$

  3. $\mathbf{u} = (6, 8)$, $\mathbf{v} = (3, -4)$ **6.** $\mathbf{u} = (1, -\sqrt{3})$, $\mathbf{v} = (-2, \sqrt{3})$

In Exercises 7–12, specify in ordered-pair form the vector with the given norm and direction angle.

7. $\|\mathbf{v}\| = 2\sqrt{2}; \theta = 45°$

8. $\|\mathbf{v}\| = 4; \theta = 30°$

9. $\|\mathbf{v}\| = 3; \theta = 180°$

10. $\|\mathbf{v}\| = 2; \theta = 270°$

11. $\|\mathbf{v}\| = 8; \theta = 225°$

12. $\|\mathbf{v}\| = 4; \theta = 120°$

In Exercises 13–20, if $\mathbf{u} = (-1, 5)$ and $\mathbf{v} = (3, -2)$, find the vector corresponding to the given expression. Illustrate the situation using geometric vectors.

13. $2\mathbf{u}$

14. $-3\mathbf{v}$

15. $2\mathbf{u} + (-3)\mathbf{v}$

16. $4\mathbf{u} + 4\mathbf{v}$

17. $4(\mathbf{u} + \mathbf{v})$

18. $\mathbf{v} + (-1)\mathbf{u}$

19. $\mathbf{u} - \mathbf{v}$

20. $\frac{1}{2}\mathbf{u} + \frac{2}{3}\mathbf{v}$

In Exercises 21–27, find the vector (x, y) for which the given statement is true.

21. $(5, 8) + (x, y) = (0, 0)$

22. $(7, 4) + (x, y) = (10, -5)$

23. $-2(5, -1) + 3(x, y) = (2, -1)$

24. $-\frac{1}{2}(x, y) = (6, 4)$

25. $4[(3, 7) + (x, y)] = (20, 16)$

26. $3(x, y) + (-1)(x, y) = (6, 10)$

27. $5(x, y) + (2, -8) = 3(x, y)$

In Exercises 28–40, let $\mathbf{u} = (a_1, b_1)$, $\mathbf{v} = (a_2, b_2)$, $\mathbf{w} = (a_3, b_3)$, r, $s \in \mathcal{R}$, and prove the stated assertion.

B 28. $\mathbf{u} + \mathbf{v} \in V$

29. $(\mathbf{u} + \mathbf{v}) + \mathbf{w} = \mathbf{u} + (\mathbf{v} + \mathbf{w})$

30. $\mathbf{u} + \mathbf{0} = \mathbf{u}, \mathbf{0} + \mathbf{u} = \mathbf{u}$

31. $\mathbf{u} + (-\mathbf{u}) = \mathbf{0}, (-\mathbf{u}) + \mathbf{u} = \mathbf{0}$

32. $\mathbf{u} + \mathbf{v} = \mathbf{v} + \mathbf{u}$

33. $r\mathbf{u} \in V$

34. $r(s\mathbf{u}) = (rs)\mathbf{u}$

35. $(r + s)\mathbf{u} = r\mathbf{u} + s\mathbf{u}$

36. $r(\mathbf{u} + \mathbf{v}) = r\mathbf{u} + r\mathbf{v}$

37. $1\mathbf{u} = \mathbf{u}$

38. $-1\mathbf{u} = -\mathbf{u}$

39. $0\mathbf{u} = \mathbf{0}$

40. $r\mathbf{0} = \mathbf{0}$

C 41. Show that $\|\mathbf{u} + \mathbf{v}\| \leq \|\mathbf{u}\| + \|\mathbf{v}\|$.

42. Show that if $\|\mathbf{v}\| \neq 0$, then $\dfrac{1}{\|\mathbf{v}\|}\mathbf{v}$ has the same direction angle as $\mathbf{v}$ and has norm 1.

43. Show that $\mathbf{u} = (x_1, y_1)$ and $\mathbf{v} = (x_2, y_2)$ are collinear if and only if $x_1 y_2 - x_2 y_1 = 0$.

6–2 *Basis Vectors*

The sum $\mathbf{a} = r\mathbf{u} + s\mathbf{v}$ of any scalar multiples of two vectors $\mathbf{u}$ and $\mathbf{v}$ is called a **linear combination** of $\mathbf{u}$ and $\mathbf{v}$. We can show that any vector in V can be expressed as a linear combination of any two *noncollinear* vectors in V.

For example, if we choose $\mathbf{u} = (2, 5)$, $\mathbf{v} = (-4, 3)$, and $\mathbf{a} = (8, 7)$, then we must show that there exist scalars r and $s \in \Re$ for which

$$\mathbf{a} = r\mathbf{u} + s\mathbf{v},$$

that is, for which
$$(8, 7) = r(2, 5) + s(-4, 3)$$
$$= (2r, 5r) + (-4s, 3s),$$

or
$$(8, 7) = (2r - 4s, 5r + 3s).$$

This vector equation is true if and only if

$$8 = 2r - 4s, \quad \text{and} \quad 7 = 5r + 3s.$$

Solving these two equations simultaneously gives

$$r = 2, s = -1, \text{ so that } \mathbf{a} = 2\mathbf{u} + (-1)\mathbf{v}.$$

The geometric situation is shown in Figure 6–7.

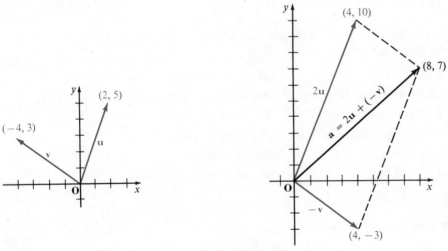

FIGURE 6–7

To show that *any* vector $\mathbf{a}$ in V can be expressed as a linear combination of any two noncollinear vectors $\mathbf{u}$ and $\mathbf{v}$ in V, we let $\mathbf{u} = (x_1, y_1)$, $\mathbf{v} = (x_2, y_2)$, and

a $= (x_3, y_3)$. We must then show that there exist scalars r, $s \in \mathcal{R}$ for which

$$\mathbf{a} = r\mathbf{u} + s\mathbf{v}, \tag{1}$$

that is,

$$(x_3, y_3) = r(x_1, y_1) + s(x_2, y_2)$$
$$= (rx_1, ry_1) + (sx_2, sy_2),$$

or

$$(x_3, y_3) = (rx_1 + sx_2, ry_1 + sy_2). \tag{2}$$

From the definition of equality of vectors, this last equation is true if and only if

$$x_3 = rx_1 + sx_2 \qquad \text{and} \qquad y_3 = ry_1 + sy_2.$$

When these equations are solved simultaneously for r and s in terms of x_1, y_1, x_2, y_2, x_3, and y_3, we find that if $x_1 y_2 - x_2 y_1 \neq 0$, then

$$r = \frac{x_3 y_2 - x_2 y_3}{x_1 y_2 - x_2 y_1}, \tag{3}$$

$$s = \frac{x_1 y_3 - x_3 y_1}{x_1 y_2 - x_2 y_1}. \tag{4}$$

Since **u** and **v** are noncollinear vectors, we know that $x_1 y_2 - x_2 y_1 \neq 0$ (Exercise 43, page 191), and so Equation (2) implies Equations (3) and (4). Since each step in the argument is reversible, we have established our assertion that we can always find r and s so as to make (1) valid.

Figure 6–8 illustrates the notion of a linear combination of **u** and **v**.

Because any two noncollinear vectors in V can be used in this way to generate every vector in V, any two such vectors are said to form a **basis** for the vector space (or to **span** the vector space), and the vectors in the pair are called **basis vectors**.

In this book, we are primarily interested in basis vectors that are **orthogonal**, that is, whose direction angles differ by 90°. Graphically, such vectors correspond to perpendicular geometric vectors.

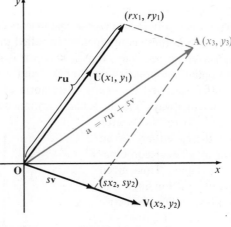

FIGURE 6–8

In particular, we are interested in the orthogonal vectors

$$\mathbf{i} = (1, 0) \qquad \text{and} \qquad \mathbf{j} = (0, 1),$$

which have **unit norm** ($\|\mathbf{v}\| = 1$) and direction angles 0° and 90°, respectively (see Figure 6–9, page 194).

As shown graphically in Figure 6–10, by adopting **i** and **j** as basis vectors, we can **resolve** (write as a sum of other vectors) any vector $\mathbf{v} = (x_1, y_1)$ into the sum of scalar multiples of **i** and **j** simply by writing

$$\mathbf{v} = (x_1, y_1) = x_1\mathbf{i} + y_1\mathbf{j}. \tag{5}$$

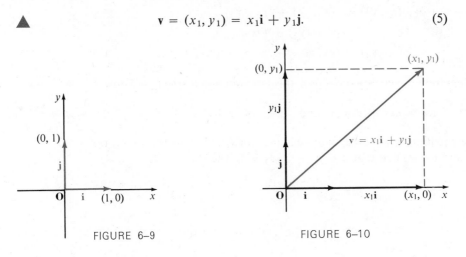

FIGURE 6–9   FIGURE 6–10

Example 1   Resolve the vector $(4, -2)$ into the sum of scalar multiples of **i** and **j**.

Solution   If $\mathbf{v} = (4, -2)$, then $\mathbf{v} = 4\mathbf{i} + (-2)\mathbf{j} = 4\mathbf{i} - 2\mathbf{j}$.

When a vector **v** is resolved into **vector components** collinear with **i** and **j**, the coefficients of **i** and **j** in these components are called the **scalar components** of **v** on the x- and y-axes, respectively; thus if a vector is given as an ordered pair (x, y), then the scalar components are simply x and y, respectively.

A vector is often specified by means of its norm and direction angle. When this is done, you can always find the scalar components of the vector on the x- and y-axes, and write the vector directly from these, either as an ordered pair or as a linear combination of the vectors **i** and **j**. Thus, given the norm $\|\mathbf{v}\|$ and direction angle θ of a vector, the corresponding geometric situation is as shown in Figure 6–11, where it is evident that the scalar components you seek are $\|\mathbf{v}\| \cos \theta$ and $\|\mathbf{v}\| \sin \theta$, respectively. Hence you can designate the vector in either of the following ways:

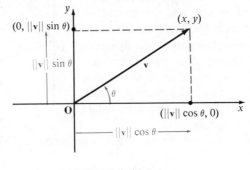

FIGURE 6–11

$$\mathbf{v} = (\|\mathbf{v}\| \cos \theta, \|\mathbf{v}\| \sin \theta), \text{ or} \tag{6}$$

$$\mathbf{v} = (\|\mathbf{v}\| \cos \theta)\mathbf{i} + (\|\mathbf{v}\| \sin \theta)\mathbf{j} \tag{7}$$

Example 2   Resolve the vector whose norm is 4 and whose direction angle is 70° into a linear combination of **i** and **j**.

Solution   The scalar component of **v** on the *x*-axis is 4 cos 70° and on the *y*-axis is 4 sin 70°. Therefore, from Table 2, we have

$$\mathbf{v} \doteq 4(0.3420)\mathbf{i} + 4(0.9397)\mathbf{j}$$
$$= 1.3680\mathbf{i} + 3.7588\mathbf{j},$$

as depicted in the sketch.

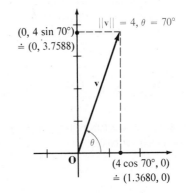

By the definition of scalar multiplication, Equations (6) and (7) may be rewritten as

$$\mathbf{v} = \|\mathbf{v}\| \,(\cos \theta, \sin \theta) \qquad (8)$$

or

$$\mathbf{v} = \|\mathbf{v}\| \,[(\cos \theta)\mathbf{i} + (\sin \theta)\mathbf{j}]. \qquad (9)$$

Both of these forms express the fact that any vector **v** can be regarded as a scalar product $\mathbf{v} = c\mathbf{u}$, in which $c = \|\mathbf{v}\|$ and **u** is the unit vector $(\cos \theta, \sin \theta)$ or $(\cos \theta)\mathbf{i} + (\sin \theta)\mathbf{j}$. To show that $(\cos \theta, \sin \theta)$ is a unit vector, we need only to observe that its norm is $\sqrt{\cos^2 \theta + \sin^2 \theta} = \sqrt{1} = 1$.

Let us define the symbol $\dfrac{\mathbf{v}}{c}$, where $\mathbf{v} = (x, y)$ is a vector and c is a nonzero real number, to mean the scalar product

$$\frac{1}{c}\mathbf{v} = \left(\frac{1}{c}x, \frac{1}{c}y\right).$$

It can be shown that if you multiply any nonzero vector **v** by the reciprocal of its norm, the result is a *unit vector with the same direction* as **v**. For example, if you multiply a vector which is in any one of the forms (6)–(9) by the reciprocal of its norm, the result is a unit vector of the form $(\cos \theta, \sin \theta)$ or $(\cos \theta)\mathbf{i} + (\sin \theta)\mathbf{j}$.

Example 3   Find a unit vector **v** in the direction of **u** = $(-6, 8)$.

Solution   Since $\|\mathbf{u}\| = \sqrt{(-6)^2 + (8)^2} = 10$, the vector we seek is

$$\mathbf{v} = \frac{1}{\|\mathbf{u}\|}\,\mathbf{u} = \tfrac{1}{10}(-6, 8) = (-\tfrac{3}{5}, \tfrac{4}{5}).$$

In Example 3, since we know that $\mathbf{v} = (-\tfrac{3}{5}, \tfrac{4}{5})$ is a unit vector, it is obvious that $\cos \theta = -\tfrac{3}{5}$ and $\sin \theta = \tfrac{4}{5}$, where θ is the direction angle of both of the vectors $\mathbf{u} = (-6, 8)$ and $\mathbf{v} = \tfrac{1}{10}(-6, 8) = (-\tfrac{3}{5}, \tfrac{4}{5})$. Thus, obtaining a unit vector in the same direction as a given vector readily identifies the values of the cos and sin of the direction angle of the vector.

Exercises 6–2

For each of the following pairs of vectors, **u** and **v**, find a vector in the form $x\mathbf{i} + y\mathbf{j}$ equal to

  (a) **u** + **v**   and   (b) **2u** + (−3)**v**

A **1.** $\mathbf{u} = (-4, 1)$, $\mathbf{v} = (5, 2)$
   2. $\mathbf{u} = (-6, 4)$, $\mathbf{v} = (1, 7)$
   3. $\mathbf{u} = (0, 8)$, $\mathbf{v} = (4, 0)$
   4. $\mathbf{u} = (-3, 3)$, $\mathbf{v} = (1, -1)$
   5. $\mathbf{u} = (10, 2)$, $\mathbf{v} = (\tfrac{1}{3}, -\tfrac{2}{3})$

For each of the following vectors: (a) express each vector as a scalar product of a real number and a unit vector, (b) find the direction angle of the vector. Use Table 2, page 392, as needed.

  6. $\sqrt{3}\,\mathbf{i} - \mathbf{j}$ **9.** $7\mathbf{i} + \mathbf{j}$
  7. $-5\mathbf{i} + 5\mathbf{j}$ **10.** $6\mathbf{i}$
  8. $-3\mathbf{i} - 4\mathbf{j}$ **11.** $\sqrt{3}\,\mathbf{i} + \sqrt{3}\,\mathbf{j}$

Find a unit vector in the same direction as each of the following vectors. Show graphically the geometric vectors corresponding to the given vector and to the corresponding unit vector.

  12. $\mathbf{i} + \mathbf{j}$ **15.** $\dfrac{1}{3}\mathbf{i} + \dfrac{1}{\sqrt{3}}\mathbf{j}$

  13. $2\mathbf{i} - 2\mathbf{j}$ **16.** $(3\cos 60°, 3\sin 60°)$
  14. $-3\mathbf{i} + 9\mathbf{j}$ **17.** $(\tfrac{1}{4}\cos 45°, \tfrac{1}{4}\sin 45°)$

In Exercises 18–22, resolve each of the vectors with the given norm and direction angle into a linear combination of **i** and **j**. Use Table 2 as needed.

18. $\|\mathbf{v}\| = 3,\ \theta = 60°$

19. $\|\mathbf{v}\| = 7,\ \theta = 90°$

20. $\|\mathbf{v}\| = \frac{1}{2},\ \theta = 150°$

21. $\|\mathbf{v}\| = 10,\ \theta = 160°$

22. $\|\mathbf{v}\| = \frac{3}{4},\ \theta = 112°$

In each of Exercises 23–28, let **k** be a unit vector with direction angle θ_k, as given, and let **m** be a unit vector with direction angle θ_m, as given. Resolve the given vector into a linear combination of **k** and **m**.

Example $4\mathbf{i} - 2\mathbf{j},\ \theta_k = 30°,\ \theta_m = 120°$

Solution   First we resolve **k** and **m** into linear combinations of **i** and **j**:

$$\mathbf{k} = (\cos 30°)\mathbf{i} + (\sin 30°)\mathbf{j} = \frac{\sqrt{3}}{2}\mathbf{i} + \frac{1}{2}\mathbf{j}$$

$$\mathbf{m} = (\cos 120°)\mathbf{i} + (\sin 120°)\mathbf{j} = -\frac{1}{2}\mathbf{i} + \frac{\sqrt{3}}{2}\mathbf{j}$$

We then use Equations (1), (3), and (4) (page 193) with $\mathbf{u} = \mathbf{k}$, $\mathbf{v} = \mathbf{m}$, $\mathbf{a} = 4\mathbf{i} - 2\mathbf{j}$, so that

$$r = \frac{x_3 y_2 - x_2 y_3}{x_1 y_2 - x_2 y_1} = \frac{(4)\left(\frac{\sqrt{3}}{2}\right) - \left(-\frac{1}{2}\right)(-2)}{\left(\frac{\sqrt{3}}{2}\right)\left(\frac{\sqrt{3}}{2}\right) - \left(-\frac{1}{2}\right)\left(\frac{1}{2}\right)} = \frac{2\sqrt{3} - 1}{1},$$

$$s = \frac{x_1 y_3 - x_3 y_1}{x_1 y_2 - x_2 y_1} = \frac{\left(\frac{\sqrt{3}}{2}\right)(-2) - (4)(\frac{1}{2})}{1} = \frac{-\sqrt{3} - 2}{1}.$$

Thus, $4\mathbf{i} - 2\mathbf{j} = r\mathbf{k} + s\mathbf{m} = (2\sqrt{3} - 1)\mathbf{k} + (-\sqrt{3} - 2)\mathbf{m}$.

B 23. $\mathbf{i} - \mathbf{j},\ \theta_k = 30°,\ \theta_m = 120°$ **26.** $4\mathbf{i} - 2\mathbf{j},\ \theta_k = 60°,\ \theta_m = 150°$

24. $2\mathbf{i} + 2\mathbf{j},\ \theta_k = 30°,\ \theta_m = 120°$ **27.** $\mathbf{i} + \mathbf{j},\ \theta_k = 90°,\ \theta_m = 180°$

25. $3\mathbf{i} + \mathbf{j},\ \theta_k = 60°,\ \theta_m = 150°$ **28.** $5\mathbf{i} - 2\mathbf{j},\ \theta_k = 90°,\ \theta_m = 180°$

C 29. Show that if $r \in \mathcal{R}$ and $r \geq -1$, then $\mathbf{v} + r\mathbf{v}$ has the same direction as **v**.

30. Let $\mathbf{u} = x_1\mathbf{i} + y_1\mathbf{j}$ and $\mathbf{v} = x_2\mathbf{i} + y_2\mathbf{j}$ be any two vectors in V. Find a relationship between x_1, y_1, x_2, and y_2 implying that **u** and **v** are orthogonal.

6–3   *The Inner Product of Two Vectors*

For some purposes, it is useful to consider still another operation involving vectors, as follows:

The **inner product** (also called **dot product**, or **scalar product**) of two vectors $\mathbf{u} = x_1\mathbf{i} + y_1\mathbf{j}$ and $\mathbf{v} = x_2\mathbf{i} + y_2\mathbf{j}$ is denoted by $\mathbf{u} \cdot \mathbf{v}$, and is defined by

$$\mathbf{u} \cdot \mathbf{v} = x_1x_2 + y_1y_2. \tag{1}$$

Example 1   If $\mathbf{u} = 2\mathbf{i} - 3\mathbf{j}$ and $\mathbf{v} = 5\mathbf{i} - \mathbf{j}$, find $\mathbf{u} \cdot \mathbf{v}$.

Solution $\mathbf{u} \cdot \mathbf{v} = (2)(5) + (-3)(-1) = 10 + 3 = 13.$

Note that this operation is not a closed operation in V, because the inner product of two vectors is not a vector but a *scalar*.

To see how another form for this product arises, consider the problem of determining $\cos \alpha$, where α $(0° \le \alpha \le 180°)$ is an angle between the geometric vectors corresponding to two given nonzero vectors $\mathbf{u} = x_1\mathbf{i} + y_1\mathbf{j}$ and $\mathbf{v} = x_2\mathbf{i} + y_2\mathbf{j}$ (see Figure 6–12).

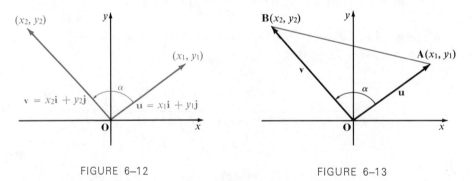

FIGURE 6–12   FIGURE 6–13

Because $x_1\mathbf{i} + y_1\mathbf{j}$ and $x_2\mathbf{i} + y_2\mathbf{j}$ represent the vectors (x_1, y_1) and (x_2, y_2), respectively, and because we can use the distance formula to find the distance between the points with coordinates (x_1, y_1) and (x_2, y_2), we can use the Law of Cosines to find $\cos \alpha$. Figure 6–13 shows a line segment drawn between $\mathbf{A}(x_1, y_1)$ and $\mathbf{B}(x_2, y_2)$. Now, consider $\triangle \mathbf{AOB}$. From the Law of Cosines, you have

$$[d(\overline{\mathbf{AB}})]^2 = \|\mathbf{u}\|^2 + \|\mathbf{v}\|^2 - 2\|\mathbf{u}\|\,\|\mathbf{v}\| \cos \alpha,$$

from which you obtain

$$\cos \alpha = \frac{\|\mathbf{u}\|^2 + \|\mathbf{v}\|^2 - [d(\overline{\mathbf{AB}})]^2}{2\|\mathbf{u}\|\,\|\mathbf{v}\|}. \tag{2}$$

By definition,

$$\|\mathbf{u}\| = \sqrt{x_1^2 + y_1^2}, \qquad \|\mathbf{v}\| = \sqrt{x_2^2 + y_2^2},$$

and from the distance formula,

$$d(\overline{\mathbf{AB}}) = \sqrt{(x_2 - x_1)^2 + (y_2 - y_1)^2}.$$

Substituting these values in equation (2), you obtain

$$\cos \alpha = \frac{(x_1^2 + y_1^2) + (x_2^2 + y_2^2) - [(x_2 - x_1)^2 + (y_2 - y_1)^2]}{2\sqrt{x_1^2 + y_1^2}\sqrt{x_2^2 + y_2^2}}$$

which simplifies to

$$\cos \alpha = \frac{x_1 x_2 + y_1 y_2}{\sqrt{x_1^2 + y_1^2}\sqrt{x_2^2 + y_2^2}}. \qquad (3)$$

Now, the numerator in (3) is just the inner product $\mathbf{u} \cdot \mathbf{v}$, so that in vector notation, Equation (3) can be written

$$\cos \alpha = \frac{\mathbf{u} \cdot \mathbf{v}}{\|\mathbf{u}\|\,\|\mathbf{v}\|}. \qquad (4)$$

From (4), we obtain

▲ $$\mathbf{u} \cdot \mathbf{v} = \|\mathbf{u}\|\,\|\mathbf{v}\| \cos \alpha. \qquad (5)$$

This gives us another expression for the inner product, this time in terms of the norms of $\mathbf{u}$ and $\mathbf{v}$ and the cosine of the angle between their geometric counterparts. Clearly, if either $\mathbf{u}$ or $\mathbf{v}$ is the zero vector, then the right-hand member of (4) is not defined, because the denominator equals zero. On the other hand, (5) is always a valid expression, even when $\mathbf{u}$ or $\mathbf{v}$ or both are zero vectors, since the statement $0 = 0 \cos \alpha$ is true for any value of α. This observation is consistent with our earlier agreement that the zero vector can be assigned any direction angle we choose.

Example 2   If $\mathbf{u}$ and $\mathbf{v}$ are vectors with norms 5 and 8 and direction angles 15° and 135°, respectively, find $\mathbf{u} \cdot \mathbf{v}$.

Solution   From (5),

$$\mathbf{u} \cdot \mathbf{v} = (5)(8) \cos (135° - 15°)$$
$$= 40 \cos 120°$$
$$= (40)(-\tfrac{1}{2}) = -20.$$

Since $\cos(-\alpha) = \cos \alpha$ and $\cos(\alpha + n360°) = \cos \alpha$, $n \in J$, Equation (5) holds for any choice of the angle α between **u** and **v**, not just for $0° \leq \alpha \leq 180°$.

From Equation (5), if neither **u** nor **v** is the zero vector, and if the dot product **u** · **v** is 0, then $\cos \alpha = 0$, and **u** and **v** determine an angle with measure $90°$; hence, **u** and **v** are orthogonal. Again, if one or both of the vectors are the zero vector, then **u** · **v** $= 0$ and the vectors can be considered to be orthogonal since we have agreed that any direction angle whatsoever might be assigned to the zero vector. Conversely, if the vectors are orthogonal, then $\cos \alpha = 0$, so that, by (5), **u** · **v** $= 0$. Hence:

▲   **u** · **v** $= 0$ if and only if **u** and **v** are orthogonal vectors.

The inner product of **v** with itself is

▲ $$\mathbf{v} \cdot \mathbf{v} = \|\mathbf{v}\| \, \|\mathbf{v}\| \cos 0° = \|\mathbf{v}\|^2.$$

More generally, if **u** and **v** are collinear, then $\alpha = 0°$ or $\alpha = 180°$, and $\cos \alpha = \pm 1$, so that, by (5),

$$\mathbf{u} \cdot \mathbf{v} = \pm \|\mathbf{u}\| \, \|\mathbf{v}\|. \tag{6}$$

Conversely, if (6) is satisfied, then either $\|\mathbf{u}\| \, \|\mathbf{v}\| = 0$ and the vectors can be considered to be collinear, or, by (5), $\cos \alpha = \pm 1$ and again the vectors are collinear. Hence:

▲   **u** · **v** $= \pm \|\mathbf{u}\| \, \|\mathbf{v}\|$ if and only if **u** and **v** are collinear vectors.

Figure 6–14 shows two nonzero geometric vectors **u** and **v**, with **u** and **v** forming a right angle. It also shows a third vector **a**, with the angle from **u** to **a** denoted by α.

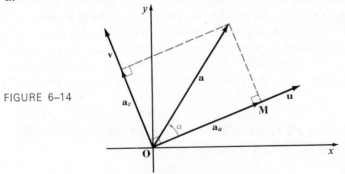

FIGURE 6–14

The **projection** $\mathbf{a}_u$ of **a** on **u** is the vector whose terminal point is obtained by dropping a perpendicular from the terminal point of **a** to the line on which **u** lies. Similarly, $\mathbf{a}_v$ is the projection of **a** on **v**.

By the definition of the sum of two vectors, you have

$$\mathbf{a} = \mathbf{a}_u + \mathbf{a}_v. \tag{7}$$

The vectors $\mathbf{a}_u$ and $\mathbf{a}_v$ are also called the **components of a** parallel to **u** and **v**, respectively.

Since $\mathbf{a}_u$ and **u** are collinear and $\mathbf{u} \neq \mathbf{0}$, $\mathbf{a}_u$ is a scalar multiple of **u**,

$$\mathbf{a}_u = r\mathbf{u}, \ r \in \Re,$$

which we can write as

$$\mathbf{a}_u = r\|\mathbf{u}\| \frac{\mathbf{u}}{\|\mathbf{u}\|} = a_u \frac{\mathbf{u}}{\|\mathbf{u}\|}, \tag{8}$$

where $\dfrac{\mathbf{u}}{\|\mathbf{u}\|}$ is the unit vector in the same direction as **u**, and where we have written a_u for $r\|\mathbf{u}\|$. Note that $|a_u|$ is equal to the norm of $\mathbf{a}_u$ and that a_u is the *directed* distance between **O** and **M**. This distance is positive if $\mathbf{a}_u$ and **u** have the same direction and is negative if they have opposite directions.

By the definition of the cosine function, a_u is given by

$$a_u = \|\mathbf{a}\| \cos \alpha. \tag{9}$$

On the other hand, substituting **a** for **v** in Equation (5), page 199, you have

$$\mathbf{u} \cdot \mathbf{a} = \|\mathbf{u}\| \|\mathbf{a}\| \cos \alpha,$$

so that

$$\|\mathbf{a}\| \cos \alpha = \frac{\mathbf{u} \cdot \mathbf{a}}{\|\mathbf{u}\|}, \tag{10}$$

and accordingly, from (9) and (10),

$$a_u = \frac{\mathbf{u} \cdot \mathbf{a}}{\|\mathbf{u}\|}. \tag{11}$$

Combining (8) and (11), we have

$$\mathbf{a}_u = \frac{\mathbf{u} \cdot \mathbf{a}}{\|\mathbf{u}\|^2} \mathbf{u}. \tag{12}$$

Similarly,

$$\mathbf{a}_v = \frac{\mathbf{v} \cdot \mathbf{a}}{\|\mathbf{v}\|^2} \mathbf{v}. \tag{13}$$

Finally, then, by (7), (12), and (13) on page 201, you have

▲

$$\mathbf{a} = \mathbf{a}_u + \mathbf{a}_v$$

$$= \frac{\mathbf{u} \cdot \mathbf{a}}{\|\mathbf{u}\|^2} \mathbf{u} + \frac{\mathbf{v} \cdot \mathbf{a}}{\|\mathbf{v}\|^2} \mathbf{v}. \tag{14}$$

This means that the coefficients r and s in (1), (3), and (4) in Section 6–2 reduce to the coefficients of $\mathbf{u}$ and $\mathbf{v}$ in (12) and (13), respectively, when $\mathbf{u}$ and $\mathbf{v}$ are orthogonal.

Example 3   Let $\mathbf{u} = \dfrac{\sqrt{3}}{2}\mathbf{i} - \dfrac{1}{2}\mathbf{j}$ and $\mathbf{v} = \dfrac{1}{2}\mathbf{i} + \dfrac{\sqrt{3}}{2}\mathbf{j}$. Find a linear combination of $\mathbf{u}$ and $\mathbf{v}$ equal to

$$2\sqrt{3}\,\mathbf{i} + 4\mathbf{j}.$$

Solution   The vectors $\mathbf{u}$ and $\mathbf{v}$ are orthogonal because

$$\mathbf{u} \cdot \mathbf{v} = \left(\frac{\sqrt{3}}{2}\right)\left(\frac{1}{2}\right) + \left(-\frac{1}{2}\right)\left(\frac{\sqrt{3}}{2}\right) = 0.$$

Moreover, they are unit vectors, because

$$\|\mathbf{u}\|^2 = \left(\frac{\sqrt{3}}{2}\right)^2 + \left(-\frac{1}{2}\right)^2 = 1,$$

and

$$\|\mathbf{v}\|^2 = \left(\frac{1}{2}\right)^2 + \left(\frac{\sqrt{3}}{2}\right)^2 = 1.$$

Letting $\mathbf{a} = 2\sqrt{3}\,\mathbf{i} + 4\mathbf{j}$, by Equation (14), we have

$$\mathbf{a} = (\mathbf{u} \cdot \mathbf{a})\mathbf{u} + (\mathbf{v} \cdot \mathbf{a})\mathbf{v}$$

$$= \left[\left(\frac{\sqrt{3}}{2}\right)(2\sqrt{3}) + (-\tfrac{1}{2})(4)\right]\mathbf{u} + \left[(\tfrac{1}{2})(2\sqrt{3}) + \left(\frac{\sqrt{3}}{2}\right)(4)\right]\mathbf{v},$$

so that

$$\mathbf{a} = \mathbf{u} + 3\sqrt{3}\,\mathbf{v}.$$

Exercises 6–3

Find the inner product $\mathbf{u} \cdot \mathbf{v}$ when $\mathbf{u}$ and $\mathbf{v}$ are as given.

A 1. $\mathbf{u} = \mathbf{j}; \mathbf{v} = \mathbf{j}$ 5. $\mathbf{u} = 5\mathbf{i} + 2\mathbf{j}; \mathbf{v} = 7\mathbf{i} - 3\mathbf{j}$

   2. $\mathbf{u} = \mathbf{i}; \mathbf{v} = \mathbf{i}$ 6. $\mathbf{u} = 2\mathbf{i} - 3\mathbf{j}; \mathbf{v} = 5\mathbf{i} + 7\mathbf{j}$

   3. $\mathbf{u} = \mathbf{i} + \mathbf{j}; \mathbf{v} = \mathbf{i} - \mathbf{j}$ 7. $\mathbf{u} = 2\mathbf{i} + 3\mathbf{j}; \mathbf{v} = 2\mathbf{u}$

   4. $\mathbf{u} = \mathbf{i}; \mathbf{v} = -\mathbf{j}$ 8. $\mathbf{u} = k_1\mathbf{i} + k_1\mathbf{j}; \mathbf{v} = k_2\mathbf{i} - k_2\mathbf{j}$

Find the angle α, $0° \leq \alpha \leq 180°$, between the geometric vectors corresponding to $\mathbf{u}$ and $\mathbf{v}$, when $\mathbf{u}$ and $\mathbf{v}$ are as given.

   9. $\mathbf{u} = (\sqrt{2}, -\sqrt{2}), \mathbf{v} = \left(\dfrac{\sqrt{3}}{2}, \dfrac{1}{2}\right)$ 12. $\mathbf{u} = (3, 2), \mathbf{v} = (-1, 4)$

  10. $\mathbf{u} = \left(\dfrac{1}{2}, \dfrac{\sqrt{3}}{2}\right), \mathbf{v} = (\tfrac{1}{2}, \tfrac{1}{2})$ 13. $\mathbf{u} = (0, 1), \mathbf{v} = \left(\dfrac{1}{2}, -\dfrac{\sqrt{3}}{2}\right)$

  11. $\mathbf{u} = (-1, 0), \mathbf{v} = (-2\sqrt{2}, 2\sqrt{2})$ 14. $\mathbf{u} = (-3, -2), \mathbf{v} = (2, -3)$

Find a linear combination of $\mathbf{u} = \left(\dfrac{\sqrt{3}}{2}, \dfrac{1}{2}\right)$ and $\mathbf{v} = \left(-\dfrac{1}{2}, \dfrac{\sqrt{3}}{2}\right)$ equal to each of the following.

  15. $2\mathbf{i}$ 17. $\dfrac{1}{2}\mathbf{i} + \dfrac{\sqrt{3}}{2}\mathbf{j}$ 19. $-\mathbf{i} + \mathbf{j}$

  16. $-2\mathbf{j}$ 18. $\dfrac{1}{2}\mathbf{i} - \dfrac{\sqrt{3}}{2}\mathbf{j}$ 20. $\mathbf{i} - \mathbf{j}$

If $\mathbf{u}, \mathbf{v}, \mathbf{t} \in V$, and $r, s \in \mathfrak{R}$, prove each of the following.

B 21. $\mathbf{u} \cdot \mathbf{v} = \mathbf{v} \cdot \mathbf{u}$

  22. $r(\mathbf{u} \cdot \mathbf{v}) = (r\mathbf{u}) \cdot \mathbf{v}$

  23. $(r\mathbf{u}) \cdot (s\mathbf{v}) = (rs)(\mathbf{u} \cdot \mathbf{v})$

  24. $\mathbf{u} \cdot (\mathbf{v} + \mathbf{t}) = \mathbf{u} \cdot \mathbf{v} + \mathbf{u} \cdot \mathbf{t}$

  25. $(\mathbf{u} + \mathbf{v}) \cdot \mathbf{t} = \mathbf{u} \cdot \mathbf{t} + \mathbf{v} \cdot \mathbf{t}$

  26. $(\mathbf{u} + \mathbf{v}) \cdot (\mathbf{u} + \mathbf{v}) = \mathbf{u} \cdot \mathbf{u} + (2\mathbf{u}) \cdot \mathbf{v} + \mathbf{v} \cdot \mathbf{v}$

  27. $(\mathbf{u} + \mathbf{v}) \cdot (\mathbf{u} - \mathbf{v}) = \mathbf{u} \cdot \mathbf{u} - \mathbf{v} \cdot \mathbf{v}$

  28. $\|\mathbf{u} + \mathbf{v}\|^2 = (\mathbf{u} + \mathbf{v}) \cdot (\mathbf{u} + \mathbf{v})$

  29. $\|\mathbf{u} + \mathbf{v}\|^2 = \|\mathbf{u}\|^2 + 2\mathbf{u} \cdot \mathbf{v} + \|\mathbf{v}\|^2$

  30. $(\mathbf{u} \cdot \mathbf{v})^2 \leq (\mathbf{u} \cdot \mathbf{u})(\mathbf{v} \cdot \mathbf{v})$

Applications

6–4   *Free Vectors; Navigational Applications*

Any geometric vector in the plane (or in space of any number of dimensions) is called a **free vector**, and is commonly used in physical applications of vectors.

The direction of a free vector in the plane is defined to be the angle formed by the vector and a ray having the same initial point as the vector, and extending in the direction of the positive x-axis. Figure 6–15 shows two free vectors in the xy-plane, with their direction angles indicated in color.

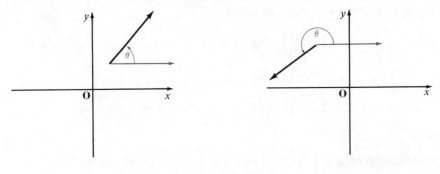

FIGURE 6–15

If two free vectors have the same magnitude (length) and the same direction, they are said to be **equivalent vectors**. Figure 6–16 shows two equivalent vectors, **u** and **v**. You can see from the figure that from *any* point in the plane as initial point, a free vector equivalent to **u** (or **v**) can be drawn. In particular, for every free vector there is an equivalent vector with initial point at the origin. Hence we can use the set of bound vectors V to discuss free vectors, because every vector in the plane can be considered as being moved parallel to itself (translated) so as to make its initial point be at the origin.

It is customary to treat two equivalent vectors as though they were the same vector, and we shall adhere to this practice.*

If **u** and **v** are free vectors, we can represent their sum as we did in Section 6–1, namely, by forming the sum of their equivalent bound vectors as shown in Figure 6–17 on page 205.

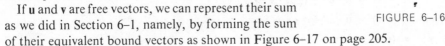

FIGURE 6–16

---

*Logically, it would be more precise to define a new concept, calling the set of *all* vectors equivalent to a given free vector a "vector."

Since, however, we can equivalently translate a free vector wherever we desire, we could also form the sum of **u** and **v** by moving the vector **v** so that its initial

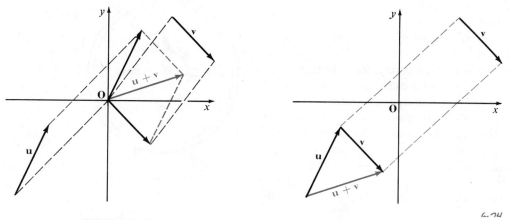

FIGURE 6–17   FIGURE 6–18

point coincides with the terminal point of **u** (Figure 6–18); the sum **u** + **v** is then the vector whose initial point is that of **u** and whose terminal point is the terminal point of **v** in its new position.

If **v** = (x, y), we have defined −**v** to be $(-x, -y)$; alternatively, we could define the vector −**v** to be the vector having the same norm as **v** but with its direction reversed. Free vectors representing **v** and −**v** are shown in Figure 6–19.

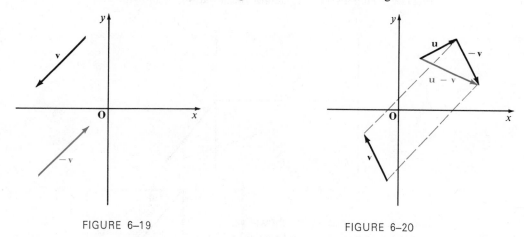

FIGURE 6–19   FIGURE 6–20

Then to form the difference **u** − **v**, which is defined to be **u** + (−**v**), you can move the vector **v** as before, except that the terminal point of **v** (the initial point of −**v**) is made to coincide with the terminal point of **u**. The difference **u** − **v** is then the vector from the initial point of **u** to the initial point of **v** (the terminal point of −**v**). Figure 6–20 shows the difference **u** − **v**.

One direct application of vectors—in particular, one in which free vectors offer an excellent model—is to the navigation of ships and aircraft. Of course, because of the curvature of the earth, vector models provide only an approximation to the actual situation; but if the distances involved are relatively small, the approximation is very good. In these applications, we shall have occasion to use the notion of a *bearing*. A **bearing** is a direction angle measured clockwise from a ray directed to the north. In discussing the direction in which a craft is headed, you use the term **heading** in place of bearing. Figure 6–21 shows a compass rose, marked at intervals of 10°, and showing lines having bearings of 50°, 140°, 220°, and 340°.

FIGURE 6–21

Example 1   A ship steams due east from a harbor. After proceeding for 120 miles on this course, it changes its heading to 140° and steams another 70 miles. How far is the ship from the harbor and what is the bearing from the harbor to the ship?

Solution   First we sketch a vector model for the situation, as shown below.

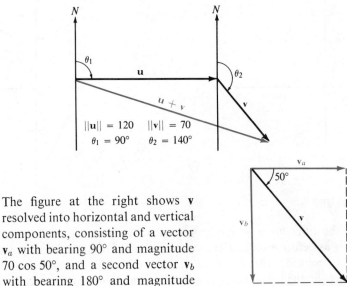

$\|\mathbf{u}\| = 120$ $\|\mathbf{v}\| = 70$
$\theta_1 = 90°$ $\theta_2 = 140°$

The figure at the right shows **v** resolved into horizontal and vertical components, consisting of a vector $\mathbf{v}_a$ with bearing 90° and magnitude 70 cos 50°, and a second vector $\mathbf{v}_b$ with bearing 180° and magnitude 70 sin 50°.

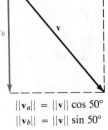

$\|\mathbf{v}_a\| = \|\mathbf{v}\| \cos 50°$
$\|\mathbf{v}_b\| = \|\mathbf{v}\| \sin 50°$

Combining these two, we have the geometric picture shown below.

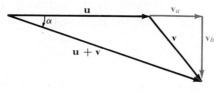

Now

$$\|\mathbf{v}_a\| = 70 \cos 50° \doteq 70(0.6428) \doteq 45.00$$

and

$$\|\mathbf{v}_b\| = 70 \sin 50° \doteq 70(0.7660) = 53.62,$$

so that we have a right triangle with one side of length

$$\|\mathbf{u} + \mathbf{v}_a\| \doteq 120 + 45.00 = 165.00,$$

and the other of length

$$\|\mathbf{v}_b\| \doteq 53.62.$$

Next, the bearing of $\mathbf{u} + \mathbf{v}$ can be obtained by finding the reference angle α using the relationship

$$\tan \alpha \doteq \frac{53.62}{165.00} \doteq 0.3250,$$

so that

$$\alpha \doteq 18°00'.$$

Hence, the bearing of the ship from the harbor is approximately

$$90° + 18° = 108°.$$

We can find the distance from the harbor to the ship by means of the relationship

$$\|\mathbf{u} + \mathbf{v}\| = \frac{\|\mathbf{u} + \mathbf{v}_a\|}{\cos \alpha} \doteq \frac{165.00}{0.9511} \doteq 173.48,$$

so the ship is approximately 173.48 miles from the harbor.

An alternative means of computing the bearing and the distance of the ship from the harbor is to use the Law of Cosines to find the distance, and then the Law of Sines to find the reference angle for the bearing. Such an approach does not depend upon vector considerations, however, and will not be discussed in detail here. Still another method of computing the bearing and distance is by means of graphical devices.

Example 2   An airliner is flying at 520 miles per hour on a compass heading of 35°. A wind of 70 miles per hour is blowing from the north, that is, from a direction of 0°. What is the **true course** (the heading parallel to the ground) of the airplane, and what is its **ground speed** (actual speed over the ground)?

Solution   A vector model of this situation is shown at the right.

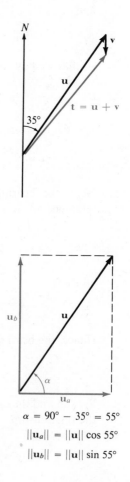

The vector **u** represents the direction and speed of the plane in still air, with $\|\mathbf{u}\| = 520$. The vector **v** represents the direction and speed of the wind, with $\|\mathbf{v}\| = 70$. The vector **t** represents the direction and speed of the plane over the ground, and we wish to find its direction and magnitude, which correspond to the true course and ground speed of the plane.

To find the horizontal and vertical components of **t**, we first resolve **u** into its components. Thus, $\mathbf{u} = \mathbf{u}_a + \mathbf{u}_b$, where $\mathbf{u}_a$ is the horizontal and $\mathbf{u}_b$ the vertical component of **u**. We have

$$\|\mathbf{u}_a\| = \|\mathbf{u}\| \cos \alpha = 520 \cos 55°$$
$$\doteq 520(0.5736) \doteq 298.27$$

and

$$\|\mathbf{u}_b\| = \|\mathbf{u}\| \sin \alpha = 520 \sin 55°$$
$$\doteq 520(0.8192)$$
$$\doteq 425.98.$$

$$\alpha = 90° - 35° = 55°$$
$$\|\mathbf{u}_a\| = \|\mathbf{u}\| \cos 55°$$
$$\|\mathbf{u}_b\| = \|\mathbf{u}\| \sin 55°$$

The resolution of **u** into $\mathbf{u}_a$ and $\mathbf{u}_b$ gives the picture at the right in terms of free vectors, from which you can see that the components of **t** are $\mathbf{u}_a$ and $\mathbf{u}_b + \mathbf{v}$. Since **v** is of opposite direction to $\mathbf{u}_b$,

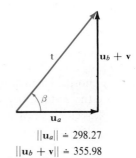

$$\|\mathbf{u}_b + \mathbf{v}\| = \|\mathbf{u}_b\| - \|\mathbf{v}\|$$
$$\doteq 425.98 - 70 = 355.98.$$

We then have the picture shown at the right. The true heading is $90° - \beta$, where β is given by

$$\tan \beta \doteq \frac{355.98}{298.27} \doteq 1.1935,$$

so that

$$\beta \doteq 50°2'.$$

$$\|\mathbf{u}_a\| \doteq 298.27$$
$$\|\mathbf{u}_b + \mathbf{v}\| \doteq 355.98$$

The true course of the plane, then, is approximately $90° - 50°2'$, or $39°58'$.

To find the ground speed, we can find $\|\mathbf{t}\|$ by using

$$\|\mathbf{t}\| = \frac{\|\mathbf{u}_a\|}{\cos \beta} \doteq \frac{298.27}{0.6424} \doteq 464.31.$$

Thus, the ground speed is approximately 464.31 miles per hour.

Again, in actual practice, computations such as this are ordinarily handled by means of various short-cut approximation devices.

Exercises 6–4

In Exercises 1–6, use scale drawings to find approximate solutions. Use the largest scale that is reasonable with the given data.

Example A ship steams 45 miles due north, turns to a heading of 45° and steams 25 miles, then turns south and steams 40 miles. How far is it from its starting place, and what is its bearing from its starting place?

(*Solution on next page*)

Solution Use a ruler and a protractor. If you use a large enough scale (say, 1 inch to 10 miles), you can obtain quite reasonable accuracy. You first lay off the vector representing the 45-mile leg to the

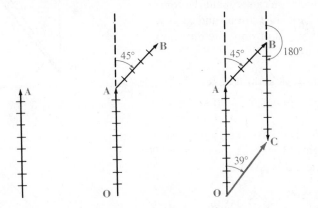

north. Then, at the terminal point **A**, lay off a vector representing the 25-mile trip on a heading of 45°. Next, from **B**, lay off the vector representing the 40-mile leg to the south, on a heading of 180°.

If you now connect points **O** and **C**, you have the sum of the geometric vectors **OA**, **AB**, and **BC**. When you measure ∠AOC, you find that it measures approximately 39°, and hence the bearing of the ship from its starting place is approximately 39°. The length of vector **OC** shows that the ship is approximately 28 miles from where it started.

A **1.** A ship steams 100 miles east, and then 40 miles on a heading of 120°. How far is the ship and how does it bear from its starting point?

2. A ship sails 150 miles on a heading of 220° and then turns and sails directly east for 50 miles. How far is the ship and how does it bear from its starting point?

3. An airplane flies on a compass heading of 90° at 200 miles per hour. The wind affecting the plane is blowing from 300° at 30 miles per hour. What is the true course and ground speed of the airplane?

4. Let the airplane in Exercise 3 fly 250 miles per hour on a heading of 180°. If the wind direction and speed are the same as given, what are the true course and ground speed of the airplane?

5. At what compass heading and air speed should an aircraft fly if a wind of 40 miles per hour is blowing from the north, and the pilot wants to maintain a ground speed of 200 miles per hour on a true course of 90°?

6. Let the wind in Exercise 5 be blowing at 40 miles per hour from 305°, while the pilot still maintains the same true course and ground speed. What should be his compass heading and air speed?

In Exercises 7–12, find answers by computation to the nearest unit for distance or speed, and the nearest degree for bearing.

7. A ship is moving through the water on a compass heading of 30° at a speed of 20 knots (nautical miles per hour). It is traveling in a current that causes the ship to move on a path with a heading of 45°. Find the speed of the current if it is flowing directly from the north.

8. A plane is flying with a compass heading of 300° at an air speed of 300 miles per hour. If its true course is observed to be 330°, and if the wind is blowing from 245°, what is the speed of the wind?

9. Two ships leave a harbor, one traveling at 20 knots on a course of 80° and the other at 24 knots on a course of 140°. How far apart are the ships after two hours? What is the bearing from the first ship to the second at that time?

10. Two airplanes leave an airport at noon, one flying on a true course of 345° and the other on a true course of 45°. If the first airplane averages 240 miles per hour ground speed and the other 200 miles per hour ground speed, how far apart are the airplanes after one hour? How does the second airplane bear from the first?

11. A pilot makes a flight plan that will take him from city A to city B, a distance of 400 miles. City B bears 60° from city A, and the wind at the planned flight altitude is 30 miles per hour from 160°. If the airplane cruises at 320 miles per hour air speed, and if the pilot takes off at noon, what will be his compass heading and what is his ETA (estimated time of arrival) at city B?

12. When the pilot in Exercise 11 decides to return to city A, the wind has shifted to 40 miles per hour from 90°. What must be his compass heading for the return trip, and, if he takes off at 6:00 P.M., what will be his ETA at city A?

6–5 *Vector Applications to Forces*

Another common application of vector models is to systems of forces. In physics, we learn the following two principles about forces acting on a body:

1. When a body is at rest, or in motion with constant velocity, the sum of the forces acting on the body is zero.

2. The force on a body due to gravity (that is, the **weight** of the body) acts vertically downward toward the center of mass of the earth.

These principles, together with the mathematical concept of a vector, make it possible to solve force problems involving inclined planes, cables, and other objects.

Example 1   A 1000-pound crate rests on a ramp that slopes upward at an angle measuring 25°. Find to the nearest pound the magnitude of the force normal (perpendicular) to the ramp exerted on the crate by the ramp, and that of the force of friction parallel to the ramp that keeps the crate from sliding down the ramp.

Solution   A diagram of the situation looks like this:

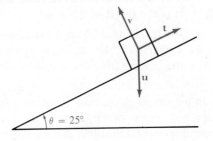

The vector **u** denotes the force on the crate due to gravity. It has a magnitude of 1000 pounds. The vectors **v** and **t** are the forces on the crate normal to the ramp and parallel to the ramp, respectively. These three are the only forces acting on the crate. According to Principle 1, page 211, the resultant of the vector sum **u** + **v** + **t** is the zero vector. Geometrically, this means that the terminal point of the third vector, which is added to the sum of the other two vectors as in the accompanying figure, coincides with the initial point of the first vector; that is, **u**, **v**, and **t** form a triangle. From the diagram at the right, we see that we must have

$$\|\mathbf{v}\| = \|\mathbf{u}\| \cos \theta$$

and

$$\|\mathbf{t}\| = \|\mathbf{u}\| \sin \theta,$$

so that

$$\|\mathbf{v}\| = \|\mathbf{u}\| \cos 25° \doteq 1000(0.9063) \doteq 906,$$

and

$$\|\mathbf{t}\| = \|\mathbf{u}\| \sin 25° \doteq 1000(0.4226) \doteq 423.$$

Hence the magnitude of the force normal to the ramp, exerted on the crate by the ramp, is approximately 906 pounds, while that of the force of friction on the crate, parallel to the ramp, is about 423 pounds.

Example 2   A loading ramp makes an angle of 22° with the horizontal. A box weighing 130 pounds slides down the ramp at constant velocity. What is the force of friction acting on the box?

Solution   A diagram of the situation looks like this:

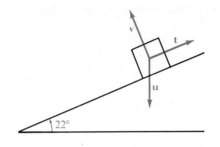

Since the box is moving with constant velocity, by Principle 1 the sum of the forces acting upon it must be zero. As in Example 1, we have

$$\|\mathbf{t}\| = \|\mathbf{u}\| \sin \theta.$$

Therefore,

$$\|\mathbf{t}\| = 130 \sin 22° = 130(0.3746) \doteq 48.7.$$

Hence the magnitude of the frictional force **t**, which acts in the direction opposite to that of the motion, must be approximately 48.7 pounds.

When a body moves with a constant speed around a circle, it can be considered to be acted upon by a force directed radially outward from the center of the circle in the plane of rotation. This force is called **centrifugal force.** (Actually, centrifugal force is an "inertial reaction" that appears to be a force when observed in a rotating system. In problem solving, however, it is usually treated as if it were a force.)

Example 3   A cable is attached to the top of a pole, and a 100-pound ball at the other end of the cable swings with constant speed in a circle parallel to the ground. As it swings around, the cable makes an angle of 30° with its support. What are the centrifugal force on the ball and the force exerted on the ball by the cable?

(Solution on next page)

Solution   A diagram of the rotating plane of the pole and the cable is shown at the right. The vector **u** represents the force exerted by the cable on the ball, **v** the centrifugal force on the ball, and **t** the force on the ball due to gravity. In accordance with Principle 1 on page 211, since the ball does not move out of the plane, the sum of these three forces must be zero. That is,

$$\mathbf{u} + \mathbf{v} + \mathbf{t} = \mathbf{0}.$$

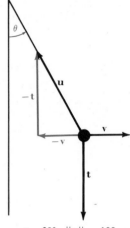

$\theta = 30°, \ \|\mathbf{t}\| = 100$

This means that the horizontal and vertical components of **u** must have norms equal to the norms of **v** and **t**, respectively, and must be of opposite direction to **v** and **t**; that is, they must be equal to $-\mathbf{v}$ and $-\mathbf{t}$, respectively. Since $\|-\mathbf{t}\| = 100$, the vertical component, $-\mathbf{t}$, of **u** must have norm equal to 100, so that

$$\|\mathbf{u}\| \cos 30° = 100,$$

$$\|\mathbf{u}\| \left(\frac{\sqrt{3}}{2} \right) = 100,$$

$$\|\mathbf{u}\| = \frac{200}{\sqrt{3}} \doteq 115.5.$$

Thus, the magnitude of the force exerted by the cable on the ball is approximately 116 pounds. Next, we can find the norm of $-\mathbf{v}$, the horizontal component of **u**, by computing

$$\|-\mathbf{v}\| = \|\mathbf{u}\| \sin 30°$$

$$\doteq 115.5(\tfrac{1}{2})$$

$$\doteq 57.8.$$

Since the norm of $-\mathbf{v}$ is equal to the norm of **v**, the magnitude of the centrifugal force exerted on the ball is approximately 58 pounds.

Exercises 6–5

In each of the following, find answers to the nearest pound or to the nearest degree.

A   **1.** An object on an inclined plane weighs 500 pounds, and the plane makes an angle of 30° with the horizontal. What force, normal to the plane, is exerted on the body by the plane? What is the resultant of this force and the force of gravity?

    2. A weight of 800 pounds is on an inclined plane making a 16° angle with the horizontal. Find the components of the weight normal to the plane and parallel to the plane.

    3. A box resting on an inclined plane weighs 120 pounds. If the plane makes an angle of 20° with the horizontal, and a force of 55 pounds parallel to the plane is necessary to keep the box moving with constant speed up the plane, what is the force of friction acting on the box in the direction parallel to and down the plane?

    4. A 400-pound motor slides with constant speed down a loading ramp that makes an angle of 18° with the horizontal. What is the frictional force acting on the motor?

    5. An object on the end of a rope that is attached to the top of a pole is swinging with constant speed around a circle. If the rope makes an angle of 35° with the pole, and if the magnitude of the centrifugal force acting on the object is 60 pounds, find the weight of the object and the pull of the rope on the object.

    6. A governor for an engine consists of two weights suspended by metal rods. As the speed of the engine increases, the rods diverge from the central supporting column. When they reach a critical position, they stop the flow of fuel to the engine. If each weight on such a governor is 40 pounds, and if the magnitude of the centrifugal force on each weight is 80 pounds, what angle will each suspension rod make with the vertical support? Assume that the weight of the rod has no effect on the situation.

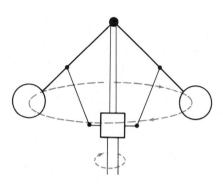

7. Three coplanar forces (forces in the same plane) act on a particle. Force *A* is 20 pounds in a direction of 30° counterclockwise from the positive *x*-direction. Forces *B* and *C* are 30 and 35 pounds, in directions 120° and 210° counterclockwise from the positive *x*-direction, respectively. What force (magnitude and direction) would have to be applied to the particle to maintain equilibrium, that is, to result in a zero sum for the forces?

8. Four coplanar forces of 30, 50, 70, and 80 pounds act on a body, with directions counterclockwise from the positive *x*-direction of 60°, 90°, 240°, and 330°, respectively. Find the magnitude and direction of the additional force necessary to maintain equilibrium.

9. A weight of 1000 pounds is suspended by two cables. One cable makes an angle of 23° with the vertical and the other an angle of 20° with the vertical. In pounds, what is the tension in each cable?

10. A 100-pound weight is suspended by two ropes making angles of 30° and 45°, respectively, with the vertical. In pounds, what is the tension in each rope?

Polar Coordinates and Graphs

6–6 *Polar Coordinates*

The concept of a vector can be used to establish a new coordinate system in the plane. In this system, called the **polar coordinate system**, we use the notion of a directed distance from a fixed point to locate other points in the plane.

Since you are familiar with the Cartesian coordinate system, let us call the ray that is the nonnegative *x*-axis the **polar axis** in the new system, and let us call the origin the **pole**. In our new system, we can locate any point in the plane by giving its directed distance from the pole. We shall ordinarily use the Greek letter ρ (rho) to denote the distance from the pole to the point, and θ to denote the direction angle from the polar axis to the direction line from the pole to the point. Thus the polar coordinates of a point having Cartesian coordinates (x, y) are (ρ, θ), as shown in Figure 6–22.

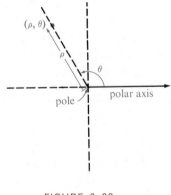

FIGURE 6–22

In the polar coordinate system, the number ρ is not necessarily the norm of the vector (x, y); rather, it is either the norm or its negative. By agreement, we shall identify positive ρ with a distance measured from the pole in the direction of the terminal side (ray) of θ, and negative ρ with a distance measured along the extension of the terminal side of θ through the pole (Figure 6-23). We shall also, of course, permit θ to assume negative values, and as usual we shall

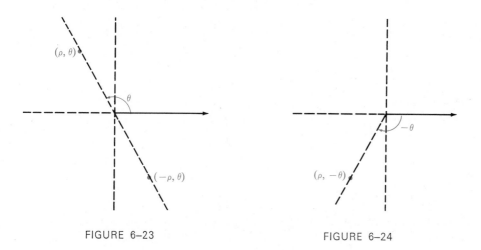

FIGURE 6–23   FIGURE 6–24

consider these to correspond to angles measured in a clockwise direction from the polar axis (Figure 6–24).

Example 1   Graph the points whose polar coordinates are (3, 60°), (−2, 135°), and (1, 0°).

Solution   It is convenient first to identify the line of direction of the angle θ and then to measure the distance ρ along this line. The figures show the procedure in each case.

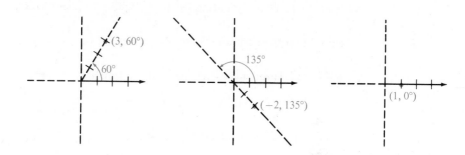

A polar coordinate system differs from a Cartesian coordinate system in that there is an unlimited number of pairs of polar coordinates associated with each point in the plane. For example, the point whose polar coordinates are (3, 45°)

[Figure 6–25] can also be identified by $(-3, 225°)$ or by $(-3, -135°)$. In fact, if n is any integer, the expressions $(3, 45° + n360°)$ and $(-3, 225° + n360°)$ can be used to designate the same point, since the addition of 360° to any value of θ does not change the direction denoted by θ.

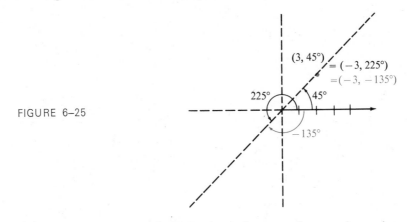

FIGURE 6–25

To describe the pole, the ordered pair $(0, \theta)$, where θ has *any* value, may be used. In polar coordinates, angles can be designated by either radian measure or degree measure. Thus, $\left(3, \dfrac{\pi^R}{4}\right)$ and $(3, 45°)$ represent the same point.

Example 2   Find three additional pairs of coordinates for the point associated with $\left(6, \dfrac{3\pi^R}{4}\right)$.

Solution   To obtain a pair of coordinates having $\rho = -6$, we simply advance θ by π^R, so that another set of coordinates for $\left(6, \dfrac{3\pi^R}{4}\right)$ is $\left(-6, \dfrac{7\pi^R}{4}\right)$. Then by adding $2\pi^R$ to $\dfrac{3\pi^R}{4}$ and $\dfrac{7\pi^R}{4}$, respectively, we can obtain the additional sets of coordinates $\left(6, \dfrac{11\pi^R}{4}\right)$ and $\left(-6, \dfrac{15\pi^R}{4}\right)$. Three additional pairs of coordinates, therefore, are $\left(-6, \dfrac{7\pi^R}{4}\right)$, $\left(6, \dfrac{11\pi^R}{4}\right)$, and $\left(-6, \dfrac{15\pi^R}{4}\right)$. Of course, there is an unlimited number of other possible answers.

Just as an equation in x and y can be represented by a graph on the geometric plane with a Cartesian coordinate system, so also does an equation in ρ and θ have a graph on the geometric plane relative to a polar coordinate system. Indeed, each equation in x and y has a counterpart in ρ and θ, and vice versa; that is, there exist both polar and Cartesian equations with the same graph. It is sometimes more convenient to use one coordinate system and sometimes the other, but you can always transform an equation in x and y to an equation in ρ and θ with the same graph by observing (Figure 6–26) that x is the scalar component of the vector associated with a given ρ and θ on the polar axis, or the polar axis extended through the pole in case $x < 0$. Consequently,

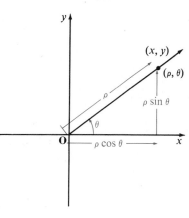

▲ $$x = \rho \cos \theta. \tag{1}$$

Similarly, y is the scalar component of the same vector on the line with equation $\theta = 90°$, which is the y-axis in the corresponding Cartesian coordinate system; hence

▲ $$y = \rho \sin \theta. \tag{2}$$

FIGURE 6–26

Equations (1) and (2) are equations of substitution when transforming from Cartesian to polar coordinates.

You are familiar with the use of rectangular-coordinate graph paper from your earlier courses. There is also a special polar-coordinate graph paper for graphing

FIGURE 6–27

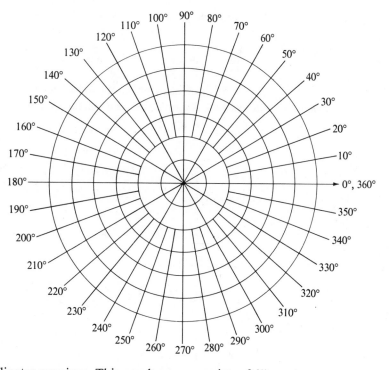

points whose polar coordinates are given. This graph paper consists of (1) a set of rays radiating from the pole and (2) a set of concentric circles with the pole as center (see Figure 6–27, page 219). The measures of angles determined by the rays are frequently shown in multiples of 10° or, alternatively, $\dfrac{\pi^R}{18}$, and the radii of the circles are multiples of some convenient unit of linear measure. To locate a point with coordinates (ρ, θ), you simply count ρ units out from the pole along the ray labeled $m°(\theta)$.

Example 3 Transform the equation defining each set into polar coordinate form and graph the set using both Cartesian and polar coordinates.

(a) $\{(x, y): x = 2\}$ (b) $\{(x, y): y = x\}$

(c) $\{(x, y): x^2 + y^2 = 9\}$

Solution (a) Since $x = \rho \cos \theta$ and $x = 2$, the set

$$\{(x, y): x = 2\}$$

is transformed into the set

$$\{(\rho, \theta): \rho \cos \theta = 2\}.$$

Writing $\rho \cos \theta = 2$ in the equivalent form

$$\rho = \frac{2}{\cos \theta}$$

may be helpful in determining points on the polar graph. For example, we note that as θ increases from 0° toward 90°, the numbers $\dfrac{2}{\cos \theta} = \rho$ increase without bound.

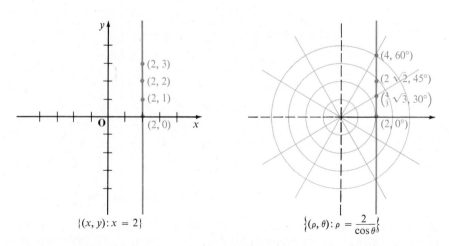

$\{(x, y): x = 2\}$ $\left\{(\rho, \theta): \rho = \dfrac{2}{\cos \theta}\right\}$

(b) Substituting $x = \rho \cos \theta$ and $y = \rho \sin \theta$ into the equation $y = x$ gives

$$\rho \cos \theta = \rho \sin \theta, \text{ or equivalently,}$$

$$\rho(\cos \theta - \sin \theta) = 0.$$

The graph of this equation is the union of the graphs of

$$\rho = 0 \tag{3}$$

and $$\cos \theta - \sin \theta = 0. \tag{4}$$

The graph of (3) is just a single point, the pole. Hence, if the graph of (4) contains the pole, then (3) contributes nothing additional to the graph, and the graph of (4) is the same as that of the given equation. Since the pole can be assigned any angle and since (4) is equivalent to

$$\frac{\sin \theta}{\cos \theta} = 1, \tan \theta = 1, \quad \text{or} \quad \theta = 45°,$$

the point $(0, 45°)$ both corresponds to the pole and satisfies (4). Therefore, (4) is the desired equation.

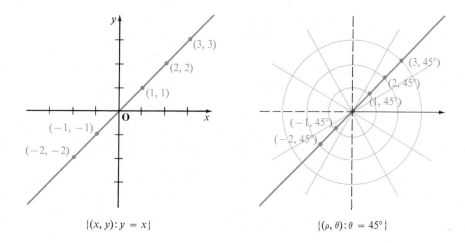

$\{(x, y): y = x\}$ $\{(\rho, \theta): \theta = 45°\}$

(c) Substituting $x = \rho \cos \theta$ and $y = \rho \sin \theta$ in $x^2 + y^2 = 9$, we have

$$(\rho \cos \theta)^2 + (\rho \sin \theta)^2 = 9,$$

$$\rho^2(\cos^2 \theta + \sin^2 \theta) = 9,$$

or simply $$\rho^2 = 9.$$

(Solution continued)

Thus we have $\{(\rho, \theta): \rho^2 = 9\}$, which is the union of the sets

$$\{(\rho, \theta): \rho = 3\} \text{ and } \{(\rho, \theta): \rho = -3\}. \qquad (5)$$

Since the conditions $\rho = 3$ and $\rho = -3$ describe the same set, namely a circle of radius 3 with center at the pole, the set can be described by either expression.

Therefore the desired description is either $\rho = 3$ or $\rho = -3$.

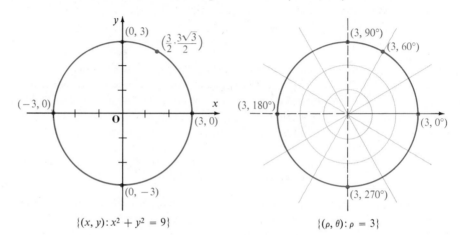

$$\{(x, y): x^2 + y^2 = 9\} \qquad\qquad \{(\rho, \theta): \rho = 3\}$$

Looking back at Figure 6–26, you can see that equations of substitution when transforming from a polar to the associated Cartesian coordinate system are given by

$$\rho = \pm\sqrt{x^2 + y^2}, \qquad (6)$$

and $\quad \theta = \mathrm{Tan}^{-1} \dfrac{y}{x}$ for x and ρ of the same sign,

$$(7)$$

$$\theta = \mathrm{Tan}^{-1} \frac{y}{x} + \pi^{R} \text{ for } x \text{ and } \rho \text{ of opposite signs.}$$

Here the selection of sign for the radical expression is governed by the sign of ρ. Thus, for $\rho < 0$ you choose $-\sqrt{x^2 + y^2}$, and for $\rho \geq 0$ you choose $\sqrt{x^2 + y^2}$.

Whenever $\sin \theta$ and $\cos \theta$ appear in polar equations, they can be replaced by

$$\sin \theta = \frac{y}{\sqrt{x^2 + y^2}} \qquad (8)$$

and $$\cos \theta = \frac{x}{\sqrt{x^2 + y^2}}, \qquad (9)$$

for $\rho > 0$, and the negatives of these expressions for $\rho < 0$.

Of course when $\rho = 0$ (that is, at the origin, where $x^2 + y^2 = 0$), $\sin \theta$ and $\cos \theta$ are indeterminate. Similar comments apply to the other trigonometric functions.

Example 4   Find a Cartesian equation for the graph of $\rho^2 = 16 \cos \theta$.

Solution   Using the substitutions given in (6) and (9), we obtain

$$(\pm\sqrt{x^2 + y^2})^2 = 16 \left(\frac{\pm x}{\sqrt{x^2 + y^2}}\right),$$

or $$x^2 + y^2 = \frac{\pm 16x}{\sqrt{x^2 + y^2}} \qquad (x^2 + y^2 \neq 0). \qquad (10)$$

The restriction $x^2 + y^2 \neq 0$ is needed at this point if the right-hand member of the equation is to have meaning. Since the graph of the given polar equation does contain the origin, however, we want $(0, 0)$ to satisfy our Cartesian equation. Thus let us multiply (10) by $\sqrt{x^2 + y^2}$ to obtain

$$(x^2 + y^2)^{\frac{3}{2}} = \pm 16x,$$

or

$$(x^2 + y^2)^3 = 256x^2,$$

which contains $(0, 0)$ in its solution set and hence is the equation we seek.

Exercises 6–6

Graph each of the given pairs of polar coordinates in the plane, and find the Cartesian coordinates of the point.

A   **1.** $(3, 180°)$ **3.** $(2, 60°)$ **5.** $(-2, 210°)$ **7.** $(-2, 300°)$

  2. $\left(4, \frac{\pi}{2}^R\right)$ **4.** $\left(7, \frac{5\pi}{6}^R\right)$ **6.** $\left(-3, \frac{11\pi}{6}^R\right)$ **8.** $\left(-3, -\frac{9\pi}{4}^R\right)$

Graph each of the given pairs of Cartesian coordinates in the plane and find a pair of polar coordinates of the point.

  9. $(3, 3)$ **11.** $\left(\frac{\sqrt{3}}{2}, -\frac{1}{2}\right)$ **13.** $\left(-\frac{5}{2}, -\frac{5\sqrt{3}}{2}\right)$ **15.** $(3, 4)$

  10. $(-2, -2)$ **12.** $\left(-\frac{3\sqrt{3}}{2}, \frac{3}{2}\right)$ **14.** $(4\sqrt{2}, -4\sqrt{2})$ **16.** $(3, 12)$

Transform the equation defining each set into polar form and graph the set using both Cartesian and polar coordinates.

17. $\{(x, y): x = 4\}$ **21.** $\{(x, y): y + x = 0\}$

18. $\{(x, y): x = -3\}$ **22.** $\{(x, y): y - x = 1\}$

19. $\{(x, y): y = 2\}$ **23.** $\{(x, y): x^2 + y^2 = 16\}$

20. $\{(x, y): y = -1\}$ **24.** $\{(x, y): x + y = 4\}$

Graph each of the following sets of points.

25. $\{(\rho, \theta): \rho = 3\}$ **28.** $\{(\rho, \theta): \theta = -60°\}$

26. $\{(\rho, \theta): \theta = 30°\}$ **29.** $\{(\rho, \theta): \rho \cos \theta = 6\}$

27. $\{(\rho, \theta): \rho = -2\}$ **30.** $\{(\rho, \theta): \rho \sin \theta = -2\}$

Transform each of the following equations from polar to Cartesian coordinates.

31. $\rho = 6$ **34.** $\rho = 3 \cos \theta$

32. $\rho = 2$ **35.** $\rho^2 = 4 \sin \theta$

33. $\theta = \frac{3}{4}\pi^R$ **36.** $\rho \sin \theta = \rho^2 \cos \theta$

Find all points in the intersection of each of the following pairs of sets.

B **37.** $\{(\rho, \theta): \rho = 4\} \cap \{(\rho, \theta): \rho = 4 \sin \theta\}$

38. $\{(\rho, \theta): \rho = 2\} \cap \{(\rho, \theta): \rho = 4 \sin 2\theta\}$

39. $\{(\rho, \theta): \rho = 3\} \cap \{(\rho, \theta): \theta = 120°\}$

40. Show that the graph of the equation $\rho = 2 \sin \theta$ is a circle containing the origin.

C **41.** Show that the distance between the points (ρ_1, θ_1) and (ρ_2, θ_2) is given by

$$\sqrt{\rho_1^2 + \rho_2^2 - 2\rho_1\rho_2 \cos (\theta_1 - \theta_2)}.$$

42. Use the result of Exercise 41 to show that a polar equation for a circle of radius a with center at (ρ_1, θ_1) is $\rho^2 + \rho_1^2 - 2\rho\rho_1 \cos (\theta - \theta_1) = a^2$.

6–7 *Graphs of Polar Equations*

In the preceding section, we established a polar coordinate system and found a way of converting polar equations to Cartesian equations, and vice versa. We discussed these conversions in terms of finding equations in the two systems whose graphs were the same. In this section, we shall examine ways of graphing solution sets of polar equations directly, without converting to Cartesian coordinates.

Example 1   Sketch the graph of $\rho = 2 \cos \theta$.

Solution   First we prepare a table showing how ρ varies with θ.

θ		$\cos \theta$		$\rho = 2 \cos \theta$	
0° to 45°	↑	1 to 0.71	↓	2 to 1.41	↓
45° to 90°	↑	0.71 to 0	↓	1.41 to 0	↓
90° to 135°	↑	0 to −0.71	↓	0 to −1.41	↓
135° to 180°	↑	−0.71 to −1	↓	−1.41 to −2	↓

From the table, we see that as θ increases from 0° to 90°, ρ decreases from 2 to 0. As θ increases from 90° to 180°, ρ decreases from 0 to −2, describing points in the fourth quadrant.

If we were to plot points for θ between 180° and 360°, we would obtain the same points obtained using θ between 0° and 180°; this follows from the identity $\cos \theta = -\cos (\theta + 180°)$.

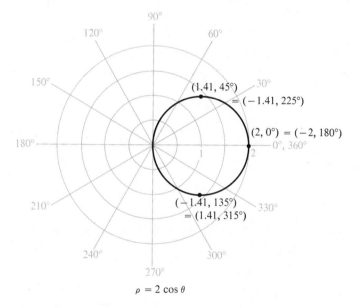

$\rho = 2 \cos \theta$

The graph appears to be a circle with center at $(1, 0°)$ and radius 1. That this is the case can be shown by transforming the polar equation $\rho = 2 \cos \theta$ to a Cartesian equation by use of Equations (6) and (9) of Section 6–6, obtaining

$$(x - 1)^2 + y^2 = 1,$$

which is the Cartesian equation of a circle with center at point $(1, 0)$ and radius 1.

Example 2   Sketch the graph of $\rho = 2 \cos 2\theta$.

Solution   Before starting the graph, we make a table showing how ρ varies with θ, thus:

θ		2θ		$\cos 2\theta$		$\rho = 2 \cos 2\theta$		Portion of The Graph
0° to 45°	↑	0° to 90°	↑	1 to 0	↓	2 to 0	↓	1
45° to 90°	↑	90° to 180°	↑	0 to −1	↓	0 to −2	↓	2
90° to 135°	↑	180° to 270°	↑	−1 to 0	↑	−2 to 0	↑	3
135° to 180°	↑	270° to 360°	↑	0 to 1	↑	0 to 2	↑	4

The numbers 1, 2, 3, 4 in the right-hand column of the above table provide one way of indicating the corresponding portions of the graph.

From the table, we see that as θ increases from 0° to 45°, ρ decreases from 2 to 0 (portion 1 of the graph, as shown at the left below). Next, we see that from $\theta = 45°$ to $\theta = 90°$, ρ decreases from 0 to −2; and that from $\theta = 90°$ to $\theta = 135°$, ρ increases from −2 to 0. Thus we add portions 2 and 3 to the sketch, shown at the right below.

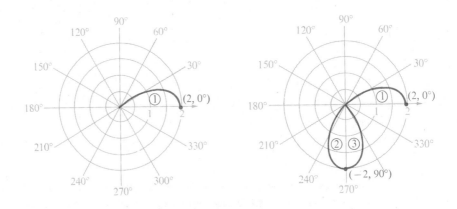

By continuing this process over successive intervals of 45° for θ, we can obtain the complete graph. This graph is an example of a **four-leafed rose**. The complete graph is shown at the top of page 227.

In the figure, the numerals (5) through (8) indicate the portions of the graph described as θ increases from 180° to 360°.

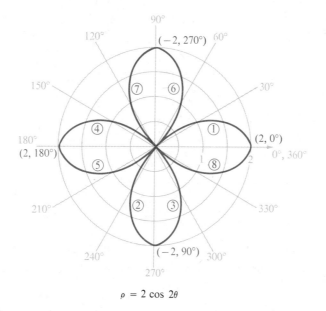

$$\rho = 2 \cos 2\theta$$

Example 3   Sketch the graph of $\rho = 1 + \sin 3\theta$.

Solution   Again, we make a table showing how ρ varies with θ.

θ		3θ		$\sin 3\theta$		$\rho = 1 + \sin 3\theta$	
0° to 30°	↑	0° to 90°	↑	0 to 1	↑	1 to 2	↑
30° to 60°	↑	90° to 180°	↑	1 to 0	↓	2 to 1	↓
60° to 90°	↑	180° to 270°	↑	0 to −1	↓	1 to 0	↓
90° to 120°	↑	270° to 360°	↑	−1 to 0	↑	0 to 1	↑
120° to 150°	↑	360° to 450°	↑	0 to 1	↑	1 to 2	↑
150° to 180°	↑	450° to 540°	↑	1 to 0	↓	2 to 1	↓

By sketching over successive intervals of 30° for θ, we obtain the graph of $\rho = 1 + \sin 3\theta$, as shown on the top of page 228. Notice that the graph is symmetric with respect to the lines $\theta = 30°$, $\theta = 150°$, and $\theta = 270°$.

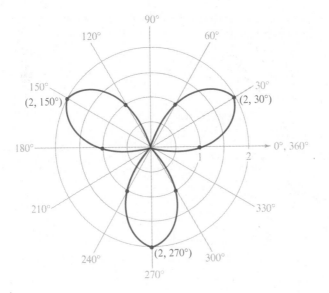

It is sometimes helpful in sketching graphs of polar equations to use the following facts.

1. If replacing θ by $-\theta$ in a polar equation does not change the solution set of the equation, then the graph of the equation is symmetric with respect to the line containing the polar axis.

   For instance, in Example 1 the solution set of the equation $\rho = 2 \cos \theta$ is unchanged if θ is replaced with $-\theta$, because $\cos (-\theta) = \cos \theta$.

2. If replacing ρ by $-\rho$ in a polar equation does not change the solution set of the equation, then the graph of the equation is symmetric with respect to the pole.

   For example, if ρ is replaced with $-\rho$ in $\rho^2 = 4 \cos 2\theta$, the solution set of the equation is unchanged because $\rho^2 = (-\rho)^2$. Figure 6-28 shows the graph of $\rho^2 = 4 \cos 2\theta$, which is symmetric with respect to the pole.

3. If replacing θ by $180° - \theta$ in a polar equation does not change the solution set of the equation, then the graph of the equation is symmetric with respect to the line $\theta = 90°$ (the y-axis in the Cartesian system).

   In Example 3, if θ is replaced with $180° - \theta$ in $\rho = 1 + \sin 3\theta$, the solution set of the equation remains unchanged.

You should note that these observations about symmetry are *sufficient* conditions for symmetry; that is, they are sufficient to assure symmetry. However, they are *not necessary* conditions for symmetry; that is, it is possible to have symmetry without these conditions. For example, although the graph of

$\rho = 2 \sin 2\theta$ (Figure 6–29) is symmetric with respect to the pole as well as with

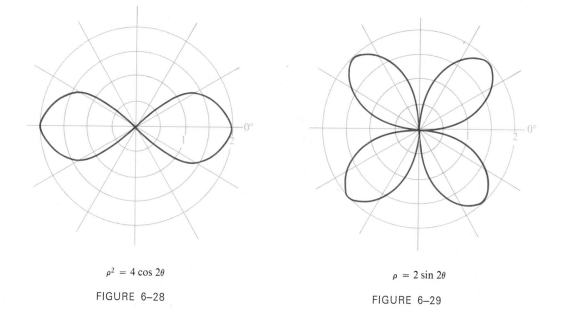

$\rho^2 = 4 \cos 2\theta$

FIGURE 6–28

$\rho = 2 \sin 2\theta$

FIGURE 6–29

respect to the line containing the polar axis and the line $\theta = 90°$, $\rho = 2 \sin 2\theta$ is not equivalent to any of the equations

$$-\rho = 2 \sin 2\theta,$$
$$\rho = 2 \sin 2(-\theta),$$
$$\rho = 2 \sin 2(180° - \theta).$$

Exercises 6–7

Sketch the graph of each of the following.

A **1.** $\rho = 4$

2. $\rho = -5$

3. $\theta = 30°$

4. $\rho = 4 \cos \theta$

5. $\rho = 2 \sin \theta$

6. $\rho = 2 \sin 2\theta$

7. $\rho = 1 + \sin 2\theta$

8. $\rho = 1 + \sin \theta$

9. $\rho \cos \theta = 3$

10. $\rho \cos \theta = -3$

11. $\rho \sin \theta = 1$

12. $\rho = 2(1 + \cos \theta)$

13. $\rho = \cos 3\theta$

18. $\rho = \cos \dfrac{\theta}{2}$

14. $\rho = 1 - \cos \theta$

19. $\rho = \theta$

15. $\rho = 1 - 2 \cos \theta$

20. $\rho = 2\theta$

16. $\rho = 1 - \sin \theta$

21. $\rho^2 = 4 \cos \theta$

17. $\rho = \sin \dfrac{\theta}{2}$

22. $\rho^2 = \sin 2\theta$

B 23. $\rho = \sin \theta + \cos \theta$

25. $\rho = 2|\sin \theta|$

24. $\rho = 2|\cos \theta|$

26. $\rho^2 - 2|\rho| = 0$

27. Sketch the region $\{(\rho, \theta): 0 \le \rho \le 2|\cos \theta|\}$.

28. Determine a polar equation for a circle of radius 6 with center at the pole.

Chapter Summary

1. A **vector** is an ordered pair (x, y) of real numbers.
2. A **geometric vector** is an arrow in the plane, from an **initial point** to a **terminal point**. If the initial point is the origin, then the geometric vector is a **bound** vector and is said to be in **standard position**; otherwise it is a **free** vector.
3. When dealing with vectors, we refer to a real number as a **scalar**.
4. A vector $\mathbf{v} = (x, y)$ can alternatively be described by giving its **norm**,

$$\|\mathbf{v}\| = \sqrt{x^2 + y^2},$$

and its **direction angle**, θ, determined for $\|\mathbf{v}\| \ne 0$ by

$$\cos \theta = \frac{x}{\|\mathbf{v}\|}, \qquad \sin \theta = \frac{y}{\|\mathbf{v}\|}, \qquad 0° \le \theta < 360°.$$

Any direction angle whatsoever might be assigned to the **zero vector** $(0, 0)$.

5. Two vector operations are **vector addition**,

$$(x_1, y_1) + (x_2, y_2) = (x_1 + x_2, y_1 + y_2),$$

and **multiplication of a vector by a scalar**,

$$r(x_1, y_1) = (rx_1, ry_1).$$

Vectors form a **commutative group** with respect to vector addition, and they form a **vector space** with respect to this operation and multiplication by a scalar.

6. Two vectors **u** and **v** form a **basis** for the set V of vectors $\mathbf{a} = (x, y)$ if every vector **a** can be written as a **linear combination** of **u** and **v**:

$$\mathbf{a} = r\mathbf{u} + s\mathbf{v},$$

where $r, s \in \Re$. In particular, the vectors $\mathbf{i} = (1, 0)$ and $\mathbf{j} = (0, 1)$ together form a basis for V.

7. The **inner product** of two vectors (x_1, y_1) and (x_2, y_2) is defined by

$$(x_1, y_1) \cdot (x_2, y_2) = x_1 x_2 + y_1 y_2.$$

An angle α between the geometric vectors corresponding to two nonzero vectors **u** and **v** satisfies

$$\cos \alpha = \frac{\mathbf{u} \cdot \mathbf{v}}{\|\mathbf{u}\| \, \|\mathbf{v}\|}.$$

These vectors are **orthogonal** if and only if $\mathbf{u} \cdot \mathbf{v} = 0$. They are **collinear** if and only if

$$\mathbf{u} \cdot \mathbf{v} = \pm \|\mathbf{u}\| \, \|\mathbf{v}\|. \tag{1}$$

If the geometric vectors corresponding to **u** and **v** are considered to be free vectors, then (1) is a necessary and sufficient condition that they be parallel.

8. If **u** and **v** are nonzero orthogonal vectors, then any vector **a** can be written as a linear combination of **u** and **v**:

$$\mathbf{a} = \frac{\mathbf{u} \cdot \mathbf{a}}{\|\mathbf{u}\|^2} \mathbf{u} + \frac{\mathbf{v} \cdot \mathbf{a}}{\|\mathbf{v}\|^2} \mathbf{v}.$$

9. Vectors are useful in physical applications—for example, in navigational and force problems.

10. Points in the plane can be specified not only by Cartesian coordinates (x, y), but also by **polar coordinates** relative to a **pole** and a **polar axis**. Polar and Cartesian coordinates are related by the equations

$$x = \rho \cos \theta, \quad y = \rho \sin \theta,$$

and

$$\rho = \pm\sqrt{x^2 + y^2}, \quad \cos \theta = \frac{x}{\rho}, \quad \sin \theta = \frac{y}{\rho}, \quad \rho \neq 0.$$

Chapter Test

6–1   **1.** Let $\mathbf{u} = (2, -6)$ and $\mathbf{v} = (3, 5)$. Find

        (a) $\|\mathbf{u} + \mathbf{v}\|$ **(b)** $4\mathbf{u} + (-1)\mathbf{v}$

        2. Find the vector with norm 5 and direction angle 120°.

6–2   **3. (a)** Express the vector $\mathbf{v} = -2\mathbf{i} + 6\mathbf{j}$ as the scalar product of a real number and a unit vector.

        (b) Find $\cos \theta$ and $\sin \theta$, where θ is the direction angle of $\mathbf{v}$.

6–3   **4.** Use the notion of inner product to find a value for x such that $\mathbf{u} = (2, 4)$ and $\mathbf{v} = (x, -3)$ are orthogonal.

6–4   **5.** A ship steams 20 miles on a heading of 60°, then south for 50 miles, and finally 40 miles on a heading of 90°. How far, to the nearest tenth of a mile, is it then from the starting point, and what is the tangent of its bearing from that point?

6–5   **6.** An object of weight 60 pounds rests on an inclined plane making an angle of 30° with the horizontal. What is the force of friction on the object?

6–6   **7.** Find three additional pairs of polar coordinates for the point associated with $(4, 75°)$.

        8. Graph the set $\{(\rho, \theta): \rho \sin \theta = 4\}$.

6–7   **9.** Graph the set $\{(\rho, \theta): \rho = 1 + \cos 2\theta\}$.

Cumulative Review · Chapters 4–6

Chapter 4

Solve for *y* over the interval $0 \leq y \leq 2\pi$.

    1. $\sin y = -\dfrac{\sqrt{3}}{2}$ **3.** $\tan y = -\sqrt{3}$

    2. $\cos y = \frac{1}{2}$ **4.** $\sec y = 2$

Find the value of each expression.

    5. $\mathrm{Sin}^{-1}(-1)$ **7.** $\sin(\mathrm{Cos}^{-1}\frac{3}{5})$

    6. $\mathrm{Cos}^{-1}(-\frac{1}{2})$ **8.** $\cos(\mathrm{Sec}^{-1} 4)$

    9. Solve $\cot^2 x + \cot x = 0$ over $0 \leq x < 2\pi$.

   10. Find the general solution of $\sin x - \cos x = 1$.

Chapter 5

11. State the degree measure of an angle α with radian measure $\dfrac{7\pi^{\text{R}}}{6}$.

12. Express cos 141° in terms of its reference angle.

13. Find **(a)** tan 1095° and **(b)** sin (−690°).

14. Prove that $\dfrac{\sin 2x}{1 + \cos 2x} = \tan x$ is an identity.

15. Determine sin θ and cos θ if the terminal side of the angle θ in standard position contains the point $(2, -5)$.

16. Solve $2 \cos^2 2\theta + \cos 2\theta - 1 = 0$ over $0 \le m°(\theta) < 360°$.

17. Solve the right triangle **ABC** if $b = 120$ and $B = 54°$. Express lengths of sides to the nearest unit.

18. In triangle **ABC**, $a = 10$, $b = 4$, and $C = 30°$. Find c to the nearest unit.

19. In triangle **ABC**, $A = 60°$, $B = 45°$, and $a = 20$. Find b to the nearest unit.

20. How many possible triangles **ABC** have $a = 4$, $b = 3$, and $B = 45°$?

Chapter 6

21. If $\mathbf{u} = (-3, 7)$ and $\mathbf{v} = (4, 7)$, find **(a)** $\|\mathbf{u} - \mathbf{v}\|$ and **(b)** $3\mathbf{u} + 2\mathbf{v}$.

22. Specify as an ordered pair the vector with norm 10 and direction angle 210°.

23. Express the vector $4\mathbf{i} - 3\mathbf{j}$ as the scalar product of a real number and a unit vector.

24. If $\mathbf{v} = (4, -5)$, find $\|\mathbf{v}\|$ to the nearest tenth and the direction angle θ of $\mathbf{v}$ to the nearest degree.

25. Use the inner product of $\mathbf{u} = (-1, 3)$ and $\mathbf{v} = (x, -4)$ to find a value of x such that $\mathbf{u}$ and $\mathbf{v}$ are orthogonal.

26. Find a linear combination of $\mathbf{u} = \left(-\dfrac{1}{2}, \dfrac{\sqrt{3}}{2}\right)$ and $\mathbf{v} = \left(\dfrac{\sqrt{3}}{2}, \dfrac{1}{2}\right)$ equal to $\mathbf{i} + \mathbf{j}$.

27. Find the angle α, $0° \le \alpha \le 180°$, between the geometric vectors corresponding to $(2, 2\sqrt{3})$ and $(-\sqrt{2}, \sqrt{2})$.

28. An airplane flies 400 miles due north and then flies 300 miles on a heading 120°. To the nearest mile, how far from its starting point would the airplane then be, neglecting any effects of wind?

29. A weight of 160 pounds is on an inclined plane making an angle of 30° with the horizontal. Find to the nearest pound the components of the weight normal to the plane and parallel to the plane.

30. A force of 40 pounds is directed on a heading 90°. What force must be directed on a heading of 180° to produce a resultant force of 80 pounds? What is the heading of the resultant force?

Applications of Trigonometry

World Maps

A cylindrical surface can be cut along one of its linear elements and smoothly spread out on a plane. A spherical surface, on the other hand, cannot be flattened out in this manner without distortion. How, then, can a plane map of the approximately spherical surface of the earth be made?

To visualize one method, consider a glass globe of radius 1 on which a map has been drawn, think of a right circular cylinder tangent to the globe along the

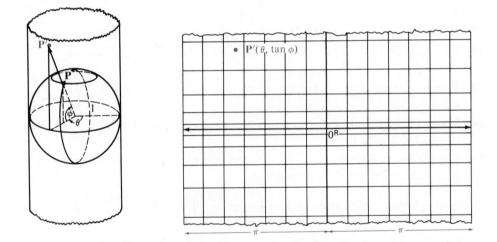

map of the equator, and imagine a bright light at the center of the globe. The shadow of the map thrown on the cylinder by the light can be taken as a new map. Then the cylinder can be cut vertically along a longitudinal line, and spread out to give a plane map. This *central cylindrical projection* is quite accurate near the equator, but distortions become very great near the poles. The point **P** on the globe with longitude θ radians and latitude ϕ radians is mapped onto the point **P′**$(\theta, \tan \phi)$ on the plane.

Next, imagine that along the vertical polar axis of the sphere, a neon tube is allowed to throw light only horizontally onto the cylinder. Now the point **P** on the globe is mapped onto the point $\mathbf{P}'(\theta, \sin \phi)$ on the plane shown below. Notice that the entire area of this map is $2 \times 2\pi$, or 4π, and that the area of the

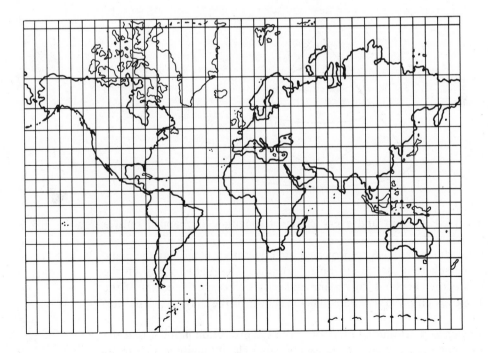

spherical surface also is 4π. Hence this is an *equal-area* map. All areas are shown in correct proportions on this map.

In a closely related map, in which lengths along the prime meridian (0°W) are mapped without distortion, the point $\mathbf{P}$ is mapped onto $\mathbf{P}'(\theta, \phi)$. This is an *even-spaced* map, in which lines of longitude and latitude with equal angular increments appear as squares, like the squares on a chessboard.

In each of the maps discussed above, every circle of latitude is mapped onto a horizontal line segment and every circle of longitude is mapped onto a vertical line or line segment. The famous *Mercator projection* of 1569 is of the same sort.

In it, any path on the globe that cuts a circle of latitude at a constant angle appears as a straight line on the map. Angles are mapped onto angles of equal measure, but areas are greatly magnified near the poles.

Another equal-area map is obtained by graphing a prime meridian without distortion onto a vertical line segment and correspondingly graphing each circle

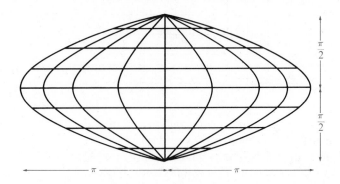

of latitude without distortion onto a horizontal line segment. Here **P** is mapped onto ($\theta \cos \phi, \phi$). In this map, all areas are in proper proportions, but shapes are accurate only near the center of the projection.

For *conical projections*, the cylinder is replaced with a right circular cone tangent to the sphere. In this map, every circle of latitude is mapped onto a

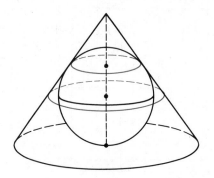

horizontal curved segment and every circle of longitude is mapped onto a straight line segment.

The spherical map can also be projected directly onto a plane, say the plane tangent to the sphere at its "south pole," from a point (light source) on the line which is perpendicular to the plane and passes through the center of the sphere. This gives an *azimuthal map*. This is shown in the diagram at the top of page 237.

A *gnomic map* is an azimuthal map for which the projection point **A** is at the center of the sphere. In a gnomic map, each great circle of longitude appears as a straight line—an important feature for navigational purposes.

An *orthographic map* is an azimuthal map for which the projection point **B** is at an infinite distance. This map *looks like* a globe.

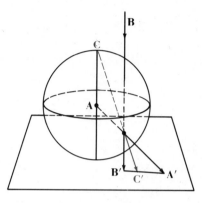

A *stereographic map* is an azimuthal map for which the projection point **C** is the "north pole" of the sphere, as shown here in color. In this map, angles are mapped onto angles of equal measure.

Since any plane map of the surface of the earth must involve distortions, no such map can be perfect. Each of the maps discussed above, like many other maps, preserves certain aspects of the earth's surface. The choice of maps to be used at any time depends on the purposes to be served by the map.

Chapter Seven

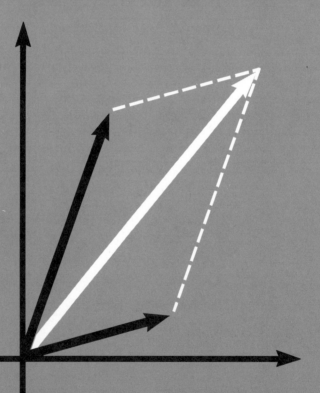

Complex Numbers

OBJECTIVES

1. *To study the properties of complex numbers and the relationship between complex numbers and vectors.*
2. *To express complex numbers in polar form.*
3. *To use De Moivre's Theorem to find products, quotients, powers, and roots of complex numbers.*

The Field of Complex Numbers

7–1 *Addition and Multiplication of Complex Numbers*

Many of the familiar properties of the set $\Re$ of real numbers are the basis of the algebraic systems called *fields*. A **field** consists of a set F of elements, together with two binary operations which satisfy the axioms listed below.

AXIOMS FOR A FIELD

Let $a, b, c \in F$.

Addition Axioms		Multiplication Axioms
$a + b \in F$	Closure property	$ab \in F$
$(a + b) + c = a + (b + c)$	Associative property	$(ab)c = a(bc)$
$a + 0 = 0 + a = a$	Existence of identity	$a \cdot 1 = 1 \cdot a = a$
$a + (-a) = (-a) + a = 0$	Existence of inverse	$a \cdot \dfrac{1}{a} = \dfrac{1}{a} \cdot a = 1 \quad (a \neq 0)$
$a + b = b + a$	Commutative property	$ab = ba$

Distributive Axiom $\qquad a(b + c) = ab + ac, \ (b + c)a = ba + ca$

The axioms are stated here in terms of addition and multiplication, since these are the operations with which we are concerned at this time. However, there are fields in which the two binary operations are not ordinarily labeled addition and multiplication.

We shall now define the set of *complex numbers* and the two basic operations of addition and multiplication of complex numbers, and we shall prove that the elements of this system satisfy the field axioms. (Proofs of some of these properties are left as exercises.) Because the complex numbers form a field, any properties of the set of real numbers that depend only on the field axioms are valid also for complex numbers.

A complex number may be defined in several equivalent ways, but in this book we shall define a complex number to be an ordered pair (x, y) of real numbers. The letter z will customarily be used to denote a complex number, and the set of complex numbers will be represented as

$$C = \{z: z = (x, y), \text{ with } x, y \in \mathcal{R}\}.$$

Equality in the set of complex numbers is defined as follows:

▲   If $z_1 = (x_1, y_1)$ and $z_2 = (x_2, y_2)$, then $z_1 = z_2$ if and only if $x_1 = x_2$ and $y_1 = y_2$.

The **sum** and **product** of two complex numbers $z_1 = (x_1, y_1)$ and $z_2 = (x_2, y_2)$ are defined as follows:

▲ $$z_1 + z_2 = (x_1 + x_2, y_1 + y_2)$$

▲ $$z_1 z_2 = (x_1 x_2 - y_1 y_2, x_1 y_2 + y_1 x_2)$$

Example   If $z_1 = (5, 2)$ and $z_2 = (-4, 1)$, find $z_1 + z_2$ and $z_1 z_2$.

Solution $z_1 + z_2 = (5, 2) + (-4, 1) = (5 - 4, 2 + 1) = (1, 3)$

$z_1 z_2 = (5, 2)(-4, 1) = ((5)(-4) - (2)(1), (5)(1) + (2)(-4))$
$= (-22, -3)$

To show that the closure axiom for addition is true:

Let $z_1 = (x_1, y_1)$ and $z_2 = (x_2, y_2)$. Then by the definition of addition of complex numbers, $z_1 + z_2 = (x_1 + x_2, y_1 + y_2)$. Since $\mathcal{R}$ is a field and hence is closed under addition, it follows that $x_1 + x_2 \in \mathcal{R}$ and $y_1 + y_2 \in \mathcal{R}$. Thus $z_1 + z_2 \in C$.

To show that there is an identity element for addition:

If $z = (x, y)$ is any complex number, then

$$(x, y) + (0, 0) = (x + 0, y + 0) = (x, y)$$

and

$$(0, 0) + (x, y) = (0 + x, 0 + y) = (x, y),$$

so that $(0, 0)$ is an identity element for addition in C. Moreover, you can show (Exercise 19, page 242) that $(0, 0)$ is the only identity element for addition in C. We call $(0, 0)$ the **zero** element in C.

To show that the additive inverse axiom holds:

First, we define the **negative** of a complex number $z = (x, y)$ to be the complex number $-z = (-x, -y)$. Then

$$(x, y) + (-x, -y) = (x + (-x), y + (-y)) = (0, 0),$$

and

$$(-x, -y) + (x, y) = ((-x) + x, (-y) + y) = (0, 0).$$

Furthermore, the additive inverse of any complex number is unique (Exercise 20, page 242).

The proofs that the commutative and associative properties for addition hold are left as exercises (Exercises 13 and 14, page 242).

To show that there is an identity element for multiplication:

If $z = (x, y)$ is any complex number, then

$$(1, 0)(x, y) = (1 \cdot x - 0 \cdot y, \ 1 \cdot y + 0 \cdot x) = (x, y),$$

and

$$(x, y)(1, 0) = (x \cdot 1 - y \cdot 0, \ x \cdot 0 + y \cdot 1) = (x, y),$$

so that the complex number $(1, 0)$ serves as an identity element for multiplication.

The proofs for closure, associativity, and commutativity for multiplication, and the proof of the distributive property are left as exercises (Exercises 15–18, page 242). The proof of the existence of a unique multiplicative inverse for any given nonzero complex number will be given in Section 7–2.

As you study this chapter, notice the ways in which the system of complex numbers and the system of vectors are alike and the ways in which they differ. From this section you can see that addition and equality are similar in the two systems. It is in regard to the operation of multiplication that the systems differ.

Exercises 7–1

Find ordered pairs corresponding to (a) $z_1 + z_2$, (b) z_1z_2.

A **1.** $z_1 = (3, 2)$, $z_2 = (1, 6)$ **4.** $z_1 = (4, 8)$, $z_2 = (-5, -1)$

    2. $z_1 = (3, -2)$, $z_2 = (-1, 6)$ **5.** $z_1 = (\frac{1}{3}, 2)$, $z_2 = (3, \frac{1}{2})$

    3. $z_1 = (4, 8)$, $z_2 = (5, 1)$ **6.** $z_1 = (\frac{1}{4}, \frac{1}{2})$, $z_2 = (\frac{1}{8}, \frac{1}{4})$

Find ordered pairs corresponding to (a) z^2, (b) z^3.

    7. $z = (1, 1)$ **9.** $z = (0, 1)$ **11.** $z = (\sqrt{3}, -\sqrt{2})$

    8. $z = (2, 3)$ **10.** $z = (5, 0)$ **12.** $z = (0, \sqrt{5})$

In Exercises 13–18, you are to prove the field properties for the complex numbers which were not proved in the text. Therefore, prove that for z_1, z_2, $z_3 \in C$:

B **13.** $z_1 + z_2 = z_2 + z_1$ **16.** $(z_1z_2)z_3 = z_1(z_2z_3)$

    14. $(z_1 + z_2) + z_3 = z_1 + (z_2 + z_3)$ **17.** $z_1z_2 = z_2z_1$

    15. $z_1z_2 \in C$ **18.** $z_1(z_2 + z_3) = z_1z_2 + z_1z_3$

C **19.** Prove that if $(x, y) + (a, b) = (a, b) + (x, y) = (x, y)$, then it follows that $(a, b) = (0, 0)$.

    20. Prove that if $(x, y) + (a, b) = (a, b) + (x, y) = (0, 0)$, then it follows that $(a, b) = (-x, -y)$.

    21. Prove that if $z_1 = (r_1 \cos \theta_1, r_1 \sin \theta_1)$ and $z_2 = (r_2 \cos \theta_2, r_2 \sin \theta_2)$, then $z_1z_2 = [r_1r_2 \cos (\theta_1 + \theta_2), r_1r_2 \sin (\theta_1 + \theta_2)]$.

7–2 *Division and Subtraction of Complex Numbers*

In Section 7–1 we verified that all the field axioms except possibly the existence of multiplicative inverses hold for the set C of complex numbers. To discover a multiplicative inverse for any nonzero complex number $z = (x, y)$, let us denote such an inverse, if there is one, by $z^{-1} = (a, b)$, and then seek an ordered pair (a, b) for which the equation

$$(x, y)(a, b) = (1, 0), \quad \text{or, equivalently,} \quad (xa - yb, xb + ya) = (1, 0),$$

is valid. By the definition of equality for complex numbers, the latter equation holds if and only if

$$xa - yb = 1 \quad \text{and} \quad xb + ya = 0.$$

Solving these equations for a and b, we obtain the unique solution

$$z^{-1} = (a, b) = \left(\frac{x}{x^2 + y^2}, \frac{-y}{x^2 + y^2} \right). \tag{1}$$

Example 1   Find the multiplicative inverse of $z = (3, -5)$.

Solution
$$(3, -5)^{-1} = \left(\frac{3}{3^2 + (-5)^2}, \frac{-(-5)}{3^2 + (-5)^2} \right)$$
$$= (\tfrac{3}{34}, \tfrac{5}{34})$$

In the system of real numbers, the operations of subtraction and division can be defined in terms of addition and multiplication, respectively, in the forms $a - b = a + (-b)$ and $a \div b = ab^{-1}$. In the field of complex numbers, similar interpretations are given to these operations. The **difference** and **quotient** of two complex numbers z_1 and z_2 are defined as follows:

$$z_1 - z_2 = z_1 + (-z_2)$$

$$\frac{z_1}{z_2} = z_1 z_2^{-1}, \qquad z_2 \neq (0, 0)$$

Example 2   If $z_1 = (5, 6)$ and $z_2 = (3, -4)$, find $z_1 - z_2$ and $\dfrac{z_1}{z_2}$.

Solution   By definition,

$$z_1 - z_2 = z_1 + (-z_2)$$
$$= (5, 6) + (-3, 4)$$
$$= (5 - 3, 6 + 4)$$
$$= (2, 10).$$

To find $\dfrac{z_1}{z_2}$, we first use Equation (1) to determine z_2^{-1}:

$$z_2^{-1} = (3, -4)^{-1}$$
$$= \left(\frac{3}{3^2 + (-4)^2}, \frac{-(-4)}{3^2 + (-4)^2} \right)$$
$$= (\tfrac{3}{25}, \tfrac{4}{25}).$$

Then, by definition,

$$\frac{z_1}{z_2} = z_1 z_2^{-1} = (5, 6)(\tfrac{3}{25}, \tfrac{4}{25}) = (\tfrac{15}{25} - \tfrac{24}{25}, \tfrac{20}{25} + \tfrac{18}{25})$$
$$= (-\tfrac{9}{25}, \tfrac{38}{25}).$$

Quotients of complex numbers often may be found more conveniently by using the *conjugate* of the divisor. The **conjugate** of a complex number $z = (x, y)$ is the complex number

$$\bar{z} = (x, -y).$$

Conjugates are useful because the ordered pair $z\bar{z}$ has 0 for its second component:

$$z\bar{z} = (x, y)(x, -y) = [(x)(x) - (y)(-y), (x)(-y) + (y)(x)]$$
$$= (x^2 + y^2, 0).$$

Now, because C is a field, we know that

$$\frac{z_1}{z_2} = \frac{z_1 z_3}{z_2 z_3}, \qquad z_2, z_3 \neq (0, 0). \tag{2}$$

If we let $z_1 = (x_1, y_1)$, $z_2 = (x_2, y_2)$, and $z_3 = \bar{z_2} = (x_2, -y_2)$, then

$$\frac{z_1}{z_2} = \frac{z_1 \bar{z_2}}{z_2 \bar{z_2}} = \frac{(x_1, y_1)(x_2, -y_2)}{(x_2, y_2)(x_2, -y_2)}$$
$$= \frac{(x_1 x_2 + y_1 y_2, -x_1 y_2 + y_1 x_2)}{(x_2^2 + y_2^2, 0)}.$$

The latter expression is equal to

$$\left(\frac{x_1 x_2 + y_1 y_2}{x_2^2 + y_2^2}, \frac{-x_1 y_2 + y_1 x_2}{x_2^2 + y_2^2} \right),$$

since, in general, for $c \neq 0$, $\dfrac{(a, b)}{(c, 0)} = \left(\dfrac{a}{c}, \dfrac{b}{c} \right)$. Thus:

$$\frac{z_1}{z_2} = \frac{(x_1, y_1)}{(x_2, y_2)} = \left(\frac{x_1 x_2 + y_1 y_2}{x_2^2 + y_2^2}, \frac{-x_1 y_2 + y_1 x_2}{x_2^2 + y_2^2} \right). \tag{3}$$

Example 3 Express the quotient $\dfrac{z_1}{z_2} = \dfrac{(5, 6)}{(3, -4)}$ as an ordered pair.

Solution We can employ the method used in obtaining Equation (3). Since $\bar{z_2} = (3, 4)$, we have

$$\frac{(5, 6)}{(3, -4)} = \frac{(5, 6)(3, 4)}{(3, -4)(3, 4)} = \frac{(15 - 24, 20 + 18)}{(9 + 16, 12 - 12)}$$
$$= \frac{(-9, 38)}{(25, 0)} = (-\tfrac{9}{25}, \tfrac{38}{25}).$$

Exercises 7–2

Multiply and divide $(0, 4)$ by the given complex number and express each result as an ordered pair.

A **1.** $(0, 1)$ **3.** $(0, 3)$ **5.** $(2, 0)$

    2. $(0, -1)$ **4.** $(0, -3)$ **6.** $(-2, 0)$

Find ordered pairs corresponding to:

(a) $z_1 - z_2$ **(b)** z_2^{-1} **(c)** $\overline{z_2}$ **(d)** $\dfrac{z_1}{z_2}$

    7. $z_1 = (1, 2),\ z_2 = (4, 3)$ **10.** $z_1 = (3, 5),\ z_2 = (5, 3)$

    8. $z_1 = (6, -2),\ z_2 = (2, 0)$ **11.** $z_1 = (12, 0),\ z_2 = (4, 0)$

    9. $z_1 = (-2, 0),\ z_2 = (1, 4)$ **12.** $z_1 = (\tfrac{1}{3}, \tfrac{1}{2}),\ z_2 = (-3, -2)$

Find an ordered pair corresponding to each quotient.

B **13.** $\dfrac{(3\sqrt{3}, 5\sqrt{3})}{(2\sqrt{3}, \sqrt{3})}$ **15.** $\dfrac{(\sqrt{3}, \sqrt{2})}{(2\sqrt{3}, -\sqrt{2})}$ **17.** $\dfrac{(15\sqrt{6}, -8)}{(7\sqrt{2}, \sqrt{3})}$

14. $\dfrac{(\sqrt{5}, -2\sqrt{5})}{(-\sqrt{5}, \sqrt{5})}$ **16.** $\dfrac{(\sqrt{5}, -\sqrt{3})}{(2\sqrt{3}, \sqrt{5})}$ **18.** $\dfrac{(\sqrt{2}, -\sqrt{2})}{(1, \sqrt{2})}$

C **19.** Prove that if $z_1 = (r_1 \cos \theta_1, r_1 \sin \theta_1)$ and $z_2 = (r_2 \cos \theta_2, r_2 \sin \theta_2)$, $r_2 \neq 0$, then

$$\frac{z_1}{z_2} = \left(\frac{r_1}{r_2} \cos (\theta_1 - \theta_2), \frac{r_1}{r_2} \sin (\theta_1 - \theta_2) \right).$$

7–3 *Complex Numbers in Standard Form*

The elements of the subset $\{(x, 0): x \in \mathcal{R}\}$ of C display the following properties:

$$(x_1, 0) + (x_2, 0) = (x_1 + x_2, 0)$$
$$(x_1, 0) - (x_2, 0) = (x_1 - x_2, 0)$$
$$(x_1, 0)(x_2, 0) = (x_1 x_2, 0)$$
$$\frac{(x_1, 0)}{(x_2, 0)} = \left(\frac{x_1}{x_2}, 0 \right), \qquad x_2 \neq 0$$

As you can see, this follows precisely the behavior of the real numbers x_1 and x_2 under the same binary operations on real numbers. Therefore, let us agree to identify the complex number $(x, 0)$ with the real number x, and write

$$(x, 0) = x. \tag{1}$$

With this agreement, the set of real numbers may be regarded as a subset of the set of complex numbers. (More precisely, the set $\mathcal{R}$ of real numbers x and the subset of complex numbers of the form $(x, 0)$ are *isomorphic*.)

Another interesting subset of C is the set of all complex numbers of the form $(0, y)$. First, note that

$$(0, y) = (y, 0)(0, 1).$$

The complex number $(0, 1)$ is customarily denoted by the letter i. Since $(y, 0)$ is the real number y, we write

$$(0, y) = (y, 0)(0, 1) = yi. \tag{2}$$

A complex number of the form $(0, y) = yi$, $y \neq 0$, is called a **pure imaginary number**. Since $i^2 = (0, 1)(0, 1) = (-1, 0) = -1$, we can also write for i:

▲
$$i = \sqrt{-1}. \tag{3}$$

We agree also that

$$yi = y\sqrt{-1} = \sqrt{y^2}\sqrt{-1} = \sqrt{y^2(-1)} = \sqrt{-y^2}, y > 0. \tag{4}$$

From (4) we have, for example,

$$\sqrt{-4} = \sqrt{2^2(-1)} = 2\sqrt{-1} = 2i.$$

Note that although $\sqrt{4}\sqrt{9} = \sqrt{36} = 6$, it is *not* true that $\sqrt{-4}\sqrt{-9} = \sqrt{36} = 6$. Instead,

$$\sqrt{-4}\sqrt{-9} = \sqrt{4(-1)}\sqrt{9(-1)} = (2i)(3i) = 6i^2 = 6(-1) = -6.$$

Radical expressions having negative-number radicands should always be rewritten in i-form before any multiplication or division operations are performed.

Any complex number $z = (x, y)$ may be regarded as the sum of two complex numbers, one from each of the two subsets of C discussed above, that is, $\{(x, 0), x \in \mathcal{R}\}$ and $\{(0, y), y \in \mathcal{R}\}$. Hence we can write

▲
$$z = (x, y) = (x, 0) + (0, y),$$
$$= x + yi, \quad x, y \in \mathcal{R}. \tag{5}$$

In the representation (5), which is known as the **standard form** of the complex number (x, y), x is called the **real part** of z, and y is called the **imaginary part**. (Note that by this definition, the imaginary part of z is not the product yi, but simply the real number y.)

A principal advantage of using the standard form $x + yi$ of complex numbers is that if complex numbers are written in this way, then the fundamental operations of addition, subtraction, multiplication, and division are performed exactly as with real numbers, with the single additional fact that $i^2 = -1$.

Example   Let $z_1 = 2 + \sqrt{-3}$ and $z_2 = 1 - 2\sqrt{-3}$. Write in the form $x + yi$, with $x, y \in \mathcal{R}$:

(a) $z_1 + z_2$ (b) $z_1 - z_2$ (c) $z_1 z_2$ (d) $\dfrac{z_1}{z_2}$

Solution   First we rewrite z_1 and z_2 in the form $x + yi$:

$$z_1 = 2 + \sqrt{3}\, i \quad \text{and} \quad z_2 = 1 - 2\sqrt{3}\, i$$

Then, from (3) and (5), page 246, and the definitions given in Sections 7–1 and 7–2,

$$(x_1 + y_1 i) + (x_2 + y_2 i) = (x_1 + x_2) + (y_1 + y_2)i,$$
$$(x_1 + y_1 i) - (x_2 + y_2 i) = (x_1 - x_2) + (y_1 - y_2)i,$$

and

$$(x_1 + y_1 i)(x_2 + y_2 i) = (x_1 x_2 - y_1 y_2) + (x_1 y_2 + y_1 x_2)i.$$

Hence,

$$z_1 + z_2 = (2 + \sqrt{3}\, i) + (1 - 2\sqrt{3}\, i) = 3 - \sqrt{3}\, i,$$
$$z_1 - z_2 = (2 + \sqrt{3}\, i) - (1 - 2\sqrt{3}\, i) = 1 + 3\sqrt{3}\, i,$$

and

$$z_1 z_2 = (2 + \sqrt{3}\, i)(1 - 2\sqrt{3}\, i) = (2 + 6) + (-4\sqrt{3} + \sqrt{3})\, i,$$
$$= 8 - 3\sqrt{3}\, i.$$

If $z = (x, y)$, then $\bar{z} = (x, -y)$. Thus it follows that if $z = x + yi$, then $\bar{z} = \overline{x + yi} = x - yi$. Therefore we have

$$\frac{z_1}{z_2} = \frac{z_1 \bar{z}_2}{z_2 \bar{z}_2} = \frac{(2 + \sqrt{3}\, i)(1 + 2\sqrt{3}\, i)}{(1 - 2\sqrt{3}\, i)(1 + 2\sqrt{3}\, i)} = \frac{-4 + 5\sqrt{3}\, i}{13}$$

$$= -\frac{4}{13} + \frac{5\sqrt{3}}{13}\, i.$$

Exercises 7–3

Find, in the form $x + yi$, with $x, y \in \mathcal{R}$:

(a) $z_1 + z_2$ **(b)** $z_1 - z_2$ **(c)** z_1z_2 **(d)** $\dfrac{z_1}{z_2}$

A **1.** $z_1 = 3 + 2i, \; z_2 = 5 + 3i$ **5.** $z_1 = 3i, \; z_2 = 6$

2. $z_1 = 5 - i, \; z_2 = 5 + i$ **6.** $z_1 = -4, \; z_2 = 2i$

3. $z_1 = 7 + i, \; z_2 = 10 - 4i$ **7.** $z_1 = \sqrt{3}\,i, \; z_2 = -i$

4. $z_1 = 7 + i, \; z_2 = 7 - i$ **8.** $z_1 = \sqrt{2}\,i, \; z_2 = -3\sqrt{2}\,i$

Match each complex number in the two left-hand columns with its correct representation in the right-hand column. Each expression in the right-hand column may be used more than once or not at all.

9. $3 - \sqrt{-16}$ **14.** $-3i^2$ **(a)** -3

10. $3 + \sqrt{-16}$ **15.** $6 \cos \dfrac{\pi}{3} + 8i \sin \left(-\dfrac{\pi}{6}\right)$ **(b)** 3

11. $3 - \sqrt{16}\,i$ **(c)** $3 - 4i$

12. $(2 + i)^2$ **16.** $6 \cos \left(-\dfrac{\pi}{3}\right) + 4i \sin \pi$ **(d)** $3 + 4i$

13. $(2 - i)^2$ **(e)** 5

Write the square of the given complex number in the form $x + yi$, with $x, y \in \mathcal{R}$.

17. $1 - i$ **19.** $5 - 2i$ **21.** $3 + 3i$ **23.** $3i$ **25.** $a + bi$

18. $1 + i$ **20.** $3 - 4i$ **22.** $2 + 6i$ **24.** $-7i$ **26.** $a - bi$

In Exercises 27–30, find all real values for x, if any, for which the given sentence is true.

Example $x^2 + 2xi = 4x + 8i$

Solution   Since $x_1 + y_1 i = x_2 + y_2 i$ if and only if $x_1 = x_2$ and $y_1 = y_2$, it follows that $x^2 + 2xi = 4x + 8i$ is true if and only if $x^2 = 4x$ and $2x = 8$. Solving these two equations gives

$$x^2 - 4x = 0 \quad \text{and} \quad 2x = 8,$$
$$x(x - 4) = 0 \quad \text{and} \quad x = 4,$$
$$x = 0 \text{ or } x = 4 \quad \text{and} \quad x = 4.$$

Thus, the desired value of x is 4.

B **27.** $(x + 3i)^2 = 18i$ **29.** $(2x + 5i) + (10 - i) = (4)(x + i)$

   28. $(x - i)^2 = x - 1$ **30.** $(x + i)(x - i) = 10$

Find all possible values of x in the interval $0 \le x < 2\pi$ for which the given sentence is true.

31. $2 \cos x + 2i \sin x = 1 + \sqrt{3}\, i$

32. $\sqrt{2} \cos x + \sqrt{2}\, i \sin x = 1 + i$

33. $4 \cos x + 4i \sin x = -2 + 2\sqrt{3}\, i$

34. $(\cos x + i \sin x)^2 = 2i$

35. $(\cos x + i \sin x)^2 = (\cos x - i \sin x)^2$

7–4   *Graphical Representation of Complex Numbers*

Since complex numbers have been defined to be ordered pairs of real numbers, they can be graphed in the plane using a Cartesian coordinate system. When the points of the plane are considered to represent complex numbers, the plane is called the **complex plane**, or the **Argand plane**, after J. R. Argand (1768–1822). The x-axis is then called the **real axis**, since the points of the form $(x, 0)$ correspond to real numbers, and the y-axis is called the **imaginary axis**, since the points of the form $(0, y)$ correspond to pure imaginary numbers. Hence the abscissa of a point z corresponds to the real part of z, and the ordinate corresponds to the imaginary part. Figure 7–1 shows the graph of $z = (-3, 2)$, or $z = -3 + 2i$, on the Argand plane.

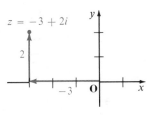

FIGURE 7–1

The representation of geometric vectors by arrows in standard position in the plane suggests a similar geometric representation for complex numbers. Using this representation, we have the graph of $z = (-3, 2) = -3 + 2i$ as shown in Figure 7–2.

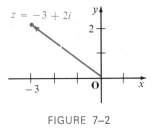

FIGURE 7–2

We define the **absolute value**, or **modulus**, of a complex number $z = (x, y) = x + yi$ by

$$|z| = \sqrt{x^2 + y^2}. \tag{1}$$

You can see that the modulus of a complex number (x, y) corresponds to the norm of the vector (x, y).

We also define the **argument**, or **amplitude**, of a complex number $z \neq 0$ to be the angle $\theta, 0 \leq \theta < 2\pi$, such that

▲
$$\cos \theta = \frac{x}{\sqrt{x^2 + y^2}} \quad \text{and} \quad \sin \theta = \frac{y}{\sqrt{x^2 + y^2}}, \quad (2)$$

although any angle differing from this by $2k\pi$, $k \in J$, might be used as an amplitude of z. Hence the amplitude of z is the direction angle of the corresponding geometric vector (x, y). Any amplitude whatsoever might be assigned to the complex number $z = (0, 0) = 0$.

Using the geometric correspondence between two-dimensional vectors and complex numbers, you can find sums and differences of complex numbers graphically. Figure 7–3 shows the graphical addition of $z_1 = -4 - i$ and $z_2 = 1 + 3i$.

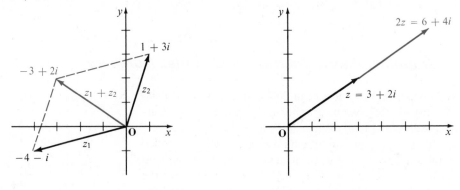

FIGURE 7–3   FIGURE 7–4

Now let us define a product of complex numbers that is analogous to the product of a vector by a scalar. We have agreed that the complex number $(x, 0)$, or $x + 0i$, can be viewed as the real number x, so we can write the product $(c, 0)(x, y)$ as

$$(c, 0)(x, y) = c(x, y), \quad \text{or} \quad c(x + yi).$$

In vector notation, of course, the symbols $c(x, y)$ denote the product of the scalar c and the vector (x, y). Hence, the geometric representation of the complex product $cz = (c, 0)(x, y)$ is the same as that of the vector (cx, cy), with the amplitude of cz the same (or differing by π^R if $c < 0$) as that of z but with modulus $|c|$ times that of z. Figure 7–4 shows the product cz of the complex numbers $c = (2, 0)$ and $z = (3, 2)$.

Complex products of the form $(0, c)(x, y)$, or $(0 + ci)(x + yi)$, can be written as

$$(0, c)(x, y) = (-cy, cx) = c(-y, x),$$

or as

$$(0 + ci)(x + yi) = ci(x + yi) = -cy + cxi.$$

If you let $z_1 = (x_1, y_1)$, then the vectors corresponding to z_1 and ciz_1 are (x_1, y_1) and $(-cy_1, cx_1)$. Since the inner product of these vectors is

$$(x_1, y_1) \cdot (-cy_1, cx_1) = -cx_1y_1 + cx_1y_1 = 0,$$

the vectors are orthogonal (Section 6–3). Thus, the geometric-vector representation of the complex product ciz is perpendicular to that of z and has magnitude $|c|$ times that of z. Figure 7–5 shows the graphs of $2 + 5i$ and $3i(2 + 5i)$. Since $3i(2 + 5i) = 3(-5 + 2i)$, you can see that the norm of the vector corresponding to $3i(2 + 5i)$ is three times the norm of the vector corresponding to $-5 + 2i$ and hence three times the norm of the vector corresponding to $2 + 5i$.

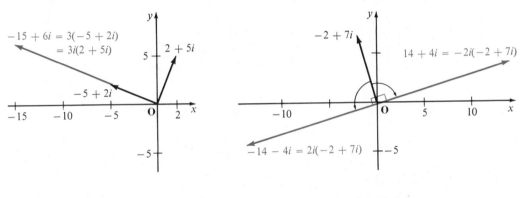

FIGURE 7–5   FIGURE 7–6

In general, for $c > 0$, multiplying a complex number $x + yi$ by ci corresponds graphically to rotating the vector (x, y) counterclockwise by $90°$ and then multiplying its length by the factor c. If $c < 0$, the rotation is in a clockwise direction, and the length is multiplied by $|c|$. Figure 7–6 shows the graphs of $-2 + 7i$, $2i(-2 + 7i)$, and $-2i(-2 + 7i)$.

From the definition $i = (0, 1)$, it follows that

$$i^2 = (0, 1)(0, 1) = (-1, 0) = -1,$$

$$i^3 = i^2i = -1(0, 1) = (0, -1) = -i,$$

$$i^4 = i^2i^2 = (-1, 0)(-1, 0) = 1,$$

$$i^5 = i^4i = 1(0, 1) = (0, 1) = i,$$

and so on. If n is a nonnegative integer, then the following statements are true:

$$i^{4n} = i^0 = 1$$
$$i^{4n+1} = i^1 = i$$
$$i^{4n+2} = i^2 = -1$$
$$i^{4n+3} = i^3 = -i$$

Example   Find a representation for i^{27} in the form i, -1, $-i$, or 1.

Solution   Upon dividing 27 by 4, we find that $27 = 4(6) + 3$, so that

$$i^{27} = i^{4(6)+3} = i^{4(6)} \cdot i^3 = 1 \cdot i^3 = i^3 = -i.$$

Graphically, repeated multiplication of the complex number (x, y), or $x + yi$, by i is analogous to repeated 90°-counterclockwise rotation of the corresponding vector (x, y). In particular, repeated multiplications of i by itself may be represented in the complex plane as shown in Figure 7–7.

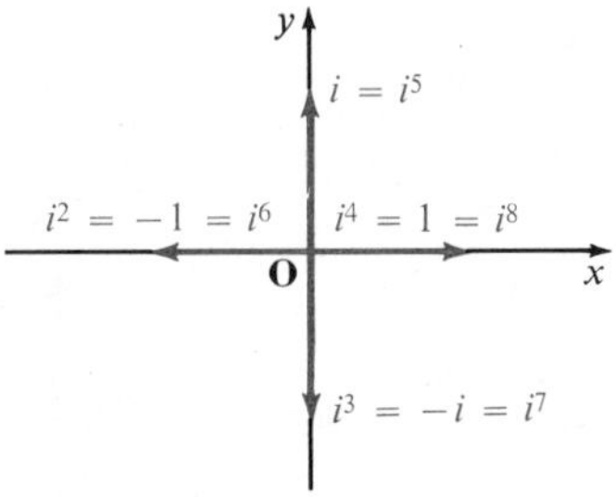

To obtain a geometric interpretation of the product $z_1 z_2$ in general, consider the following.

If $z_1 = (x_1, y_1)$,

and $z_2 = (x_2, y_2) = (x_2, 0) + (0, y_2)$,

then

$$
\begin{aligned}
z_1 z_2 &= (x_1, y_1)[(x_2, 0) + (0, y_2)] \\
&= (x_1, y_1)(x_2, 0) + (x_1, y_1)(0, y_2) \\
&= (x_2, 0)(x_1, y_1) + (0, y_2)(x_1, y_1) \\
&= x_2(x_1, y_1) + (y_2 i)(x_1, y_1) \\
&= x_2(x_1, y_1) + y_2[i(x_1, y_1)] \\
&= x_2(x_1, y_1) + y_2(-y_1, x_1). \qquad (3)
\end{aligned}
$$

Equation (3) shows that the product $z_1 z_2$ corresponds to the sum of two orthogonal vectors, one of which is the product of z_1 and the real part of z_2, and the other of which is the product of z_1 rotated 90° counterclockwise and the imaginary part of z_2. Figure 7–8 shows the graphical depiction of

$$z_1 z_2 = (2, 1)(3, 4) = 3(2, 1) + 4(-1, 2) = (2, 11).$$

FIGURE 7-7

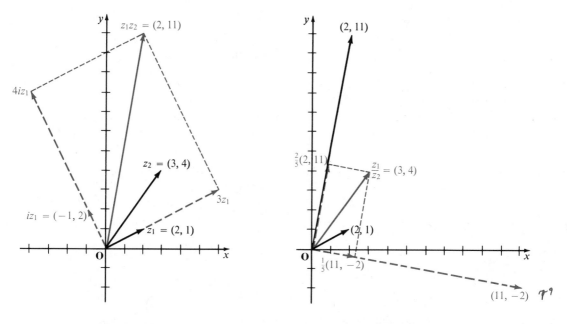

FIGURE 7–8   FIGURE 7–9

To find the quotient $\dfrac{z_1}{z_2} = \dfrac{(x_1, y_1)}{(x_2, y_2)}$ geometrically, we write

$$\frac{z_1}{z_2} = \frac{(x_1, y_1)(x_2, -y_2)}{(x_2, y_2)(x_2, -y_2)}$$

$$= \frac{(x_1, y_1)(x_2, -y_2)}{x_2^2 + y_2^2}$$

$$= \frac{x_2(x_1, y_1) - y_2(-y_1, x_1)}{x_2^2 + y_2^2} \qquad \text{[from (3), page 252]}$$

$$= \frac{x_2}{x_2^2 + y_2^2}(x_1, y_1) + \frac{y_2}{x_2^2 + y_2^2}(y_1, -x_1).$$

Figure 7–9 shows the graphical representation of the quotient of $z_1 = (2, 11)$ and $z_2 = (2, 1)$:

$$\frac{z_1}{z_2} = \frac{(2, 11)}{(2, 1)} = \frac{2}{5}(2, 11) + \frac{1}{5}(11, -2) = \left(\frac{15}{5}, \frac{20}{5}\right)$$

$$= (3, 4)$$

Note that in Figure 7–8 we multiplied $(2, 1)$ by $(3, 4)$ to obtain $(2, 11)$, while in Figure 7–9, we divided $(2, 11)$ by $(2, 1)$ to obtain $(3, 4)$.

Exercises 7–4

Show graphically on one coordinate plane the vectors corresponding to z_1, z_2, and $z_1 + z_2$.

A   **1.** $z_1 = 2 + 3i$, $z_2 = 3 - i$ **4.** $z_1 = 1 - i$, $z_2 = 2 + i$

   2. $z_1 = 0 + 4i$, $z_2 = 7 + 0i$ **5.** $z_1 = 3 - 4i$, $z_2 = -1 - i$

   3. $z_1 = 0 + 4i$, $z_2 = 0 - 2i$ **6.** $z_1 = \dfrac{1}{2} - \dfrac{\sqrt{3}}{2}i$, $z_2 = \dfrac{\sqrt{3}}{2} + \dfrac{1}{2}i$

7–12.   Repeat Exercises 1–6, showing graphically on one coordinate plane the vectors corresponding to iz_1, iz_2, and $iz_1 + iz_2$.

To which of the numbers i, -1, $-i$, or 1 is each of the following equal?

13. i^7 **15.** i^{18} **17.** $-i^{206}$ **19.** $\dfrac{1}{i^3}$

14. i^{12} **16.** i^{12345} **18.** $(-i)^{13}$ **20.** $\dfrac{1}{i^5}$

Find each indicated product or quotient and show the graphical representation of all complex numbers involved.

21. $(1 - i)(2 + 7i)$ **23.** $(3 + 0i)(2 + 4i)$ **25.** $(2 + 2i)(-1 + i)$

22. $(6 + 2i)(3 + 2i)$ **24.** $(0 + 4i)(0 - 2i)$ **26.** $(3 + i)(-2 + 6i)$

B   **27.** $\dfrac{1 + i}{2 + i}$ **28.** $\dfrac{2 + 2i}{1 + 2i}$ **29.** $\dfrac{1 + i}{1 - i}$ **30.** $\dfrac{6 - i}{3 + 4i}$

C   **31.**   Using Figure 7–8, show that the modulus of the product $(2 + i)(3 + 4i)$ is the product of the moduli of $2 + i$ and $3 + 4i$ and that an amplitude of the product is the sum of the amplitudes of $2 + i$ and $3 + 4i$.

Polar Representation of Complex Numbers

7–5   *Polar Form for Complex Numbers*

From Section 6–6 it follows that a point in the plane with Cartesian coordinates (x, y) can be represented in terms of polar coordinates (ρ, θ) by means of the equations $|\rho| = \sqrt{x^2 + y^2}$ and $\cos \theta = \dfrac{x}{\rho}$, $\sin \theta = \dfrac{y}{\rho}$, and that a point with polar coordinates (ρ, θ) can be represented in terms of Cartesian coordinates by means of the equations $x = \rho \cos \theta$ and $y = \rho \sin \theta$. Similarly, the complex number $x + yi$ can be represented in **polar,** or **trigonometric, form** as

▲ $$x + yi = \rho(\cos \theta + i \sin \theta).^* \tag{1}$$

To convert $z = x + yi, z \neq 0$, to the polar form of (1), we use the facts $\rho = |z| = \sqrt{x^2 + y^2}$, $\cos \theta = \dfrac{x}{\rho}$, and $\sin \theta = \dfrac{y}{\rho}$ to write

$$x + yi = \sqrt{x^2 + y^2} \left(\frac{x}{\sqrt{x^2 + y^2}} + \frac{y}{\sqrt{x^2 + y^2}} i \right). \tag{2}$$

Then, by observing that $\cos \theta = \dfrac{x}{\rho} = \dfrac{x}{\sqrt{x^2 + y^2}}$, and $\sin \theta = \dfrac{y}{\rho} = \dfrac{y}{\sqrt{x^2 + y^2}}$, we can find a value for θ, either by inspection or from Table 2. Note that here we are taking

$$\rho = \sqrt{x^2 + y^2} > 0.$$

Example 1 Write $3 + 4i$ in polar form.

Solution Since $$\rho = \sqrt{x^2 + y^2} = \sqrt{3^2 + 4^2} = 5,$$

it follows that $$3 + 4i = 5(\tfrac{3}{5} + \tfrac{4}{5}i),$$

by Equation (2). The latter expression signifies that $\cos \theta = \tfrac{3}{5}$ and $\sin \theta = \tfrac{4}{5}$, and we can use either of these facts, together with the fact that θ is in the first quadrant, to find from Table 2 that $\theta \doteq 53°8'$. Therefore, $3 + 4i \doteq 5(\cos 53°8' + i \sin 53°8')$.

By expressing $x + yi$ in terms of ρ and θ, you can obtain a simple expression for the product of two complex numbers. Let

$$z_1 = \rho_1(\cos \theta_1 + i \sin \theta_1) \quad \text{and} \quad z_2 = \rho_2(\cos \theta_2 + i \sin \theta_2).$$

Then

$$z_1 z_2 = \rho_1(\cos \theta_1 + i \sin \theta_1)\rho_2(\cos \theta_2 + i \sin \theta_2)$$
$$= \rho_1\rho_2[(\cos \theta_1 \cos \theta_2 - \sin \theta_1 \sin \theta_2) + i(\sin \theta_1 \cos \theta_2 + \cos \theta_1 \sin \theta_2)],$$

so that, by the trigonometric identities corresponding to formulas 9 and 10, page 30,

▲ $$z_1 z_2 = \rho_1\rho_2[\cos (\theta_1 + \theta_2) + i \sin (\theta_1 + \theta_2)]. \tag{3}$$

*Sometimes abbreviated ρ cis θ.

Example 2   If $z_1 = 4 - 4i$ and $z_2 = \sqrt{3} + i$, use the polar form of z_1 and z_2 to find $z_1 z_2$, and express the product in the form $x + yi$.

Solution   For $z_1 = 4 - 4i$, we have

$$\rho_1 = \sqrt{4^2 + 4^2} = 4\sqrt{2},$$

so

$$z_1 = 4\sqrt{2}\left(\frac{1}{\sqrt{2}} - \frac{1}{\sqrt{2}}i\right).$$

Since $\cos \theta_1 = \dfrac{1}{\sqrt{2}}$, $\sin \theta_1 = -\dfrac{1}{\sqrt{2}}$, and θ_1 is in the fourth quadrant, we have $\theta_1 = 315°$. For $z_2 = \sqrt{3} + i$,

$$\rho_2 = \sqrt{(\sqrt{3})^2 + 1^2} = 2, \qquad \text{so} \qquad z_2 = 2\left(\frac{\sqrt{3}}{2} + \frac{1}{2}i\right).$$

Since $\cos \theta_2 = \dfrac{\sqrt{3}}{2}$, $\sin \theta_2 = \frac{1}{2}$, and θ_2 is in the first quadrant, we have $\theta_2 = 30°$. We have now shown that

$$z_1 = 4\sqrt{2}\,(\cos 315° + i \sin 315°)$$

and

$$z_2 = 2(\cos 30° + i \sin 30°).$$

Using Equation (3), page 255, we obtain

$$\begin{aligned}
z_1 z_2 &= (4\sqrt{2})(2)[\cos(315° + 30°) + i \sin(315° + 30°)] \\
&= 8\sqrt{2}\,(\cos 345° + i \sin 345°) \\
&= 8\sqrt{2}\,(\cos 15° - i \sin 15°).
\end{aligned}$$

From Table 2, $\cos 15° \doteq 0.9659$, $\sin 15° \doteq 0.2588$, so that $z_1 z_2 \doteq 8(1.414)(0.9659 - 0.2588i)$, or $z_1 z_2 \doteq 10.9 - 2.9i$.

The quotient of two complex numbers also has a relatively simple expression in polar form. If

$$z_1 = \rho_1(\cos \theta_1 + i \sin \theta_1) \qquad \text{and} \qquad z_2 = \rho_2(\cos \theta_2 + i \sin \theta_2), \ \rho_2 \neq 0,$$

then

$$\frac{z_1}{z_2} = \frac{\rho_1(\cos \theta_1 + i \sin \theta_1)}{\rho_2(\cos \theta_2 + i \sin \theta_2)}$$

and $\dfrac{z_1 \bar{z}_2}{z_2 \bar{z}_2} = \dfrac{\rho_1(\cos \theta_1 + i \sin \theta_1)\rho_2(\cos \theta_2 - i \sin \theta_2)}{\rho_2(\cos \theta_2 + i \sin \theta_2)\rho_2(\cos \theta_2 - i \sin \theta_2)}$

$$= \left(\frac{\rho_1}{\rho_2}\right) \frac{(\cos \theta_1 \cos \theta_2 + \sin \theta_1 \sin \theta_2) + i(\sin \theta_1 \cos \theta_2 - \cos \theta_1 \sin \theta_2)}{\cos^2 \theta_2 + \sin^2 \theta_2},$$

or

▲ $$\frac{z_1}{z_2} = \frac{\rho_1}{\rho_2}[\cos (\theta_1 - \theta_2) + i \sin (\theta_1 - \theta_2)]. \tag{4}$$

The effect of multiplying or dividing a complex number z by i is made particularly clear when the process is viewed in polar form. To express i in polar form, we note that $i = 0 + 1i$, so $\rho = 1$, $\cos \theta = \dfrac{0}{1}$, and $\sin \theta = \dfrac{1}{1}$. Hence $\theta = 90°$ and

$$i = 1(\cos 90° + i \sin 90°).$$

Then

$$iz = (\cos 90° + i \sin 90°)\rho(\cos \theta + i \sin \theta)$$
$$= \rho[\cos (\theta + 90°) + i \sin (\theta + 90°)]$$

and

$$\frac{z}{i} = \frac{\rho(\cos \theta + i \sin \theta)}{\cos 90° + i \sin 90°} = \rho[\cos (\theta - 90°) + i \sin (\theta - 90°)].$$

Thus you can see that the multiplication, or division, of a complex number z by i leaves the modulus of z unchanged, but changes the direction of the vector corresponding to z by 90° counterclockwise, or clockwise, respectively.

Exercises 7–5

Change each of the following to the form $x + yi$.

A **1.** $\cos 30° + i \sin 30°$ **4.** $2(\cos 120° + i \sin 120°)$

2. $\cos 60° + i \sin 60°$ **5.** $4(\cos 315° + i \sin 315°)$

3. $\cos 90° + i \sin 90°$ **6.** $4[\cos (-60°) + i \sin (-60°)]$

Change each of the following to polar form. Use Table 2 as needed.

7. $\dfrac{1}{2} + \dfrac{\sqrt{3}}{2} i$ **9.** $1 - \sqrt{3} i$ **11.** $1 + i$ **13.** $6i$ **15.** $6 - 3i$

8. $-\dfrac{1}{2} + \dfrac{\sqrt{3}}{2} i$ **10.** $4 + 4\sqrt{3} i$ **12.** $-4i$ **14.** 7 **16.** $-8 - 6i$

Find an expression of the form $x + yi$ for (a) z_1z_2, (b) $\dfrac{z_1}{z_2}$.

17. $z_1 = 2(\cos 60° + i \sin 60°)$, $z_2 = 3(\cos 30° + i \sin 30°)$
18. $z_1 = 6(\cos 90° + i \sin 90°)$, $z_2 = 2[\cos (-60°) + i \sin (-60°)]$
19. $z_1 = 10(\cos 120° + i \sin 120°)$, $z_2 = 5(\cos 60° + i \sin 60°)$
20. $z_1 = 8(\cos 270° + i \sin 270°)$, $z_2 = 6(\cos 30° + i \sin 30°)$

Find an expression of the form $\rho(\cos \theta + i \sin \theta)$ for (a) z_1z_2, (b) $\dfrac{z_1}{z_2}$.

21. $z_1 = -2 - 2i$, $z_2 = -1 + i$ **23.** $z_1 = -3i$, $z_2 = 5 - 5i$
22. $z_1 = -3 + 3i$, $z_2 = 1 + i$ **24.** $z_1 = 4i$, $z_2 = 1 - \sqrt{3}\,i$

B 25. Show that if $z = \rho(\cos \theta + i \sin \theta)$, then $z^2 = \rho^2(\cos 2\theta + i \sin 2\theta)$.
26. Show that if $z = \rho(\cos \theta + i \sin \theta)$, then $z^3 = \rho^3(\cos 3\theta + i \sin 3\theta)$.
27. Show that if $z = \rho(\cos \theta + i \sin \theta)$, $z \neq 0$, then

$$\frac{1}{z} = \frac{1}{\rho}[\cos (-\theta) + i \sin (-\theta)].$$

7–6   De Moivre's Theorem

From the relationship (3) of the preceding section, that is,

$$z_1z_2 = \rho_1\rho_2[\cos (\theta_1 + \theta_2) + i \sin (\theta_1 + \theta_2)],$$

we obtain, as a special case,

$$z^2 = zz = \rho\rho[\cos (\theta + \theta) + i \sin (\theta + \theta)] = \rho^2(\cos 2\theta + i \sin 2\theta).$$

Applying the same formula again, we find that

$$z^3 = z^2z = \rho^2\rho[\cos (2\theta + \theta) + i \sin (2\theta + \theta)] = \rho^3(\cos 3\theta + i \sin 3\theta).$$

Indeed, it is true that for any positive integer n,

$$z^n = \rho^n(\cos n\theta + i \sin n\theta),$$

as the next theorem states. The proof of this theorem, which was named for the mathematician Abraham De Moivre (1667–1754), is left as an exercise (Exercise 19, page 261).

De Moivre's Theorem

▲ If $z = \rho(\cos \theta + i \sin \theta)$ and $n \in N$, then

$$z^n = [\rho(\cos \theta + i \sin \theta)]^n = \rho^n(\cos n\theta + i \sin n\theta).$$

It can be shown (Exercise 17, page 261) that the theorem also holds for $n = 0$.

Example 1   Express $(-1 + i)^4$ in the form $x + yi$.

Solution   We first express $-1 + i$ in polar form. We have

$$-1 + i = \sqrt{2} \ (\cos 135° + i \sin 135°).$$

Then, by De Moivre's Theorem,

$$
\begin{aligned}
(-1 + i)^4 &= (\sqrt{2})^4[\cos (4 \cdot 135°) + i \sin (4 \cdot 135°)] \\
&= 4(\cos 540° + i \sin 540°) \\
&= 4(\cos 180° + i \sin 180°) \\
&= -4 = -4 + 0i.
\end{aligned}
$$

In Exercise 27, page 258, you were asked to show that if $z \neq 0$ and $z = \rho(\cos \theta + i \sin \theta)$, then $\dfrac{1}{z} = \dfrac{1}{\rho} [\cos (-\theta) + i \sin (-\theta)]$. You can use this result to prove (Exercise 20, page 261) that for $z \neq 0$ and $n \in N$,

▲ $$z^{-n} = \rho^{-n}[\cos (-n\theta) + i \sin (-n\theta)]. \tag{1}$$

This is De Moivre's Theorem extended to negative integers, for $z \neq 0$.

Example 2   Express $(1 + \sqrt{3} \ i)^{-6}$ in the form $x + yi$.

Solution   First we express $1 + \sqrt{3} \ i$ in polar form. Since $\rho = 2$, we have

$$1 + \sqrt{3} \ i = 2 \left(\frac{1}{2} + \frac{\sqrt{3}}{2} i \right) = 2(\cos 60° + i \sin 60°).$$

Then, by Equation (1),

$$
\begin{aligned}
(1 + \sqrt{3} \ i)^{-6} &= 2^{-6}[\cos (-6)(60°) + i \sin (-6)(60°)] \\
&= \tfrac{1}{64}[\cos (-360°) + i \sin (-360°)] \\
&= \tfrac{1}{64}(1) = \tfrac{1}{64}.
\end{aligned}
$$

De Moivre's Theorem can be used to prove certain identities, as, for example, $\cos 2\theta = \cos^2 \theta - \sin^2 \theta$ and $\sin 2\theta = 2 \sin \theta \cos \theta$. To prove these two particular identities, we proceed, as in Section 7–3, to evaluate $(\cos \theta + i \sin \theta)^2$, obtaining

$$(\cos \theta + i \sin \theta)(\cos \theta + i \sin \theta) = \cos^2 \theta + 2i \sin \theta \cos \theta + i^2 \sin^2 \theta$$
$$= (\cos^2 \theta - \sin^2 \theta) + i(2 \sin \theta \cos \theta).$$

By De Moivre's Theorem, however,

$$(\cos \theta + i \sin \theta)^2 = \cos 2\theta + i \sin 2\theta.$$

Thus

$$(\cos^2 \theta - \sin^2 \theta) + i(2 \sin \theta \cos \theta) = \cos 2\theta + i \sin 2\theta,$$

and, by the definition of equality of complex numbers, it must be true that

$$\cos 2\theta = \cos^2 \theta - \sin^2 \theta,$$

and

$$\sin 2\theta = 2 \sin \theta \cos \theta.$$

Exercises 7–6

Use De Moivre's Theorem, or its extension, to find each of the following in the form $x + yi$.

A   **1.** $[2(\cos 10° + i \sin 10°)]^6$

     2. $[3(\cos 15° + i \sin 15°)]^4$

     3. $[\frac{1}{10}(\cos 20° + i \sin 20°)]^3$

     4. $[\frac{1}{2}(\cos 60° + i \sin 60°)]^{-5}$

     5. $(1 - \sqrt{3} i)^3$

     6. $(3 + 3i)^4$

     7. $(-\frac{1}{3} - \frac{1}{3}i)^{-4}$

     8. $(3 - \sqrt{3} i)^{-3}$

Find each of the following in the form $x + yi$.

     9. $[3(\cos 10° + i \sin 10°)]^3[\frac{1}{3}(\cos 12° + i \sin 12°)]^5$

     10. $(\sqrt{3} + i)^4(1 - i)^2$

     11. $(1 + i)^4(2 - 2i)^3$

     12. $\dfrac{(1 + i)^4}{(2 - 2i)^3}$

     13. $\dfrac{(\sqrt{3} + i)^3}{(1 - i)^2}$

     14. $\dfrac{(1 + \sqrt{3} i)^2}{(\sqrt{3} + i)^3}$

B   **15.** Apply De Moivre's Theorem to $(\cos \theta + i \sin \theta)^3$ to prove the identities:
(a) $\cos 3\theta = 4 \cos^3 \theta - 3 \cos \theta$, (b) $\sin 3\theta = 3 \sin \theta - 4 \sin^3 \theta$.

     16. Apply De Moivre's Theorem to $(\cos \theta + i \sin \theta)^4$ to discover identities involving: (a) $\cos 4\theta$, (b) $\sin 4\theta$.

17. Prove that if we define z^0 by $z^0 = 1$, then De Moivre's Theorem holds for the case $n = 0$.

18. Let $z_1 = \cos 0° + i \sin 0°$, $z_2 = \cos 120° + i \sin 120°$, and $z_3 = \cos 240° + i \sin 240°$. Show that $z_1^3 = z_2^3 = z_3^3 = 1$.

C 19. Prove De Moivre's Theorem (page 259). (*Hint:* Use mathematical induction, showing that the statement of the theorem is true for $n = 1$ and that if the statement is true for any given positive integer k, then it is true for $k + 1$.)

20. Prove the extension of De Moivre's Theorem to the negative integers, for $z \neq 0$. Define $z^{-n} = \dfrac{1}{z^n}$ and employ Exercise 27, page 258, and De Moivre's Theorem.

7–7 *Roots of Complex Numbers*

To find a qth root of the complex number z means to find a complex number $x + yi$, or $\rho(\cos \theta + i \sin \theta)$, such that

$$(x + yi)^q = [\rho(\cos \theta + i \sin \theta)]^q = z.$$

For $z \neq 0$, consider the complex number in polar form,

$$\rho^{\frac{1}{q}} \left(\cos \frac{\theta}{q} + i \sin \frac{\theta}{q} \right),$$

where $\rho > 0$ and $q \in N$. Since $\rho > 0$, $\rho^{\frac{1}{q}}$ is a positive real number, and $\rho^{\frac{1}{q}}$ exists for every such q. By De Moivre's Theorem,

$$\left[\rho^{\frac{1}{q}} \left(\cos \frac{\theta}{q} + i \sin \frac{\theta}{q} \right) \right]^q = \left[\rho^{(\frac{1}{q})q} \left(\cos q\frac{\theta}{q} + i \sin q\frac{\theta}{q} \right) \right]$$

$$= \rho(\cos \theta + i \sin \theta),$$

so $\rho^{\frac{1}{q}} \left(\cos \dfrac{\theta}{q} + i \sin \dfrac{\theta}{q} \right)$ is certainly a qth root of z.

Moreover, because $\cos \theta = \cos (\theta + k360°)$ and $\sin \theta = \sin (\theta + k360°)$ for every $k \in J$, it follows that

$$\rho^{\frac{1}{q}} \left[\cos \left(\frac{\theta + k360°}{q} \right) + i \sin \left(\frac{\theta + k360°}{q} \right) \right] \qquad (1)$$

is also a qth root of z whenever $k \in J$.

There are not infinitely many *distinct* qth roots of z, however, for if we take $k = 1, 2, \ldots$, then as soon as $k \geq q$, we begin to obtain repetitions. For example, for $k = q$, we have

$$\rho^{\frac{1}{q}} \left[\cos \left(\frac{\theta + q360°}{q} \right) + i \sin \left(\frac{\theta + q360°}{q} \right) \right]$$

$$= \rho^{\frac{1}{q}} \left[\cos \left(\frac{\theta}{q} + 360° \right) + i \sin \left(\frac{\theta}{q} + 360° \right) \right] = \rho^{\frac{1}{q}} \left(\cos \frac{\theta}{q} + i \sin \frac{\theta}{q} \right),$$

which is the same as the result with $k = 0$. Thus, the distinct roots of z are obtained for values $k \in \{0, 1, 2, \ldots, q - 1\}$, and there are exactly q such values. That is, every complex number z other than 0 has *exactly* q distinct complex qth roots. The graphs of these roots are uniformly distributed on a circle of radius $|z|^{\frac{1}{q}}$ with center at the origin.

Example 1   Find the three cube roots of $z = \dfrac{\sqrt{3}}{2} + \dfrac{1}{2} i$.

Solution   Changing $\dfrac{\sqrt{3}}{2} + \dfrac{1}{2} i$ to polar form, we have

$$z = \frac{\sqrt{3}}{2} + \frac{1}{2} i = \cos (30° + k360°) + i \sin (30° + k360°).$$

Then the cube roots ω_k are of the form

$$\cos \left(\frac{30° + k360°}{3} \right) + i \sin \left(\frac{30° + k360°}{3} \right),$$

and for $k = 0, 1,$ and 2, respectively, we find

$$\omega_0 = \left(\frac{\sqrt{3}}{2} + \frac{1}{2} i \right)^{\frac{1}{3}} = \cos 10° + i \sin 10°,$$

$$\omega_1 = \cos (10° + 120°) + i \sin (10° + 120°)$$
$$= \cos 130° + i \sin 130°,$$

$$\omega_2 = \cos (10° + 240°) + i \sin (10° + 240°)$$
$$= \cos 250° + i \sin 250°.$$

Using Table 2, we find that these are approximately equal to $0.98 + 0.17i$, $-0.64 + 0.77i$, and $-0.34 - 0.94i$, respectively.

The roots found in the foregoing example are shown graphically in Figure 7–10. You can see that the arguments of the roots differ by 120°.

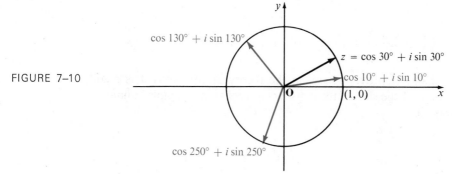

FIGURE 7–10

Example 2 Find the solution set in C of $z^3 + 1 = 0$.

Solution Solving the equation $z^3 + 1 = 0$, or $z^3 = -1$, is a matter of finding all the cube roots of -1. In polar form, the complex number $-1 + 0i$ is equal to $\cos 180° + i \sin 180°$, so that the roots we seek are of the form

$$\cos\left(\frac{180° + k360°}{3}\right) + i \sin\left(\frac{180° + k360°}{3}\right).$$

Replacing k with 0, 1, and 2, respectively, we find that the solution set of $x^3 + 1 = 0$ is

$$\{\cos 60° + i \sin 60°, \cos 180° + i \sin 180°, \cos 300° + i \sin 300°\},$$

or

$$\left\{\frac{1}{2} + \frac{\sqrt{3}}{2} i, -1, \frac{1}{2} - \frac{\sqrt{3}}{2} i\right\}.$$

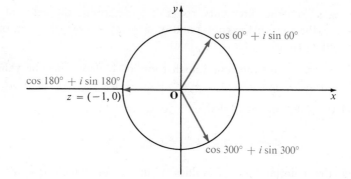

FIGURE 7–11

The graph of the solution set in Example 2 is shown in Figure 7–11. It is interesting to note also that the sum of the cube roots of -1 is 0; that is, you have

$$\left(\frac{1}{2} + \frac{\sqrt{3}}{2}i\right) + (-1 + 0i) + \left(\frac{1}{2} - \frac{\sqrt{3}}{2}i\right) = 0.$$

Although we shall not prove it here, in the theory of equations it is readily shown that for $q > 1$ the sum of the q distinct qth roots of a complex number z, $z \neq 0$, is always 0.

Exercises 7–7

In each of the following, find the required roots and show a sketch of their graphs. Use Table 2 as required.

A **1.** The three cube roots of 1.

 2. The four fourth roots of i.

 3. The four fourth roots of $16(\cos 120° + i \sin 120°)$.

 4. The three cube roots of $27(\cos 240° + i \sin 240°)$.

 5. The five fifth roots of $16\sqrt{2} + 16\sqrt{2}\,i$.

 6. The three cube roots of $-4\sqrt{3} + 4i$.

Find the solution set in C of each of the following.

 7. $z^5 - 1 = 0$ **9.** $z^3 + 4 + 4\sqrt{3}\,i = 0$

 8. $z^5 - i = 0$ **10.** $z^4 + 8\sqrt{3} - 8i = 0$

C **11.** Show that the three cube roots of 1 can be represented by expressions of the form 1, ω, and ω^2.

 12. Show that the four fourth roots of 1 can be represented by expressions of the form 1, ω, ω^2, and ω^3.

 13. If 1, ω, ω^2 are the three cube roots of 1, determine the value of $1 + \omega + \omega^2$ (the sum of the roots) and of $\omega + \omega^2 + \omega\omega^2$ (the sum of the products of the roots two at a time).

 14. If 1, ω, ω^2, ω^3 are the four fourth roots of 1, determine the value of $1 + \omega + \omega^2 + \omega^3$, and of $\omega + \omega^2 + \omega^3 + \omega\omega^2 + \omega\omega^3 + \omega^2\omega^3$.

 15. Find the solution set of values z in C for which

$$z = \omega^3 \quad \text{and} \quad \omega^4 - 1 - i = 0.$$

 16. Find the solution set of values z in C for which $z = \omega^4$ and

$$\omega^3 + \frac{1}{2} - \frac{\sqrt{3}\,i}{2} = 0.$$

Chapter Summary

1. If sums and products of ordered pairs (x, y) of real numbers are defined by

$$(x_1, y_1) + (x_2, y_2) = (x_1 + x_2, y_1 + y_2),$$
$$(x_1, y_1)(x_2, y_2) = (x_1 x_2 - y_1 y_2, x_1 y_2 + y_1 x_2),$$

then the set $\mathcal{R} \times \mathcal{R}$ is called the set C of **complex numbers**, and this set with the given operations constitutes a field.

2. The symbol i is defined by $i = (0, 1)$. We have

$$i^2 = (\sqrt{-1})^2 = -1.$$

Each complex number (x, y) can be denoted by the sum $x + yi$. The **conjugate**, $\bar{z} = (x, -y)$, of $z = (x, y)$ is then denoted by $x - yi$.

3. The **modulus** of the complex number $z = x + yi$ is defined by $|z| = |x + yi| = \sqrt{x^2 + y^2}$, and for $z \neq 0$ the **amplitude** of z is defined as the angle θ, $0 \leq \theta < 2\pi$, such that

$$\cos \theta = \frac{x}{\sqrt{x^2 + y^2}} \quad \text{and} \quad \sin \theta = \frac{y}{\sqrt{x^2 + y^2}}.$$

Each complex number z corresponds to a vector; the modulus of z is equal to the norm of the corresponding vector, and the amplitude of z is equal to its direction angle.

4. Each complex number $x + yi$ can be expressed in **polar form**,

$$x + yi = \rho(\cos \theta + i \sin \theta),$$

where

$$\rho = |x + yi|, \text{ and, for } z \neq 0, \cos \theta = \frac{x}{\sqrt{x^2 + y^2}}, \sin \theta = \frac{y}{\sqrt{x^2 + y^2}}.$$

5. By **De Moivre's Theorem**, if $z = \rho(\cos \theta + i \sin \theta)$, then $z^n = \rho^n(\cos n\theta + i \sin n\theta)$ for each $n \in N$. This theorem can be extended to $n = 0$ and to the negative integers.

6. Each nth root of z $(n \in N)$ can be written in the form

$$\rho^{\frac{1}{n}} \left[\cos \left(\frac{\theta + k360°}{n} \right) + i \sin \left(\frac{\theta + k360°}{n} \right) \right],$$

where $k \in J$. For $z \neq 0$, there are n distinct roots, corresponding to $k = 0, 1, \ldots, n - 1$.

Chapter Test

7–1   **1.** Let $z_1 = (5, -2)$, $z_2 = (1, 4)$. Find an ordered pair equal to
(a) $z_1 + z_2$, (b) $z_1 z_2$.

7–2   **2.** Let $z_1 = (5, -2)$, $z_2 = (1, 4)$. Find an ordered pair equal to
(a) $z_1 - z_2$, (b) z_2^{-1}, (c) $\overline{z_2}$, (d) $\dfrac{z_1}{z_2}$.

7–3   **3.** Find all real numbers x for which

$$(x + i)(x - 2i) = 6 + 2i.$$

7–4   **4.** Show the graphical representation of z and iz if $z = -2 + 3i$.

5. Let $z_1 = 1 + 4i$, $z_2 = 2 + 3i$. Find $z_1 z_2$ and show the graphical representation of z_1, z_2, and $z_1 z_2$.

7–5   **6.** Express in polar form: (a) $4 - 4i$, (b) $7i$.

7. Let $z_1 = 1 + i$, $z_2 = \sqrt{3} - i$. Find an expression of the form $\rho(\cos \theta + i \sin \theta)$ for (a) $z_1 z_2$, (b) $\dfrac{z_1}{z_2}$.

7–6   **8.** Find each of the following, in the form $x + yi$:
(a) $[\frac{1}{2}(\cos 130° + i \sin 130°)]^3$ (b) $\dfrac{(\sqrt{3} - i)^4}{i^3}$

7–7   **9.** Find the four fourth roots of $\dfrac{1}{2} + \dfrac{\sqrt{3}}{2} i$.

Applications of Trigonometry

Exploring the Universe

Laser beams returning from reflectors placed on the moon by astronauts make it possible to determine the distance to the moon with an error of no more than about six inches.

What a wealth of technical achievement is implied by that simple statement! —the recent invention of the laser, the flights of the astronauts, and the accurate determination of the speed of light and of an interval of elapsed time.

Yet this remarkable measurement is only a relatively minor achievement in the current burgeoning of space exploration.

Giant astronomical interferometers consisting of paired radiotelescopes separated by distances almost as great as the diameter of the earth are today being used to examine the structure of radio galaxies and quasars.

The Lunar Roving Vehicle provides the astronauts with a means of transportation on the moon's surface. Here, Astronaut David Scott conducts experiments at the Hadley-Apennine landing site. In the background, Hadley Delta rises approximately 13,124 feet above the plain.

Optical telescopes in orbiting astronomical observatories above the earth's atmosphere already are returning valuable information. By about 1980 there will quite possibly be a large national or international observatory in space, having reflecting telescopes up to three meters in diameter. The station might gradually be enlarged to house perhaps a hundred scientists.

A "grand tour" of all the outer planets except Pluto is projected for the late 1970's, the entire trip to take 11 years. Jupiter, Saturn, and Uranus will be aligned in such a way that a vehicle will be accelerated as it passes each of them and will then continue on its way to Neptune.

Although some of the physical technology involved in these achievements is new, much of the basic mathematics is quite old.

Aristarchus of Samos (310–230 B.C.) inferred from lunar eclipses that the distance to the moon is about 20 times the radius of the earth. To do this he noted that the diameter of the earth's shadow on the moon is about $2\frac{1}{2}$ times the diameter of the moon, that a conical shadow cast from the sun tapers down at an angle of about $\frac{1}{2}°$, and that the moon subtends an arc of about 2°. (This last estimate unfortunately was off by a factor of about 4.) Notice that these measurements involve the ratios of sides of triangles with known angles; that is, they use trigonometry.

A century later, Hipparchus (who made tables of chord lengths and is generally considered as the actual founder of trigonometry) used more accurate values and computed the distance to the moon as being 59 earth radii. (The true mean distance actually is about 60.3 earth radii.)

The measurements of Aristarchus and Hipparchus give *relative* distances. Relative distances can be converted to *true* distances when one of these distances

A 360-degree panoramic view of the entire equatorial region of Mars is shown in the mosaic of pictures at the right, taken by Mariner 9 over a period of two months. Several hundred individual television photo frames were scaled to size for this mosaic, which covers 27 million square miles, or 50% of the surface of Mars! Visible at left center is the complex of newly-discovered giant volcanic mountains and their summit craters. The largest of these, Nix Olympica, measures 310 miles across at its base. Nine huge volcanoes have been seen in the Mariner 9 pictures. The center section of the mosaic contains an enormous canyon—2500 miles long, 75 miles wide, and, at its maximum depth, nearly 20,000 feet deep. On Earth, this Mars feature would extend from Los Angeles to New York, and its maximum depth is four times that of the Grand Canyon.

has been determined. This step was taken by Eratosthenes (276–195 B.C.). Being told that at Syene, 5000 stadii to the south of Alexandria, light from the sun penetrated to the bottom of a well at noon on the first day of summer each year, he measured the deviation of the sun from the zenith at Alexandria on that day. Finding it to be about 7°, or about $\frac{1}{50} \times 360°$, he concluded that the circumference of the earth is about 50×5000 stadii, or about 250,000 stadii. This is about 20% too large if his measurements were based on the common Olympic stadium (the course length

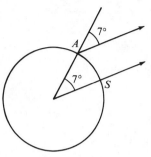

of a popular foot race of the day), but is less than 1% in error if the alternative definition of the stadium as $\frac{1}{10}$ of a mile was intended.

Modern space investigations have both practical and theoretical value, as discussed in the essay on environmental exploration at the end of Chapter 4.

In basic theory, the ability to measure the distance between a place on earth and a place on the moon at any time with a precision of less than a foot can, for example, help determine how the mass of the moon is distributed, the rate at which continental drift on earth is proceeding, and changes in the location of the earth's poles. As astronomical observations are extended and made more accurate, we can expect to find answers to questions about the processes by which stars and even galaxies are born, grow old, and die; and about the nature of quasars, pulsers, and black holes in the universe. This is by far the most active of all times in space investigations, and the heightened activity quite surely will continue for many years to come.

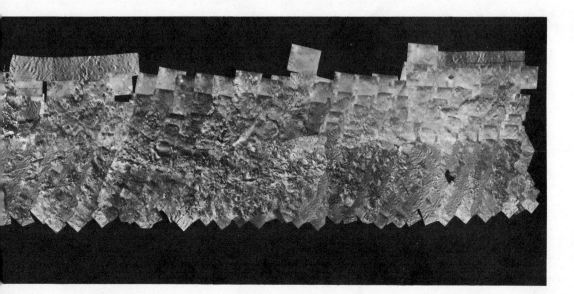

Chapter Eight

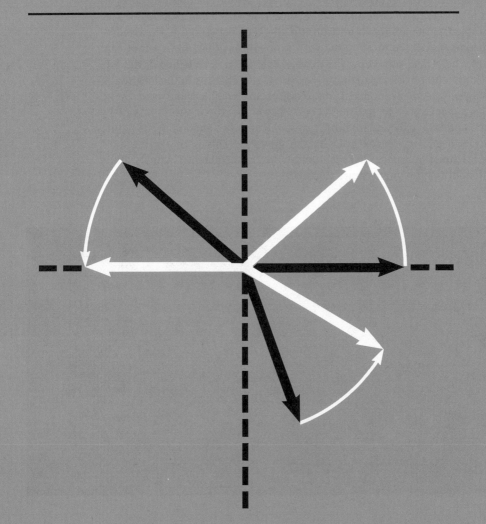

Matrices

OBJECTIVES

1. To learn the properties of the set of 2 × 2 matrices.
2. To use 2 × 2 matrices to perform computations involving complex numbers.
3. To use 2 × 2 matrices to effect simple transformations of the plane, including magnifications, shrinkings, stretchings, shearings, reflections in the origin, reflections in an axis, and rotations.

Operations with Matrices

8–1 Basic Properties of 2 × 2 Matrices

In Chapter 6, you saw that a vector can be represented as an ordered pair (x, y), as the sum $x\mathbf{i} + y\mathbf{j}$ of scalar multiples of unit basis vectors $\mathbf{i}$ and $\mathbf{j}$, and in polar form as $\rho[(\cos \theta)\mathbf{i} + (\sin \theta)\mathbf{j}]$. In Chapter 7, you saw that a complex number can be represented as an ordered pair (x, y), as the sum $x + yi$, and in polar form as $\rho(\cos \theta + i \sin \theta)$. There is still another way in which both vectors and complex numbers can be represented—by means of *matrices*. In this chapter we shall study some basic properties of matrices, and then we shall use these to find matrix representations for complex numbers and vectors.

Any rectangular array of numbers, such as

$$\begin{bmatrix} 1 & 2 & 7 \\ 3 & 0 & -5 \end{bmatrix} \quad \text{or} \quad \begin{bmatrix} 1 \\ 0 \\ 0 \end{bmatrix},$$

is called a **matrix**. To identify the array, we enclose it in square brackets, as shown. The numbers, such as 1, 2, and 7, are called the **entries** of the matrix in which they appear.

In this section, we shall be concerned primarily with a special set of matrices, namely, the set $S_{2\times 2}$ of square matrices having two (horizontal) **rows** and two (vertical) **columns** of real-number entries. Thus,

$$\begin{bmatrix} -1 & 4 \\ 2 & 3 \end{bmatrix}, \quad \begin{bmatrix} 1 & 0 \\ 0 & 1 \end{bmatrix}, \quad \text{and} \quad \begin{bmatrix} 0 & 0 \\ 0 & 0 \end{bmatrix}$$

are members of $S_{2\times 2}$. Since these matrices have two rows and two columns, they are said to be 2 × 2 (read "two-by-two") matrices. (In stating the dimensions of a matrix, the number of rows is always specified first, and then the number of columns. For example, a matrix with 3 rows and 2 columns is a 3 × 2 matrix.)

Capital letters are frequently used to denote matrices; for example, we may write

$$A = \begin{bmatrix} 1 & -2 \\ -7 & 3 \end{bmatrix} \quad \text{or} \quad B = \begin{bmatrix} 1 & 0 \\ 1 & 0 \end{bmatrix}.$$

We define two matrices in $S_{2\times 2}$ to be **equal** if and only if their corresponding entries are equal. Thus

$$\begin{bmatrix} 1 & 2 \\ 6 & -1 \end{bmatrix} = \begin{bmatrix} 2-1 & \frac{4}{2} \\ 3 \times 2 & 2-3 \end{bmatrix},$$

but

$$\begin{bmatrix} 0 & 1 \\ 2 & 3 \end{bmatrix} \neq \begin{bmatrix} 1 & 0 \\ 3 & 2 \end{bmatrix}.$$

If all the entries of a matrix are zeros, the matrix is called a **zero matrix** and is denoted by O. Thus, in the set $S_{2\times 2}$, the zero matrix is

$$O = \begin{bmatrix} 0 & 0 \\ 0 & 0 \end{bmatrix}.$$

The **negative** of a matrix A is defined to be the matrix $-A$, each of whose entries is the negative of the corresponding entry in A. Thus if

$$A = \begin{bmatrix} 7 & -1 \\ -4 & 3 \end{bmatrix}, \quad \text{then} \quad -A = -\begin{bmatrix} 7 & -1 \\ -4 & 3 \end{bmatrix} = \begin{bmatrix} -7 & 1 \\ 4 & -3 \end{bmatrix}.$$

The **sum** of matrices A and B in $S_{2\times 2}$ is the matrix $A + B$, each of whose entries is the sum of the corresponding entries in A and B. For example, if

$$A = \begin{bmatrix} 1 & 3 \\ 5 & 7 \end{bmatrix} \text{ and } B = \begin{bmatrix} 2 & -3 \\ 6 & 9 \end{bmatrix}, \text{ then}$$

$$A + B = \begin{bmatrix} 1 & 3 \\ 5 & 7 \end{bmatrix} + \begin{bmatrix} 2 & -3 \\ 6 & 9 \end{bmatrix} = \begin{bmatrix} 1+2 & 3+(-3) \\ 5+6 & 7+9 \end{bmatrix} = \begin{bmatrix} 3 & 0 \\ 11 & 16 \end{bmatrix}.$$

You can prove the following facts about the addition of 2×2 matrices.

▲   If A, B, and $C \in S_{2\times 2}$, then:

1. $A + B \in S_{2\times 2}$
2. $(A + B) + C = A + (B + C)$
3. $A + O = O + A = A$
4. $A + (-A) = -A + A = O$
5. $A + B = B + A$

In words, addition in the set $S_{2\times 2}$ is closed, commutative, and associative; there is an additive identity element in the set, and each member of the set has an additive inverse in the set. Thus (recall page 190), the set of 2×2 matrices forms a commutative group under matrix addition.

The **product** of a scalar (in this book, a real number) c and a matrix A is defined to be the matrix cA, each of whose entries is c times the corresponding entry of A. Thus, if

$$A = \begin{bmatrix} 7 & -1 \\ 2 & 4 \end{bmatrix}, \qquad \text{then} \qquad 3A = 3\begin{bmatrix} 7 & -1 \\ 2 & 4 \end{bmatrix} = \begin{bmatrix} 21 & -3 \\ 6 & 12 \end{bmatrix}.$$

You can prove the following facts about the multiplication of a member of the set $S_{2\times 2}$ by a scalar.

▲   If A, $B \in S_{2\times 2}$ and c, $d \in \mathcal{R}$, then:

6. $cA \in S_{2\times 2}$
7. $c(dA) = (cd)A$
8. $(c + d)A = cA + dA$
9. $c(A + B) = cA + cB$
10. $1A = A$
11. $-1A = -A$
12. $0A = O$
13. $cO = O$

By comparing these thirteen properties of the addition of 2×2 matrices and the multiplication of a 2×2 matrix by a scalar with the properties of vectors listed on page 190, you can see that under these operations the set $S_{2\times 2}$ is a vector space.

We can also define a **subtraction** operation for matrices in a manner comparable to that used to define subtraction in the set of real numbers, namely:

If A and B are 2×2 matrices, then

$$A - B = A + (-B).$$

Example   If $A = \begin{bmatrix} 6 & -2 \\ 4 & 3 \end{bmatrix}$ and $B = \begin{bmatrix} -4 & 5 \\ 2 & 0 \end{bmatrix}$, find:

(a) $A - B$ (b) $3A + 2B$ (c) $3A - 2B$

Solution   (a) $A - B = \begin{bmatrix} 6 & -2 \\ 4 & 3 \end{bmatrix} + \left(-\begin{bmatrix} -4 & 5 \\ 2 & 0 \end{bmatrix} \right)$

$= \begin{bmatrix} 6 & -2 \\ 4 & 3 \end{bmatrix} + \begin{bmatrix} 4 & -5 \\ -2 & 0 \end{bmatrix} = \begin{bmatrix} 10 & -7 \\ 2 & 3 \end{bmatrix}$

(b) $3A + 2B = 3\begin{bmatrix} 6 & -2 \\ 4 & 3 \end{bmatrix} + 2\begin{bmatrix} -4 & 5 \\ 2 & 0 \end{bmatrix}$

$= \begin{bmatrix} 18 & -6 \\ 12 & 9 \end{bmatrix} + \begin{bmatrix} -8 & 10 \\ 4 & 0 \end{bmatrix} = \begin{bmatrix} 10 & 4 \\ 16 & 9 \end{bmatrix}$

(c) $3A - 2B = 3\begin{bmatrix} 6 & -2 \\ 4 & 3 \end{bmatrix} + \left(-2\begin{bmatrix} -4 & 5 \\ 2 & 0 \end{bmatrix} \right)$

$= \begin{bmatrix} 18 & -6 \\ 12 & 9 \end{bmatrix} + \begin{bmatrix} 8 & -10 \\ -4 & 0 \end{bmatrix} = \begin{bmatrix} 26 & -16 \\ 8 & 9 \end{bmatrix}$

Although we have restricted our discussion in this section to the set $S_{2\times2}$ of 2×2 matrices, the definitions made here carry over to matrices with any given number m of rows and any given number n of columns. If, however, two matrices are to be equal or to have a sum, it is clear that, under the definitions adopted here, they must have both the same number of rows and the same number of columns; that is, they must be of the same **order**. For example, the following pair of matrices does not have a sum:

$$A = \begin{bmatrix} 1 & 2 & 0 \\ -6 & 0 & 3 \end{bmatrix} \quad \text{and} \quad B = \begin{bmatrix} 1 & 0 \\ -3 & 5 \\ 2 & -1 \end{bmatrix}.$$

The vector-space properties of the set $S_{2\times2}$ discussed in this section also carry over to the set $S_{m\times n}$ of matrices of order $m \times n$, that is, to the set of matrices having m rows and n columns for any fixed m and $n \in N$. Accordingly, the set $S_{m\times n}$ is a commutative group under the operation of matrix addition, and is a vector space under this operation and the operation of scalar multiplication.

Exercises 8–1

In Exercises 1–6, let $A = \begin{bmatrix} 1 & -2 \\ 5 & 3 \end{bmatrix}$ and $B = \begin{bmatrix} 0 & 5 \\ -4 & -6 \end{bmatrix}$. Find a 2 × 2 matrix equal to the given expression.

A   1. $A + B$ **3.** $3A + B$ **5.** $3(A + B)$

    2. $A - 2B$ **4.** $4A + 4B$ **6.** $-2(B - A)$

In Exercises 7–12, express each matrix in the form cA, where all entries of matrix A are integers and c is the greatest possible scalar (not necessarily an integer).

Example $\begin{bmatrix} 36 & -12 \\ 6 & 0 \end{bmatrix}$ Solution $\begin{bmatrix} 36 & -12 \\ 6 & 0 \end{bmatrix} = 6\begin{bmatrix} 6 & -2 \\ 1 & 0 \end{bmatrix}$

7. $\begin{bmatrix} 8 & 0 \\ 0 & 8 \end{bmatrix}$ **9.** $\begin{bmatrix} 6 & 21 \\ -15 & 0 \end{bmatrix}$ **11.** $\begin{bmatrix} -8 & \frac{1}{3} \\ 1 & \frac{3}{4} \end{bmatrix}$

8. $\begin{bmatrix} 2 & -2 \\ -2 & 2 \end{bmatrix}$ **10.** $\begin{bmatrix} 3 & \frac{1}{2} \\ 12 & 6 \end{bmatrix}$ **12.** $\begin{bmatrix} 168 & 84 \\ 252 & 378 \end{bmatrix}$

In Exercises 13–20, find the matrix X satisfying the given equation.

Example $2X + 4\begin{bmatrix} 3 & -\frac{1}{2} \\ 1 & 0 \end{bmatrix} = \begin{bmatrix} 8 & 6 \\ 5 & -3 \end{bmatrix}$

Solution   By first completing the scalar multiplication, you obtain

$$2X + \begin{bmatrix} 12 & -2 \\ 4 & 0 \end{bmatrix} = \begin{bmatrix} 8 & 6 \\ 5 & -3 \end{bmatrix}.$$

Adding the negative of $\begin{bmatrix} 12 & -2 \\ 4 & 0 \end{bmatrix}$ to each member, you have

$$2X + \begin{bmatrix} 12 & -2 \\ 4 & 0 \end{bmatrix} + \begin{bmatrix} -12 & 2 \\ -4 & 0 \end{bmatrix} = \begin{bmatrix} 8 & 6 \\ 5 & -3 \end{bmatrix} + \begin{bmatrix} -12 & 2 \\ -4 & 0 \end{bmatrix},$$

$$2X + O = \begin{bmatrix} -4 & 8 \\ 1 & -3 \end{bmatrix}, \quad \text{or} \quad 2X = \begin{bmatrix} -4 & 8 \\ 1 & -3 \end{bmatrix}.$$

Multiplying each member by $\frac{1}{2}$ gives

$$X = \frac{1}{2}\begin{bmatrix} -4 & 8 \\ 1 & -3 \end{bmatrix} = \begin{bmatrix} -2 & 4 \\ \frac{1}{2} & -\frac{3}{2} \end{bmatrix}.$$

13. $X + \begin{bmatrix} 2 & 0 \\ 0 & 2 \end{bmatrix} = \begin{bmatrix} 5 & 0 \\ 0 & 5 \end{bmatrix}$

17. $2X + \frac{1}{2}\begin{bmatrix} -4 & 10 \\ 6 & 0 \end{bmatrix} = 4\begin{bmatrix} 1 & 0 \\ 0 & 1 \end{bmatrix}$

14. $\begin{bmatrix} 2 & 1 \\ 1 & 3 \end{bmatrix} + X = \begin{bmatrix} 0 & 1 \\ 0 & 7 \end{bmatrix}$

18. $4X = \begin{bmatrix} 8 & -16 \\ -16 & 8 \end{bmatrix}$

15. $2X + \begin{bmatrix} 3 & 1 \\ -1 & 11 \end{bmatrix} = \begin{bmatrix} 0 & 0 \\ 0 & 0 \end{bmatrix}$

19. $X + \begin{bmatrix} 1 & 0 \\ 0 & 1 \end{bmatrix} = \begin{bmatrix} 0 & 1 \\ 1 & 0 \end{bmatrix}$

16. $3X - \begin{bmatrix} 1 & 7 \\ 6 & -2 \end{bmatrix} = \begin{bmatrix} 3 & 10 \\ 2 & -3 \end{bmatrix}$

20. $6X = \begin{bmatrix} 20 & 10 \\ -10 & 20 \end{bmatrix} - 4X$

In Exercises 21–32, let

$$A = \begin{bmatrix} a_1 & b_1 \\ c_1 & d_1 \end{bmatrix}, \qquad B = \begin{bmatrix} a_2 & b_2 \\ c_2 & d_2 \end{bmatrix}, \qquad \text{and} \qquad C = \begin{bmatrix} a_3 & b_3 \\ c_3 & d_3 \end{bmatrix}$$

be members of the set $S_{2\times2}$, and let $c, d \in \Re$. Prove each assertion.

Example $A + B \in S_{2\times2}$

Solution   By definition, $A + B = \begin{bmatrix} a_1 + a_2 & b_1 + b_2 \\ c_1 + c_2 & d_1 + d_2 \end{bmatrix}$.

Since addition in the set of real numbers is closed, $a_1 + a_2$, $b_1 + b_2$, $c_1 + c_2$, and $d_1 + d_2$ are real numbers. Thus $A + B$ is a member of $S_{2\times2}$.

B 21. $(A + B) + C = A + (B + C)$

22. $A + O = A$

23. $A + (-A) = O$

24. $A + B = B + A$

25. $cA \in S_{2\times2}$

26. $c(dA) = (cd)A$

27. $(c + d)A = cA + dA$

28. $c(A + B) = cA + cB$

29. $1A = A$

30. $-1A = -A$

31. $0A = O$

32. $cO = O$

8–2 Products of 2 × 2 Matrices

The **product** of matrices A and B in $S_{2\times 2}$ is the matrix AB which is defined as follows:

$$\text{If} \quad A = \begin{bmatrix} a_1 & b_1 \\ c_1 & d_1 \end{bmatrix} \quad \text{and} \quad B = \begin{bmatrix} a_2 & b_2 \\ c_2 & d_2 \end{bmatrix}, \quad \text{then}$$

$$AB = \begin{bmatrix} a_1 & b_1 \\ c_1 & d_1 \end{bmatrix}\begin{bmatrix} a_2 & b_2 \\ c_2 & d_2 \end{bmatrix} = \begin{bmatrix} a_1a_2 + b_1c_2 & a_1b_2 + b_1d_2 \\ c_1a_2 + d_1c_2 & c_1b_2 + d_1d_2 \end{bmatrix}.$$

For example, consider the product AB, where

$$A = \begin{bmatrix} 3 & -1 \\ -6 & 4 \end{bmatrix} \quad \text{and} \quad B = \begin{bmatrix} 2 & 5 \\ 1 & -3 \end{bmatrix}.$$

We can find this product using "row by column" multiplication, as follows: Computing the entry in the first row and first column of the product matrix, we have

$$AB = \begin{bmatrix} 3 & -1 \\ -6 & 4 \end{bmatrix}\begin{bmatrix} 2 & 5 \\ 1 & -3 \end{bmatrix} = \begin{bmatrix} 6 + (-1) & \\ & \end{bmatrix} = \begin{bmatrix} 5 & \\ & \end{bmatrix}.$$

In the first row and second column, we find

$$AB = \begin{bmatrix} 3 & -1 \\ -6 & 4 \end{bmatrix}\begin{bmatrix} 2 & 5 \\ 1 & -3 \end{bmatrix} = \begin{bmatrix} 5 & 15 + 3 \\ & \end{bmatrix} = \begin{bmatrix} 5 & 18 \\ & \end{bmatrix}.$$

In the second row and first column, we have

$$AB = \begin{bmatrix} 3 & -1 \\ -6 & 4 \end{bmatrix}\begin{bmatrix} 2 & 5 \\ 1 & -3 \end{bmatrix} = \begin{bmatrix} 5 & 18 \\ -12 + 4 & \end{bmatrix} = \begin{bmatrix} 5 & 18 \\ -8 & \end{bmatrix},$$

and in the second row and second column,

$$AB = \begin{bmatrix} 3 & -1 \\ -6 & 4 \end{bmatrix}\begin{bmatrix} 2 & 5 \\ 1 & -3 \end{bmatrix} = \begin{bmatrix} 5 & 18 \\ -8 & -30 - 12 \end{bmatrix}.$$

Thus,

$$AB = \begin{bmatrix} 5 & 18 \\ -8 & -42 \end{bmatrix}.$$

It is evident from the results of the following example that *matrix multiplication is not always commutative.*

Example 1   If $A = \begin{bmatrix} 2 & 4 \\ 7 & 5 \end{bmatrix}$ and $B = \begin{bmatrix} 3 & -2 \\ 0 & 1 \end{bmatrix}$, find AB and BA.

Solution
$$AB = \begin{bmatrix} 2 & 4 \\ 7 & 5 \end{bmatrix}\begin{bmatrix} 3 & -2 \\ 0 & 1 \end{bmatrix}$$

$$= \begin{bmatrix} (2)(3) + (4)(0) & (2)(-2) + (4)(1) \\ (7)(3) + (5)(0) & (7)(-2) + (5)(1) \end{bmatrix}$$

$$= \begin{bmatrix} 6 & 0 \\ 21 & -9 \end{bmatrix}, \text{ but}$$

$$BA = \begin{bmatrix} 3 & -2 \\ 0 & 1 \end{bmatrix}\begin{bmatrix} 2 & 4 \\ 7 & 5 \end{bmatrix}$$

$$= \begin{bmatrix} (3)(2) + (-2)(7) & (3)(4) + (-2)(5) \\ (0)(2) + (1)(7) & (0)(4) + (1)(5) \end{bmatrix}$$

$$= \begin{bmatrix} -8 & 2 \\ 7 & 5 \end{bmatrix}.$$

Although the commutative law of multiplication does not hold in the set $S_{2\times2}$ of 2×2 matrices, the following properties do hold. You will be asked to prove the first six of these in the exercises (page 281); the matrix I will be defined and the seventh property will be established in the following paragraph.

   If $A, B, C \in S_{2\times2}$, and c is a scalar, then:
1. $AB \in S_{2\times2}$
2. $(AB)C = A(BC)$
3. $A(B + C) = AB + AC$
4. $(B + C)A = BA + CA$
5. $A(cB) = (cA)B = c(AB)$
6. $AO = OA = O$
7. $AI = IA = A$

The matrix
$$I = \begin{bmatrix} 1 & 0 \\ 0 & 1 \end{bmatrix},$$

called the **identity matrix**, serves as the unique identity element for multiplication in the set $S_{2\times2}$ of 2×2 matrices. To show that $AI = IA = A$, we let $A = \begin{bmatrix} a & b \\ c & d \end{bmatrix}$ be any matrix in $S_{2\times2}$. Then

$$AI = \begin{bmatrix} a & b \\ c & d \end{bmatrix}\begin{bmatrix} 1 & 0 \\ 0 & 1 \end{bmatrix} = \begin{bmatrix} a+0 & 0+b \\ c+0 & 0+d \end{bmatrix} = \begin{bmatrix} a & b \\ c & d \end{bmatrix} = A, \text{ and}$$

$$IA = \begin{bmatrix} 1 & 0 \\ 0 & 1 \end{bmatrix} \begin{bmatrix} a & b \\ c & d \end{bmatrix} = \begin{bmatrix} a+0 & b+0 \\ 0+c & 0+d \end{bmatrix} = \begin{bmatrix} a & b \\ c & d \end{bmatrix} = A.$$

Matrix multiplication has several properties which are strikingly different from those of multiplication of either real or complex numbers. We have already noted that multiplication of matrices is not, in general, commutative. As the following example indicates, it is possible for two nonzero matrices to have the zero matrix for their product. Thus if

$$A = \begin{bmatrix} 10 & 5 \\ 2 & 1 \end{bmatrix} \quad \text{and} \quad B = \begin{bmatrix} 4 & 1 \\ -8 & -2 \end{bmatrix},$$

then

$$AB = \begin{bmatrix} 40-40 & 10-10 \\ 8-8 & 2-2 \end{bmatrix} = \begin{bmatrix} 0 & 0 \\ 0 & 0 \end{bmatrix}.$$

Moreover, there are nonzero matrices A for which $A^2 = O$. One such matrix is $A = \begin{bmatrix} 2 & 1 \\ -4 & -2 \end{bmatrix}$, for which

$$A^2 = A \cdot A = \begin{bmatrix} 2 & 1 \\ -4 & -2 \end{bmatrix} \begin{bmatrix} 2 & 1 \\ -4 & -2 \end{bmatrix} = \begin{bmatrix} 0 & 0 \\ 0 & 0 \end{bmatrix}.$$

Since the commutative law for multiplication does not hold for matrices, care has to be exercised in carrying out certain seemingly familiar operations.

Example 2 If $A = \begin{bmatrix} 3 & 2 \\ -1 & 3 \end{bmatrix}$ and $B = \begin{bmatrix} 7 & -1 \\ 6 & 2 \end{bmatrix}$, find a 2 × 2 matrix equal to $(A + B)^2$.

Solution   The most direct way to compute $(A + B)^2$ in this example is to perform first the addition and then the squaring operation. We have

$$A + B = \begin{bmatrix} 3 & 2 \\ -1 & 3 \end{bmatrix} + \begin{bmatrix} 7 & -1 \\ 6 & 2 \end{bmatrix} = \begin{bmatrix} 10 & 1 \\ 5 & 5 \end{bmatrix},$$

and then

$$(A + B)^2 = \begin{bmatrix} 10 & 1 \\ 5 & 5 \end{bmatrix}^2 = \begin{bmatrix} 10 & 1 \\ 5 & 5 \end{bmatrix} \begin{bmatrix} 10 & 1 \\ 5 & 5 \end{bmatrix} = \begin{bmatrix} 105 & 15 \\ 75 & 30 \end{bmatrix}.$$

Note, however, that if we try to compute $(A + B)^2$ from the

(*Solution continued*)

usual expression $A^2 + 2AB + B^2$, we obtain

$$\begin{bmatrix} 3 & 2 \\ -1 & 3 \end{bmatrix}^2 + 2\begin{bmatrix} 3 & 2 \\ -1 & 3 \end{bmatrix}\begin{bmatrix} 7 & -1 \\ 6 & 2 \end{bmatrix} + \begin{bmatrix} 7 & -1 \\ 6 & 2 \end{bmatrix}^2$$

$$= \begin{bmatrix} 7 & 12 \\ -6 & 7 \end{bmatrix} + 2\begin{bmatrix} 33 & 1 \\ 11 & 7 \end{bmatrix} + \begin{bmatrix} 43 & -9 \\ 54 & -2 \end{bmatrix}$$

$$= \begin{bmatrix} 7 & 12 \\ -6 & 7 \end{bmatrix} + \begin{bmatrix} 66 & 2 \\ 22 & 14 \end{bmatrix} + \begin{bmatrix} 43 & -9 \\ 54 & -2 \end{bmatrix}$$

$$= \begin{bmatrix} 116 & 5 \\ 70 & 19 \end{bmatrix}.$$

Hence $(A + B)^2 \neq A^2 + 2AB + B^2$. The difficulty here is that $AB \neq BA$, and the expansion of $(A + B)^2$ to $A^2 + AB + BA + B^2$ cannot be simplified to $A^2 + 2AB + B^2$ by combining the two terms AB and BA. You can verify, however, that $A^2 + AB + BA + B^2$ is equal to $(A + B)^2$.

The definition given for the product of two matrices in $S_{2\times2}$ may be extended to find the product of matrices having other dimensions, provided the number of columns in the matrix forming the first factor of the product is equal to the number of rows in the matrix forming the second factor. Thus, if A and B are matrices which have a product, then the entry in the ith row and the jth column $(i, j \in N)$ of the matrix AB is the sum of the products formed by multiplying each entry in the ith row of A by the corresponding entry in the jth column of B.

In Section 8–5 we shall be particularly interested in products of 2 × 2 matrices and 2 × 1 matrices. Note that these products are defined, since a 2 × 2 matrix has two columns and a 2 × 1 matrix has two rows. The product of a 2 × 2 matrix and a 2 × 1 matrix is a 2 × 1 matrix; and, in general, the product of an $m \times n$ matrix and an $n \times p$ matrix is an $m \times p$ matrix.

Example 3   For $A = \begin{bmatrix} 2 & 7 \\ 0 & -4 \end{bmatrix}$ and $B = \begin{bmatrix} 10 \\ -3 \end{bmatrix}$, find AB.

Solution   Since the number of columns in A is the same as the number of rows in B, the product AB is defined. It is computed as follows:

$$AB = \begin{bmatrix} 2 & 7 \\ 0 & -4 \end{bmatrix}\begin{bmatrix} 10 \\ -3 \end{bmatrix} = \begin{bmatrix} (2)(10) + (7)(-3) \\ (0)(10) + (-4)(-3) \end{bmatrix} = \begin{bmatrix} -1 \\ 12 \end{bmatrix}.$$

Note that the product BA is not defined for the two matrices in Example 3 above, because the number of columns in B (one) is not equal to the number of rows in A (two).

Exercises 8–2

Find each product.

A 1. $\begin{bmatrix} 2 & -3 \\ -4 & 5 \end{bmatrix}\begin{bmatrix} 6 & -5 \\ 4 & 7 \end{bmatrix}$

5. $\begin{bmatrix} 5 & 2 \\ 1 & 3 \end{bmatrix}\begin{bmatrix} 1 & 4 \\ 2 & -1 \end{bmatrix}$

2. $\begin{bmatrix} 1 & 2 \\ 3 & 4 \end{bmatrix}\begin{bmatrix} 1 & -1 \\ 0 & 0 \end{bmatrix}$

6. $\begin{bmatrix} 3 & 1 \\ 0 & 3 \end{bmatrix}\begin{bmatrix} -1 & 2 \\ 2 & 4 \end{bmatrix}$

3. $\begin{bmatrix} 3 & 1 \\ 2 & -1 \end{bmatrix}\begin{bmatrix} 0 & 1 \\ 1 & 0 \end{bmatrix}$

7. $\begin{bmatrix} 2 & 5 \\ 1 & 3 \end{bmatrix}\begin{bmatrix} -1 & 2 \\ 3 & -5 \end{bmatrix}$

4. $\begin{bmatrix} -1 & 0 \\ -2 & -1 \end{bmatrix}\begin{bmatrix} 1 & 0 \\ -2 & 1 \end{bmatrix}$

8. $\begin{bmatrix} 3 & 4 \\ 2 & 9 \end{bmatrix}\begin{bmatrix} -6 & 4 \\ 5 & 0 \end{bmatrix}$

In Exercises 9–12, let

$$A = \begin{bmatrix} 3 & -1 \\ 0 & 5 \end{bmatrix} \quad \text{and} \quad B = \begin{bmatrix} 6 & -2 \\ 8 & 1 \end{bmatrix},$$

and find a 2 × 2 matrix equal to each of the following.

9. $(A - B)^2$ 10. $A^2 - B^2$ 11. $(A + B)(A - B)$ 12. $(A - B)(A + B)$

Determine values of x_1 and x_2 for which the given equation is true.

13. $\begin{bmatrix} 5 & 1 \\ 0 & 4 \end{bmatrix}\begin{bmatrix} -2 & x_1 \\ 3 & x_2 \end{bmatrix} = \begin{bmatrix} -7 & 21 \\ 12 & 4 \end{bmatrix}$

16. $\begin{bmatrix} 3 & 5 \\ 4 & 7 \end{bmatrix}\begin{bmatrix} 7 & x_2 \\ x_1 & 3 \end{bmatrix} = \begin{bmatrix} 1 & 0 \\ 0 & 1 \end{bmatrix}$

14. $\begin{bmatrix} -1 & 1 \\ 2 & 3 \end{bmatrix}\begin{bmatrix} x_1 & x_2 \\ 3 & 7 \end{bmatrix} = \begin{bmatrix} -1 & 5 \\ 17 & 25 \end{bmatrix}$

17. $\begin{bmatrix} -1 & 1 \\ 3 & -2 \end{bmatrix}\begin{bmatrix} x_1 & 1 \\ x_2 & 5 \end{bmatrix} = \begin{bmatrix} 4 & 4 \\ -6 & -7 \end{bmatrix}$

15. $\begin{bmatrix} x_1 & 3 \\ 1 & x_2 \end{bmatrix}^2 = \begin{bmatrix} 7 & -9 \\ -3 & 4 \end{bmatrix}$

18. $\begin{bmatrix} x_1 & x_2 \\ x_2 & x_1 \end{bmatrix}^2 = \begin{bmatrix} 2 & -2 \\ -2 & 2 \end{bmatrix}$

In Exercises 19–24, let A, B, and C be members of the set $S_{2 \times 2}$, and let $c \in \mathcal{R}$. Prove the given assertion.

B 19. $AB \in S_{2 \times 2}$

22. $(B + C)A = BA + CA$

20. $(AB)C = A(BC)$

23. $A(cB) = (cA)B$

21. $A(B + C) = AB + AC$

24. $AO = O, \; OA = O$

25. Find a scalar c, in terms of a, such that

$$\begin{bmatrix} a & 0 \\ 0 & a \end{bmatrix}^2 = cI \quad \text{for every } a \in \mathcal{R}.$$

26. Letting $J = \begin{bmatrix} 0 & 1 \\ -1 & 0 \end{bmatrix}$, show that $(I + J)(I - J) = 2I$.

8–3   *The Inverse of a Matrix*

A natural question now arises: Does every 2×2 matrix have a multiplicative inverse? As you know, every nonzero real number a has a multiplicative inverse $\frac{1}{a}$, because $\frac{1}{a} \cdot a = 1$. Similarly, you saw in Chapter 7 that every nonzero complex number (x, y) has a multiplicative inverse

$$\left(\frac{x}{x^2 + y^2}, \frac{-y}{x^2 + y^2} \right),$$

because

$$\left(\frac{x}{x^2 + y^2}, \frac{-y}{x^2 + y^2} \right) (x, y) = (1, 0).$$

If $A = \begin{bmatrix} a & b \\ c & d \end{bmatrix}$ *does* have a **multiplicative inverse** $A^{-1} = \begin{bmatrix} w & x \\ y & z \end{bmatrix}$, then, by definition, it must be true that

$$A^{-1}A = \begin{bmatrix} 1 & 0 \\ 0 & 1 \end{bmatrix} \quad \text{and} \quad AA^{-1} = \begin{bmatrix} 1 & 0 \\ 0 & 1 \end{bmatrix}.$$

Thus, we must have

$$A^{-1}A = \begin{bmatrix} w & x \\ y & z \end{bmatrix} \begin{bmatrix} a & b \\ c & d \end{bmatrix} = \begin{bmatrix} 1 & 0 \\ 0 & 1 \end{bmatrix},$$

or

$$\begin{bmatrix} wa + xc & wb + xd \\ ya + zc & yb + zd \end{bmatrix} = \begin{bmatrix} 1 & 0 \\ 0 & 1 \end{bmatrix}.$$

From the definition of equality of matrices, this matrix equation is true if and only if:

$$wa + xc = 1 \qquad wb + xd = 0 \tag{1}$$

and

$$ya + zc = 0 \qquad yb + zd = 1 \tag{2}$$

Solving Equations (1) for a multiple of w and x, and Equations (2) for a multiple of y and z, in terms of a, b, c, and d, we have:

$$(ad - bc)w = d \qquad (ad - bc)x = -b$$
$$\tag{3}$$
$$(ad - bc)y = -c \qquad (ad - bc)z = a$$

Accordingly, if $ad - bc \neq 0$, we obtain

$$w = \frac{d}{ad - bc} \qquad x = \frac{-b}{ad - bc}$$

$$y = \frac{-c}{ad - bc} \qquad z = \frac{a}{ad - bc}$$

as the unique solution of the system.

The number $ad - bc$ is called the **determinant** of the matrix A, and is denoted by the symbol $\delta(A)$ (read "delta of A," or "the determinant of A"). Thus, you can verify by substitution that:

▲   If A is a 2×2 matrix with $\delta(A) \neq 0$, then the matrix

$$A^{-1} = \begin{bmatrix} \dfrac{d}{\delta(A)} & \dfrac{-b}{\delta(A)} \\ \dfrac{-c}{\delta(A)} & \dfrac{a}{\delta(A)} \end{bmatrix} = \frac{1}{\delta(A)} \begin{bmatrix} d & -b \\ -c & a \end{bmatrix} \qquad (4)$$

satisfies the equation $A^{-1}A = I$.

Furthermore, as was shown above, it is the only matrix having this property. You can also readily verify by direct substitution that $AA^{-1} = I$. By definition, then, the matrix A^{-1} given by (4) is the multiplicative inverse of A.

On the other hand, if $\delta(A) = 0$ and A had a multiplicative inverse $\begin{bmatrix} w & x \\ y & z \end{bmatrix}$, then by Equations (3) you would have $a = b = c = d = 0$, so that A would be the zero matrix O. Then you would have

$$A \begin{bmatrix} w & x \\ y & z \end{bmatrix} = O, \quad \text{not} \quad A \begin{bmatrix} w & x \\ y & z \end{bmatrix} = I.$$

Accordingly, if $\delta(A) = 0$, then A does not have a multiplicative inverse.

In conclusion, we have shown that:

▲   A matrix A in $S_{2 \times 2}$ has a multiplicative inverse A^{-1} if and only if $\delta(A) \neq 0$.

If $\delta(A) \neq 0$, then A is said to be **invertible** (or **nonsingular**), whereas if $\delta(A) = 0$, then A is said to be **singular**.

Example   If $A = \begin{bmatrix} 9 & 4 \\ 3 & 2 \end{bmatrix}$, find A^{-1}.

Solution   We first compute $\delta(A)$, obtaining

$$\delta(A) = (9)(2) - (4)(3) = 6.$$

Then, using Equation (4) on page 283, we interchange the entries 9 and 2, replace the entries 3 and 4 with their negatives, and multiply the resulting matrix by $\dfrac{1}{\delta(A)}$, or $\dfrac{1}{6}$, to obtain

$$A^{-1} = \tfrac{1}{6}\begin{bmatrix} 2 & -4 \\ -3 & 9 \end{bmatrix} = \begin{bmatrix} \frac{1}{3} & -\frac{2}{3} \\ -\frac{1}{2} & \frac{3}{2} \end{bmatrix}.$$

As a check, we may use either of the forms $\begin{bmatrix} \frac{1}{3} & -\frac{2}{3} \\ -\frac{1}{2} & \frac{3}{2} \end{bmatrix}$ or $\tfrac{1}{6}\begin{bmatrix} 2 & -4 \\ -3 & 9 \end{bmatrix}$ for A^{-1} to show that $A^{-1}A = I$ (or that $AA^{-1} = I$). Thus

$$\begin{bmatrix} \frac{1}{3} & -\frac{2}{3} \\ -\frac{1}{2} & \frac{3}{2} \end{bmatrix}\begin{bmatrix} 9 & 4 \\ 3 & 2 \end{bmatrix} = \begin{bmatrix} 1 & 0 \\ 0 & 1 \end{bmatrix},$$

or

$$\left(\tfrac{1}{6}\begin{bmatrix} 2 & -4 \\ -3 & 9 \end{bmatrix}\right)\begin{bmatrix} 9 & 4 \\ 3 & 2 \end{bmatrix} = \tfrac{1}{6}\left(\begin{bmatrix} 2 & -4 \\ -3 & 9 \end{bmatrix}\begin{bmatrix} 9 & 4 \\ 3 & 2 \end{bmatrix}\right)$$

$$= \tfrac{1}{6}\begin{bmatrix} 6 & 0 \\ 0 & 6 \end{bmatrix} = \begin{bmatrix} 1 & 0 \\ 0 & 1 \end{bmatrix},$$

as desired.

Exercises 8–3

Find the inverse A^{-1} of each matrix A. If the matrix has no inverse, so state. Check each inverse by computing the product $A^{-1}A$.

A 1. $\begin{bmatrix} 1 & 1 \\ -2 & 3 \end{bmatrix}$ **3.** $\begin{bmatrix} -5 & 2 \\ 10 & -4 \end{bmatrix}$ **5.** $\begin{bmatrix} \sqrt{3} & -\frac{1}{2} \\ \frac{1}{2} & \frac{\sqrt{3}}{2} \end{bmatrix}$ **6.** $\begin{bmatrix} 9 & 6 \\ 3 & 2 \end{bmatrix}$

2. $\begin{bmatrix} 1 & 1 \\ 1 & 0 \end{bmatrix}$ **4.** $\begin{bmatrix} 0 & 1 \\ 1 & 0 \end{bmatrix}$ **7.** $\begin{bmatrix} \frac{1}{2} & \frac{2}{3} \\ \frac{2}{3} & \frac{1}{3} \end{bmatrix}$

In Exercises 8–13, solve each system of equations using matrices and the fact that if $AX = B$, then $(A^{-1}A)X = A^{-1}B$, or $X = A^{-1}B$. Check each answer.

Example

$$2x + 5y = 14$$
$$3x + 4y = 7$$

Solution

Since $\begin{bmatrix} 2 & 5 \\ 3 & 4 \end{bmatrix}\begin{bmatrix} x \\ y \end{bmatrix} = \begin{bmatrix} 2x + 5y \\ 3x + 4y \end{bmatrix}$, the given pair of equations may be represented in matrix notation by

$$\begin{bmatrix} 2 & 5 \\ 3 & 4 \end{bmatrix}\begin{bmatrix} x \\ y \end{bmatrix} = \begin{bmatrix} 14 \\ 7 \end{bmatrix}.$$

Multiplying both members of this equation on the left by the inverse of $\begin{bmatrix} 2 & 5 \\ 3 & 4 \end{bmatrix}$, namely, $-\frac{1}{7}\begin{bmatrix} 4 & -5 \\ -3 & 2 \end{bmatrix}$, gives

$$\left(-\frac{1}{7}\begin{bmatrix} 4 & -5 \\ -3 & 2 \end{bmatrix}\right)\left(\begin{bmatrix} 2 & 5 \\ 3 & 4 \end{bmatrix}\begin{bmatrix} x \\ y \end{bmatrix}\right) = \left(-\frac{1}{7}\begin{bmatrix} 4 & -5 \\ -3 & 2 \end{bmatrix}\right)\begin{bmatrix} 14 \\ 7 \end{bmatrix},$$

or, by the associative property,

$$\left(-\frac{1}{7}\begin{bmatrix} 4 & -5 \\ -3 & 2 \end{bmatrix}\begin{bmatrix} 2 & 5 \\ 3 & 4 \end{bmatrix}\right)\begin{bmatrix} x \\ y \end{bmatrix} = -\frac{1}{7}\left(\begin{bmatrix} 4 & -5 \\ -3 & 2 \end{bmatrix}\begin{bmatrix} 14 \\ 7 \end{bmatrix}\right).$$

Then

$$\begin{bmatrix} 1 & 0 \\ 0 & 1 \end{bmatrix}\begin{bmatrix} x \\ y \end{bmatrix} = -\frac{1}{7}\begin{bmatrix} 21 \\ -28 \end{bmatrix}, \quad \text{so that} \quad \begin{bmatrix} x \\ y \end{bmatrix} = \begin{bmatrix} -3 \\ 4 \end{bmatrix},$$

which means that $x = -3$ and $y = 4$.

You can check that these values do satisfy the given equations as follows:

$$(2)(-3) + (5)(4) = -6 + 20 = 14,$$

$$(3)(-3) + (4)(4) = -9 + 16 = 7.$$

8. $x - y = 1$
$2x + y = 11$

9. $5x - 2y = 8$
$6x + 3y = -12$

10. $9x - 5y = 4$
$-2x + 3y = 1$

11. $2x - 5y = 16$
$7x + 9y = 3$

12. $8x + 3y = 4$
$-3x + 2y = 11$

13. $-5x + 2y = 3$
$3x - y = 1$

Let $A = \begin{bmatrix} a_1 & b_1 \\ c_1 & d_1 \end{bmatrix}$ be any invertible 2×2 matrix and c a scalar. Prove each assertion.

14. $\delta(cA) = c^2\delta(A)$ **15.** $\delta(A^{-1}) = \dfrac{1}{\delta(A)}$ **16.** $(A^{-1})^{-1} = A$

In Exercises 17–19, show that the given property is true:

(a) for $A = \begin{bmatrix} 2 & -1 \\ -3 & 4 \end{bmatrix}$ and $B = \begin{bmatrix} 3 & 8 \\ 1 & 5 \end{bmatrix}$,

(b) for any two invertible 2×2 matrices $A = \begin{bmatrix} a_1 & b_1 \\ c_1 & d_1 \end{bmatrix}$ and $B = \begin{bmatrix} a_2 & b_2 \\ c_2 & d_2 \end{bmatrix}$.

B 17. $\delta(AB) = \delta(A)\,\delta(B)$ **18.** $(AB)^{-1} = B^{-1}A^{-1}$ **19.** AB and BA are invertible

20. Prove that each matrix of the form

$$\begin{bmatrix} \cos\theta & \sin\theta \\ -\sin\theta & \cos\theta \end{bmatrix}$$

has determinant equal to 1, and hence is invertible.

21. Show that the product of two matrices of the form

$$\begin{bmatrix} \cos\theta & \sin\theta \\ -\sin\theta & \cos\theta \end{bmatrix}$$

is another matrix of the same form.

C 22. Show that if A is any invertible 2×2 matrix of the form $\begin{bmatrix} a & b \\ -b & a \end{bmatrix}$ for which $\delta(A) = 1$, then

$$A = \begin{bmatrix} \cos\theta & \sin\theta \\ -\sin\theta & \cos\theta \end{bmatrix}$$

for some angle θ such that $0° \le \theta < 360°$.

23. Show that for a given matrix $A = \begin{bmatrix} a & b \\ c & d \end{bmatrix}$,

$$\delta(A - xI) = x^2 - (a + d)x + \delta(A).$$

The polynomial $x^2 - (a + d)x + \delta(A)$ is called the **characteristic polynomial** of A. It can be shown that for each $A \in S_{2\times2}$, there exist complex solutions of the **characteristic equation** of A, $\delta(A - xI) = 0$. These solutions are called the **eigenvalues** of A (or the **characteristic roots** of A).

Find the characteristic polynomial and the eigenvalues (see Exercise 23) of each matrix.

24. $\begin{bmatrix} 5 & 2 \\ -3 & -2 \end{bmatrix}$ **25.** $\begin{bmatrix} 3 & 2 \\ 2 & 4 \end{bmatrix}$

Matrix Representation of Complex Numbers and Vectors

8–4 *Complex Numbers and Matrices*

If you identify the real number a with the matrix $\begin{bmatrix} a & 0 \\ 0 & a \end{bmatrix}$, and the imaginary number bi with the matrix $\begin{bmatrix} 0 & b \\ -b & 0 \end{bmatrix}$, you can discover a startling association between the set of complex numbers of the form $a + bi$ and the set of 2×2 matrices of the form

$$\begin{bmatrix} a & b \\ -b & a \end{bmatrix}.$$

To show that these identifications make sense, first note that

$$\begin{bmatrix} a & 0 \\ 0 & a \end{bmatrix} = a \begin{bmatrix} 1 & 0 \\ 0 & 1 \end{bmatrix} = aI.$$

Then, observe the following parallels:

Matrices	Real Numbers
$a_1 I + a_2 I = (a_1 + a_2)I$	$(a_1) + (a_2) = a_1 + a_2$
$a_1 I - a_2 I = (a_1 - a_2)I$	$(a_1) - (a_2) = a_1 - a_2$
$(a_1 I)(a_2 I) = a_1 a_2 I^2 = a_1 a_2 I$	$(a_1)(a_2) = a_1 a_2$
$(a_1 I)(a_2 I)^{-1} = (a_1 I)\left(\dfrac{1}{a_2} I\right) = \dfrac{a_1}{a_2} I \quad (a_2 \neq 0)$	$\dfrac{(a_1)}{(a_2)} = \dfrac{a_1}{a_2} \quad (a_2 \neq 0)$

Thus, the members of the set S_R of matrices of the form aI behave exactly like the members of the set $\mathcal{R}$ of real numbers under the four basic operations. Moreover, it is easy to show that the set S_R is a field (page 239) by showing that the addition and multiplication axioms and the distributive axiom are satisfied by the members of S_R.

Now, consider the matrix

$$J = \begin{bmatrix} 0 & 1 \\ -1 & 0 \end{bmatrix}.$$

We have:

$$J^2 = \begin{bmatrix} 0 & 1 \\ -1 & 0 \end{bmatrix}\begin{bmatrix} 0 & 1 \\ -1 & 0 \end{bmatrix} = \begin{bmatrix} -1 & 0 \\ 0 & -1 \end{bmatrix} = -\begin{bmatrix} 1 & 0 \\ 0 & 1 \end{bmatrix} = -I$$

$$J^3 = J^2 \cdot J = -I \cdot J = -J$$

$$J^4 = J^2 \cdot J^2 = (-I) \cdot (-I) = I^2 = I$$

$$J^5 = J^4 \cdot J = I \cdot J = J$$

$$\cdot\ \cdot\ \cdot\ \cdot\ \cdot$$

When you compare these properties of J with the properties of the imaginary number i,

$$i^2 = -1$$
$$i^3 = -i$$
$$i^4 = 1$$
$$i^5 = i$$

$$\cdot\ \cdot\ \cdot$$

you find that powers of the matrix J parallel the powers of i. Moreover,

$$bJ = b\begin{bmatrix} 0 & 1 \\ -1 & 0 \end{bmatrix} = \begin{bmatrix} 0 & b \\ -b & 0 \end{bmatrix},$$

so that the matrix $\begin{bmatrix} 0 & b \\ -b & 0 \end{bmatrix}$ corresponds strikingly to the imaginary number bi. Then, if you define the quotient $\dfrac{A}{B}$ of matrices A and B to be the product AB^{-1}, you can show that with regard to the fundamental operations of addition, subtraction, multiplication, and division, the set of matrices of the form bJ, with $b \in \mathcal{R}$, behaves exactly like the set of pure imaginary numbers bi, with $b \in \mathcal{R}$.

Then, taking one step more:

▲   We identify the complex number $a + bi$ with the matrix sum

$$aI + bJ = \begin{bmatrix} a & 0 \\ 0 & a \end{bmatrix} + \begin{bmatrix} 0 & b \\ -b & 0 \end{bmatrix} = \begin{bmatrix} a & b \\ -b & a \end{bmatrix}.$$

With this identification, the definition of equality and the fundamental operations of complex numbers of the form $a + bi$ are entirely consistent with those of matrices of the form $\begin{bmatrix} a & b \\ -b & a \end{bmatrix}$.

Example 1   Use matrices to write the product $(2 - i)(3 + 2i)$ in the form $a + bi$.

Solution   In matrix notation, we have

$$\begin{bmatrix} 2 & -1 \\ 1 & 2 \end{bmatrix} \begin{bmatrix} 3 & 2 \\ -2 & 3 \end{bmatrix} = \begin{bmatrix} 8 & 1 \\ -1 & 8 \end{bmatrix},$$

so that

$$(2 - i)(3 + 2i) = 8 + i.$$

If $\rho(\cos \theta + i \sin \theta)$ is the polar form of $a + bi$, then, in matrix notation, we have

$$\rho \begin{bmatrix} \cos \theta & \sin \theta \\ -\sin \theta & \cos \theta \end{bmatrix}$$

in place of

$$\begin{bmatrix} a & b \\ -b & a \end{bmatrix},$$

where, as usual, $\rho = \sqrt{a^2 + b^2}$ and θ is determined, for $\rho \neq 0$, by the equations

$$\frac{a}{\rho} = \cos \theta, \quad \frac{b}{\rho} = \sin \theta, \quad 0° \leq \theta < 360°.$$

Example 2   Show that

$$\rho_1 \begin{bmatrix} \cos \theta_1 & \sin \theta_1 \\ -\sin \theta_1 & \cos \theta_1 \end{bmatrix} \cdot \rho_2 \begin{bmatrix} \cos \theta_2 & \sin \theta_2 \\ -\sin \theta_2 & \cos \theta_2 \end{bmatrix} = \rho_1 \rho_2 \begin{bmatrix} \cos (\theta_1 + \theta_2) & \sin (\theta_1 + \theta_2) \\ -\sin (\theta_1 + \theta_2) & \cos (\theta_1 + \theta_2) \end{bmatrix}.$$

Solution   By direct multiplication, the product of the factors in the left-hand member of the given equation is

$$\rho_1 \rho_2 \begin{bmatrix} \cos \theta_1 \cos \theta_2 - \sin \theta_1 \sin \theta_2 & \cos \theta_1 \sin \theta_2 + \sin \theta_1 \cos \theta_2 \\ -(\sin \theta_1 \cos \theta_2 + \cos \theta_1 \sin \theta_2) & -\sin \theta_1 \sin \theta_2 + \cos \theta_1 \cos \theta_2 \end{bmatrix}.$$

By the sum and difference formulas for angles (see page 66), this expression reduces to the right-hand member of the given equation.

Exercises 8–4

Use matrices to compute each of the following. Express your answer both in matrix form and in the form $a + bi$.

A 1. $(2 + i) + (5 - 2i)$

2. $(1 + 3i) + (0 - 4i)$

3. $(1 - 2i) - (-4 + i)$

4. $(-5 + i) - (3 - 4i)$

5. $(2 - i)(4 - 2i)$

6. $(-1 + 5i)(3 - 2i)$

7. $(1 + i)^2$

8. $(1 - i)^3$

Use matrices to find an expression both in the form $\rho(\cos \theta + i \sin \theta)$ and in the form $a + bi$ for each of the following.

9. $3 \left(\cos \frac{\pi}{3} + i \sin \frac{\pi}{3} \right) \cdot 2 \left(\cos \frac{\pi}{6} + i \sin \frac{\pi}{6} \right)$

10. $4 \left(\cos \frac{\pi}{6} + i \sin \frac{\pi}{6} \right) \cdot 3 \left(\cos \frac{2\pi}{3} + i \sin \frac{2\pi}{3} \right)$

11. $-2(\cos 20° + i \sin 20°) \cdot (-2)(\cos 10° + i \sin 10°)$

12. $-4(\cos 40° + i \sin 40°) \cdot 3(\cos 80° + i \sin 80°)$

B 13. Show that $|a + bi| = \sqrt{\delta(A)}$, where $A = \begin{bmatrix} a & b \\ -b & a \end{bmatrix}$.

14. Verify that the matrix product corresponding to the product of the complex number $a + bi$ and its conjugate $a - bi$ is

$$\begin{bmatrix} a^2 + b^2 & 0 \\ 0 & a^2 + b^2 \end{bmatrix}.$$

15. Show that $\begin{bmatrix} \rho \cos \theta & \rho \sin \theta \\ -\rho \sin \theta & \rho \cos \theta \end{bmatrix}^3 = \rho^3 \begin{bmatrix} \cos 3\theta & \sin 3\theta \\ -\sin 3\theta & \cos 3\theta \end{bmatrix}.$

16. Show that if

$$A = \begin{bmatrix} a & b \\ -b & a \end{bmatrix}, \quad B = \begin{bmatrix} c & d \\ -d & c \end{bmatrix},$$

and B is invertible, then the product AB^{-1} corresponds to the quotient

$$\frac{a + bi}{c + di}.$$

Use the results of Exercise 16 to write each of the following in the form $a + bi$.

17. $\dfrac{1 + 2i}{i}$

18. $\dfrac{3 - 2i}{2 + i}$

19. $\dfrac{4(\cos 60° + i \sin 60°)}{2(\cos 15° + i \sin 15°)}$

20. $\dfrac{8(\cos 90° + i \sin 90°)}{2(\cos 30° + i \sin 30°)}$

8–5 *Vectors and Matrices*

In the preceding section, we identified complex numbers of the form $a + bi$ with 2×2 matrices of the form $\begin{bmatrix} a & b \\ -b & a \end{bmatrix}$, and found that under this identification the basic properties of complex numbers parallel those of the corresponding matrices. In this section we shall establish a similar correspondence between *vectors* and matrices.

Because vectors have been defined to be ordered pairs of real numbers, it seems reasonable to identify the vector (x, y) with either the 2×1 matrix $\begin{bmatrix} x \\ y \end{bmatrix}$ or the 1×2 matrix $[x \quad y]$. If we make either of these identifications, we find that the results of addition and scalar multiplication of vectors are consistent with the results of the same operations on the corresponding matrices.

For example, if we let the vectors (x_1, y_1) and (x_2, y_2) correspond to the matrices $\begin{bmatrix} x_1 \\ y_1 \end{bmatrix}$ and $\begin{bmatrix} x_2 \\ y_2 \end{bmatrix}$, respectively, we can observe the following parallels:

Vectors	Matrices
$(x_1, y_1) + (x_2, y_2) = (x_1 + x_2, y_1 + y_2)$	$\begin{bmatrix} x_1 \\ y_1 \end{bmatrix} + \begin{bmatrix} x_2 \\ y_2 \end{bmatrix} = \begin{bmatrix} x_1 + x_2 \\ y_1 + y_2 \end{bmatrix}$
$c(x_1, y_1) = (cx_1, cy_1)$	$c\begin{bmatrix} x_1 \\ y_1 \end{bmatrix} = \begin{bmatrix} cx_1 \\ cy_1 \end{bmatrix}$

Since the operations of addition and scalar multiplication as defined for two-dimensional vectors parallel those for either 2×1 or 1×2 matrices, both $S_{2 \times 1}$ and $S_{1 \times 2}$ can be shown to be vector spaces over $\Re$. Therefore, it makes sense to speak of the matrices $[x \quad y]$ and $\begin{bmatrix} x \\ y \end{bmatrix}$ as vectors and to associate either of them with the same geometric vector that we associated earlier with the ordered pair (x, y). In the remainder of this chapter, we shall frequently be concerned with two-rowed column matrices, that is, with elements of the set

$$S_{2 \times 1} = \left\{ \begin{bmatrix} x \\ y \end{bmatrix} : x, y \in \Re \right\}.$$

From Section 8–2 we know that the product of a 2×2 matrix and a 2×1 matrix is defined and is a 2×1 matrix. We have just associated 2×1 matrices with geometric vectors. Therefore, when we multiply a 2×1 matrix (a geometric vector) by a 2×2 matrix to get another 2×1 matrix (a geometric vector), we are led to ask if we can find any connection between these two geometric vectors that would explain the significance of the 2×2 matrix which relates them.

Let us begin by considering the particular 2×2 matrix $\begin{bmatrix} 1 & 1 \\ 0 & 0 \end{bmatrix}$, whose product with $\begin{bmatrix} x \\ y \end{bmatrix}$ is

$$\begin{bmatrix} 1 & 1 \\ 0 & 0 \end{bmatrix}\begin{bmatrix} x \\ y \end{bmatrix} = \begin{bmatrix} x + y \\ 0 \end{bmatrix} = \begin{bmatrix} x' \\ y' \end{bmatrix}, \qquad \text{where} \quad \begin{matrix} x' = x + y \\ y' = 0 \end{matrix}. \qquad (1)$$

The matrix equation (1) pairs each matrix $\begin{bmatrix} x \\ y \end{bmatrix}$ with a unique matrix $\begin{bmatrix} x' \\ y' \end{bmatrix}$ and, therefore, defines a function, which we shall call τ (tau), with domain $S_{2\times1}$ and range a subset of $S_{2\times1}$. For example,

$$\tau\left(\begin{bmatrix} 1 \\ 1 \end{bmatrix}\right) = \begin{bmatrix} 2 \\ 0 \end{bmatrix} \quad \text{and} \quad \tau\left(\begin{bmatrix} -3 \\ 2 \end{bmatrix}\right) = \begin{bmatrix} -1 \\ 0 \end{bmatrix}.$$

We can illustrate the function τ geometrically by considering the matrices $\begin{bmatrix} x \\ y \end{bmatrix}$ and $\begin{bmatrix} x' \\ y' \end{bmatrix}$ to be vectors in the plane. Figure 8–1 depicts the vectors $\begin{bmatrix} 1 \\ 1 \end{bmatrix}$ and

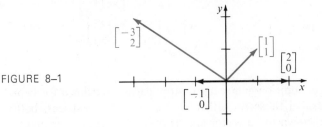

FIGURE 8–1

$\begin{bmatrix} -3 \\ 2 \end{bmatrix}$ in the domain of τ, together with the corresponding members of the range of τ, namely, $\begin{bmatrix} 2 \\ 0 \end{bmatrix}$ and $\begin{bmatrix} -1 \\ 0 \end{bmatrix}$. We note that the *domain* of τ is the set of *all vectors in the plane*, whereas the *range* of τ is the set of *all vectors on the x-axis*.

A function, such as τ, which maps each vector in the plane into another vector in the plane, is called a **transformation** (or a **mapping**) **of the plane**, and the 2×2 matrix used to define the transformation is called the **matrix of the transformation**. The vectors $\begin{bmatrix} x \\ y \end{bmatrix}$ in the domain are called the **pre-images** of the vectors $\begin{bmatrix} x' \\ y' \end{bmatrix}$ in the range, and the vectors $\begin{bmatrix} x' \\ y' \end{bmatrix}$ in the range are called the **images** of the corresponding vectors $\begin{bmatrix} x \\ y \end{bmatrix}$ in the domain.

Any matrix equation of the form $AV = V'$, where

$$V = \begin{bmatrix} x \\ y \end{bmatrix}, \qquad V' = \begin{bmatrix} x' \\ y' \end{bmatrix}, \qquad \text{and} \qquad A = \begin{bmatrix} a & b \\ c & d \end{bmatrix},$$

determines a mapping of the plane **into** itself; that is, the image of every vector in the plane under the mapping is again a vector in the plane. If, in addition, every vector in the plane is the image of some vector under this mapping, then we say that the plane is mapped **onto** itself.

The preceding example, with $A = \begin{bmatrix} 1 & 1 \\ 0 & 0 \end{bmatrix}$, constitutes a mapping of the plane *into*, but *not onto*, the plane. All the remaining examples in this section are concerned with "onto transformations."

One means of visualizing the results of a given transformation of the plane is to determine the effect the transformation has on a familiar geometric figure. This will be done in each of the remaining examples in this section.

Example 1   Describe the geometric effect of the transformation of the plane with matrix $\begin{bmatrix} 3 & 0 \\ 0 & 3 \end{bmatrix}$ and sketch the figure into which the triangle with vertices $A(2, 1)$, $B(2, 0)$, and $C(0, 0)$ is mapped by this transformation.

Solution   By inspection of the matrix equation

$$\begin{bmatrix} 3 & 0 \\ 0 & 3 \end{bmatrix} \begin{bmatrix} x \\ y \end{bmatrix} = \begin{bmatrix} 3x \\ 3y \end{bmatrix},$$

we can see that each vector $\begin{bmatrix} x \\ y \end{bmatrix}$ is mapped into a vector whose magnitude is three times that of $\begin{bmatrix} x \\ y \end{bmatrix}$ and which has the same direction as $\begin{bmatrix} x \\ y \end{bmatrix}$.

The diagram below shows that the transformation maps $\triangle ABC$ into the similar $\triangle A'B'C'$. Such a transformation is called a **magnification**.

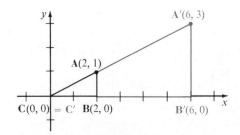

Example 2 Describe the geometric effect of the transformation of the plane with matrix $\begin{bmatrix} 1 & 3 \\ 0 & 1 \end{bmatrix}$ and sketch the figure into which the square with vertices **A(0, 1)**, **B(1, 1)**, **C(1, 0)**, and **D(0, 0)** is mapped.

Solution From the matrix equation

$$\begin{bmatrix} 1 & 3 \\ 0 & 1 \end{bmatrix}\begin{bmatrix} x \\ y \end{bmatrix} = \begin{bmatrix} x + 3y \\ y \end{bmatrix},$$

we can see that the x-component of each vector is changed by an amount $3y$ and the y-component is unchanged. The net effect is to **shear** the plane along the x-axis.

As shown in the diagram below, the square **ABCD** is transformed into parallelogram **A'B'C'D'**. Such a transformation is called a **shearing**.

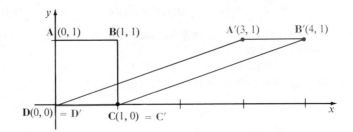

Example 3 If A is the matrix $\begin{bmatrix} 2 & 0 \\ 0 & -1 \end{bmatrix}$:

(a) Describe the geometric effect of the transformation of the plane with matrix A and sketch the figure into which the square with vertices **P(0, 1)**, **Q(1, 1)**, **R(1, 0)**, and **S(0, 0)** is mapped.

(b) Show that A can be factored into the product of two separate transformation matrices.

Solution (a) Since $\begin{bmatrix} 2 & 0 \\ 0 & -1 \end{bmatrix}\begin{bmatrix} x \\ y \end{bmatrix} = \begin{bmatrix} 2x \\ -y \end{bmatrix}$, the x-component of each vector $\begin{bmatrix} x \\ y \end{bmatrix}$ is doubled and the y-component is transformed into its additive inverse. As shown in the diagram, square **PQRS** is transformed into rectangle **P′Q′R′S′**.

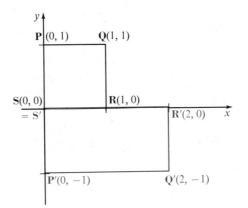

(b) The transformation given by $A \begin{bmatrix} x \\ y \end{bmatrix} = \begin{bmatrix} 2x \\ -y \end{bmatrix}$ suggests that

we can first transform $\begin{bmatrix} x \\ y \end{bmatrix}$ to $\begin{bmatrix} 2x \\ y \end{bmatrix}$ and then transform

$\begin{bmatrix} 2x \\ y \end{bmatrix}$ to $\begin{bmatrix} 2x \\ -y \end{bmatrix}$. The matrix $\begin{bmatrix} 2 & 0 \\ 0 & 1 \end{bmatrix}$ transforms $\begin{bmatrix} x \\ y \end{bmatrix}$ to $\begin{bmatrix} 2x \\ y \end{bmatrix}$,

and the matrix $\begin{bmatrix} 1 & 0 \\ 0 & -1 \end{bmatrix}$ transforms $\begin{bmatrix} 2x \\ y \end{bmatrix}$ to $\begin{bmatrix} 2x \\ -y \end{bmatrix}$. By direct

multiplication, we find that

$$\begin{bmatrix} 2 & 0 \\ 0 & 1 \end{bmatrix} \begin{bmatrix} 1 & 0 \\ 0 & -1 \end{bmatrix} = \begin{bmatrix} 2 & 0 \\ 0 & -1 \end{bmatrix} = A.$$

Note that the matrix $\begin{bmatrix} 2 & 0 \\ 0 & 1 \end{bmatrix}$ **stretches** the square **PQRS** into

the rectangle with vertices $(0, 1)$, $(2, 1)$, $(2, 0)$, and $(0, 0)$, and that this rectangle is **reflected in the x-axis** by the matrix

$\begin{bmatrix} 1 & 0 \\ 0 & -1 \end{bmatrix}$. Thus the transformation given by the matrix $\begin{bmatrix} 2 & 0 \\ 0 & -1 \end{bmatrix}$

is a combination of a **stretching** and a **reflection in the x-axis**.

The general forms for the matrices of the basic types of mappings of the plane onto itself are listed on page 296. The matrix of any transformation of the plane onto itself can be factored into the product of matrices of the types listed. (This product might have more than two factors.)

Magnification, $a > 1$: $\begin{bmatrix} a & 0 \\ 0 & a \end{bmatrix}$
    (or **shrinking** for $0 < a < 1$)

Stretching, $a > 1$: $\begin{bmatrix} 1 & 0 \\ 0 & a \end{bmatrix}$ or $\begin{bmatrix} a & 0 \\ 0 & 1 \end{bmatrix}$
    (or **contracting** for $0 < a < 1$)

Shearing: $\begin{bmatrix} 1 & a \\ 0 & 1 \end{bmatrix}$ or $\begin{bmatrix} 1 & 0 \\ a & 1 \end{bmatrix}$

Reflection in the origin: $\begin{bmatrix} -1 & 0 \\ 0 & -1 \end{bmatrix}$

Reflection in an axis: $\begin{bmatrix} -1 & 0 \\ 0 & 1 \end{bmatrix}$ or $\begin{bmatrix} 1 & 0 \\ 0 & -1 \end{bmatrix}$

Reflection in the line $y = x$: $\begin{bmatrix} 0 & 1 \\ 1 & 0 \end{bmatrix}$

Reflection in the line $y = -x$: $\begin{bmatrix} 0 & -1 \\ -1 & 0 \end{bmatrix}$

Rotation: $\begin{bmatrix} \cos\theta & -\sin\theta \\ \sin\theta & \cos\theta \end{bmatrix}$

Rotations will be discussed in Section 8–6.

Exercises 8–5

Describe the geometric effect of the transformation of the plane having the given matrix and sketch the figure into which the square with vertices $(0, 0)$, $(1, 0)$, $(0, 1)$, and $(1, 1)$ is mapped by this transformation.

A   **1.** $\begin{bmatrix} 3 & 0 \\ 0 & 3 \end{bmatrix}$ **3.** $\begin{bmatrix} -2 & 0 \\ 0 & -2 \end{bmatrix}$ **5.** $\begin{bmatrix} 3 & 0 \\ 0 & -1 \end{bmatrix}$ **7.** $\begin{bmatrix} 0 & -1 \\ 1 & 0 \end{bmatrix}$

     2. $\begin{bmatrix} -1 & 0 \\ 0 & 1 \end{bmatrix}$ **4.** $\begin{bmatrix} 1 & 0 \\ 0 & -1 \end{bmatrix}$ **6.** $\begin{bmatrix} 0 & 1 \\ 1 & 0 \end{bmatrix}$ **8.** $\begin{bmatrix} 2 & 1 \\ 1 & 2 \end{bmatrix}$

Describe the geometric effect of the transformation of the plane with the given matrix A and sketch the graph of set S and its image set T under this transformation.

     9. $A = \begin{bmatrix} 4 & 0 \\ 0 & 4 \end{bmatrix}$; S is the triangle whose vertices are $(0, 0)$, $(6, 0)$, and $(8, 4)$.

     10. $A = \begin{bmatrix} 1 & 0 \\ 0 & -1 \end{bmatrix}$; S is the triangle in Exercise 9.

11. $A = \begin{bmatrix} -1 & 0 \\ 0 & -1 \end{bmatrix}$; S is the parallelogram whose vertices are $(0, 0)$, $(4, 0)$, $(3, 2)$, and $(7, 2)$.

12. $A = \begin{bmatrix} -2 & 0 \\ 0 & 1 \end{bmatrix}$; S is the parallelogram in Exercise 11.

13. $A = \begin{bmatrix} \frac{1}{2} & 0 \\ 0 & -\frac{1}{2} \end{bmatrix}$; S is the triangle whose vertices are $(1, 0)$, $(1, 4)$, and $(5, 0)$.

14. $A = \begin{bmatrix} -1 & 0 \\ 0 & 1 \end{bmatrix}$; S is the triangle in Exercise 13.

15. $A = \begin{bmatrix} 0 & -1 \\ -1 & 0 \end{bmatrix}$; S is the line segment whose endpoints are $(2, 0)$ and $(4, 1)$.

16. $A = \begin{bmatrix} 0 & 1 \\ 1 & 0 \end{bmatrix}$; S is the line segment whose endpoints are $(1, 3)$ and $(2, 6)$.

Determine the net effect of each of the following composite reflections of the plane:

17. A reflection in the x-axis followed by a reflection in the y-axis.

18. A reflection in the x-axis followed by a reflection in the origin.

19. A reflection in the line $y = -x$ followed by a reflection in the line $y = x$.

Determine the geometric effect which the transformation given by matrix A has upon set S. Graph S and T, the image set of S, on the same coordinate plane.

B 20. $A = \begin{bmatrix} 3 & 0 \\ 0 & 3 \end{bmatrix}$; $S = \{(x, y): x^2 + y^2 = 1\}$

21. $A = \begin{bmatrix} -1 & 0 \\ 0 & 1 \end{bmatrix}$; $S = \{(x, y): x^2 + y^2 = 4, 0 \le x \le 2\}$
(S is a semicircle.)

22. $A = \begin{bmatrix} 0 & 1 \\ 1 & 0 \end{bmatrix}$; $S = \{(x, y): y = 2x + 1, 1 \le x \le 3\}$

23. $A = \begin{bmatrix} 1 & 0 \\ 0 & -1 \end{bmatrix}$; $S = \{(x, y): y = x - 2, -1 \le x \le 4\}$

In Exercises 24–29, find a 2×2 transformation matrix which transforms set S into set T. Graph S and T on the same coordinate plane.

24. $S = \{(x, y): x^2 + y^2 = 1\}$, $T = \{(x, y): x^2 + y^2 = 16\}$

25. $S = \{(x, y): y = x^3, 0 \le x \le 2\}$, $T = \{(x, y): y = -x^3, 0 \le x \le 2\}$

26. $S = \{(x, y): y = 2x, 1 \le x \le 3\}$, $T = \{(x, y): y = -2x, -3 \le x \le -1\}$

27. $S = \{(x, y): y = x + 1, -1 \le x \le 3\}$, $T = \{(x, y): y = -x + 1, -3 \le x \le 1\}$

28. $S = \{(x, y): x^2 + y^2 = 36\}$, $T = \{(x, y): x^2 + y^2 = 4\}$
29. $S = \{(x, y): y = \sin x, 0 \le x \le 2\pi\}$, $T = \{(x, y): y = \sin 2x, 0 \le x \le \pi\}$
30. Describe the transformation of the plane given by:

(a) $\begin{bmatrix} 1 & 1 \\ 1 & 1 \end{bmatrix}$ (b) $\begin{bmatrix} 1 & 0 \\ 0 & 0 \end{bmatrix}$ (c) $\begin{bmatrix} 0 & 0 \\ 1 & 1 \end{bmatrix}$

Which, if any, of these transformations are *onto*?

C 31. Show that if A is an invertible 2×2 matrix that maps $\begin{bmatrix} x \\ y \end{bmatrix}$ onto $\begin{bmatrix} x' \\ y' \end{bmatrix}$, then A^{-1} maps $\begin{bmatrix} x' \\ y' \end{bmatrix}$ onto $\begin{bmatrix} x \\ y \end{bmatrix}$.

8–6   Rotations

A rotation may be viewed in either of two ways: as a rotation of the plane while the axes remain fixed or as a rotation of the axes while the plane remains fixed. We shall look at each viewpoint separately.

First, think of the entire plane as rotating in a counterclockwise direction about the origin while the axes remain fixed. If the rotation is made through an angle θ with positive measure, and if each point in the plane is expressed in terms of polar coordinates ρ and ϕ (phi), then, as shown in Figure 8–2, each point (ρ, ϕ) rotates into the point $(\rho, \phi + \theta)$. If (x, y) represents the Cartesian coordinates of the point with polar coordinates (ρ, ϕ), we have

$$(x, y) = (\rho \cos \phi, \rho \sin \phi).$$

Then, the image (x', y') of (x, y) after the rotation is

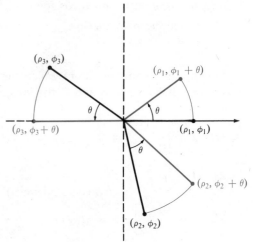

FIGURE 8–2

$$(x', y') = (\rho \cos (\phi + \theta), \rho \sin (\phi + \theta))$$
$$= (\rho \cos \phi \cos \theta - \rho \sin \phi \sin \theta, \rho \sin \phi \cos \theta + \rho \cos \phi \sin \theta).$$

Therefore, since $\rho \cos \phi = x$ and $\rho \sin \phi = y$, we have

$$(x', y') = (x \cos \theta - y \sin \theta, x \sin \theta + y \cos \theta).$$

Thus, such a rotation of the plane maps the point (x, y) into the point $(x \cos \theta - y \sin \theta, x \sin \theta + y \cos \theta)$, or, in terms of vectors, maps the vector

$\begin{bmatrix} x \\ y \end{bmatrix}$ into the vector $\begin{bmatrix} x \cos \theta - y \sin \theta \\ x \sin \theta + y \cos \theta \end{bmatrix}$. By inspection,

$$\begin{bmatrix} x' \\ y' \end{bmatrix} = \begin{bmatrix} x \cos \theta - y \sin \theta \\ x \sin \theta + y \cos \theta \end{bmatrix} = \begin{bmatrix} \cos \theta & -\sin \theta \\ \sin \theta & \cos \theta \end{bmatrix} \begin{bmatrix} x \\ y \end{bmatrix}.$$

Consequently, the matrix

▲
$$A = \begin{bmatrix} \cos \theta & -\sin \theta \\ \sin \theta & \cos \theta \end{bmatrix}$$

defines the transformation that rotates the plane counterclockwise about the origin through an angle θ. For vectors $V = \begin{bmatrix} x \\ y \end{bmatrix}$ and $V' = \begin{bmatrix} x' \\ y' \end{bmatrix}$, the matrix equation $AV = V'$ determines a mapping of the plane onto itself; the mapping can be interpreted as a rotation of the plane in a counterclockwise direction if $m°(\theta) > 0$ or in a clockwise direction if $m°(\theta) < 0$.

Example 1   Find the images of the vertices $A(0, 0)$, $B(2, 0)$, and $C(0, 4)$ of $\triangle ABC$ after a rotation of the plane through an angle of $30°$. Sketch the triangle and its image.

Solution   The matrix of the transformation is

$$A = \begin{bmatrix} \cos 30° & -\sin 30° \\ \sin 30° & \cos 30° \end{bmatrix} = \begin{bmatrix} \dfrac{\sqrt{3}}{2} & -\dfrac{1}{2} \\ \dfrac{1}{2} & \dfrac{\sqrt{3}}{2} \end{bmatrix}.$$

Using the equation $AV = V'$ to transform each vertex produces

$$\begin{bmatrix} \dfrac{\sqrt{3}}{2} & -\dfrac{1}{2} \\ \dfrac{1}{2} & \dfrac{\sqrt{3}}{2} \end{bmatrix} \begin{bmatrix} 0 \\ 0 \end{bmatrix} = \begin{bmatrix} 0 \\ 0 \end{bmatrix},$$

$$\begin{bmatrix} \dfrac{\sqrt{3}}{2} & -\dfrac{1}{2} \\ \dfrac{1}{2} & \dfrac{\sqrt{3}}{2} \end{bmatrix} \begin{bmatrix} 2 \\ 0 \end{bmatrix} = \begin{bmatrix} \sqrt{3} \\ 1 \end{bmatrix},$$

$$\begin{bmatrix} \dfrac{\sqrt{3}}{2} & -\dfrac{1}{2} \\ \dfrac{1}{2} & \dfrac{\sqrt{3}}{2} \end{bmatrix} \begin{bmatrix} 0 \\ 4 \end{bmatrix} = \begin{bmatrix} -2 \\ 2\sqrt{3} \end{bmatrix}.$$

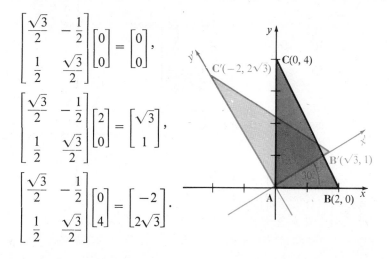

Another way of thinking of a rotation is to consider the plane to be fixed and then to rotate the axes. Figure 8–3 shows a set of x'- and y'-axes resulting from a counterclockwise rotation of the x- and y-axes through an angle θ. Notice that if (ρ, ϕ) are the polar coordinates of a point in the xy-system of coordinates, then the polar coordinates of the point in the $x'y'$-system are $(\rho, \phi - \theta)$. Therefore, we have

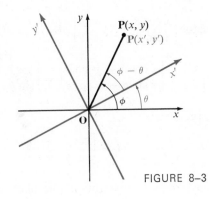

FIGURE 8–3

$$x' = \rho \cos (\phi - \theta) = \rho \cos \phi \cos \theta + \rho \sin \phi \sin \theta$$
$$y' = \rho \sin (\phi - \theta) = -\rho \cos \phi \sin \theta + \rho \sin \phi \cos \theta.$$

Then, since $x = \rho \cos \phi$ and $y = \rho \sin \phi$, we have

$$x' = x \cos \theta + y \sin \theta$$
$$y' = -x \sin \theta + y \cos \theta.$$

In terms of matrices, this is expressed as

$$\begin{bmatrix} x' \\ y' \end{bmatrix} = \begin{bmatrix} \cos \theta & \sin \theta \\ -\sin \theta & \cos \theta \end{bmatrix} \begin{bmatrix} x \\ y \end{bmatrix}.$$

Example 2   Find the new coordinates, after a rotation of axes through an angle of 30°, of the points whose old coordinates are $P(5, \sqrt{3})$, $Q(\sqrt{3}, 5)$, and $R(\sqrt{3}, 1)$.

Solution   The matrix of the rotation is

$$\begin{bmatrix} \cos 30° & \sin 30° \\ -\sin 30° & \cos 30° \end{bmatrix} = \begin{bmatrix} \dfrac{\sqrt{3}}{2} & \dfrac{1}{2} \\ -\dfrac{1}{2} & \dfrac{\sqrt{3}}{2} \end{bmatrix}.$$

The image of the vector $\begin{bmatrix} 5 \\ \sqrt{3} \end{bmatrix}$ is

$$\begin{bmatrix} \dfrac{\sqrt{3}}{2} & \dfrac{1}{2} \\ -\dfrac{1}{2} & \dfrac{\sqrt{3}}{2} \end{bmatrix} \begin{bmatrix} 5 \\ \sqrt{3} \end{bmatrix} = \begin{bmatrix} 3\sqrt{3} \\ -1 \end{bmatrix}.$$

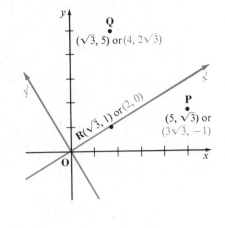

Similarly, the image of $\begin{bmatrix} \sqrt{3} \\ 5 \end{bmatrix}$ is $\begin{bmatrix} 4 \\ 2\sqrt{3} \end{bmatrix}$, and the image of $\begin{bmatrix} \sqrt{3} \\ 1 \end{bmatrix}$ is $\begin{bmatrix} 2 \\ 0 \end{bmatrix}$.

The two interpretations of rotations that we have discussed are related as follows:

▲   A rotation of the plane about the origin through an angle θ has the same effect on the coordinates of points as a rotation of the axes through an angle $-\theta$.

Thus any rotational transformation can be viewed in either of these two ways. Because a rotation of the plane in effect maps each point in the plane into another point, whereas a rotation of the axes assigns new coordinates to each point, these transformations are sometimes referred to as "alibi" (I was somewhere else) and "alias" (I have another name) transformations, respectively.

For example, if the plane is rotated about the origin through an angle of 60°, then the point **P**(2, 0) is mapped into the point with coordinates $(1, \sqrt{3})$. On the other hand, if the point **P**(2, 0) remains in the same location, but the axes are rotated through an angle of $-60°$, then point **P** will have the "new name" $(1, \sqrt{3})$.

Exercises 8–6

Find the images of the vertices of each of the following polygons after a rotation of the plane through the given angle θ. Sketch the polygon and its image.

A   **1.** $\theta = 30°$; triangle with vertices (0, 0), $(\sqrt{3}, 0)$, and $(2\sqrt{3}, 4)$.

2. $\theta = 45°$; triangle with vertices $(\sqrt{2}, 0)$, (1, 3), and (2, 4).

3. $\theta = 60°$; square with vertices (0, 0), (2, 0), (2, 2), and (0, 2).

4. $\theta = -30°$; square with vertices (0, 0), (2, 0), (2, 2), and (0, 2).

5. $\theta = -135°$; triangle with vertices $(\sqrt{2}, 0)$, $(\sqrt{2}, \sqrt{2})$, and $(0, \sqrt{2})$.

6. $\theta = 120°$; rectangle with vertices $(-2, \sqrt{3})$, $(-2, 2\sqrt{3})$, $(3, \sqrt{3})$, and $(3, 2\sqrt{3})$.

7–12. Determine the images of the vertices of each of the polygons in Exercises 1–6 following a rotation of the coordinate axes through the given angle.

Determine the 2 × 2 matrix A of the transformation that maps the first vector into the second by rotating the plane about the origin.

B 13. $\begin{bmatrix} 2 \\ 1 \end{bmatrix}, \begin{bmatrix} -1 \\ 2 \end{bmatrix}$ **14.** $\begin{bmatrix} -4\sqrt{2} \\ -7 \end{bmatrix}, \begin{bmatrix} 4 \\ 7 \end{bmatrix}$ **15.** $\begin{bmatrix} 3 \\ 5 \end{bmatrix}, \begin{bmatrix} -4 \\ -3\sqrt{2} \end{bmatrix}$ **16.** $\begin{bmatrix} 5 \\ -5 \end{bmatrix}, \begin{bmatrix} 1 \\ 7 \end{bmatrix}$

C 17. Show that if $\begin{bmatrix} x' \\ y' \end{bmatrix}$ is the image of $\begin{bmatrix} x \\ y \end{bmatrix}$ under a rotation of the plane through an angle θ, then the norm $\|(x', y')\|$ is equal to the norm $\|(x, y)\|$.

18. Show that if $\begin{bmatrix} x' \\ y' \end{bmatrix}$ is the image of $\begin{bmatrix} x \\ y \end{bmatrix}$ under a rotation of coordinate axes through an angle θ, then $\begin{bmatrix} x \\ y \end{bmatrix}$ is the image of $\begin{bmatrix} x' \\ y' \end{bmatrix}$ under a rotation of the plane about the origin through the same angle θ.

19. Show that the distance between the images of any two points in the plane after any rotation of the plane about the origin is the same as the distance between the points.

20. Show that if $\begin{bmatrix} x' \\ y' \end{bmatrix}$ is the image of $\begin{bmatrix} x \\ y \end{bmatrix}$ under a rotation of the plane through an angle measuring π radians, then $\begin{bmatrix} x' \\ y' \end{bmatrix} = -\begin{bmatrix} x \\ y \end{bmatrix}$.

21. Show that if A is the matrix of the transformation that rotates the plane through an angle θ, then A has real eigenvalues if and only if $\theta = n \cdot 180°$ for some $n \in J$. Moreover, show at the same time that such eigenvalues are equal either to 1 or to -1. (See Exercise 23, page 286.)

Chapter Summary

1. A **matrix** is a rectangular array of numbers. The set of all 2 × 2 matrices with real-number entries is a vector space under the operations of matrix addition and multiplication of a matrix by a scalar.

2. Matrix multiplication is associative but not commutative. A 2 × 2 matrix has a multiplicative inverse if and only if the determinant of the matrix is not 0.

3. The complex number $a + bi$ can be represented by the matrix

$$\begin{bmatrix} a & b \\ -b & a \end{bmatrix}.$$

Operations with such matrices parallel corresponding operations with complex numbers.

4. Each vector (x, y) can be represented by a 2×1 matrix $\begin{bmatrix} x \\ y \end{bmatrix}$. Each 2×2 matrix $\begin{bmatrix} a & b \\ c & d \end{bmatrix}$ defines a transformation of the plane.

5. Each 2×2 matrix of the form $\begin{bmatrix} \cos \theta & -\sin \theta \\ \sin \theta & \cos \theta \end{bmatrix}$ can be viewed either as the matrix of a rotation of the plane about the origin in a counterclockwise (positive) direction through the angle θ or as the matrix of a rotation of the axes about the origin in a clockwise (negative) direction through the angle θ.

Chapter Test

Let $A = \begin{bmatrix} 2 & 5 \\ 0 & 1 \end{bmatrix}$ and $B = \begin{bmatrix} 0 & -1 \\ 2 & 3 \end{bmatrix}$. Find a 2×2 matrix equal to the given expression.

8–1   1. $A - 3B$

8–2   2. AB

    3. $A^2 - 2A$

8–3   4. BA^{-1}

    5. Solve for x_1 and x_2: $\begin{bmatrix} 6 & 1 \\ 12 & 4 \end{bmatrix} \begin{bmatrix} -1 & x_1 \\ 7 & x_2 \end{bmatrix} = \begin{bmatrix} 1 & 7 \\ 16 & -8 \end{bmatrix}$.

8–4   6. Use matrices to compute $(4 + i)(3 - 6i)$ and express the product both in matrix form and in the form $a + bi$.

8–5   7. Describe the geometric effect of the transformation of the plane with matrix $\begin{bmatrix} -2 & 0 \\ 0 & -2 \end{bmatrix}$.

    8. Sketch the triangle with vertices $(0, 0)$, $(1, 4)$, and $(-1, 4)$, and its image under the transformation with matrix $\begin{bmatrix} 0 & 1 \\ 1 & 0 \end{bmatrix}$.

    9. Determine the net effect of a reflection of the plane in the x-axis followed by a reflection of the plane in the origin.

8–6   10. Find the images of the points with coordinates $(4, 0)$ and $(1, \sqrt{3})$ after a rotation of the *plane* through an angle of $60°$.

Computer Investigations

If you have access to an electronic computer that will accept BASIC, you may wish to experiment with the matrix operations.

You can use computer matrix operations to solve systems of n linear equations in n variables. For example, to solve the system

$$2x + y = 4$$
$$x - 3y = -5$$

form these matrices:

$$A = \begin{bmatrix} 2 & 1 \\ 1 & -3 \end{bmatrix} \quad B = \begin{bmatrix} 4 \\ -5 \end{bmatrix} \quad X = \begin{bmatrix} x \\ y \end{bmatrix}$$

This system can then be described by the matrix equation

$$AX = B,$$

for which the solution is

$$X = A^{-1}B.$$

Use the program shown at the right to find X.

To solve other systems of 2 equations in 2 variables, change the DATA line. Try the exercises in Section 8–3.

```
10 DIM A(2,2),B(2),V(2,2),X(2)
20 MAT READ A,B
30 MAT PRINT A;B
40 PRINT
50 MAT V=INV(A)
60 MAT X=V*B
70 MAT PRINT X
80 DATA 2,1,1,-3,4,-5
90 END
```

By changing both the DIM and DATA lines, you can solve systems of different numbers of linear equations. For example, to solve

$$2x - y - z = 1$$
$$2x - 3y - 4z = 0$$
$$x + y - z = 4$$

form the matrices

$$A = \begin{bmatrix} 2 & -1 & -1 \\ 2 & -3 & -4 \\ 1 & 1 & -1 \end{bmatrix} \quad B = \begin{bmatrix} 1 \\ 0 \\ 4 \end{bmatrix} \quad X = \begin{bmatrix} x \\ y \\ z \end{bmatrix}$$

and make these changes in the program:

10 DIM A(3, 3), B(3), V(3, 3), X(3)
80 DATA 2, −1, −1, 2, −3, −4, 1, 1, −1, 1, 0, 4

Experiment with other systems of equations.

To find the coordinates of the points into which the points

$$(0, 0), \quad (0, 1), \quad (1, 1), \quad (1, 0)$$

are mapped by the transformation with matrix

$$\begin{bmatrix} 1 & 2 \\ 0 & 1 \end{bmatrix}$$

```
10  DIM M(2,2),A(2),P(2)
20  MAT READ M
30  FOR N=1 TO 4
40  MAT READ A
50  MAT P=M*A
60  MAT PRINT P
70  PRINT
80  NEXT N
90  DATA 1,2,0,1
100 DATA 0,0,0,1,1,1,1,0
110 END
```

use the program shown at the right.

To solve other similar problems, change **DATA** line 90. Try the exercises in Section 8–5.

The matrix of a rotation of the plane is:

$$\begin{bmatrix} \cos \theta & -\sin \theta \\ \sin \theta & \cos \theta \end{bmatrix}$$

This matrix can be expressed in the form:

$$(\cos \theta) \begin{bmatrix} 1 & 0 \\ 0 & 1 \end{bmatrix} + (\sin \theta) \begin{bmatrix} 0 & -1 \\ 1 & 0 \end{bmatrix}$$

In the following program, we let

$$I = \begin{bmatrix} 1 & 0 \\ 0 & 1 \end{bmatrix}$$

$$T = \begin{bmatrix} 0 & -1 \\ 1 & 0 \end{bmatrix}$$

$$R = (\cos \theta)I$$
$$S = (\sin \theta)T$$
$$M = R + S$$

```
10  DIM T(2,2),R(2,2),S(2,2),M(2,2),A(2),P(2)
20  MAT I=IDN(2,2)
30  MAT READ T
40  PRINT "WHAT IS ANGLE OF ROTATION (DEGREES)";
50  INPUT D
60  PRINT
70  LET D1=D*3.14159/180
80  MAT R=(COS(D1))*I
90  MAT S=(SIN(D1))*T
100 MAT M=R+S
110 FOR N=1 TO 4
120 MAT READ A
130 MAT P=M*A
140 MAT PRINT P
150 PRINT
160 NEXT N
170 DATA 0,-1,1,0
180 DATA 0,0,0,1,1,1,1,0
190 END
```

The program finds the coordinates of the points into which the points

$$(0, 0), \quad (0, 1), \quad (1, 1), \quad (1, 0)$$

are mapped by a rotation of the plane. To find the images of other points, change **DATA** line 180.

Chapter Nine

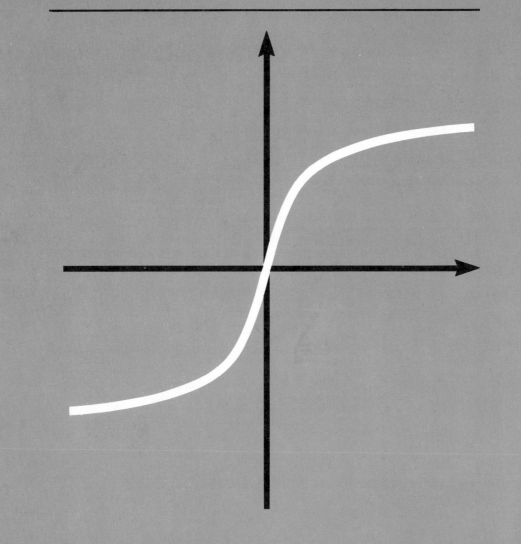

Infinite Series
and Circular Functions

OBJECTIVES

1. *To learn the meaning of "limit of a sequence," and to apply limit theorems to find limits of some simple sequences:*
2. *To identify intervals of convergence for simple power series.*
3. *To use infinite binomial expansions to obtain series for sin x and cos x.*
4. *To prove identities involving hyperbolic functions.*

Fundamental Concepts

9–1 *Sequences*

A **sequence** (often called an **infinite sequence**) is a function whose domain is the set N of natural numbers. The members of the range are called the **terms** of the sequence.

To designate a sequence, we select a letter of the alphabet, such as a, and let a_1 (read "a sub one") designate the first term of the sequence, a_2 the second term, and so on; we call a_n the general term. The notation $\{a_n\}$ (read "the sequence a sub n") denotes the entire sequence.

The terms of a sequence are in one-to-one correspondence with the set N of natural numbers. For example, if $\{a_n\} = \left\{\dfrac{n}{2^{n-1}}\right\}$, we display the first few terms and the general term of the sequence as follows:

Natural Numbers: $\quad 1 \quad 2 \quad 3 \quad 4 \quad 5 \quad 6 \;\ldots\; n \;\ldots$

$\qquad\qquad\qquad\quad \updownarrow \;\; \updownarrow \;\; \updownarrow \;\; \updownarrow \;\; \updownarrow \;\; \updownarrow \qquad\;\; \updownarrow$

Terms of the Sequence: $\quad 1 \quad 1 \quad \dfrac{3}{4} \quad \dfrac{1}{2} \quad \dfrac{5}{16} \quad \dfrac{3}{16} \;\cdots\; \dfrac{n}{2^{n-1}} \;\cdots$

Thus $a_1 = 1$, $a_2 = 1$, $a_3 = \frac{3}{4}$, and so on.

The terms of some sequences tend to concentrate around certain values. For example, the terms in the sequence

$$\frac{1}{2}, \frac{3}{4}, \frac{7}{8}, \frac{15}{16}, \ldots, \left[1 - \left(\frac{1}{2}\right)^n\right], \ldots$$

tend to approach the number 1. In fact, we can find a natural number m sufficiently large so that the mth term, and *all terms after the mth term*, differ from 1 by less than any positive value determined in advance. For instance, to find a natural number m so that the mth term, and all terms after the mth term, differ from 1 by less than $\frac{1}{100}$, we determine m so that $|1 - [1 - (\frac{1}{2})^m]| < \frac{1}{100}$, or $(\frac{1}{2})^m < \frac{1}{100}$. Since this inequality holds if $m \geq 7$, we can take $m = 7$. We call a sequence with this kind of "concentrating" property a *convergent sequence*. Thus we make the following definition:

▲ Let $\{s_n\}$ be a sequence and L a real number. Suppose that corresponding to any positive real number d (no matter how small), there is a natural number m such that for all natural numbers $n \geq m$ the difference $|L - s_n|$ is less than d. Then L is called the **limit** of $\{s_n\}$ as n increases without bound, $\{s_n\}$ is said to be a **convergent sequence**, and we write

$$\lim_{n \to \infty} s_n = L.$$

If $\{s_n\}$ does not have a limit, we call $\{s_n\}$ a **divergent sequence**.

Example 1   Using the definition of limit, prove that the sequence $\{a_n\} = \left\{\dfrac{3n}{n+1}\right\}$ converges to 3.

Solution   We wish to show that for any positive real number d there is a natural number m such that for all natural numbers $n \geq m$, the difference $|a_n - 3|$ is less than d. Since

$$|a_n - 3| = \left|\frac{3n}{n+1} - 3\right| = \left|\frac{-3}{n+1}\right| = \frac{3}{n+1},$$

and since $\dfrac{3}{n+1} < d$ is equivalent to $\dfrac{3}{d} < n + 1$ and, con-

sequently, to $n > \dfrac{3}{d} - 1$, we see that

$$|a_n - 3| < d \quad \text{if and only if} \quad n > \frac{3}{d} - 1.$$

Therefore, given any positive real number d, we choose m to be any natural number greater than $\dfrac{3}{d} - 1$.

Several values for d and corresponding values for $\dfrac{3}{d} - 1$ are shown in the table:

d	1	0.1	0.01	0.0001
$\dfrac{3}{d} - 1$	2	29	299	29999

The definition of limit of a sequence, as we have stated it and applied it here, expresses the basic meaning of a limit. To show that a given sequence has a number L as its limit, we shall sometimes apply the definition directly, but, more frequently, we shall apply one or more theorems or techniques which are *consequences of the definition.* A list of such theorems is shown below.

1. $\displaystyle\lim_{n\to\infty} \frac{a}{n} = 0$ for every $a \in \Re$.

2. $\displaystyle\lim_{n\to\infty} \left(\frac{a}{b}\right)^n = 0$ for every $a, b \in \Re$ satisfying $|a| < |b|$.

3. $\displaystyle\lim_{n\to\infty} c = c$ for every $c \in \Re$ (a constant sequence).

Similarly, it can be shown that if $\{a_n\}$ and $\{b_n\}$ are convergent sequences, then

4. $\displaystyle\lim_{n\to\infty} (a_n + b_n) = \lim_{n\to\infty} a_n + \lim_{n\to\infty} b_n$,

5. $\displaystyle\lim_{n\to\infty} (a_n - b_n) = \lim_{n\to\infty} a_n - \lim_{n\to\infty} b_n$,

6. $\displaystyle\lim_{n\to\infty} (a_n b_n) = \left(\lim_{n\to\infty} a_n\right)\left(\lim_{n\to\infty} b_n\right)$,

7. $\displaystyle\lim_{n\to\infty} \frac{a_n}{b_n} = \frac{\displaystyle\lim_{n\to\infty} a_n}{\displaystyle\lim_{n\to\infty} b_n} \quad (b_n \neq 0 \text{ and } \lim_{n\to\infty} b_n \neq 0)$,

8. $\displaystyle\lim_{n\to\infty} (a_n^x) = \left(\lim_{n\to\infty} a_n\right)^x \quad (a_n > 0, \ x \in \Re)$.

As a consequence of Properties 6 and 3,

9. $\displaystyle\lim_{n\to\infty} c a_n = c \lim_{n\to\infty} a_n$.

To see how these properties are applied, study the examples on the next page.

Example 2 Find $\lim\limits_{n \to \infty} \dfrac{2n - 1}{3n + 2}$ if the limit exists.

Solution Let us first rewrite the fraction $\dfrac{2n - 1}{3n + 2}$ as $\dfrac{2 - \dfrac{1}{n}}{3 + \dfrac{2}{n}}$ by dividing numerator and denominator by n. Then, by Properties (7), (4), and (5) of limits, we have

$$\lim_{n \to \infty} \left(\frac{2 - \dfrac{1}{n}}{3 + \dfrac{2}{n}} \right) = \frac{\lim\limits_{n \to \infty} \left(2 - \dfrac{1}{n} \right)}{\lim\limits_{n \to \infty} \left(3 + \dfrac{2}{n} \right)} = \frac{\lim\limits_{n \to \infty} 2 - \lim\limits_{n \to \infty} \dfrac{1}{n}}{\lim\limits_{n \to \infty} 3 + \lim\limits_{n \to \infty} \dfrac{2}{n}} = \frac{2 - 0}{3 + 0} = \frac{2}{3}.$$

Justification for these steps comes only after we see that the final four limits exist.

Example 3 Find $\lim\limits_{n \to \infty} (-1)^n$ if the limit exists.

Solution Since the terms of $\{(-1)^n\} = \{-1, 1, -1, 1, \ldots\}$ alternate between 1 and -1, there is no $m \in N$ such that for all $n \geq m$, $(-1)^n$ is arbitrarily close (say as close as $\frac{1}{2}$) to any real number. Hence, the sequence is divergent.

Example 4 Find $\lim\limits_{n \to \infty} \left(3 + \dfrac{1}{n^2 + 2} \right)$ if this limit exists.

Solution Rewriting $\dfrac{1}{n^2 + 2}$ as $\dfrac{\dfrac{1}{n^2}}{1 + \dfrac{2}{n^2}}$, we find that

$$\lim_{n \to \infty} \frac{1}{n^2 + 2} = \lim_{n \to \infty} \left(\frac{\dfrac{1}{n^2}}{1 + \dfrac{2}{n^2}} \right) = \lim_{n \to \infty} \left(\frac{\dfrac{1}{n} \cdot \dfrac{1}{n}}{1 + \dfrac{2}{n} \cdot \dfrac{1}{n}} \right)$$

$$= \frac{\left(\lim\limits_{n \to \infty} \dfrac{1}{n} \right) \left(\lim\limits_{n \to \infty} \dfrac{1}{n} \right)}{\lim\limits_{n \to \infty} 1 + \left(\lim\limits_{n \to \infty} \dfrac{2}{n} \right) \left(\lim\limits_{n \to \infty} \dfrac{1}{n} \right)}$$

$$= \frac{0 \cdot 0}{1 + 0 \cdot 0} = \frac{0}{1} = 0.$$

It is now easy to see, by Properties (3) and (4) of limits, that

$$\lim_{n \to \infty} \left(3 + \frac{1}{n^2 + 2} \right) = \lim_{n \to \infty} 3 + \lim_{n \to \infty} \frac{1}{n^2 + 2} = 3 + 0 = 3.$$

Exercises 9–1

Write the first four terms of the given sequence.

A   **1.** $\{3n\}$ **3.** $\left\{ \dfrac{2n + 1}{2n - 1} \right\}$ **5.** $\{\sin^n 30°\}$ **7.** $\{i^n\}$

     2. $\{4 - 3n\}$ **4.** $\left\{ \dfrac{n^2 + 1}{n} \right\}$ **6.** $\{\cos^n 30°\}$ **8.** $\left\{ (-1)^n \sin \dfrac{n\pi}{2} \right\}$

Determine the limit of each sequence, as n increases without bound, whenever it exists. If no limit exists, so state.

9. $\{1\}$ **12.** $\left\{ \dfrac{7}{n} \right\}$ **15.** $\left\{ \dfrac{2n - 1}{n} \right\}$ **18.** $\left\{ \dfrac{n}{3n - 2} \right\}$

10. $\left\{ -\dfrac{6}{n} \right\}$ **13.** $\{ (-\tfrac{3}{5})^n \}$ **16.** $\left\{ 3 - \dfrac{1}{n} \right\}$ **19.** $\left\{ \dfrac{(n - 1)^2}{n^2} \right\}$

11. $\left\{ \dfrac{3^n}{4^n} \right\}$ **14.** $\left\{ \dfrac{(-1)^n}{3^n} \right\}$ **17.** $\{ 1 + (\tfrac{3}{4})^n \}$ **20.** $\left\{ 1 - \dfrac{n^2}{n + 1} \right\}$

9–2   *Infinite Series*

If $\{a_n\}$ is a sequence, a new sequence, which we shall denote by $\{A_n\}$, can be formed by letting

$$A_1 = a_1,$$
$$A_2 = a_1 + a_2,$$
$$A_3 = a_1 + a_2 + a_3, \text{ and so on,}$$

for n any natural number. This new sequence $\{A_n\}$ is called the **sequence of partial sums** corresponding to $\{a_n\}$.

     Furthermore, for any sequence $\{a_n\}$, the expression

$$a_1 + a_2 + a_3 + \cdots + a_n + \cdots$$

is called an **infinite series**, or simply a **series**.

For example, corresponding to the sequence

$$\left\{ \frac{1}{2}, \frac{2}{3}, \frac{3}{4}, \ldots, \frac{n}{n+1}, \ldots \right\},$$

we have the infinite series

$$\frac{1}{2} + \frac{2}{3} + \frac{3}{4} + \cdots + \frac{n}{n+1} + \cdots.$$

The first four terms of the corresponding sequence of partial sums are

$$\tfrac{1}{2},\ \tfrac{1}{2} + \tfrac{2}{3},\ \tfrac{1}{2} + \tfrac{2}{3} + \tfrac{3}{4}, \text{ and } \tfrac{1}{2} + \tfrac{2}{3} + \tfrac{3}{4} + \tfrac{4}{5},$$

which simplify to

$$\tfrac{1}{2},\ \tfrac{7}{6},\ \tfrac{23}{12}, \text{ and } \tfrac{163}{60}.$$

If we can find a general expression to denote the terms of the sequence $\{a_n\}$, then we can use this expression, together with the Greek capital letter Σ (sigma), to describe the corresponding series and the terms of the corresponding sequence of partial sums. Thus

$$\sum_{i=1}^{\infty} a_i$$

is a short form for representing the series

$$a_1 + a_2 + a_3 + \cdots + a_n + \cdots.$$

Moreover, the nth term of the corresponding sequence of partial sums is denoted by

$$A_n = \sum_{i=1}^{n} a_i.$$

This signifies that

$$A_n = a_1 + a_2 + a_3 + \cdots + a_n.$$

That is, the **sigma**, or **summation**, **notation**

$$\sum_{i=1}^{n} a_i$$

represents the number obtained by adding the terms obtained by successively replacing the **index** i with the natural numbers $1, 2, 3, \ldots, n$. It is read, "the sum from i equals 1 to i equals n of a sub i."

Example 1 Write in expanded form:

(a) $\displaystyle\sum_{i=1}^{n} (2i + 1)$ (b) $\displaystyle\sum_{i=1}^{\infty} \frac{3}{i^2}$

Solution (a) Replacing i with $1, 2, 3, \ldots, n$, in turn, produces

$$\sum_{i=1}^{n} (2i + 1) = [2(1) + 1] + [2(2) + 1] + [2(3) + 1] + \cdots + (2n + 1)$$

$$= 3 + 5 + 7 + \cdots + (2n + 1).$$

(b) $\displaystyle\sum_{i=1}^{\infty} \frac{3}{i^2} = \frac{3}{1^2} + \frac{3}{2^2} + \frac{3}{3^2} + \cdots + \frac{3}{n^2} + \cdots.$

Example 2 Write the series

$$\frac{1}{1^2 + 5} + \frac{3}{2^2 + 5} + \frac{5}{3^2 + 5} + \cdots + \frac{(2n - 1)}{n^2 + 5} + \cdots$$

in sigma notation.

Solution $\displaystyle\sum_{i=1}^{\infty} \frac{(2i - 1)}{i^2 + 5}$

The index i used in the examples of sigma notation displayed thus far is called a **dummy symbol**. That is, any symbol may be used as the index (except the symbols you are using for other purposes, such as n in the examples above). Thus

$$\sum_{i=1}^{n} s_i = \sum_{j=1}^{n} s_j = \sum_{k=1}^{n} s_k.$$

Sigma notation may indicate that an expression starts with a value other than 1 for the index, and terminates with a value other than n, as in

$$\sum_{i=5}^{7} s_i = s_5 + s_6 + s_7,$$

and

$$\sum_{i=3}^{n-1} s_i = s_3 + s_4 + \cdots + s_{n-1}.$$

Just as the terms of a sequence may or may not approach a limit, similarly, a series may or may not have a limit, called its "sum."

Specifically, an infinite series

$$a_1 + a_2 + a_3 + \cdots + a_n + \cdots$$

is said to be **convergent** if the corresponding sequence of partial sums

$$\{A_n\} = \left\{ \sum_{i=1}^{n} a_i \right\}$$

is convergent, and is said to be **divergent** if $\{A_n\}$ is divergent.

If $\lim\limits_{n \to \infty} A_n = S$, we write

$$a_1 + a_2 + a_3 + \cdots + a_n + \cdots = S$$

or

$$\sum_{i=1}^{\infty} a_i = S,$$

and we refer to the number S as the **sum** of the infinite series.

Use of the word *sum* does not imply that any term of $\{A_n\}$ is necessarily equal to the number S. Nor does it imply that all of the numbers $a_1, a_2, a_3, \ldots,$ $a_n, \ldots$ have been added; this obviously is impossible. It is simply another name for the limit of the sequence of partial sums which corresponds to a given infinite series.

Exercises 9–2

For each sequence $\{a_n\}$ whose general term is given, find the first four terms of the corresponding sequence of partial sums.

A **1.** $a_n = \dfrac{n+1}{n}$ **3.** $a_n = \dfrac{1}{n}(-1)^n$ **5.** $a_n = \dfrac{2}{n}$

2. $a_n = \dfrac{1}{2^n}$ **4.** $a_n = 3^n - 2^n$ **6.** $a_n = (-1)^n$

In Exercises 7–12, write the first four terms of the sequence of partial sums associated with the given series.

7. $\displaystyle\sum_{i=1}^{n} 2^{i-1}$ **9.** $\displaystyle\sum_{j=1}^{n} j^j$ **11.** $\displaystyle\sum_{i=1}^{n} [(-1)^{i+1}(2^i - 1)]$

8. $\displaystyle\sum_{i=1}^{n} (3 - 2i)$ **10.** $\displaystyle\sum_{k=1}^{n} \dfrac{k}{k+4}$ **12.** $\displaystyle\sum_{i=1}^{n} \cos i\pi$

In Exercises 13–18, write the fifth term of the sequence of partial sums associated with the given series.

13. $\displaystyle\sum_{i=1}^{\infty} i^2$ **15.** $\displaystyle\sum_{j=1}^{\infty} (\tfrac{2}{3})^j$ **17.** $\displaystyle\sum_{i=2}^{\infty} \left(\frac{i}{i^2 - 1}\right)$

14. $\displaystyle\sum_{i=1}^{\infty} \left(1 - \frac{1}{i}\right)$ **16.** $\displaystyle\sum_{j=1}^{\infty} (-\tfrac{1}{2})^j$ **18.** $\displaystyle\sum_{i=1}^{\infty} \left(\frac{i - 1}{i + 1} - 1\right)$

B **19.** Show that if a is a constant, then $\displaystyle\sum_{i=1}^{n} a s_i = a \sum_{i=1}^{n} s_i$.

20. Show that $\displaystyle\sum_{i=1}^{n} s_i + \sum_{i=1}^{n} r_i = \sum_{i=1}^{n} (s_i + r_i)$.

21. Show by a counterexample that

$$\left(\sum_{i=1}^{n} s_i\right)\left(\sum_{i=1}^{n} r_i\right) = \sum_{i=1}^{n} s_i r_i$$

is not an identity for $s_i, r_i \in \mathcal{R}$.

Some Important Sequences and Series

9–3 *Geometric Sequences and Series*

If the first term in a sequence is not 0, and if each term after the first term is the product of a constant r and the preceding term, then the sequence is called a **geometric sequence** or a **geometric progression**. Thus,

$$\{2, 4, 8, \ldots, 2^n, \ldots\},$$

$$\left\{\frac{1}{3}, \frac{1}{9}, \frac{1}{27}, \ldots, \frac{1}{3^n}, \ldots\right\},$$

$$\left\{2, -\frac{2}{5}, \frac{2}{25}, \ldots, 2\left(-\frac{1}{5}\right)^{n-1}, \ldots\right\},$$

and

$$\{1, 1, 1, \ldots, 1^n, \ldots\}$$

are geometric sequences.

If a denotes the first term in a geometric sequence, r the constant multiplier, or **common ratio** as it is called, and $n \in N$ the number of the term, then, by inspecting the first few terms in the sequence

$$a, ar, ar^2, ar^3, ar^4,$$

it is evident that the nth term is given by

$$ar^{n-1}.$$

Example 1 Find the seventh term in the geometric progression

$$\{2, -\tfrac{2}{5}, \tfrac{2}{25}, \ldots, 2(-\tfrac{1}{5})^{n-1}, \ldots\}.$$

Solution   The seventh term is

$$2\left(-\frac{1}{5}\right)^6 = 2(-1)^6\left(\frac{1}{5^6}\right) = 2\left(\frac{1}{15,625}\right) = \frac{2}{15,625}.$$

To find an expression in terms of a, r, and n for the sum of the finite **geometric series**

▲
$$S_n = \sum_{i=1}^{n} ar^{i-1},$$

we can start by writing the series in expanded form,

$$S_n = a + ar + ar^2 + \cdots + ar^{n-1}. \tag{1}$$

Multiplying each member of this equation by r produces

$$rS_n = ar + ar^2 + ar^3 + \cdots + ar^n. \tag{2}$$

If (2) is then subtracted from (1) as indicated,

$$
\begin{aligned}
S_n &= a + ar + ar^2 + \cdots + ar^{n-1} \\
-\ rS_n &= \quad\ - ar - ar^2 - \cdots - ar^{n-1} - ar^n \\
\hline
S_n - rS_n &= a \qquad\qquad\qquad\qquad\qquad - ar^n
\end{aligned}
$$

we have $S_n(1 - r) = a - ar^n$, or

▲
$$S_n = \frac{a - ar^n}{1 - r} \quad (r \neq 1). \tag{3}$$

Example 2 Find S_8 if $S_n = \sum_{i=1}^{n} (\frac{1}{2})^{i-1}$.

Solution By inspection, $\sum_{i=1}^{n} (\frac{1}{2})^{i-1}$ is a geometric series with $a = 1$ and $r = \frac{1}{2}$. By (3),

$$S_8 = \frac{a - ar^8}{1 - r} = \frac{1 - (\frac{1}{2})^8}{1 - \frac{1}{2}}$$

$$= \frac{1 - \dfrac{1}{2^8}}{\frac{1}{2}} = 2(1 - \tfrac{1}{256}) = \tfrac{255}{128}.$$

Now, consider the infinite geometric series

$$\sum_{i=1}^{\infty} ar^{i-1} = a + ar + ar^2 + ar^3 + \cdots + ar^{n-1} + \cdots.$$

From (3), we know that for each $n \in N$,

$$S_n = \frac{a - ar^n}{1 - r} = \frac{a}{1 - r}(1 - r^n) \qquad (r \neq 1).$$

If $|r| < 1$, then, by Property 2, page 309,

$$\lim_{n \to \infty} r^n = 0.$$

In this case,

$$\lim_{n \to \infty} \sum_{i=1}^{n} ar^{i-1} = \lim_{n \to \infty} S_n$$

$$= \lim_{n \to \infty} \frac{a}{1 - r}(1 - r^n)$$

$$= \frac{a}{1 - r}\left(\lim_{n \to \infty} 1 - \lim_{n \to \infty} r^n\right)$$

$$= \frac{a}{1 - r}(1 - 0) = \frac{a}{1 - r}.$$

That is, every infinite geometric series with ratio r satisfying $|r| < 1$ converges, and we can write for such a series

$$S_\infty = \sum_{i=1}^{\infty} ar^{i-1} = \frac{a}{1 - r}.$$

Example 3   Find a fraction of the form $\dfrac{a}{b}$ equivalent to the number with the repeating decimal numeral $0.323232\ldots$.

Solution   The number $0.323232\ldots = \dfrac{32}{100} + \dfrac{32}{10,000} + \dfrac{32}{1,000,000} + \cdots$

can be represented by the infinite geometric series

$$a + ar + ar^2 + ar^3 + \cdots$$

where $a = \frac{32}{100}$ and $r = \frac{1}{100}$. Since $|r| < 1$,

$$S_\infty = \frac{a}{1 - r} = \frac{\frac{32}{100}}{1 - \frac{1}{100}} = \frac{32}{99}.$$

Therefore, $0.323232\ldots = \frac{32}{99}$.

Exercises 9–3

A **1.** Find the fifth term in the geometric progression whose first two terms are 12 and 4.

2. Find the seventh term in the geometric progression whose first two terms are 24 and 12.

Find the sum of the indicated geometric series.

3. $\displaystyle\sum_{i=1}^{4} (\tfrac{1}{3})^{i-1}$

4. $\displaystyle\sum_{j=1}^{5} 5(4^{j-1})$

5. $\displaystyle\sum_{i=1}^{6} 27(\tfrac{1}{3})^{i-1}$

6. $\displaystyle\sum_{j=1}^{\infty} 64(\tfrac{1}{2})^{j-1}$

7. $\displaystyle\sum_{i=1}^{\infty} 12(\tfrac{1}{2})^{i-1}$

8. $\displaystyle\sum_{j=1}^{\infty} (-4)(-\tfrac{1}{3})^{j-1}$

9. $\displaystyle\sum_{i=1}^{\infty} 18(\tfrac{2}{3})^{i-1}$

10. $\displaystyle\sum_{i=1}^{\infty} (\tfrac{2}{3})(\tfrac{3}{4})^{i-1}$

11. $\displaystyle\sum_{i=1}^{\infty} (\tfrac{1}{3})(-\tfrac{2}{6})^{i-1}$

Write the given repeating decimal as an equivalent fraction of the form $\dfrac{a}{b}$, where $a, b \in J$.

12. $0.666\ldots$

13. $0.273273\ldots$

14. $1.363363\ldots$

15. $2.324324\ldots$

16. $0.128888\ldots$

17. $0.823333\ldots$

Show that each of the statements in Exercises 18–20 is true, given that each geometric series converges.

B **18.** $\displaystyle\sum_{i=1}^{\infty} a_1 r_1^{i-1} + \sum_{i=1}^{\infty} a_2 r_2^{i-1} = \frac{a_1 + a_2 - (a_1 r_2 + a_2 r_1)}{(1 - r_1)(1 - r_2)}$

19. $\dfrac{\displaystyle\sum_{j=1}^{\infty} a_1 r_1^{j-1}}{\displaystyle\sum_{j=1}^{\infty} a_2 r_2^{j-1}} = \dfrac{a_1(1-r_2)}{a_2(1-r_1)}$ $(a_2, r_2 \neq 0)$

20. $\left(\displaystyle\sum_{i=1}^{\infty} a_1 r_1^{i-1}\right)\left(\displaystyle\sum_{i=1}^{\infty} a_2 r_2^{i-1}\right) = \dfrac{a_1 a_2}{(1-r_1)(1-r_2)}$

C 21. Consider the repeating decimal $0.a_1 a_2 a_1 a_2 a_1 a_2 \ldots$, where a_1 and a_2 are different digits. Show that using $a_1 a_2$ for the repeating group produces the same result as using $a_2 a_1$ for the repeating group when finding an equivalent fraction of the form $\dfrac{p}{q}$, $p, q \in J$.

22. Extend Exercise 21 to the repeating decimal $0.a_1 a_2 a_3 a_1 a_2 a_3 \ldots$. That is, show that using $a_1 a_2 a_3$, $a_2 a_3 a_1$, or $a_3 a_1 a_2$ as the repeating group produces the same result.

9–4 *Power Series*

A series formed from a sequence of the form $\{a_{n-1}x^{n-1}\}$, where the a's are constants, is called a **power series**. Thus

$$\sum_{i=1}^{\infty} a_{i-1}x^{i-1} = a_0 x^0 + a_1 x^1 + a_2 x^2 + \cdots + a_{n-1}x^{n-1} + \cdots$$
$$= a_0 + a_1 x^1 + a_2 x^2 + \cdots + a_{n-1}x^{n-1} + \cdots$$

is a power series.

Since every real number x determines a particular series when substituted in a given power series, a power series is actually a *set* of series (or a "family" of series). For example, some particular members of the power series

$$\sum_{i=1}^{\infty} \frac{1}{i}x^i = x + \tfrac{1}{2}x^2 + \tfrac{1}{3}x^3 + \cdots + \frac{1}{n}x^n + \cdots$$

are as follows:

For $x = 1$: $\displaystyle\sum_{i=1}^{\infty} \frac{1}{i} = 1 + \tfrac{1}{2} + \tfrac{1}{3} + \cdots + \frac{1}{n} + \cdots$

For $x = 2$: $\displaystyle\sum_{i=1}^{\infty} \frac{1}{i}2^i = 2 + \frac{2^2}{2} + \frac{2^3}{3} + \frac{2^4}{4} + \cdots + \frac{2^n}{n} + \cdots$

For $x = \tfrac{1}{3}$: $\displaystyle\sum_{i=1}^{\infty} \frac{1}{i}(\tfrac{1}{3})^i = \tfrac{1}{3} + \tfrac{1}{2}(\tfrac{1}{3})^2 + \tfrac{1}{3}(\tfrac{1}{3})^3 + \cdots + \frac{1}{n}(\tfrac{1}{3})^n + \cdots$

$$= \tfrac{1}{3} + \tfrac{1}{18} + \tfrac{1}{81} + \cdots + \frac{1}{n}(\tfrac{1}{3})^n + \cdots$$

Given a power series, an important question is: For what values of x are the resulting series convergent? The set of all values of x for which a power series converges is called its **interval of convergence**.

Before we investigate convergence of power series in detail, it will be helpful for you to become familiar with the following two series. The first is the **harmonic series**

$$\sum_{i=1}^{\infty} \frac{1}{i} = 1 + \tfrac{1}{2} + \tfrac{1}{3} + \cdots + \frac{1}{n} + \cdots.$$

Although it appears at first sight that this series might converge, it is actually divergent. Thus if we designate the nth partial sum by b_n, we note that $b_1 = 1$, $b_2 = b_1 + \tfrac{1}{2} > b_1$, $b_3 = b_2 + \tfrac{1}{3} > b_2$, and $\{b_n\}$ is an increasing sequence. Moreover, grouping successive terms so that the denominator of the last term in each group is a power of 2, we find

$$b_4 = b_2 + (\tfrac{1}{3} + \tfrac{1}{4}) > b_2 + (\tfrac{1}{4} + \tfrac{1}{4}) = b_2 + \tfrac{1}{2},$$
$$b_8 = b_4 + (\tfrac{1}{5} + \tfrac{1}{6} + \tfrac{1}{7} + \tfrac{1}{8}) > b_4 + (\tfrac{1}{8} + \tfrac{1}{8} + \tfrac{1}{8} + \tfrac{1}{8}) = b_4 + \tfrac{1}{2},$$
$$b_{16} = b_8 + (\tfrac{1}{9} + \cdots + \tfrac{1}{16}) > b_8 + (\tfrac{1}{16} + \cdots + \tfrac{1}{16}) = b_8 + \tfrac{1}{2},$$

and so on. Thus $\{b_{2^k}\}$ increases without bound. Consequently, $\{b_n\}$ increases without bound, and the series diverges. It diverges very slowly, however, since the sum of the first billion terms is less than 22!

The second series we want to consider is the **alternating harmonic series**

$$\sum_{i=1}^{\infty} (-1)^{i-1} \left(\frac{1}{i}\right) = 1 - \tfrac{1}{2} + \tfrac{1}{3} - \tfrac{1}{4} + \cdots + (-1)^{n-1} \frac{1}{n} + \cdots.$$

This series is convergent, although we do not prove its convergence here.

Example 1   Find the interval of convergence of the power series $\displaystyle\sum_{i=1}^{\infty} x^{i-1}$.

Solution   We have

$$\sum_{i=1}^{\infty} x^{i-1} = 1 + x + x^2 + x^3 + \cdots + x^{n-1} + \cdots,$$

which is a geometric series with $a = 1$ and $r = x$. Therefore, the series converges provided $|x| < 1$, and diverges for $|x| \geq 1$.

There exist numerous methods for testing the convergence of power series. Although we shall not prove its validity here, we shall state one of these tests, called the **ratio test**, that is widely used and that applies not only to power series but also to any infinite series of real or complex terms.

▲ If the sequence of ratios $\dfrac{a_{n+1}}{a_n}$ of the $(n+1)$st to the nth terms in the series $\displaystyle\sum_{i=1}^{\infty} a_i$ has a limit L, and if $|L| < 1$, then the series converges. If $|L| > 1$, the series diverges, and if $|L| = 1$, the test fails.

Example 2   Use the ratio test to find the interval of convergence of

$$\sum_{i=1}^{\infty} \frac{x^{i-1}}{i}.$$

Solution   The $(n+1)$st term of this series is $\dfrac{x^n}{n+1}$, and the nth term is $\dfrac{x^{n-1}}{n}$. Therefore, the series converges as long as the sequence

$$\left\{\frac{a_{n+1}}{a_n}\right\} = \left\{\frac{\dfrac{x^n}{n+1}}{\dfrac{x^{n-1}}{n}}\right\} = \left\{\frac{n}{n+1}\left(\frac{x^n}{x^{n-1}}\right)\right\} = \left\{\frac{n}{n+1}x\right\}$$

converges to a number L with $|L| < 1$, that is, as long as

$$\lim_{n\to\infty} \left|\frac{n}{n+1}x\right| < 1.$$ If we rewrite $\left|\dfrac{n}{n+1}\right|$ as $\left|\dfrac{1}{1+\dfrac{1}{n}}\right|$,

and note that $\left|\dfrac{1}{1+\dfrac{1}{n}}\cdot x\right| = \left|\dfrac{1}{1+\dfrac{1}{n}}\right|\cdot|x|$, we require that

$$\lim_{n\to\infty}\left|\frac{1}{1+\dfrac{1}{n}}\right| \cdot \lim_{n\to\infty}|x| = 1\cdot\lim_{n\to\infty}|x| = 1\cdot|x| < 1.$$

Then, by the ratio test, the series certainly converges for $|x| < 1$ and diverges for $|x| > 1$. We have not yet determined convergence or divergence in case $|x| = 1$. To do this, we examine the specific series associated with the endpoints 1 and -1 of the interval $-1 \le x \le 1$; that is,

$$\sum_{i=1}^{\infty} \frac{1^{i-1}}{i} \quad \text{and} \quad \sum_{i=1}^{\infty} \frac{(-1)^{i-1}}{i}.$$

From page 320, we know that the first of these series diverges, while the second converges, so that $\{x:\ -1 \le x < 1\}$ is the interval of convergence of the given series.

With each $x \in \mathfrak{R}$ in the interval of convergence of an infinite power series there is associated a unique real number

$$\sum_{i=1}^{\infty} a_{i-1}x^{i-1}.$$

This pairing constitutes a function f, and we can write

$$f(x) = \sum_{i=1}^{\infty} a_{i-1}x^{i-1} = a_0 + a_1x + a_2x^2 + \cdots + a_{n-1}x^{n-1} + \cdots.$$

Moreover, if we have another such function

$$g(x) = \sum_{i=1}^{\infty} b_{i-1}x^{i-1} = b_0 + b_1x + b_2x^2 + \cdots + b_{n-1}x^{n-1} + \cdots,$$

then for all values of x for which both f and g converge, it can be shown that $f(x) + g(x)$ and $f(x) \cdot g(x)$ also converge, where

▲   I. $f(x) + g(x) = (a_0 + b_0) + (a_1 + b_1)x + \cdots + (a_{n-1} + b_{n-1})x^{n-1} + \cdots,$

  II. $f(x) \cdot g(x) = a_0b_0 + (a_1b_0 + a_0b_1)x + (a_2b_0 + a_1b_1 + a_0b_2)x^2 + \cdots$

  $+ (a_{n-1}b_0 + a_{n-2}b_1 + \cdots + a_1b_{n-2} + a_0b_{n-1})x^{n-1} + \cdots.$

Example 3   If $f(x) = \sum_{i=1}^{\infty} \frac{1}{i}x^{i-1}$ and $g(x) = \sum_{i=1}^{\infty} \frac{i}{3^{i-1}}x^{i-1}$, find the first four terms of $f(x) + g(x)$ and of $f(x) \cdot g(x)$.

Solution   We first write four terms of f and of g:

$$f(x) = \sum_{i=1}^{\infty} \frac{1}{i}x^{i-1} = 1 + \tfrac{1}{2}x + \tfrac{1}{3}x^2 + \tfrac{1}{4}x^3 + \cdots$$

$$g(x) = \sum_{i=1}^{\infty} \frac{i}{3^{i-1}}x^{i-1} = 1 + \tfrac{2}{3}x + \tfrac{3}{9}x^2 + \tfrac{4}{27}x^3 + \cdots$$

Then from Formula I, above,

$$f(x) + g(x) = (1 + 1) + (\tfrac{1}{2} + \tfrac{2}{3})x + (\tfrac{1}{3} + \tfrac{3}{9})x^2 + (\tfrac{1}{4} + \tfrac{4}{27})x^3 + \cdots$$
$$= 2 + \tfrac{7}{6}x + \tfrac{2}{3}x^2 + \tfrac{43}{108}x^3 + \cdots;$$

and, from Formula II, above,

$$f(x) \cdot g(x) = (1 \cdot 1) + (\tfrac{1}{2} \cdot 1 + 1 \cdot \tfrac{2}{3})x + (\tfrac{1}{3} \cdot 1 + \tfrac{1}{2} \cdot \tfrac{2}{3} + 1 \cdot \tfrac{3}{9})x^2$$
$$+ (\tfrac{1}{4} \cdot 1 + \tfrac{1}{3} \cdot \tfrac{2}{3} + \tfrac{1}{2} \cdot \tfrac{3}{9} + 1 \cdot \tfrac{4}{27})x^3 + \cdots$$
$$= 1 + \tfrac{7}{6}x + x^2 + \tfrac{85}{108}x^3 + \cdots.$$

Exercises 9–4

In Exercises 1–9, find the interval of convergence of the given power series. Do not investigate convergence at endpoints.

A 1. $\displaystyle\sum_{i=1}^{\infty} x^i$

4. $\displaystyle\sum_{i=1}^{\infty} \frac{i}{2^{i-1}} x^{i-1}$

7. $\displaystyle\sum_{i=1}^{\infty} \frac{2i-1}{2^{i-1}} x^{i-1}$

2. $\displaystyle\sum_{i=1}^{\infty} x^{-i}$

5. $\displaystyle\sum_{i=1}^{\infty} i x^i$

8. $1 + \displaystyle\sum_{i=1}^{\infty} \frac{x^i}{1 \cdot 2 \cdot 3 \cdots (2i)}$

3. $\displaystyle\sum_{i=1}^{\infty} \frac{1}{i(i+1)} x^i$

6. $\displaystyle\sum_{i=1}^{\infty} \frac{1}{i(4^{i-1})} x^{i-1}$

9. $1 + \displaystyle\sum_{i=1}^{\infty} \frac{x^{2i}}{1 \cdot 2 \cdot 3 \cdots (2i)}$

If $f(x)$ and $g(x)$ are series as shown, write (a) the first four terms of $f(x) + g(x)$ and (b) the first four terms of $f(x) \cdot g(x)$.

B 10. $f(x) = \displaystyle\sum_{i=1}^{\infty} \frac{1}{2i} x^{i-1}, \ g(x) = \sum_{i=1}^{\infty} \frac{1}{3i} x^{i-1}$

11. $f(x) = \displaystyle\sum_{i=1}^{\infty} \frac{1}{i(i+1)} x^{i-1}, \ g(x) = \sum_{i=1}^{\infty} \frac{1}{i^2} x^{i-1}$

12. $f(x) = \displaystyle\sum_{i=1}^{\infty} (-1)^{i-1} \frac{1}{1 \cdot 2 \cdot 3 \cdots (2i-2)} x^{i-1}, \ g(x) = f(x)$.

(We define $1 \cdot 2 \cdot 3 \cdots (2i - 2)$ to be 1 for $i = 1$.)

9–5 Binomial Series

When the binomial power

$$(1 + x)^n$$

is expanded by means of the distributive law, we find that for $x \in \mathfrak{R}$ and n a nonnegative integer, we have

$$(1 + x)^0 = 1$$
$$(1 + x)^1 = 1 + x$$
$$(1 + x)^2 = 1 + 2x + x^2$$
$$(1 + x)^3 = 1 + 3x + 3x^2 + x^3$$
$$(1 + x)^4 = 1 + 4x + 6x^2 + 4x^3 + x^4$$

and, in general,

▲ $(1 + x)^n = 1 + nx + \dfrac{n(n-1)}{2!} x^2 + \dfrac{n(n-1)(n-2)}{3!} x^3 + \cdots$

$$+ \frac{n(n-1) \cdots [n - (r-1)]}{r!} x^r + \cdots + x^n. \quad (1)$$

In (1), the **factorial notation** $r!$, which appears in the denominator of the $(r + 1)$st term, denotes the product $1 \cdot 2 \cdot 3 \cdots (r - 1)(r)$ for $r \geq 2$. For $r = 1$ or 0, we have $1! = 1$ and $0! = 1$.

Although the right-hand member of (1) terminates with the term x^n, this series can be considered to be a special case of the infinite series

$$1 + nx + \frac{n(n - 1)}{2!} x^2 + \cdots + \frac{n(n - 1) \cdots [n - (r - 1)]}{r!} x^r + \cdots, \quad (2)$$

because for every $n \in N$, each term in (2) after the $(n + 1)$st term is zero. (In Exercise 23, page 327, you will be asked to verify that this is true.) Thus we can write binomial powers such as $(1 + x)^2$ and $(1 + x)^3$ in the form (2) as

$$(1 + x)^2 = 1 + 2x + x^2 + 0x^3 + 0x^4 + \cdots$$

and

$$(1 + x)^3 = 1 + 3x + 3x^2 + x^3 + 0x^4 + 0x^5 + \cdots.$$

So far as natural-number exponents are concerned, then,

$$\blacktriangle \ (1 + x)^n = 1 + nx + \frac{n(n - 1)}{2!} x^2 + \cdots + \frac{n(n - 1) \cdots [n - (r - 1)]}{r!} x^r + \cdots \quad (3)$$

is an identity in x over $\mathfrak{R}$. It can be (and is in the calculus) proved that (3) is a valid equality for *every* real number n and *every* complex number x as long as the infinite series in the right-hand member converges, which it does for all x satisfying $|x| < 1$. Therefore (3) can be used in particular to approximate certain irrational numbers.

Example 1 Write the first four terms in the expansion of $(1 + \frac{1}{10})^{\frac{1}{2}}$, and use them to approximate $\sqrt{1.1}$.

Solution Using (3) with $n = \frac{1}{2}$ and $x = \frac{1}{10}$, we have

$$(1 + \tfrac{1}{10})^{\frac{1}{2}} = 1 + \tfrac{1}{2}(\tfrac{1}{10}) + \frac{(\frac{1}{2})(-\frac{1}{2})}{2!} (\tfrac{1}{10})^2$$

$$+ \frac{(\frac{1}{2})(-\frac{1}{2})(-\frac{3}{2})}{3!} (\tfrac{1}{10})^3 + \cdots.$$

Upon simplifying each term, we find that

$$(1 + \tfrac{1}{10})^{\frac{1}{2}} = 1 + \tfrac{1}{20} - \tfrac{1}{800} + \tfrac{1}{16000} + \cdots.$$

Since

$$\sqrt{1.1} = (1 + \tfrac{1}{10})^{\frac{1}{2}},$$

we have $\quad\sqrt{1.1} = (1 + \tfrac{1}{10})^{\frac{1}{2}} \doteq 1 + 0.05 - 0.00125 + 0.0000625,$

or $\quad\sqrt{1.1} \doteq 1.0488125 \doteq 1.0488.$

Example 2 Find an infinite-series expansion for $\left(1 + \dfrac{1}{n}\right)^{nx}$, $n \in N$, and deduce a plausible expression for $\lim\limits_{n\to\infty}\left(1 + \dfrac{1}{n}\right)^{nx}$.

Solution By (3), for $n \neq 1$,

$$\left(1 + \frac{1}{n}\right)^{nx} = 1 + nx\left(\frac{1}{n}\right) + \frac{nx(nx - 1)}{2!}\left(\frac{1}{n}\right)^2$$

$$+ \frac{nx(nx - 1)(nx - 2)}{3!}\left(\frac{1}{n}\right)^3 + \cdots$$

$$+ \frac{nx(nx - 1)(nx - 2)\cdots[nx - (r - 1)]}{r!}\left(\frac{1}{n}\right)^r + \cdots.$$

We now rewrite the right-hand member of this equality by multiplying each term by $\dfrac{x^r}{x^r}$, where $r + 1$ is the number of the term, and then parcelling out factors of nx from the denominator of $\left(\dfrac{1}{nx}\right)^r$. For example, for the fourth term we have

$$\frac{nx(nx - 1)(nx - 2)}{3!}\left(\frac{1}{n}\right)^3 = \frac{nx(nx - 1)(nx - 2)}{3!}\left(\frac{1}{n}\right)^3 \frac{x^3}{x^3}$$

$$= \frac{nx(nx - 1)(nx - 2)}{3!}\left(\frac{1}{nx}\right)^3 x^3$$

$$= \frac{\left(\dfrac{nx}{nx}\right)\left(\dfrac{nx - 1}{nx}\right)\left(\dfrac{nx - 2}{nx}\right)}{3!} x^3$$

$$= \frac{\left(1 - \dfrac{1}{nx}\right)\left(1 - \dfrac{2}{nx}\right)}{3!} x^3.$$

Thus we have

$$\left(1 + \frac{1}{n}\right)^{nx} = 1 + x + \frac{\left(1 - \dfrac{1}{nx}\right)}{2!} x^2 + \frac{\left(1 - \dfrac{1}{nx}\right)\left(1 - \dfrac{2}{nx}\right)}{3!} x^3 + \cdots$$

$$+ \frac{\left(1 - \dfrac{1}{nx}\right)\left(1 - \dfrac{2}{nx}\right)\cdots\left(1 - \dfrac{r - 1}{nx}\right)}{r!} x^r + \cdots.$$

(Solution continued)

Now clearly, as n increases without bound, each factor, other than the power of x, in the numerator of each of the terms in the right-hand member approaches 1, since for each real number a, $\lim\limits_{n \to \infty} \dfrac{a}{n} = 0$. Hence it is reasonable to write

▲
$$\lim_{n \to \infty} \left(1 + \frac{1}{n}\right)^{nx} = 1 + x + \frac{x^2}{2!} + \frac{x^3}{3!} + \cdots + \frac{x^r}{r!} + \cdots . \quad (4)$$

The series (4) determines a function with domain $\mathcal{R}$, as can be shown by the ratio test. In fact, it can be shown that (4) is convergent for all complex x as well as all real x. In the work that follows, we shall use this result and other valid results involving complex exponents, although it is beyond the scope of this book to give their proof. You should regard operations with complex exponents as purely formal operations whose use here is justified by the fact that they lead to important results that we shall need. For $x = 1$, (4) becomes

$$\lim_{n \to \infty} \left(1 + \frac{1}{n}\right)^{n} = 1 + 1 + \frac{1}{2!} + \frac{1}{3!} + \cdots + \frac{1}{r!} + \cdots ,$$

and it can be shown that this series converges to an irrational number approximately equal to 2.718; this number is denoted by the letter e. Thus, by (4) and Property 8 on page 309, we have

▲
$$e^x = 1 + x + \frac{x^2}{2!} + \frac{x^3}{3!} + \cdots + \frac{x^r}{r!} + \cdots . \quad (5)$$

Exercises 9–5

In Exercises 1–6 simplify each of the expressions.

Example
$$\frac{(2n)!(n + 1)!}{(2n - 1)!(n + 1)}$$

Solution

Using expanded notation to help visualize the factors involved, you find

$$\frac{(2n)!(n + 1)!}{(2n - 1)!(n + 1)} = \frac{[1 \cdot 2 \cdots (2n - 1)(2n)][1 \cdot 2 \cdot 3 \cdots (n - 1)n(n + 1)]}{[1 \cdot 2 \cdots (2n - 1)](n + 1)} .$$

By dividing common factors from numerator and denominator, you obtain

$$\frac{[1 \cdot 2 \cdots (2n - 1)(2n)][1 \cdot 2 \cdot 3 \cdots (n - 1)n(n + 1)]}{[1 \cdot 2 \cdots (2n - 1)](n + 1)} = 2n(n!).$$

A **1.** $\dfrac{n!}{(n-2)!}$ **3.** $\dfrac{(n+2)(n+3)!}{(n+4)!}$ **5.** $\dfrac{(2n+2)!}{(2n-1)!2n}$

2. $\dfrac{(n+2)!}{n!}$ **4.** $\dfrac{(2n+2)!}{(2n)!}$ **6.** $\dfrac{(n+1)!}{(n-2)!(n^2-n)}$

Write the first four terms in the expansion of the given binomial.

7. $(1+x)^8$ **8.** $(1-x)^{12}$ **9.** $\left(1-\dfrac{1}{x}\right)^{10}$ **10.** $(1+\tfrac{1}{2})^{\frac{1}{4}}$

Use an appropriate binomial expansion to approximate the given expression to two decimal places.

11. $\sqrt{1.03}$ **12.** $(1.01)^{\frac{1}{3}}$ **13.** $(0.99)^{20}$ **14.** $(1.02)^{20}$

Use the ratio test to find the interval of convergence of the given infinite series. Do not investigate convergence at endpoints.

B **15.** $\displaystyle\sum_{i=1}^{\infty} \dfrac{(x+2)^{i-1}}{i(i+1)}$

16. $\displaystyle\sum_{i=1}^{\infty} \sqrt{i}\,(x-3)^i$

17. $\displaystyle\sum_{i=1}^{\infty} \dfrac{(x-2)^i}{3i+1}$

18. $\displaystyle\sum_{i=1}^{\infty} \dfrac{(x+1)^i}{i!}$

19. Use Equation (5) on page 326 to find a four-decimal-place approximation to e.

20. Show that the power series for e^x converges for all $x \in \Re$.

21. Find a power series expansion for e^{-x}.

22. Determine the interval of convergence of the power series for e^{-x}. Assume the validity of the ratio test for this series.

23. Show that in Equation (2), page 324, each term after the $(n+1)$st term is zero.

24. Given that

$$e^x = \sum_{i=1}^{\infty} \frac{x^{i-1}}{(i-1)!}$$

is valid for all complex numbers x, use the first four terms of the right-hand member to find an approximation for $e^{i\pi}$.

Infinite Series and Circular Functions

9–6 *Series for cos x and sin x*

In earlier chapters, we have seen how the symmetry of the unit circle and the properties of special right triangles can be used to determine values of $\cos x$ and $\sin x$ for certain values of x, and how reduction formulas, double-angle formulas, and half-angle formulas then enable us to use these known values to find additional values. We now wish, however, to establish a relationship between infinite series and circular functions which will enable us to find values of $\cos x$ and $\sin x$ for *any* given x.

Given any real number x, we first assume that we have chosen a natural number n which is very large compared to $|x|$, so that the number $\dfrac{x}{n}$ is very close to zero. Let $\mathbf{P}(u, v)$ be the point on the unit circle $u^2 + v^2 = 1$ such that the arc distance from $(1, 0)$ to $\mathbf{P}(u, v)$ is the number $\left|\dfrac{x}{n}\right|$, as shown in Figure 9–1.

As we have seen in Section 7–5, since $\mathbf{P}(u, v)$ is on the unit circle, the *complex number* (u, v) can be written in the polar form

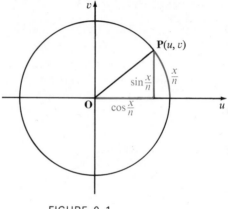

FIGURE 9–1

$$(u, v) = 1\left(\cos\frac{x}{n} + i\sin\frac{x}{n}\right).$$

Since $\dfrac{x}{n}$ is very close to 0, $\cos\dfrac{x}{n}$ and $\sin\dfrac{x}{n}$ are very close to 1 and to $\dfrac{x}{n}$, respectively. It is therefore plausible that

$$\cos\frac{x}{n} + i\sin\frac{x}{n} \doteq 1 + i\frac{x}{n} \tag{1}$$

for x any real number and for n any natural number for which $\left|\dfrac{x}{n}\right|$ is very close to 0.

To carry the approximations a step farther, we write

$$\left(\cos\frac{x}{n} + i\sin\frac{x}{n}\right)^n \doteq \left(1 + i\frac{x}{n}\right)^n,$$

and since by De Moivre's Theorem,

$$\left(\cos\frac{x}{n} + i\sin\frac{x}{n}\right)^n \doteq \cos x + i\sin x,$$

we have

$$\cos x + i\sin x \doteq \left(1 + i\frac{x}{n}\right)^n \qquad (2)$$

for $x \in \mathcal{R}$ and n any natural number for which $\left|\dfrac{x}{n}\right|$ is close to 0.

The larger the values of n, the smaller the numbers $\left|\dfrac{x}{n}\right|$ become, and the more nearly equal we would expect the members of (2) to be. In fact, as is shown in the calculus, we can actually assert that

$$\cos x + i\sin x = \lim_{n\to\infty}\left(1 + \frac{ix}{n}\right)^n.$$

Now, if we replace n with nix in the right-hand member of this expression, we have

$$\cos x + i\sin x = \lim_{n\to\infty}\left(1 + \frac{ix}{n}\right)^n$$

$$= \lim_{n\to\infty}\left(1 + \frac{ix}{nix}\right)^{nix}$$

$$= \lim_{n\to\infty}\left(1 + \frac{1}{n}\right)^{nix}$$

$$= \lim_{n\to\infty}\left[\left(1 + \frac{1}{n}\right)^n\right]^{ix}$$

$$= \left[\lim_{n\to\infty}\left(1 + \frac{1}{n}\right)^n\right]^{ix}.$$

Recalling from Section 9–5 that

$$\lim_{n\to\infty}\left(1 + \frac{1}{n}\right)^n = e,$$

we have

▲ $$\cos x + i\sin x = e^{ix}. \qquad (3)$$

Thus we have come upon a rather fascinating relationship involving complex numbers, the cos and sin functions, and the number e.

Example 1   Find a complex number in the form $a + bi$ that is equal to $e^{i\pi}$.

Solution   From (3),

$$e^{i\pi} = \cos \pi + i \sin \pi = -1 + i0.$$

Therefore, $e^{i\pi} = -1 + 0i = -1$.

On page 326, we found that for complex numbers x,

$$e^x = 1 + x + \frac{x^2}{2!} + \frac{x^3}{3!} + \cdots,$$

so that, in particular,

$$e^{ix} = 1 + (ix) + \frac{(ix)^2}{2!} + \frac{(ix)^3}{3!} + \frac{(ix)^4}{4!} + \frac{(ix)^5}{5!} + \cdots.$$

Also, on page 251, we observed that powers of i are periodic, taking on the values i, -1, $-i$, 1, in sequence. It follows that

$$e^{ix} = 1 + ix - \frac{x^2}{2!} - \frac{ix^3}{3!} + \frac{x^4}{4!} + \frac{ix^5}{5!} + \cdots$$

$$= \left(1 - \frac{x^2}{2!} + \frac{x^4}{4!} - \frac{x^6}{6!} + \cdots\right) + i\left(x - \frac{x^3}{3!} + \frac{x^5}{5!} - \frac{x^7}{7!} + \cdots\right).$$

From (3), then,

$$\cos x + i \sin x = \left(1 - \frac{x^2}{2!} + \frac{x^4}{4!} - \frac{x^6}{6!} + \cdots\right) + i\left(x - \frac{x^3}{3!} + \frac{x^5}{5!} - \frac{x^7}{7!} + \cdots\right).$$

Now complex numbers are equal if and only if their real parts are equal and their imaginary parts are equal, so that this latter equality implies that

▲ $\cos x = 1 - \dfrac{x^2}{2!} + \dfrac{x^4}{4!} - \dfrac{x^6}{6!} + \cdots + (-1)^{n+1} \dfrac{x^{2n-2}}{(2n-2)!} + \cdots$ (4)

and

▲ $\sin x = x - \dfrac{x^3}{3!} + \dfrac{x^5}{5!} - \dfrac{x^7}{7!} + \cdots + (-1)^{n+1} \dfrac{x^{2n-1}}{(2n-1)!} + \cdots.$ (5)

Example 2   Find three-decimal-place approximations for $\cos 0.2$ and $\sin 0.2$.

Solution   From (4), we have

$$\cos 0.2 = 1 - \frac{(0.2)^2}{2!} + \frac{(0.2)^4}{4!} - \frac{(0.2)^6}{6!} + \frac{(0.2)^8}{8!} + \cdots,$$

or $\quad \cos 0.2 = 1 - \dfrac{0.04}{2} + \dfrac{0.0016}{24} - \dfrac{0.000064}{720} + \dfrac{0.00000256}{40320} + \cdots$.

By inspection, the contribution made by the fourth and fifth terms is too small to affect the value of a three-decimal-place approximation; this is true also of the sum of all the remaining terms of the infinite series. In fact, the third term is only about 0.00007, and thus

$$\cos 0.2 \doteq 1 - \dfrac{0.04}{2} = 0.980.$$

The value of $\cos 0.2$ correct to six decimal places is 0.980067, so that the error in our approximation is quite small.

Using (5), we find in a similar way that

$$\sin 0.2 \doteq 0.2 - \dfrac{(0.2)^3}{3!} = 0.2 - \dfrac{0.008}{6} \doteq 0.2 - 0.0013.$$

Therefore,

$$\sin 0.2 \doteq 0.199.$$

Correct to six decimal places, $\sin 0.2 \doteq 0.198669$, so that, again, the error here is very small.

The series (4) and (5), together with the arithmetic of series (page 322), can be used to explore some of the properties of the functions sin and cos, although, clearly, the work involved would be laborious. For our purposes, the chief importance of these series is that they can be used to find approximations to the values of $\cos x$ and $\sin x$.

Exercises 9–6

Compute each of the following correct to two decimal places. Check your result against the value given in Table 3 or Table 2.

A **1.** $\sin 0.1$ **3.** $\cos 1$ **5.** $\sin \frac{1}{2}$ **7.** $\cos \dfrac{\pi}{6}$

   2. $\cos 0.1$ **4.** $\sin 1$ **6.** $\cos \frac{1}{2}$ **8.** $\sin \dfrac{\pi}{6}$

By making appropriate substitutions in (4) and (5) on page 330, find series representations for each of the following.

B **9.** $\sin \dfrac{x}{2}$ **10.** $\cos \dfrac{x}{2}$ **11.** $\sin 2x$ **12.** $\cos 2x$

   13. Show that the power series for $\cos x$ converges for all $x \in \Re$. (Assume the validity of the ratio test.)

C 14. Use the definition of the product of convergent series on page 322 to show that

$$\cos^2 x = \frac{1}{0!0!} - \left(\frac{1}{0!2!} + \frac{1}{2!0!}\right) x^2 + \left(\frac{1}{0!4!} + \frac{1}{2!2!} + \frac{1}{4!0!}\right) x^4 - \cdots$$

$$+ (-1)^{n+1} \left[\frac{1}{0!(2n-2)!} + \frac{1}{2!(2n-4)!} + \cdots\right.$$

$$\left. + \frac{1}{(2n-4)!2!} + \frac{1}{(2n-2)!0!}\right] x^{2n-2} + \cdots.$$

9–7 *Hyperbolic Functions*

If x is replaced with $-x$ in the identity

$$\cos x + i \sin x = e^{ix}, \qquad (1)$$

we have

$$\cos(-x) + i \sin(-x) = e^{i(-x)},$$

or, since cos is an even and sin an odd function,

$$\cos x - i \sin x = e^{-ix}. \qquad (2)$$

If we add the corresponding members of (1) and (2), we find that

$$2 \cos x = e^{ix} + e^{-ix},$$

from which we have

▲
$$\cos x = \frac{e^{ix} + e^{-ix}}{2}. \qquad (3)$$

Similarly, it can be shown that

▲
$$\sin x = \frac{e^{ix} - e^{-ix}}{2i}. \qquad (4)$$

Equations (3) and (4) are called **Euler's equations**, after Leonhard Euler (1707–1783).

Since (1) is valid for complex as well as real numbers x, we can replace each x in (3) and (4) with ix to obtain

$$\cos ix = \frac{e^x + e^{-x}}{2} \qquad (5)$$

and

$$\sin ix = i\left(\frac{e^x - e^{-x}}{2}\right). \qquad (6)$$

The exponential expressions in the right-hand members of (5) and (6) are used to define two important real-valued functions, called the **hyperbolic cosine function** (abbreviated **cosh**) and the **hyperbolic sine function** (abbreviated **sinh**). Thus,

▲
$$\cosh = \left\{(x, y): y = \cosh x = \frac{e^x + e^{-x}}{2}\right\}$$

and

▲
$$\sinh = \left\{(x, y): y = \sinh x = \frac{e^x - e^{-x}}{2}\right\}.$$

When the domains of cosh and sinh are taken to be $\Re$, the range of cosh is $\{x: x \geq 1\}$, and the range of sinh is $\Re$. The use of the names *hyperbolic cosine* and *hyperbolic sine* stems from the fact that these functions are related to the equilateral hyperbola with equation $u^2 - v^2 = 1$ in a manner analogous to a relationship existing between the sine and cosine functions and the unit circle.

Example 1   Prove that $\cosh^2 x - \sinh^2 x = 1$.

Solution   We have

$$\cosh^2 x - \sinh^2 x = \left(\frac{e^x + e^{-x}}{2}\right)^2 - \left(\frac{e^x - e^{-x}}{2}\right)^2$$

$$= \frac{e^{2x} + 2 + e^{-2x}}{4} - \frac{e^{2x} - 2 + e^{-2x}}{4}$$

$$= \frac{4}{4} = 1.$$

Other hyperbolic functions are defined in terms of cosh and sinh, as follows:

▲
$$\tanh = \left\{(x, y): y = \tanh x = \frac{\sinh x}{\cosh x}\right\}$$

$$\coth = \left\{(x, y): y = \coth x = \frac{\cosh x}{\sinh x}\right\}$$

$$\operatorname{sech} = \left\{(x, y): y = \operatorname{sech} x = \frac{1}{\cosh x}\right\}$$

$$\operatorname{ccsh} = \left\{(x, y): y = \operatorname{csch} x = \frac{1}{\sinh x}\right\}$$

Example 2   Show that, for each $x \in \Re$,

$$\tanh x = \frac{e^x - e^{-x}}{e^x + e^{-x}}.$$

(Solution on next page)

Solution   Using the definition of tanh, we find

$$\tanh x = \frac{\sinh x}{\cosh x} = \frac{\dfrac{e^x - e^{-x}}{2}}{\dfrac{e^x + e^{-x}}{2}} = \frac{e^x - e^{-x}}{e^x + e^{-x}}.$$

Since $\cosh x \geq 1$ for all $x \in \Re$, the demonstration is complete.

The graphs of cosh, sinh, and tanh are shown in Figure 9–2. Notice that both sinh and tanh are one-to-one functions, and hence have inverses that are

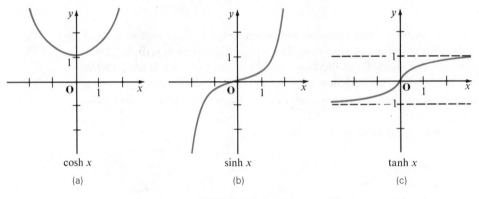

| cosh *x* | sinh *x* | tanh *x* |
| (a) | (b) | (c) |

FIGURE 9–2

functions. To obtain an inverse function for cosh, the restriction $y \geq 0$ is placed on the range. Figure 9–3 shows the graphs of Cosh^{-1}, $\sinh^{-1}$, and $\tanh^{-1}$.

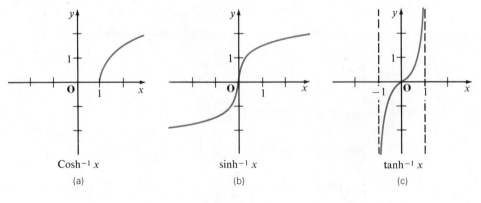

| Cosh⁻¹ *x* | sinh⁻¹ *x* | tanh⁻¹ *x* |
| (a) | (b) | (c) |

FIGURE 9–3

The hyperbolic functions, as well as their inverses, appear in many different physical situations, as you will discover when you study the calculus. For example, Figure 9–2(a), the graph of cosh, suggests that cosh could serve as a mathematical model for a hanging flexible cable, which is indeed the case.

Exercises 9–7

Use the definitions of cosh x, sinh x, and tanh x to prove each of the following identities.

A **1.** $\cosh(-x) = \cosh x$ **4.** $\coth^2 x - \operatorname{csch}^2 x = 1$

2. $\sinh(-x) = -\sinh x$ **5.** $\cosh x + \sinh x = e^x$

3. $\tanh^2 x + \operatorname{sech}^2 x = 1$ **6.** $\cosh x - \sinh x = e^{-x}$

B **7.** Use Equation (5), page 326, the result of Exercise 21, page 327, and the definition of the sum of power series on page 322 to show that

$$\cosh x = 1 + \frac{x^2}{2!} + \frac{x^4}{4!} + \cdots + \frac{x^{2n-2}}{(2n-2)!} + \cdots.$$

8. Repeat Exercise 7 for

$$\sinh x = x + \frac{x^3}{3!} + \frac{x^5}{5!} + \cdots + \frac{x^{2n-1}}{(2n-1)!} + \cdots.$$

Use the results of Exercises 7 and 8 to find three-place decimal approximations for each of the following.

9. $\cosh 1$ **10.** $\sinh 1$ **11.** $\sinh\left(-\tfrac{1}{2}\right)$ **12.** $\cosh\left(-\tfrac{1}{2}\right)$

Chapter Summary

1. A **sequence** (often called an **infinite sequence**) is a function whose domain is the set N of natural numbers. The members of the range are called the **terms** of the sequence. Thus the terms of a sequence form a set which is in one-to-one correspondence with the set N of natural numbers.

   An expression of the form

$$a_1 + a_2 + a_3 + \cdots + a_n + \cdots$$

is called an infinite **series** and can be represented using **summation notation** by

$$\sum_{i=1}^{\infty} a_i.$$

2. A sequence $\{s_n\}$ is said to **converge** to a real number L if for any positive real number d (no matter how small) there is a natural number m such that for all natural numbers $n \geq m$ the difference $|L - s_n|$ is less than d. The real number L is called the **limit** of the sequence. A sequence that does not converge is said to **diverge**. The limits of sums, differences, products, and quotients of sequences are equal to the sums, differences, products, and quotients of the limits of the sequences, respectively, provided that (for quotients) denominators are not 0 and do not converge to 0. A series is said to **converge** if and only if the corresponding sequence of partial sums converges.

3. The **infinite geometric series** $\sum\limits_{i=1}^{\infty} ar^{i-1}$, $a \neq 0$, converges for all $|r| < 1$ and diverges for $|r| \geq 1$. The sum of a convergent infinite geometric series is given by

$$S_\infty = \lim_{n \to \infty} \sum_{i=1}^{n} ar^{i-1} = \frac{a}{1-r}.$$

4. A series of the form $\sum\limits_{i=1}^{\infty} a_{i-1}x^{i-1}$ is called a **power series.** The ratio test can be used to determine the **interval of convergence** of a power series.

5. The **binomial expansion**

$$(1+x)^n = 1 + nx + \frac{n(n-1)}{2!}x^2 + \cdots + \frac{n(n-1)\cdots[n-(r-1)]}{r!}x^r + \cdots$$

is valid for all $n \in \mathfrak{R}$ and for all complex numbers x such that $|x| < 1$. The infinite-series representation of e^x,

$$e^x = 1 + x + \frac{x^2}{2!} + \frac{x^3}{3!} + \cdots + \frac{x^r}{r!} + \cdots,$$

is valid for all complex numbers x.

6. Infinite-series representations for $\cos x$ and $\sin x$ are given by

$$\cos x = 1 - \frac{x^2}{2!} + \frac{x^4}{4!} + \cdots + (-1)^{n+1}\frac{x^{2n-2}}{(2n-2)!} + \cdots$$

and

$$\sin x = x - \frac{x^3}{3!} + \frac{x^5}{5!} + \cdots + (-1)^{n+1}\frac{x^{2n-1}}{(2n-1)!} + \cdots.$$

They converge for all $x \in \mathfrak{R}$.

7. The **hyperbolic cosine** and **hyperbolic sine** functions are defined by

$$\cosh x = \frac{e^x + e^{-x}}{2}$$

and

$$\sinh x = \frac{e^x - e^{-x}}{2}.$$

Other hyperbolic functions are defined in terms of cosh x and sinh x.

Chapter Test

9–1   **1.** Find $\lim\limits_{n \to \infty} \dfrac{n}{3n - 2}$, if it exists.

2. Find $\lim\limits_{n \to \infty} (-1)^n \dfrac{1}{n}$, if it exists.

9–2   **3.** Given the sequence of partial sums $\left\{ \sum\limits_{i=1}^{n} \dfrac{i}{i + 2} \right\}$, find:

   (a) the third term
   (b) the number obtained by subtracting the fifth term from the sixth term.

9–3   **4.** Find the sixth term in the geometric progression whose first two terms are 9 and 6.

5. Given the series $\sum\limits_{i=1}^{\infty} 6(\tfrac{1}{4})^{i-1}$, find:

   (a) the first three terms of the corresponding sequence of partial sums.
   (b) the sum of the series, if it exists.

9–4   **6.** Find the interval of convergence of the power series $\sum\limits_{i=1}^{\infty} \dfrac{i}{3^i} x^i$. Do not investigate convergence at endpoints.

9–5   **7.** Use an appropriate binomial expansion to approximate $\sqrt[3]{1.06}$ to two decimal places.

8. Simplify $\dfrac{n!(n + 3)!}{(n + 2)!(n - 1)!}$.

9–6   **9.** Find a complex number in the form $a + bi$ that is equal to $e^{\frac{\pi i}{2}}$.

9–7   **10.** Graph $y = \cosh x$.

Cumulative Review · Chapters 7–9

Chapter 7

If $z_1 = (-4, 2)$ and $z_2 = (6, -5)$, find:

1. $z_1 + z_2$ **2.** $z_1 - z_2$ **3.** $z_1 z_2$ **4.** $\dfrac{z_1}{z_2}$ **5.** $\dfrac{z_2}{z_1}$

Express in the form $a + bi$:

6. $(3 - i)(4 + i)$ **7.** $\dfrac{2 - i}{1 + 3i}$ **8.** $2(\cos 5° + i \sin 5°)^6$

9. Express $-\dfrac{1}{2} - \dfrac{\sqrt{3}}{2} i$ in polar form.

If $z_1 = 5(\cos 30° + i \sin 30°)$ and $z_2 = 2[\cos (-30°) + i \sin (-30°)]$, find in polar form:

10. $z_1 z_2$ **11.** $\dfrac{z_1}{z_2}$

12. Find the three cube roots of -8.

Chapter 8

If $A = \begin{bmatrix} -3 & 7 \\ 1 & 2 \end{bmatrix}$ and $B = \begin{bmatrix} 4 & 7 \\ 1 & 2 \end{bmatrix}$, find:

13. $A + B$ **14.** $A - 2B$ **15.** AB **16.** $B(A + I)$

17. Find the inverse of $\begin{bmatrix} -4 & -2 \\ 1 & 1 \end{bmatrix}$.

18. Use matrices to solve the system: $3x - y = -5$

$x + 2y = 3$

19. Use matrices to compute $(4 - i)(1 + 3i)$, expressing your answer both in matrix form and in the form $a + bi$.

20. Use matrices to find an expression of the form $\rho(\cos \theta + i \sin \theta)$ for

$$2\left(\cos \frac{\pi}{3} + i \sin \frac{\pi}{3}\right) \cdot (-3)\left(\cos \frac{2\pi}{3} + i \sin \frac{2\pi}{3}\right).$$

In Exercises 21 and 22, describe the geometric effect of the transformation of the plane with the given matrix A and sketch the graph of set S and its image set T under this transformation.

21. $A = \begin{bmatrix} -2 & 0 \\ 0 & 2 \end{bmatrix}$; S is the square with vertices $(0, 0)$, $(1, 0)$, $(1, 1)$, and $(0, 1)$.

22. $A = \begin{bmatrix} 0 & -3 \\ -3 & 0 \end{bmatrix}$; S is the triangle with vertices $(0, 0)$, $(6, 0)$, and $(3, 4)$.

Find the images of the vertices of the given polygon after a rotation of the plane through the angle θ. Sketch the polygon and its image.

23. $\theta = 150°$; triangle with vertices $(0, 0)$, $(2, 0)$, and $(0, 2)$.

24. $\theta = -60°$; rectangle with vertices $(1, 1)$, $(1, 3)$, $(4, 1)$, and $(4, 3)$.

Chapter 9

25. Write the first four terms of $\left\{ \dfrac{3n + 2}{n + 5} \right\}$.

26. Find $\lim\limits_{n \to \infty} \dfrac{2n}{3n^2 + 1}$.

27. If $A_n = \sum\limits_{i=1}^{n} \dfrac{3i}{i + 2}$, find A_1, A_2, A_3, and A_4.

28. Find $\sum\limits_{i=1}^{\infty} 3(\frac{2}{3})^i$.

29. Simplify $\dfrac{(n + 1)!}{(n - 2)!}$.

30. Write the first four terms of the expansion of $(1 + x)^{\frac{1}{3}}$.

31. Compute sin 0.4 to the nearest hundredth using the series for sin x.

32. Prove that $[\cosh(-x) + \sinh(-x)][\cosh x + \sinh x] = 1$.

Applications of Trigonometry

Synthesis and Analysis of Waves

Pythagoras discovered that the sound emitted by two plucked strings of the same material and under the same tension produces a pleasant effect provided the lengths of the strings are in the ratio of two small integers, such as 2 and 3. On the basis of this empirical evidence that there are numerical relationships in nature, he and his followers developed a mystic philosophy that sought to explain the entire universe in terms of numbers. Thus arose, for example, the concept of the "music of the spheres," or planets, in ancient astronomy.

The strings plucked by Pythagoras vibrated with fundamental frequencies in the same ratio as their lengths. In the air, their vibrations accordingly created regular waves, or musical notes, with these same relative frequencies, say 2 and 3. While the first wave was going through two cycles, the second went through three, and then the pattern repeated itself. It appears that the human ear reacts pleasurably to such regular repetitions of sound patterns.

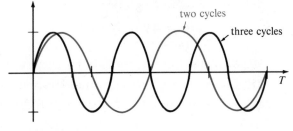

two cycles

three cycles

T

Actually, however, the situation is more complicated than we have thus far indicated, for a string vibrates not only with its fundamental frequency f but also with integral multiples of f, namely $2f$ (the first harmonic), $3f$ (the second harmonic), etc. Thus if a string vibrates twice in a time interval of length T, then it is in the same phase at times $t = \dfrac{T}{2}$ and $t = T$ as it is at $t = 0$; its first harmonic is in the same phase at times $t = 0, \dfrac{T}{4}, \dfrac{T}{2}, \dfrac{3T}{4}$, and T; and its second harmonic at times $t = 0, \dfrac{T}{6}, \dfrac{T}{3}, \dfrac{T}{2}, \dfrac{2T}{3}, \dfrac{5T}{6}$, and T. If a second string vibrates three times in the same time interval T, then, for instance, at times $t = \dfrac{T}{6}, \dfrac{T}{3}, \dfrac{T}{2}$, etc., the third harmonic of the first string is in the same phase relationship to the second harmonic of the second string as it is at times $t = 0$.

The proportions of these various harmonics, or overtones, make differences of *quality* in musical notes of the same pitch and loudness, when these notes are produced by different instruments. Thus a piano and a clarinet are easily distinguishable, even when they sound notes of the same pitch and volume. The versatile German philosopher and scientist Hermann Ludwig Ferdinand von

Helmholtz (1821–1894) devised ingenious laboratory methods of demonstrating this fact. Through the observation of resonant reactions in such pure instruments as tuning forks mounted on hollow boxes, he *analyzed* the complicated but periodic oscillations of a musical sound produced, for instance, by an oboe. He then verified his analysis by *synthesizing* the observed pure tone and pure overtones to simulate the original sound.

It was shown by the French mathematical physicist Jean Baptiste Joseph Fourier (1768–1830) how all this can be handled mathematically. A pure wave, whether sound, electromagnetic, or any other, with period $T = \dfrac{2\pi}{\omega}$

can be represented by an expression of the form $a_1 \cos \omega t + b_1 \sin \omega t$, where two terms are used to allow for an arbitrary phase shift. Any combination of such a wave and its first harmonic can then be represented by

$$a_1 \cos \omega t + b_1 \sin \omega t + a_2 \cos 2\omega t + b_2 \sin 2\omega t,$$

and so on. From this, he made the startling conjecture that any ordinary function f of period $T = \dfrac{2\pi}{\omega}$ can be represented by a series of the form

$$f(t) = a_0 + a_1 \cos \omega t + b_1 \sin \omega t + \cdots + a_n \cos n\omega t + b_n \sin n\omega t + \cdots.$$

The four musicians in the foreground are playing Moog synthesizers, accompanied by the Boston Symphony Orchestra under the direction of Arthur Fiedler. The Moog synthesizer produces sound entirely by electronic means. Almost every known musical sound, and many new sounds, can be synthesized on electronic instruments such as these.

This was found to be true, at least for any periodic function f having a smooth graph, and methods were found for determining the constants $a_0, a_1, b_1, \ldots$ when f is given.

For example, the periodic function f, which satisfies $f(t) = t$ for $-\pi < t < \pi$, has the *Fourier-series* representation

$$f(t) = 2\left(\frac{\sin t}{1} - \frac{\sin 2t}{2} + \frac{\sin 3t}{3} - \cdots\right).$$

In particular, for $t = \dfrac{\pi}{2}$, this gives the interesting formula $\dfrac{\pi}{4} = 1 - \dfrac{1}{3} + \dfrac{1}{5} - \cdots$.

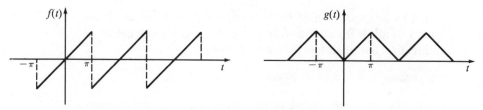

You might compute the first few terms of the series given at the right above for $\dfrac{\pi}{4}$ and note that the partial sums $1, 1 - \frac{1}{3}, 1 - \frac{1}{3} + \frac{1}{5}$, and so on, are successively greater than and less than $\dfrac{\pi}{4}$. The average of your last two partial sums should be a good approximation to $\dfrac{\pi}{4}$.

You might also sketch the graphs of the first few approximations

$$y = 2\left(\frac{\sin t}{1}\right), \qquad y = 2\left(\frac{\sin t}{1} - \frac{\sin 2t}{2}\right),$$

and so on, for $-\pi < t < \pi$.

Again, the function g shown at the right, above, of period 2π, satisfying $g(t) = |t|$ for $-\pi \le t \le \pi$, can be represented by the Fourier series

$$g(t) = \frac{\pi}{2} - \frac{4}{\pi}\left(\frac{\cos t}{1^2} + \frac{\cos 3t}{3^2} + \frac{\cos 5t}{5^2} + \cdots\right).$$

Substitution of $t = 0$ in the formula for $g(t)$ gives $\dfrac{\pi^2}{8} = \dfrac{1}{1^2} + \dfrac{1}{3^2} + \dfrac{1}{5^2} + \cdots$.

Note that the above functions f and g, which are represented by different series, actually are identical for $0 \le t < \pi$, since $f(t) = g(t) = t$ in this interval.

The methods of *Fourier analysis*, as the study of such sine and cosine series is called, are widely applicable, and today they are extensively used in virtually all branches of engineering and of the physical, life, and social sciences.

Computer Investigations

If you have access to an electronic computer that will accept BASIC, you may wish to try the programs on this page and the next.

You can use a computer to print the terms of a geometric series and its partial sums. We use the form:

$$a + ar + ar^2 + ar^3 + \cdots + ar^{n-1} + \cdots$$

The adjoining program will print the first 10 terms (and sums) of such a series after you IN-PUT values of A and R. Try

$$A = .5, \qquad R = .5$$

and then

$$A = 1, \qquad R = .5$$

and compare the results. Try other values of A and R.

```
10    PRINT "INPUT A AND R ";
20    INPUT A, R
30    PRINT
40    PRINT "NUMBER", "TERM", "SUM"
45    LET S=0
50    FOR N=0 TO 9
60    LET T=A*R↑N
70    LET S=S+T
80    PRINT N+1, T, S
90    NEXT N
100   END
```

The preceding program used the formula to compute each term. We can also compute each term after the first by using:

$$T = T * R$$

Make the following changes in the program:

```
42 LET T = A
45 LET S = A
48 PRINT 1, T, S
50 FOR N = 2 to 10
60 LET T = T * R
80 PRINT N, T, S
```

RUN the resulting program for A = 1, R = .5, and compare the results with those obtained above.

Try also:

$$A = 1, \qquad R = .25$$
$$A = 1, \qquad R = .125$$
$$A = 1, \qquad R = .0625$$

You found in Section 9–5 that:

$$e = 1 + \left[\frac{1}{1!} + \frac{1}{2!} + \frac{1}{3!} + \cdots \frac{1}{n!} + \cdots \right]$$

The terms in the series in brackets (after the first) can be found from:

$$T = T * (1/N)$$

Use the adjoining program to find the first 10 terms (and sums) of this series and, hence, 11 terms in the approximation of e.

```
10   PRINT "NUMBER", "TERM", "SUM"
20   LET T=1
30   LET S=1
40   PRINT 1, T, S
50   FOR N=1 TO 10
60   LET T=T*(1/N)
70   LET S=S+T
80   PRINT N+1, T, S
90   NEXT N
100  END
```

Notice that the last 3 values of e in the printout are the same. We can change the program to stop when the value of the next T will be less than .000005. Try these changes:

```
40 LET N = 1
50 PRINT N, T, S
80 IF T < .000005 THEN 100
90 LET N = N + 1
95 GO TO 50
```

RUN this revised program to find how many terms are needed to give the value of e to 5 decimal places.

You found in Section 9–6 that:

$$\cos x = 1 - \frac{x^2}{2!} + \frac{x^4}{4!} - \frac{x^6}{6!} + \cdots + (-1)^{n+1} \frac{x^{2n-2}}{(2n-2)!} + \cdots$$

Each term after the first can be found from:

$$t = t(-1)\left(\frac{x^2}{(2n-3)(2n-2)}\right)$$

The adjoining program prints out terms of the series with each corresponding sum, and then the value of COS as a check. Try D = 10, 20, 30, 45, 60, 70, and 80, and notice the number of terms needed for each.

Write a similar program for SIN.

```
10   PRINT "INPUT ANGLE IN DEGREES ";
20   INPUT D
30   LET D1=D*3.14159/180
40   PRINT
50   PRINT "NUMBER", "TERM", "COS"; D
60   LET T=1
70   LET N=1
75   LET S=0
80   LET S=S+T
90   PRINT N, T, S
100  LET N=N+1
110  LET T=T*(-1)*D1*2/((2*N-3)*(2*N-2))
120  IF ABS(T)<5.E-07 THEN 140
130  GO TO 80
140  PRINT
150  PRINT "COS"; D; " ="; COS(D1)
160  END
```

Comprehensive Test

Chapter 1

1. If $f(x + 3) = f(x)$, and $f(2) = 6$, then $f(5) =$

   (a) 11   (c) 7

   (b) 6   (d) 9

2. If t is the length of arc on the unit circle measured in a clockwise direction from the point $(1, 0)$ to the point **P**, then the ordinate of **P** is always

   (a) positive   (c) equal to $\cos t$

   (b) negative   (d) equal to $\sin t$

3. The expression $\sin a \cos b + \cos a \sin b$ is equal to

   (a) $\sin (a + b)$ (c) $\cos (a + b)$

   (b) $\sin (a - b)$ (d) $\cos (a - b)$

4. If $\dfrac{3\pi}{2} < x < 2\pi$, then

   (a) $\sin x = -\sqrt{1 - \cos^2 x}$ (c) $\sin x = \sqrt{1 - \cos^2 x}$

   (b) $\cos x = -\sqrt{1 - \sin^2 x}$ (d) None of (a), (b), or (c) is true.

5. Given that $\cos x = \dfrac{\sqrt{5}}{4}$ and x is in Quadrant I, then $\sin x$ is equal to

   (a) $\dfrac{4}{\sqrt{5}}$ (c) $\dfrac{\sqrt{11}}{4}$

   (b) $1 - \dfrac{\sqrt{5}}{4}$ (d) $\dfrac{\sqrt{5}}{4} - 1$

6. If $x = \dfrac{3\pi}{4}$, then

   (a) $\sin x < \cos x$ (c) $\sin x = \cos x$

   (b) $\sin x > \cos x$ (d) $\sin x < 0$

7. Which of the following is *never* true for any value of x?

   (a) $\sin x = 1 + \cos \dfrac{\pi}{2}$ (c) $\sin x = 1 - \cos \dfrac{\pi}{2}$

   (b) $\cos x = 1 + \sin \dfrac{\pi}{2}$ (d) $\cos x = 1 - \sin \dfrac{\pi}{2}$

8. If $\sin 2x = -\frac{1}{2}$ and $\cos 2x = -\dfrac{\sqrt{3}}{2}$, then x is equal to

   (a) 105°   (c) 240°

   (b) 210°   (d) 120°

9. If $\cos x = \frac{3}{5}$ and $\sin x < 0$, then $\cos\left(x + \frac{\pi}{3}\right)$ is equal to

(a) $\dfrac{3}{5} - \dfrac{2\sqrt{3}}{5}$

(c) $\dfrac{3\sqrt{3}}{5} - \dfrac{2}{5}$

(b) $\dfrac{3}{10} - \dfrac{2\sqrt{3}}{5}$

(d) $\dfrac{3}{10} + \dfrac{2\sqrt{3}}{5}$

10. If $\sin x = \dfrac{\sqrt{5}}{3}$ and $\dfrac{\pi}{2} \leq x \leq \pi$, then $\cos x =$

(a) $\dfrac{3}{\sqrt{5}}$

(c) $-\frac{2}{3}$

(b) $\frac{2}{3}$

(d) $-\dfrac{3}{\sqrt{5}}$

Chapter 2

1. If $\cos x = m$ and $\sin x = n$, then $\tan x$ is equal to

(a) $\dfrac{n}{m}$

(c) $\dfrac{1}{n}$

(b) $\dfrac{m}{n}$

(d) $\dfrac{1}{m}$

2. If $\sin x = \frac{4}{5}$, then $\csc x$ is equal to

(a) $\frac{3}{5}$

(c) $\frac{5}{4}$

(b) $\frac{5}{3}$

(d) $\frac{4}{5}$

3. In terms of $\sin x$ or $\cos x$ or both, $\dfrac{\csc x}{\tan x + \cot x}$ is equal to

(a) $\sin x$

(c) $\sin^2 x \cos x$

(b) $\cos x$

(d) $\sin x \cos^2 x$

4. Which of the following is *not true* about the tangent function.

(a) Its fundamental period is π.

(b) It is an odd function.

(c) It is not defined for $\sin x = 0$.

(d) It is not defined for $\cos x = 0$.

5. $\sec \dfrac{8\pi}{3}$ is equal to

(a) 2

(c) $\dfrac{\sqrt{3}}{2}$

(b) -2

(d) $\dfrac{-\sqrt{3}}{2}$

6. If $\cot x = \frac{3}{4}$ and $\sin x < 0$, then $\cos x$ is equal to

(a) $-\frac{4}{5}$

(c) $\frac{4}{5}$

(b) $-\frac{3}{5}$

(d) $\frac{3}{5}$

7. Over the interval $0 \leq x \leq \dfrac{\pi}{2}$, the graph of cot x appears as

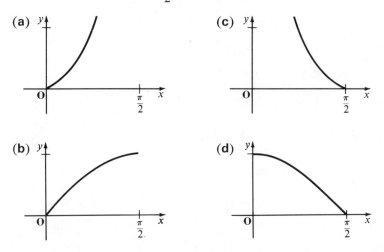

(a)

(c)

(b)

(d)

8. For each x for which $\dfrac{\tan x}{\cot x}$ is defined, this expression is equal to

(a) $\cot^2 x$

(c) $\tan^2 x$

(b) $\sec^2 x$

(d) $\csc^2 x$

9. If $\tan^2 x = \frac{4}{3}$, then $\sec^2 x$ is equal to

(a) $\frac{1}{4}$

(c) $\frac{7}{3}$

(b) $\frac{16}{9}$

(d) $\frac{25}{9}$

10. Which of the following is *not true* for every x for which sec x is defined?

(a) $\sec x = \dfrac{1}{\cos x}$

(c) $\sec^2 x - 1 = \tan^2 x$

(b) $|\sec x| \geq 1$

(d) $\sec^2 x + \csc^2 x = 1$

Chapter 3

1. The diagram shows a portion of the graph of

(a) $\{(x, y): y = 3 \cos \frac{1}{2} x\}$

(b) $\{(x, y): y = 3 \cos 2x\}$

(c) $\{(x, y): y = 3 \sin \frac{1}{2} x\}$

(d) $\{(x, y): y = 3 \sin 2x\}$

2. The graph of $\left\{(x, y): y = \sin\left(x - \dfrac{\pi}{3}\right)\right\}$

    (a) leads the graph of $\{(x, y): y = \sin x\}$ by $\dfrac{\pi}{6}$

    (b) leads the graph of $\{(x, y): y = \sin x\}$ by $\dfrac{\pi}{3}$

    (c) lags the graph of $\{(x, y): y = \sin x\}$ by $\dfrac{\pi}{6}$

    (d) lags the graph of $\{(x, y): y = \sin x\}$ by $\dfrac{\pi}{3}$

3. The period of the function $\{(x, y): y = \sin \frac{3}{2}x\}$ is

    (a) $\frac{3}{2}\pi$ **(c)** $\frac{3}{4}\pi$

    (b) $\frac{4}{3}\pi$ **(d)** $\frac{2}{3}\pi$

4. At $x = \dfrac{\pi}{3}$, the ordinate of the point on the graph of $y = \cos 2x + \sin x$ is equal to

    (a) $1 + \dfrac{\sqrt{3}}{2}$ **(c)** $-\dfrac{1}{2} + \dfrac{\sqrt{3}}{2}$

    (b) $\sqrt{3} + \frac{1}{2}$ **(d)** $-\dfrac{\sqrt{3}}{2} + \dfrac{1}{2}$

5. If a point **P** is moving with constant speed in a counterclockwise direction around the unit circle starting at the point $(1, 0)$ in such a fashion that it completes $\frac{3}{4}$ of a revolution per second, then its rotational velocity is

    (a) $\dfrac{3\pi}{2}$ **(c)** $\frac{4}{3}\pi$

    (b) 2π **(d)** $\frac{8}{3}\pi$

6. If a point **P** is moving with a rotational velocity of $\dfrac{2\pi}{3}$ radians per second along a circle of radius 3 inches, then in 5 seconds it traverses an arc of

    (a) $\dfrac{10\pi}{3}$ inches   **(c)** 10π inches

    (b) $\dfrac{5\pi}{3}$ inches   **(d)** $\frac{10}{3}$ inches

7. The amplitude of the graph of $\left\{(x, y): y = -2 \sin\left(3x + \dfrac{\pi}{6}\right)\right\}$ is

    (a) 2   **(c)** 3

    (b) -2 **(d)** $\frac{2}{3}$

8. The y-intercept of the graph of $\left\{(x, y): y = 2 \cos\left(3x - \dfrac{\pi}{2}\right)\right\}$ is

    (a) 0   **(c)** -2

    (b) 2   **(d)** $\dfrac{\sqrt{3}}{2}$

Chapter 4

1. $\text{Sin}^{-1}(-\frac{1}{2})$ is equal to

(a) $-\dfrac{\pi}{3}$

(c) $\dfrac{4\pi}{3}$

(b) $-\dfrac{\pi}{6}$

(d) $\dfrac{5\pi}{3}$

2. $\cos(\text{Sin}^{-1} b)$ is equal to

(a) $\dfrac{1}{\sqrt{1-b^2}}$

(c) $\dfrac{b}{\sqrt{1-b^2}}$

(b) $\sqrt{1-b^2}$

(d) $\dfrac{\sqrt{1-b^2}}{b}$

3. The graph shown at the right is that of

(a) $\{(x, y): y = \text{Cot}^{-1} x\}$

(b) $\{(x, y): y = \text{Tan}^{-1} x\}$

(c) $\{(x, y): y = \text{Sin}^{-1} x\}$

(d) $\{(x, y): y = \text{Cos}^{-1} x\}$

4. $\text{Sin}^{-1} \frac{1}{2} + \text{Sin}^{-1} - \dfrac{\sqrt{3}}{2}$ is equal to

(a) $-\dfrac{\pi}{6}$

(c) $-\dfrac{\pi}{2}$

(b) $-\dfrac{\pi}{3}$

(d) $\dfrac{\pi}{6}$

5. The solution set over $\{t: 0 \le t < 2\pi\}$ of $2 \cos 3t - 1 = 0$ is

(a) $\left\{\dfrac{\pi}{9}, \dfrac{7\pi}{9}, \dfrac{13\pi}{9}\right\}$

(b) $\left\{\dfrac{\pi}{9}, \dfrac{5\pi}{9}, \dfrac{7\pi}{9}, \dfrac{11\pi}{9}, \dfrac{13\pi}{9}, \dfrac{17\pi}{9}\right\}$

(c) $\left\{\dfrac{5\pi}{9}, \dfrac{11\pi}{9}, \dfrac{17\pi}{9}\right\}$

(d) $\left\{\dfrac{\pi}{2}, \dfrac{5\pi}{3}\right\}$

6. The general solution set of $\tan^2 x - \sqrt{3} \tan x = 0$ is

(a) $\{x: x = k\pi\}$

(b) $\left\{x: x = \dfrac{\pi}{3} + k\pi\right\}$

(c) $\{x: x = k\pi\} \cup \left\{x: x = \dfrac{\pi}{3} + k\pi\right\}$

(d) $\{x: x = k\pi\} \cup \left\{x: x = \dfrac{\pi}{3} + k\pi\right\} \cup \left\{x: x = \dfrac{5\pi}{3} + k\pi\right\}$

7. Over the interval $\{x: 0 \le x < 2\pi\}$, the solution set of $2\cos x \csc x = \csc x$ is

(a) $\left\{\dfrac{\pi}{3}, 0\right\}$

(c) $\left\{\dfrac{\pi}{3}, \dfrac{2\pi}{3}, \dfrac{4\pi}{3}, \dfrac{5\pi}{3}\right\}$

(b) $\left\{\dfrac{\pi}{3}, \dfrac{5\pi}{3}\right\}$

(d) $\left\{\dfrac{\pi}{3}, \dfrac{5\pi}{3}, 0\right\}$

8. The general solution set of $\cos 2x + \cos x + 1 = 0$ is

(a) $\left\{x: x = \dfrac{\pi}{2} + k\pi\right\} \cup \left\{x: x = \dfrac{2\pi}{3} + k\pi\right\} \cup \left\{x: x = \dfrac{4\pi}{3} + k\pi\right\}$

(b) $\left\{x: x = \dfrac{\pi}{2} + k\pi\right\} \cup \left\{x: x = \dfrac{2\pi}{3} + 2k\pi\right\} \cup \left\{x: x = \dfrac{4\pi}{3} + 2k\pi\right\}$

(c) $\left\{x: x = \dfrac{\pi}{2} + 2k\pi\right\} \cup \left\{x: x = \dfrac{5\pi}{3} + 2k\pi\right\}$

(d) $\left\{x: x = \dfrac{\pi}{2} + 2k\pi\right\} \cup \left\{x: x = \dfrac{4\pi}{3} + k\pi\right\}$

Chapter 5

1. The reference angle for an angle measuring $803°$ measures

(a) $7°$

(c) $-97°$

(b) $83°$

(d) $443°$

2. The radian measure of an angle measuring $210°$ is

(a) $\dfrac{4\pi}{3}$

(c) $\dfrac{7\pi}{6}$

(b) $\dfrac{7\pi}{12}$

(d) $\dfrac{5\pi}{4}$

3. In terms of a reference angle, $\sin 215°$ is equal to

(a) $\sin 35°$

(c) $\cos 35°$

(b) $\sin 15°$

(d) none of (a), (b), or (c)

4. Given that $\cot 54°10' \doteq 0.7221$ and $\cot 54°20' \doteq 0.7177$, the closest approximation to $\cot 54°12'$ is

(a) 0.7186

(c) 0.7212

(b) 0.7230

(d) 0.7217

5. If the terminal side of θ contains the point $(-4, -3)$, then $\sec \theta$ is equal to

(a) $-\frac{5}{4}$

(c) $\frac{4}{3}$

(b) $-\frac{5}{3}$

(d) $\frac{3}{4}$

6. In right triangle **ABC**, if $a = 7$, $A = 30°$ and $C = 90°$, then b is equal to

(a) $7\sqrt{3}$

(c) $\frac{7}{2}$

(b) $\frac{7}{2}\sqrt{3}$

(d) none of (a), (b), or (c)

7. In the triangle shown at the right, y is equal to

    (**a**) $\dfrac{x}{\sin \theta}$

    (**b**) $\dfrac{z}{\sec \theta}$

    (**c**) $z \cos \theta$

    (**d**) $x \tan \theta$

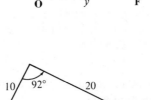

8. The area of the triangle shown is

    (**a**) $100 \sin 10°$

    (**b**) $100 \sin 92°$

    (**c**) $100 \sin 26°10'$

    (**d**) none of (**a**), (**b**), or (**c**)

9. For given line segments of lengths a and b, and given acute angle A, if $b > a > b \sin A$, then the number of triangles that can be formed using these quantities is

    (**a**) 1   (**c**) 3

    (**b**) 2   (**d**) 0

10. In any triangle **ABC**,

    (**a**) $a = \dfrac{b \sin B}{\sin A}$ (**c**) $a = \dfrac{\sin A \sin B}{\sin b}$

    (**b**) $a = b \sin A \sin B$ (**d**) $a = \dfrac{b \sin A}{\sin B}$

Chapter 6

1. The norm of **v** is 6 and its direction angle is $120°$, so **v** is equal to

    (**a**) $(-3, 3\sqrt{3})$ (**c**) $(-6, 6\sqrt{3})$

    (**b**) $\left(3, -\dfrac{\sqrt{3}}{2}\right)$ (**d**) $(6, -6\sqrt{3})$

2. The norm of the vector $(6, 2)$ is

    (**a**) 40   (**c**) $10\sqrt{2}$

    (**b**) $2\sqrt{10}$ (**d**) 64

3. A unit vector in the direction of $(-4, 3)$ is

    (**a**) $(-1, 1)$ (**c**) $(-\tfrac{4}{5}, \tfrac{3}{5})$

    (**b**) $(-\tfrac{1}{4}, \tfrac{1}{3})$ (**d**) none of (**a**), (**b**), or (**c**)

4. If $\mathbf{u} = (-2, 1)$ and $\mathbf{v} = (6, 3)$, then $2\mathbf{u} + (-3)\mathbf{v}$ is equal to

    (**a**) $(-22, -7)$ (**c**) $(22, 7)$

    (**b**) $(14, 11)$ (**d**) $(-14, -11)$

5. If $\mathbf{u} = (7, 3)$ and $\mathbf{v} = (3, -2)$, then $\mathbf{u} \cdot \mathbf{v}$ is equal to

(a) $(21, -6)$ (c) 15

(b) $(15, -5)$ (d) 27

6. A ship sails 50 miles west and then 40 miles on a heading of 350°. To find how far the ship then was from its starting point, you would

(a) use the Law of Sines

(b) use the Law of Cosines

(c) find the inner product of the two direction vectors

(d) need to know how long it took to cover the distance

7. The Cartesian equation that corresponds to the given polar equation $\rho = 2 \sin \theta \cot \theta$ is

(a) $\sqrt{x^2 + y^2} = 2xy$ (c) $x^2 + y^2 = 2x$

(b) $x^2 + y^2 = 2y$ (d) $(x^2 + y^2)\sqrt{x^2 + y^2} = 2$

8. The Cartesian coordinates of the point whose polar coordinates are $\left(3, -\dfrac{\pi^R}{6}\right)$ are

(a) $\left(\dfrac{3\sqrt{3}}{2}, -\dfrac{3}{2}\right)$ (c) $\left(\dfrac{3}{2}, -\dfrac{3\sqrt{3}}{2}\right)$

(b) $\left(-\dfrac{3\sqrt{3}}{2}, \dfrac{3}{2}\right)$ (d) $\left(-\dfrac{3}{2}, \dfrac{3\sqrt{3}}{2}\right)$

Chapter 7

1. The product of the complex numbers $(-2, 3)$ and $(4, 6)$ is

(a) $(-8, 18)$ (c) $(10, 0)$

(b) $(-26, 0)$ (d) $(10, -24)$

2. If $z_1 = (5, -3)$ and $z_2 = (1, 5)$, then $\dfrac{z_1}{z_2}$ is equal to

(a) $(-\frac{10}{13}, -\frac{14}{13})$ (c) $(-\frac{5}{13}, -\frac{14}{13})$

(b) $(-\frac{17}{5}, 0)$ (d) $(\frac{10}{13}, \frac{11}{13})$

3. If $z = -2 + 4i$, then $z\bar{z}$ is equal to

(a) $2\sqrt{5}$ (c) $4 - 16i$

(b) $2\sqrt{5}i$ (d) 20

4. i^{33} is equal to

(a) 1 (c) i

(b) -1 (d) $-i$

5. In polar form, $3 - 3\sqrt{3}\,i$ is equal to

(a) $3\sqrt{3}(\cos 120° + i \sin 120°)$ (c) $6(\cos 240° + i \sin 240°)$

(b) $6(\cos 300° + i \sin 300°)$ (d) $-3\sqrt{3}(\cos 150° + i \sin 150°)$

6. If $z_1 = a(\cos \alpha + i \sin \alpha)$ and $z_2 = b(\cos \beta + i \sin \beta)$, then $z_1 \cdot z_2$ is equal to

(a) $ab(\cos \alpha \cos \beta + i \sin \alpha \sin \beta)$
(b) $ab(\cos \alpha\beta + i \sin \alpha\beta)$
(c) $(a + b)(\cos \alpha\beta + i \sin \alpha\beta)$
(d) $ab[\cos (\alpha + \beta) + i \sin (\alpha + \beta)]$

7. If $z = a(\cos \alpha + i \sin \alpha)$, then z^4 is equal to

(a) $a^4(\cos^4 \alpha + i \sin^4 \alpha)$
(b) $a^4(\cos 4\alpha + i \sin 4\alpha)$
(c) $4a(\cos^4 \alpha i \sin^4 \alpha)$
(d) $4a(\cos 4\alpha + i \sin 4\alpha)$

8. Which of the following is *not* a fourth root of -1?

(a) $\cos 180° + i \sin 180°$ (c) $\cos 315° + i \sin 315°$
(b) $\cos 135° + i \sin 135°$ (d) $\cos 225° + i \sin 225°$

Chapter 8

1. If $2X + \begin{bmatrix} -1 & 3 \\ 2 & 0 \end{bmatrix} = \begin{bmatrix} 6 & 1 \\ -1 & 2 \end{bmatrix}$, then X is equal to

(a) $\begin{bmatrix} 7 & -2 \\ -3 & 2 \end{bmatrix}$ (c) $\begin{bmatrix} \frac{7}{2} & -1 \\ -\frac{3}{2} & 1 \end{bmatrix}$

(b) $\begin{bmatrix} 3 & \frac{1}{2} \\ -\frac{1}{2} & 1 \end{bmatrix}$ (d) $\begin{bmatrix} -\frac{7}{2} & \frac{1}{2} \\ -3 & -1 \end{bmatrix}$

2. If $A = \begin{bmatrix} -1 & 2 \\ 0 & 1 \end{bmatrix}$ and $B = \begin{bmatrix} 2 & 1 \\ -1 & 3 \end{bmatrix}$, then AB is equal to

(a) $\begin{bmatrix} -4 & 5 \\ -1 & 3 \end{bmatrix}$ (c) $\begin{bmatrix} 1 & 0 \\ 0 & 1 \end{bmatrix}$

(b) $\begin{bmatrix} -5 & -7 \\ -1 & 4 \end{bmatrix}$ (d) $\begin{bmatrix} 0 & 1 \\ 1 & 0 \end{bmatrix}$

3. The inverse of $\begin{bmatrix} 4 & 3 \\ 3 & 2 \end{bmatrix}$

(a) is $\begin{bmatrix} -4 & 3 \\ 3 & -2 \end{bmatrix}$ (c) is $\begin{bmatrix} 2 & -3 \\ -3 & 4 \end{bmatrix}$

(b) is $\begin{bmatrix} -2 & 3 \\ 3 & -4 \end{bmatrix}$ (d) does not exist

4. If $\begin{bmatrix} 2 & -1 \\ 3 & 4 \end{bmatrix}\begin{bmatrix} x \\ y \end{bmatrix} = \begin{bmatrix} 4 \\ 1 \end{bmatrix}$, then $\begin{bmatrix} x \\ y \end{bmatrix}$ is equal to

(a) $\begin{bmatrix} 1 \\ 7 \end{bmatrix}$ (c) $\begin{bmatrix} 1 \\ -2 \end{bmatrix}$

(b) $\begin{bmatrix} \frac{17}{11} \\ -\frac{10}{11} \end{bmatrix}$ (d) $\begin{bmatrix} \frac{4}{11} \\ \frac{1}{11} \end{bmatrix}$

5. In matrix form, the complex number $3 - 2i$ appears as

(a) $\begin{bmatrix} 3 & 3 \\ -2 & -2 \end{bmatrix}$ (c) $\begin{bmatrix} 3 & 2 \\ -2 & 3 \end{bmatrix}$

(b) $\begin{bmatrix} 3 & 2 \\ 3 & -2 \end{bmatrix}$ (d) $\begin{bmatrix} 3 & -2 \\ 2 & 3 \end{bmatrix}$

6. The transformation of the plane with transformation matrix $\begin{bmatrix} -2 & 0 \\ 0 & -2 \end{bmatrix}$ is
   (a) a magnification and reflection in the origin
   (b) a magnification and reflection in the line $y = x$
   (c) a shearing
   (d) a stretching and shearing

7. To rotate the plane through an angle of $30°$ in a clockwise direction, you
   could use the matrix

(a) $\begin{bmatrix} \dfrac{1}{2} & -\dfrac{\sqrt{3}}{2} \\ \dfrac{\sqrt{3}}{2} & \dfrac{1}{2} \end{bmatrix}$ (c) $\begin{bmatrix} -\dfrac{1}{2} & \dfrac{\sqrt{3}}{2} \\ \dfrac{\sqrt{3}}{2} & -\dfrac{1}{2} \end{bmatrix}$

(b) $\begin{bmatrix} \dfrac{\sqrt{3}}{2} & -\dfrac{1}{2} \\ \dfrac{1}{2} & \dfrac{\sqrt{3}}{2} \end{bmatrix}$ (d) $\begin{bmatrix} \dfrac{\sqrt{3}}{2} & \dfrac{1}{2} \\ -\dfrac{1}{2} & \dfrac{\sqrt{3}}{2} \end{bmatrix}$

8. If the plane is rotated through an angle of $90°$ in a clockwise direction, the
   new coordinates of $(2, 1)$ are

(a) $(-1, 2)$ (c) $(-2, 1)$

(b) $(1, -2)$ (d) $(2, -1)$

Chapter 9

1. The first four terms of $\left\{ \dfrac{2n + 1}{n - 5} \right\}$ are

(a) $-\frac{3}{4}, \frac{5}{3}, -\frac{7}{2}, 9$ (c) $\frac{1}{2}, \frac{5}{7}, \frac{7}{8}, 1$

(b) $-\frac{3}{4}, -\frac{5}{3}, -\frac{7}{2}, -9$ (d) $-\frac{1}{2}, -\frac{5}{7}, -\frac{7}{8}, -1$

2. $\lim\limits_{n \to \infty} \dfrac{2n}{n^2 - 5}$

(a) is equal to 0   (c) is equal to $\frac{1}{2}$

(b) is equal to $\frac{2}{5}$ (d) does not exist

3. The fifth term of the sequence of partial sums associated with $\sum\limits_{i=1}^{n} (2 - 3i)$ is

(a) -35 (c) -22

(b) -13 (d) -52

4. $\sum\limits_{j=1}^{\infty} 2(\frac{3}{2})^j$

   (a) is equal to $-\frac{3}{2}$ **(c)** is equal to 6

   (b) is equal to -6 **(d)** does not exist

5. Excluding the endpoints, the interval of convergence of $\sum\limits_{i=1}^{n} 2x^i$ is

   (a) $\{x:\ x < 2\}$ **(c)** $\{x:\ |x| < 1\}$

   (b) $\{x:\ x < 1\}$ **(d)** $\{x:\ |x| < \frac{1}{2}\}$

6. $\dfrac{(n+2)!}{(n+1)(n-1)!}$ is equal to

   (a) n^2 **(c)** $\dfrac{n+2}{n+1}$

   (b) $n^2 + 2n$ **(d)** none of **(a)**, **(b)**, or **(c)**

7. Given that $\cos x + i \sin x = e^{ix}$, $e^{\frac{\pi}{2}i}$ is equal to

   (a) $e^{i\pi}$ **(c)** 1

   (b) i **(d)** $-i$

8. Given that $\cosh x = \dfrac{e^x + e^{-x}}{2}$, $\cosh 0$ is

   (a) equal to $\frac{1}{2}$ **(c)** equal to $\frac{3}{4}$

   (b) equal to 1   **(d)** not defined

Appendix A

Sets, Relations, and Functions

A–1 *Sets and Real Numbers*

In trigonometry, as in other branches of mathematics, the concept of a **set** and the properties of sets are highly useful. A set may be described simply as a *well-defined* collection of objects. In speaking of a *well-defined* collection, we mean that it is possible to determine whether or not a given object belongs to the collection.

An object in a set is called a **member** or **element** of the set. The symbol $\in$ is used to denote set membership. Thus $a \in S$ is read "*a* is a member of *S*."

A set is **specified** either by listing the names of its members in *braces*, { }, or by stating a *rule* by which its members can be identified. Thus

$$\{3, 4, 5\} \quad \text{and} \quad \{\text{the integers between 2 and 6}\}$$

both specify the same set.

The rule identifying the members of a set may be presented in conjunction with **set-builder** notation. For example, $\{x\colon x^2 = 4\}$ is read "the set of all x such that $x^2 = 4$."

If all members of a set A are also members of a set B, then A is said to be a **subset** of B, and we denote this by $A \subseteq B$ (read "A is a subset of B" or "A is contained in B"). If A is a subset of B, and B has at least one element that is not an element of *A*, then *A* is a **proper subset** of *B*, and we write $A \subset B$ (read "*A* is a proper subset of *B*" or "*A* is properly contained in *B*"). Every subset of a set *A* except *A* itself is a proper subset of *A*.

If each member of a set *A* is also a member of a set *B*, and vice versa, then the two sets are said to be **equal**, and we write $A = B$. That is, $A = B$ is true if and only if $A \subseteq B$ and $B \subseteq A$.

The set having no members is denoted by $\emptyset$ and is called the **empty set** or the **null set**. Thus, $\emptyset$ is a subset of every set and is a proper subset of every set except itself.

A slash, /, is used in conjunction with other symbols to denote **negation**. Thus, $\notin$ means "is not a member of," and $\nsubseteq$ means "is not a subset of."

The **union** of two sets *A* and *B*, denoted by $A \cup B$, is the set of all elements contained in *either A or B*. The **intersection** of two sets *A* and *B*, denoted by $A \cap B$, is the set of all elements contained in *both A and B*.

A general set from which subsets used in a discussion are drawn is called a **universal set**.

One of the most commonly used universal sets is the set $\mathfrak{R}$ of real numbers. In algebra, you studied many of the properties of $\mathfrak{R}$ and learned to apply these properties in working with algebraic expressions.

On page 358 is a list of axioms that determine the entire structure of $\mathfrak{R}$. Note that addition and multiplication are *binary operations* on real numbers; that is, each assigns a unique real number to each ordered pair of real numbers. Any mathematical system consisting of a set of elements and two binary operations in which the Addition Axioms, the Multiplication Axioms, and the Distributive Axiom given on page 358 are satisfied is said to form a **field**. A field in which the Order Axioms are also satisfied is said to be an **ordered field**. An ordered field in which the Completeness Axiom is satisfied is said to be a **complete ordered field**. The set $\mathfrak{R}$, with the operations addition and multiplication, forms a complete ordered field.

The set $\mathfrak{R}$ of real numbers contains several subsets of interest; each of these sets is often used as a universal set:

1. The set *N* of **natural numbers**, or **counting numbers**:

$$N = \{1, 2, 3, \ldots\}.$$

2. The set *J* of **integers**:

$$J = \{\ldots, -2, -1, 0, 1, 2, \ldots\}.$$

3. The set *Q* of **rational numbers**:

$$Q = \left\{ \frac{a}{b} : a \in J, b \in J, b \neq 0 \right\}.$$

(Continued on page 359)

AXIOMS FOR THE REAL NUMBERS

Let $a, b, c \in \Re$.

Equality Axioms

E–1	$a = a$.	Reflexive property
E–2	If $a = b$, then $b = a$.	Symmetric property
E–3	If $a = b$ and $b = c$, then $a = c$.	Transitive property
E–4	If $a = b$ and $c = d$, then	Substitution property
	$a + c = b + d$ and $ac = bd$.	

Addition Axioms

A–1	$a + b \in \Re$.	Closure property
A–2	$(a + b) + c = a + (b + c)$.	Associative property
A–3	$a + 0 = 0 + a = a$.	Existence of identity
A–4	$a + (-a) = (-a) + a = 0$.	Existence of inverse
A–5	$a + b = b + a$.	Commutative property

Multiplication Axioms

M–1	$ab \in \Re$.	Closure property
M–2	$(ab)c = a(bc)$.	Associative property
M–3	$a \cdot 1 = 1 \cdot a = a$.	Existence of identity
M–4	$a \cdot \dfrac{1}{a} = \dfrac{1}{a} \cdot a = 1 \quad (a \neq 0)$.	Existence of inverse
M–5	$ab = ba$.	Commutative property

Distributive Axiom

D $a(b + c) = ab + ac, \quad (b + c)a = ba + ca$.

Order Axioms

O–1	Exactly one of the following statements is true:	
	$a < b, \quad a = b, \quad b < a$.	Trichotomy property
O–2	If $a > 0$ and $b > 0$, then	Closure properties for
	$a + b > 0$ and $ab > 0$.	positive numbers

Completeness Axiom

C   If A and B are nonempty subsets of $\Re$, and $a < b$ for each $a \in A$ and each $b \in B$, then there is at least one real number c with the property that $a \le c$ for each $a \in A$, and $c \le b$ for each $b \in B$.

Rational numbers can also be characterized as being numbers with terminating or repeating decimal representations, and every terminating or repeating decimal represents a rational number; thus

$$\tfrac{1}{2} = 0.5 \quad \text{and} \quad -\tfrac{2}{3} = -0.6\overline{6},$$

where the bar indicates that the digit 6 repeats indefinitely, are both rational numbers.

4. The set Q' of **irrational numbers**:

$$Q' = \{x: \ x \in \mathfrak{R}, \ x \notin Q\}.$$

Every irrational number has a nonterminating and nonrepeating decimal representation, and every nonterminating and nonrepeating decimal represents an irrational number.

For example, $\sqrt{2} \in Q'$ and $\pi \in Q'$, as is the number $0.121121112\ldots$.

A–2 *Open Sentences*

A **variable** is a symbol which may represent any element of some specified set, called the **replacement set**, or **domain**, of the variable. An **open sentence in one variable** is a sentence which contains a variable; if the variable is replaced by any member of the replacement set, the resulting statement will be either true or false. The subset of the replacement set for which the open sentence becomes a true statement is called the **solution set**, or the **truth set**, of the open sentence. Two open sentences are **equivalent** if they have the same solution set.

Any statement of equality is an **equation**. The following **transformations** on the members of an equation produce *equivalent equations*:

1. Replacing either member of the equation with an equal expression. Frequent use is made of the axioms for the real numbers (on page 358) and algebraic properties derived from these axioms.

2. Adding to, or subtracting from, each member of the given equation the same polynomial in the same variable appearing in the equation.

3. Multiplying or dividing each member by the same nonzero number.

Applying these transformations to

$$5(x + 4) - x = 11x - 15,$$

you have:

$$5x + 20 - x = 11x - 15$$
$$4x + 20 = 11x - 15$$
$$-7x = -35$$
$$x = 5$$

The solution set is $\{5\}$.

To find the solution set of a *quadratic equation,* you may use one of three methods.

1. If the quadratic expression is *factorable,* you factor it and apply the principle that if $a, b, \in \mathcal{R}$, then $ab = 0$ if and only if $a = 0$ or $b = 0$ or both. For example:

$$6x^2 + 7x = 3$$
$$6x^2 + 7x - 3 = 0$$
$$(2x + 3)(3x - 1) = 0$$

$2x + 3 = 0$ or $3x - 1 = 0$

$x = -\frac{3}{2}$ or $x = \frac{1}{3}$

The solution set is $\{-\frac{3}{2}, \frac{1}{3}\}$.

2. You can use the method of *completing the square:*

$$2x^2 - 5x - 2 = 0$$
$$x^2 - \tfrac{5}{2}x = 1$$
$$x^2 - \tfrac{5}{2}x + (\tfrac{5}{4})^2 = 1 + (\tfrac{5}{4})^2$$
$$(x - \tfrac{5}{4})^2 = \tfrac{41}{16}$$

$x - \dfrac{5}{4} = \dfrac{\sqrt{41}}{4}$ or $x - \dfrac{5}{4} = -\dfrac{\sqrt{41}}{4}$

$x = \dfrac{5}{4} + \dfrac{\sqrt{41}}{4}$ or $x = \dfrac{5}{4} - \dfrac{\sqrt{41}}{4}$

The solution set is $\left\{\dfrac{5 + \sqrt{41}}{4}, \dfrac{5 - \sqrt{41}}{4}\right\}$.

3. You may use the *quadratic formula:*

The solution set of $ax^2 + bx + c = 0$, $a, b, c \in \mathcal{R}$ and $a \neq 0$, is

$$\left\{\frac{-b + \sqrt{b^2 - 4ac}}{2a}, \frac{-b - \sqrt{b^2 - 4ac}}{2a}\right\}.$$

Thus, the solution set of $2x^2 - 5x - 2 = 0$ is $\left\{\dfrac{5 + \sqrt{41}}{4}, \dfrac{5 - \sqrt{41}}{4}\right\}$.

Solutions of open sentences in two variables are **ordered pairs** of numbers. If the variables are x and y, then their customary ordering is first x and then y. For example, $(5, 1)$ and $(-1, 4)$ are solutions of $x + 2y = 7$, but $(1, 5)$ and $(4, -1)$ are not. The solution set of a *system* of two linear equations in two variables is the set of all ordered pairs satisfying *both* equations.

A–3 *Inequalities and Absolute Value*

In the preceding section, we discussed certain principles for finding solution sets of linear and quadratic equations. Let us now continue the discussion of open sentences, with emphasis on inequalities and the notion of absolute value.

The following transformations produce *equivalent inequalities:*

1. Replacing either member of the given inequality with an equal expression.

2. Adding to, or subtracting from, each member the same polynomial in any variables appearing in the inequality.

3. Multiplying or dividing each member by the same positive number.

4. Multiplying or dividing each member by the same negative number and then reversing the sense of the inequality.

Applying these transformations to

$$4x - 1 > 7x + 5,$$

you have:

$$4x - 7x > 5 + 1$$
$$-3x > 6$$
$$x < -2$$

The solution set is $\{x: x < -2\}$.

To specify that $a < x$ *and* $x < b$, we sometimes write the continued inequality $a < x < b$.

The set of all real numbers between (and, possibly, including) two given real numbers is called an **interval**. If the interval contains both of its endpoints, as in $\{x: 1 \leq x \leq 3\}$, then the interval is said to be **closed**; if it contains neither of its endpoints, as in $\{x: -2 < x < 2\}$, then it is said to be **open**.

Of course, an interval may contain one but not the other of its endpoints. In this case, it is neither open nor closed, but it is said to be "half-open."

Figure A–1 shows the graphs of some intervals of ℜ. Note that a solid dot at an endpoint indicates that the point is included in the interval, whereas an open dot indicates that the endpoint is excluded from the interval.

Closed interval:
$\{x: -1 \le x \le 3\}$

Open interval:
$\{x: -2 < x < 2\}$

Half-open interval:
$\{x: -2 < x \le 2\}$

FIGURE A–1

If a and x are any two real numbers, then the **absolute value** of $x - a$, denoted by $|x - a|$, is defined by:

$$|x - a| = \begin{cases} x - a & \text{if } x \ge a \\ -(x - a) & \text{if } x < a \end{cases}$$

In particular, if $a = 0$, then the absolute value of x is given by:

$$|x| = \begin{cases} x & \text{if } x \ge 0 \\ -x & \text{if } x < 0 \end{cases}$$

Geometrically, if a and x are coordinates of two points on a real number line, then the number $|x - a|$ is the (undirected) **distance** between these two points.

Absolute-value notation can be used to describe any closed or open interval, using x as the variable and a as the midpoint of the interval. For example, in Figure A–1, the closed interval $\{x: -1 \le x \le 3\}$ can be described by $\{x: |x - 1| \le 2\}$, and the open interval $\{x: -2 < x < 2\}$ can be described by $\{x: |x| < 2\}$.

As another example, the closed interval $\{x: -5 \le x \le 1\}$ can be described by $\{x: |x - (-2)| \le 3\}$, or $\{x: |x + 2| \le 3\}$.

A–4 *Graphs of Relations and Functions*

The **Cartesian product** $A \times B$ (read "A cross B") of two sets A and B is the set of all *ordered pairs* whose first components are in A and whose second components are in B. Thus, if $A = \{1, 2, 3\}$ and $B = \{5, 7\}$, then

$$A \times B = \{(1, 5), (1, 7), (2, 5), (2, 7), (3, 5), (3, 7)\}.$$

The Cartesian product of the set of real numbers with itself is denoted by $\Re \times \Re$; it consists of all ordered pairs of real numbers.

Because of the one-to-one correspondence between the set of real numbers and the set of points on each geometric line, you can establish a one-to-one correspondence between $\Re \times \Re$ and the set of points in the geometric plane by means of the familiar rectangular Cartesian coordinate system (Figure A–2). You can use this system to visualize the solution sets of open sentences in two variables by graphing the ordered pairs that are members of the solution sets.

The distance between any two points $\mathbf{A}(x_1, y_1)$ and $\mathbf{B}(x_2, y_2)$ in the plane can be found using the distance formula:

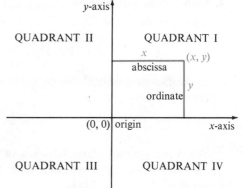

FIGURE A–2

$$d = d(\overline{\mathbf{AB}}) = \sqrt{(x_2 - x_1)^2 + (y_2 - y_1)^2}$$

It is customary in modern mathematics to call any set of ordered pairs a **relation**. In most cases of mathematical interest, the pairing is accomplished by means of an open sentence. For example, the equation $y = 2x$ pairs each value x with twice that value and defines the relation $\{(x, y): y = 2x\}$. The set of all first components in the ordered pairs in a relation is called the **domain**, and the set of all second components is called the **range**. Unless otherwise stated, all relations referred to hereafter are assumed to be subsets of $\Re \times \Re$.

If *no two* ordered pairs in a relation have the same first component and different second components, then the relation is said to be a **function**. Figure A–3

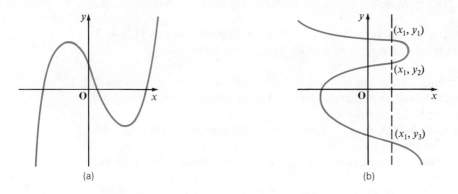

FIGURE A–3

shows the graphs of two relations. Here (a) is a function; (b), however, is not, because for certain elements in the domain (values of x) of (b) there are more than one element in the range (values of y).

We can describe a function in either of two ways:

1. **Using set-builder notation:**

   For example,

   $$f = \{(x, y): y = 2x + 3, x \in \mathcal{R}\}$$

   is the function whose *domain* is $\mathcal{R}$, whose *name* is f, and whose *rule of correspondence* is

   $$y = 2x + 3.$$

   When we use set-builder notation to describe a function, the expression "$x \in \mathcal{R}$" is sometimes omitted when the domain is understood to be the set $\mathcal{R}$ of all real numbers.

2. **Stating the domain, name, and rule of correspondence of the function:**

   The name of the function and the rule of correspondence are often combined in the same statement by using $f(x)$ (read "f of x") notation, as in the following example. The function

   $$f = \{(x, y): y = 2x + 3, x \in \mathcal{R}\}$$

   can be described by

   $$f(x) = 2x + 3, \quad x \in \mathcal{R},$$

   or by

   $$f(x) = 2x + 3, \quad \text{Dom}_f = \mathcal{R} \text{ (read "Domain of } f \text{ is } \mathcal{R}\text{")}.$$

   The notation $f(x)$ is very useful for making statements such as $f(2) = 7$, which means that the ordered pair $(2, 7) \in f$.

When describing a function, it is not essential that the range be mentioned. It is necessary, however, to be certain that the rule of correspondence does hold true for all members of the domain.

In Figures A–4, A–5, A–6, A–7, A–8, A–9, A–10, and A–11, on page 365, graphs of some of the more common functions are shown.

It often happens that a function may have a **restricted domain**. Such a function is

$$s = \{(x, y): y = x^2, -1 \leq x \leq 2\}.$$

By referring to Figure A–6, you can see that the range for the function s is $\{y: 0 \leq y \leq 4\}$. Thus, this function is a different function from the function h whose graph appears in Figure A–6; even though both functions have the same rule of correspondence, they have different domains.

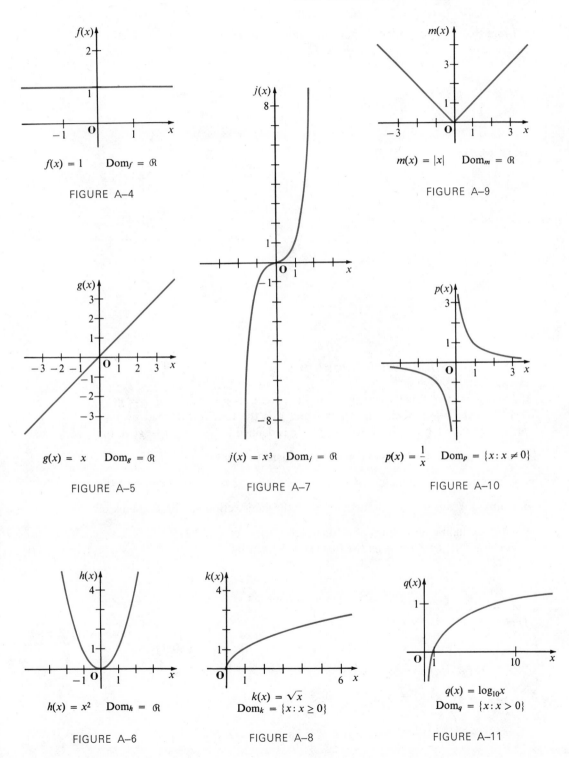

$f(x) = 1$ $\text{Dom}_f = \mathcal{R}$

FIGURE A–4

$g(x) = x$ $\text{Dom}_g = \mathcal{R}$

FIGURE A–5

$h(x) = x^2$ $\text{Dom}_h = \mathcal{R}$

FIGURE A–6

$j(x) = x^3$ $\text{Dom}_j = \mathcal{R}$

FIGURE A–7

$k(x) = \sqrt{x}$
$\text{Dom}_k = \{x : x \geq 0\}$

FIGURE A–8

$m(x) = |x|$ $\text{Dom}_m = \mathcal{R}$

FIGURE A–9

$p(x) = \dfrac{1}{x}$ $\text{Dom}_p = \{x : x \neq 0\}$

FIGURE A–10

$q(x) = \log_{10} x$
$\text{Dom}_q = \{x : x > 0\}$

FIGURE A–11

More than one rule of correspondence may be used in describing a function, as in the example shown in Figure A–12.

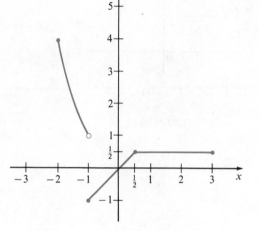

$$f(x) = \begin{cases} x^2 & \text{for } -2 \le x < -1 \\ x & \text{for } -1 \le x \le \tfrac{1}{2} \\ \tfrac{1}{2} & \text{for } \tfrac{1}{2} < x \le 3 \end{cases}$$

$\text{Dom}_f = \{x: -2 \le x \le 3\}$

$\text{Range} = \{y: -1 \le y \le \tfrac{1}{2} \text{ or } 1 < y \le 4\}$

FIGURE A–12

A–5   Operations with Functions

If f and g are two functions defined by the equations $y = f(x)$ and $y = g(x)$, then the **sum** $f + g$ of the functions f and g is the function defined by $y = f(x) + g(x)$. Similarly, the **difference** $f - g$ is defined by $y = f(x) - g(x)$, the **product** $f \cdot g$ by $y = f(x) \cdot g(x)$, and the **quotient** $\dfrac{f}{g}$ by $y = \dfrac{f(x)}{g(x)}$, $g(x) \ne 0$.

Furthermore, the domain of $f + g$, $f - g$, and $f \cdot g$ is the *intersection* of the domains of f and g. The domain of $\dfrac{f}{g}$ is the intersection of the domains of f and g, excluding any values of x for which $g(x) = 0$.

For example, let f and g be the functions defined by:

$$f(x) = x^2 \qquad \text{Dom}_f = \{x: -3 \le x \le 3\}$$
$$g(x) = x(x - 2) \quad \text{Dom}_g = \{x: -1 \le x \le 4\}$$

Then:

$$(f + g)(x) = x^2 + x(x - 2) = 2x^2 - 2x = 2x(x - 1)$$
$$(f - g)(x) = x^2 - x(x - 2) = 2x$$
$$(f \cdot g)(x) = x^2[x(x - 2)] = x^3(x - 2)$$
$$\left(\frac{f}{g}\right)(x) = \frac{x^2}{x(x - 2)} = \frac{x}{x - 2}$$

The domain of $f + g, f - g,$ and $f \cdot g$ is

$$\text{Dom}_f \cap \text{Dom}_g = \{x\colon -3 \le x \le 3\} \cap \{x\colon -1 \le x \le 4\}$$
$$= \{x\colon -1 \le x \le 3\}.$$

The domain of $\dfrac{f}{g}$ is $\text{Dom}_f \cap \text{Dom}_g$ excluding any values of x for which $g(x) = 0$, that is, for which $x(x - 2) = 0$. Thus,

$$\text{Dom}_{\frac{f}{g}} = \{x\colon -1 \le x \le 3,\ x \ne 0,\ x \ne 2\}.$$

Of special interest are the sum and the product of two functions when one of the functions is a *constant* function. The *sum* of the function $g(x) = x$, $x \in \mathfrak{R}$, and various constant functions are depicted graphically in Figure A–13; note that the effect of adding a constant function defined by $y = c$ to g is to *raise* the graph if $c > 0$ and to *lower* the graph if $c < 0$.

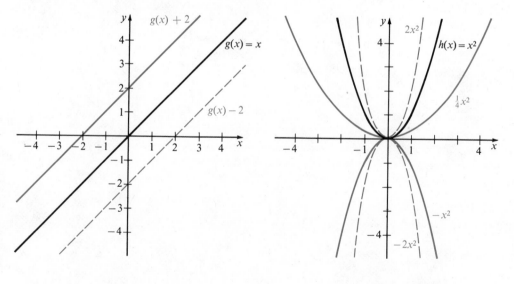

FIGURE A–13   FIGURE A–14

The product of $h(x) = x^2$, $x \in \mathfrak{R}$, and various constant functions are shown in Figure A–14. We note that if $|c| > 1$, the graph is *contracted*; if $0 < |c| < 1$, the graph is *magnified*; and if $c < 0$, the graph is also reflected in the x-axis.

A somewhat different operation on functions is that of *composition*. The **composition** $f \circ g$ of two functions f and g is the function whose rule of correspondence is given by

$$(f \circ g)(x) = f(g(x)).$$

For example, if $f(x) = x^2 - 2x$ and $g(x) = 2x + 1$, then

$$(f \circ g)(x) = (2x + 1)^2 - 2(2x + 1) = 4x^2 - 1.$$

The *domain* of the composite function $f \circ g$ is the subset of the domain of g for which the elements $g(x)$ in the range of g are in the domain of f. If $\text{Dom}_f = \mathfrak{R}$ and $\text{Dom}_g = \mathfrak{R}$ in the example above, then

$$\text{Dom}_{f \circ g} = \mathfrak{R}.$$

On the other hand, if $h(x) = \sqrt{x}$ with $\text{Dom}_h = \{x: x \geq 0\}$ and $j(x) = 2x - 1$ with $\text{Dom}_j = \{x: -5 \leq x \leq 5\}$, then

$$(h \circ j)(x) = \sqrt{2x - 1},$$

and the domain of $h \circ j$ is the subset of Dom_j for which $j(x) = 2x - 1 \geq 0$, or $x \geq \frac{1}{2}$. Thus,

$$\text{Dom}_{h \circ j} = \{x: \tfrac{1}{2} \leq x \leq 5\}.$$

Appendix B

Using Logarithms

B–1 *Logarithms to the Base 10*

The properties of the function

▲
$$\log_{10} = \{(x, y)\colon\ x = 10^{y}\}$$

are useful in making certain numerical computations. This function is called the **logarithmic function to the base 10**, and the values y in the range of $\log_{10}$ are called **logarithms to the base 10**. By definition, an equivalent form for the equation $x = 10^{y}$ is $y = \log_{10} x$. Thus, $\log_{10} x$ is just the exponent y needed in order that the power 10^{y}, or $10^{\log_{10} x}$, be equal to x. That is, we have the fundamental identity for all positive real numbers x,

$$10^{\log_{10} x} = x. \tag{1}$$

You should recall the laws of exponents given on page 370 from your study of algebra.

If $a, b, x, y \in \mathfrak{R}$, and $a, b > 0$, then

1. $\qquad a^x a^y = a^{x+y}$,

2. $\qquad \dfrac{a^x}{a^y} = a^{x-y}$,

3. $\qquad (ab)^x = a^x b^x$,

4. $\qquad \left(\dfrac{a}{b}\right)^x = \dfrac{a^x}{b^x}$,

5. $\qquad a^x = a^y$ if and only if $x = y$.

Using these laws of real-number exponents, you can prove the following properties for $\log_{10}$.

For $k, x_1, x_2 \in \mathfrak{R}, x_1 > 0$ and $x_2 > 0$,

1. $\quad \log_{10} x_1 x_2 = \log_{10} x_1 + \log_{10} x_2$,

2. $\quad \log_{10} \dfrac{x_1}{x_2} = \log_{10} x_1 - \log_{10} x_2$,

3. $\quad \log_{10} x_1^k = k \log_{10} x_1$,

4. $\quad \log_{10} x_1 = \log_{10} x_2$ if and only if $x_1 = x_2$.

To show that Property 1 is true, from identity (1) we have

$$x_1 x_2 = 10^{\log_{10} x_1 x_2}, \quad x_1 = 10^{\log_{10} x_1}, \quad x_2 = 10^{\log_{10} x_2},$$

so that

$$10^{\log_{10} x_1 x_2} = x_1 x_2 = 10^{\log_{10} x_1} 10^{\log_{10} x_2}.$$

By the first law of exponents, $10^{\log_{10} x_1} 10^{\log_{10} x_2} = 10^{\log_{10} x_1 + \log_{10} x_2}$. Thus, we have

$$10^{\log_{10} x_1 x_2} = 10^{\log_{10} x_1 + \log_{10} x_2}.$$

But, by the fifth law of exponents, this implies that

$$\log_{10} x_1 x_2 = \log_{10} x_1 + \log_{10} x_2,$$

as was to be shown.

In order to use logarithms with reasonable ease in computations, it is necessary to apply the four properties of logarithms listed above to express the logarithm of a product, quotient, power or root, or combination of these, in expanded form.

Example 1 Expand $\log_{10} \dfrac{(214)(709)}{127}$.

Solution   By Property 2,

$$\log_{10} \frac{(214)(709)}{127} = \log_{10} (214)(709) - \log_{10} 127.$$

By Property 1,

$$\log_{10} (214)(709) = \log_{10} 214 + \log_{10} 709.$$

Therefore,

$$\log_{10} \frac{(214)(709)}{127} = \log_{10} 214 + \log_{10} 709 - \log_{10} 127.$$

Example 2   Expand $\log_{10} \dfrac{(21)^2 \sqrt[3]{15}}{3\sqrt{3}}$.

Solution   It is helpful first to rewrite the expression $\dfrac{(21)^2 \sqrt[3]{15}}{3\sqrt{3}}$ using fractional exponents where necessary. Thus,

$$\frac{(21)^2 \sqrt[3]{15}}{3\sqrt{3}} = \frac{(21)^2 (15)^{\frac{1}{3}}}{3^{\frac{3}{2}}}.$$

Then

$$\log_{10} \frac{(21)^2 \sqrt[3]{15}}{3\sqrt{3}} = \log_{10} \frac{(21)^2 (15)^{\frac{1}{3}}}{3^{\frac{3}{2}}}$$

$$= \log_{10} (21)^2 (15)^{\frac{1}{3}} - \log_{10} 3^{\frac{3}{2}} \qquad \text{(Property 2)}$$

$$= \log_{10} (21)^2 + \log_{10} (15)^{\frac{1}{3}} - \log_{10} 3^{\frac{3}{2}} \qquad \text{(Property 1)}$$

$$= 2 \log_{10} 21 + \tfrac{1}{3} \log_{10} 15 - \tfrac{3}{2} \log_{10} 3 \qquad \text{(Property 3)}.$$

Exercises B–1

Find the value of each of the following.

Example $\log_{10} 1000$

Solution   Let $y = \log_{10} 1000$. Then $10^y = 1000$, $10^y = 10^3$, and $y = 3$.

A **1.** $\log_{10} 10$ **4.** $\log_{10} \frac{1}{10}$

   2. $\log_{10} 100$ **5.** $\log_{10} \frac{1}{100}$

   3. $\log_{10} 1$ **6.** $\log_{10} \sqrt{10}$

Expand the given logarithm.

7. $\log_{10} (235)(172)$

8. $\log_{10} (3.1)(0.172)$

9. $\log_{10} 28^{18}$

10. $\log_{10} \sqrt[3]{84}$

11. $\log_{10} \dfrac{81.7}{23.9}$

12. $\log_{10} \dfrac{3.07}{0.0123}$

13. $\log_{10} \dfrac{(21.2)(7.6)^2}{1.15}$

14. $\log_{10} \dfrac{(\sqrt{31})(\sqrt[3]{17})}{\sqrt[5]{8}}$

15. $\log_{10} \dfrac{[(21.3)^2(\sqrt[3]{5})]^{\frac{1}{2}}}{(6.1)(8.7)^2}$

16. $\log_{10} \dfrac{(\sqrt{5.1})(\sqrt[4]{3})}{\sqrt{(\sqrt[3]{21})(18)^5}}$

Express the logarithm of each of the following numbers as the sum of an integer and the logarithm of a number between 1 and 10.

Example   0.08173

Solution   Since $0.08173 = 8.173 \times \frac{1}{100}$,

$$\log_{10} 0.08173 = \log_{10} (8.173 \times \tfrac{1}{100})$$
$$= \log_{10} 8.173 + \log_{10} \tfrac{1}{100}$$
$$= \log_{10} 8.173 + \log_{10} 10^{-2}$$
$$= \log_{10} 8.173 + (-2).$$

B 17. 83

18. 1741

19. 0.675

20. 0.0021

21. 823.1

22. 671.5

B–2   *Tables of Values for log₁₀*

Just as Table 2, page 392, gives values for trigonometric functions, Table 5, page 402, gives values for $\log_{10} x$. Also, as is the case for values found in the trigonometric tables, the values for $\log_{10} x$ shown in Table 5 are rational approximations for irrational numbers, and we frequently use the symbol $\doteq$ in discussing them.

Table 5 contains logarithms (or, rather, their approximations) only for certain numbers x between 1 and 10. In order to extend the use of this table to numbers between 0 and 1 or to numbers greater than 10, it is helpful first to express such numbers in **scientific notation**. You should recall that scientific notation involves the product of a number between 1 and 10 and a power of 10. For example, in scientific notation,

$$231 = 2.31 \times 10^2, \qquad 0.231 = 2.31 \times 10^{-1},$$
$$23.1 = 2.31 \times 10^1, \qquad 0.00231 = 2.31 \times 10^{-3}.$$

To save space in the entries in Table 5, all decimal points have been omitted. A decimal point is understood to belong between each pair of digits in the left-hand column of the table, and before each four-digit entry in the body of the table.

Example 1   Find $\log_{10} 23.1$.

Solution   We write 23.1 as 2.31×10^1. To find $\log_{10} 2.31$, we locate 23 in the left-hand column of Table 5 and 1 in the top row. The intersection of the *row* containing 23 and the *column* containing 1 contains the numeral 3636. Therefore, $\log_{10} 2.31 \doteq 0.3636$. Now

$$\log_{10} 23.1 = \log_{10} (2.31 \times 10^1) = \log_{10} 2.31 + \log_{10} 10^1,$$

and since $\log_{10} 10^1 = 1$, we have

$$\log_{10} 23.1 \doteq (0.3636) + 1 = 1.3636.$$

Notice in the foregoing example that finding $\log_{10} 23.1$ requires determining two numbers: $\log_{10} 2.31$, which is a number between 0 and 1, and $\log_{10} 10^1$, which is an integer, 1. In general, $\log_{10} x$, for any positive real number x, can be thought of as consisting of two parts. One part is a nonnegative decimal fraction that represents the logarithm of a number between 1 and 10, and is called the **mantissa** of the logarithm. The other part is an integer that represents the logarithm of a power of ten, and is called the **characteristic** of the logarithm.

Thus, for any positive real number a, we have

$$\log_{10} a = \underbrace{\log_{10} m}_{\text{mantissa}} + \underbrace{c}_{\text{characteristic}},$$

where $1 \leq m < 10, 0 \leq \log_{10} m < 1$, and c is an integer. If the characteristic of $\log_{10} a$ is negative, that is, if $c < 0$, then we frequently write $\log_{10} a$ in the form

$$\log_{10} a = \underbrace{\log_{10} m}_{\text{mantissa}} + \underbrace{b - d}_{\text{characteristic}},$$

where $0 < b < d$, and $b - d = c$. (See Example 2, page 374.)

Example 2   Find $\log_{10} 0.0231$.

Solution   We have $0.0231 = 2.31 \times 10^{-2}$. Then

$$
\begin{aligned}
\log_{10} 0.0231 &\doteq \log_{10} 2.31 + \log_{10} 10^{-2} \\
&\doteq 0.3636 + (-2) \\
&= 0.3636 + 8 - 10 \\
&= 8.3636 - 10.
\end{aligned}
$$

Of course, instead of $8 - 10$ you could use $1 - 3$, $2 - 4$, or any other pair of nonnegative integers b and d such that $b - d = -2$. Although $8 - 10$ is customary, it is sometimes convenient to use another form.

By means of linear interpolation, you can use Table 5 to find approximations for $\log_{10} x$ when x is a number having a four-significant-digit numeral.

Example 3   Find $\log_{10} 1.374$.

Solution   It is helpful to use the same condensed form for interpolation of logarithms as was used for values of trigonometric functions.

x	$\log_{10} x$
1.370	0.1367
1.374	$\log_{10} 1.374$
1.380	0.1399

$$0.010 \left[0.004 \left[\begin{array}{l} 1.370 \\ 1.374 \end{array} \right] \right. \quad \left. \begin{array}{l} 0.1367 \\ \log_{10} 1.374 \end{array} \right] y \left] 0.0032 \right.$$

$$\frac{y}{0.0032} \doteq \frac{0.004}{0.010},$$

$$y \doteq \tfrac{4}{10}(0.0032) = 0.00128 \doteq 0.0013.$$

Therefore,

$$\log_{10} 1.374 \doteq 0.1367 + 0.0013 = 0.1380.$$

If $\log_{10} a = b$, then a is called the **antilogarithm** of b, and we write

$$\text{antilog}_{10} b = a.$$

You can use Table 5 to find an approximation for $\text{antilog}_{10} b$ for any positive real number b whose numeral has four significant digits to the right of the decimal point.

Example 4   Find $\text{antilog}_{10} 3.8414$.

Solution   If $a = $ antilog$_{10}$ 3.8414, then log$_{10}$ $a = 3.8414 = 0.8414 + 3$.
Now we locate the mantissa, 0.8414, in the body of Table 5 and
record the corresponding value for a, 6.94. Since the characteristic of log$_{10}$ a is 3, $a \doteq 6.94 \times 10^3 = 6940$.

You can also use interpolation to find antilog$_{10}$ b when the mantissa of b has
a numeral with four significant digits that is not an entry in the table. Note,
however, that when antilog$_{10}$ b is found by interpolation in a four-place table,
such as Table 5, the result may not be correct to four significant digits, even
through the mantissa of b has four significant digits in its numeral.

Example 5   Find antilog$_{10}$ 1.0875.

Solution   If $a = $ antilog$_{10}$ 1.0875, then log$_{10}$ $a = 1.0875 = 0.0875 + 1$.
Noting that the characteristic is 1, we can turn our attention to
finding antilog$_{10}$ 0.0875, and multiply the result by 10^1, or 10.
We have:

x	$\log_{10} x$
1.220	0.0864
x	0.0875
1.230	0.0899

$$0.010 \begin{bmatrix} y \begin{bmatrix} \\ \\ \end{bmatrix} \end{bmatrix} \quad \begin{bmatrix} 0.0011 \end{bmatrix} 0.0035$$

$$\frac{y}{0.010} \doteq \frac{0.0011}{0.0035}, \quad \text{or} \quad y \doteq 0.01(\tfrac{11}{35}) \doteq 0.003.$$

Then $x \doteq 1.220 + 0.003 = 1.223$, and since $a = x \times 10^1$, we
find that $a \doteq 1.223 \times 10^1 = 12.23$.

Exercises B–2

Find log$_{10}$ x.

A **1.** $x = 9.23$ **4.** $x = 40$ **7.** $x = 720{,}000$ **10.** $x = 3.855$

   2. $x = 7.81$ **5.** $x = 0.0140$ **8.** $x = 32{,}500$ **11.** $x = 0.01542$

   3. $x = 60$ **6.** $x = 0.00140$ **9.** $x = 2.176$ **12.** $x = 0.01257$

Find antilog$_{10}$ y.

13. $y = 1.4048$ **17.** $y = 1.8756 - 3$ **21.** $y = 9.9225 - 10$

14. $y = 2.9727$ **18.** $y = 4.6776 - 5$ **22.** $y = 8.8135 - 10$

15. $y = 9.6875 - 10$ **19.** $y = 0.6028$ **23.** $y = 5.6017$

16. $y = 8.7903 - 10$ **20.** $y = 1.6700$ **24.** $y = 5.7237$

B-3 *Computations*

You can use the properties of logarithms on page 370 to compute products, quotients, powers, and roots, as well as combinations of these.

Example 1   Compute $\dfrac{(1.83)^2(5.3)}{(1.12)^3}$.

Solution   We let $N = \dfrac{(1.83)^2(5.3)}{(1.12)^3}$. Then, by Property 4,

$$\log_{10} N = \log_{10} \frac{(1.83)^2(5.3)}{(1.12)^3}.$$

Using Properties 1, 2, and 3, we have

$$\log_{10} N = 2 \log_{10} 1.83 + \log_{10} 5.3 - 3 \log_{10} 1.12.$$

From Table 5,

$$
\begin{aligned}
2 \log_{10} 1.83 &\doteq 2(0.2625) = 0.5250 \\
\log_{10} 5.3 & = \underline{0.7243} \quad (+) \\
& \phantom{\doteq 2(0.2625) = {}} 1.2493 \\
3 \log_{10} 1.12 &\doteq 3(0.0492) = \underline{0.1476} \quad (-) \\
& \phantom{\doteq 3(0.0492) = {}} 1.1017
\end{aligned}
$$

Therefore, $\log_{10} N \doteq 1.1017$, and

$$N \doteq \text{antilog}_{10} 1.1017 \doteq 12.64.$$

Example 2   Compute $\sqrt[8]{0.0815}$.

Solution

$$N = \sqrt[8]{0.0815} = (0.0815)^{\frac{1}{8}} ;$$

$$\log_{10} N = \log_{10}(0.0815)^{\frac{1}{8}} = \tfrac{1}{8}\log_{10} 0.0815.$$

From Table 5, $\log_{10} 0.0815 \doteq 6.9112 - 8$. Notice that we use $6 - 8$ rather than $8 - 10$ for the characteristic of $\log_{10} 0.0815$ because we wish to divide this logarithm by 8.

$$\log_{10} N \doteq \tfrac{1}{8} (6.9112 - 8) = 0.8639 - 1$$

$$N \doteq \text{antilog}_{10}(0.8639 - 1) \doteq 0.7310$$

When sums or differences are involved in numerical expressions, logarithms can be of help only if some of the terms involve products, quotients, powers, or roots. Electronic calculators offer the best means of evaluating such expressions. However, you may find logarithms helpful if one or more terms in an expression is a power or a root.

Example 3   Compute $(3.15)^3 - \sqrt[4]{(18.3)^3}$.

Solution   Although logarithms offer no help in computing the difference here, they can be of help in simplifying each term separately. You can then find the difference directly. Let $N = (3.15)^3$ and $M = \sqrt[4]{(18.3)^3}$. Then

$$\log_{10} N = 3 \log_{10} 3.15 \qquad \log_{10} M = \tfrac{3}{4} \log_{10} 18.3$$
$$\log_{10} N \doteq 3(0.4983) \qquad \log_{10} M \doteq \tfrac{3}{4}(1.2625)$$
$$\log_{10} N \doteq 1.4949 \qquad \log_{10} M \doteq 0.9469$$
$$N \doteq \text{antilog}_{10} 1.4949 \qquad M \doteq \text{antilog}_{10} 0.9469$$
$$\doteq 31.25 \qquad \doteq 8.85$$

Therefore, $N - M \doteq 31.25 - 8.85 = 22.4$.

If any product, quotient, power, or root involves negative numbers, you can still use logarithms for computations on absolute values of these numbers, and then make appropriate adjustments for signs.

Exercises B–3

Write the logarithmic equation you would use to compute the expression in each of Exercises 1–16.

A   **1.** $(26.7)(811)$

2. $(0.0821)(1.370)$

3. $\dfrac{256}{72.6}$

4. $\dfrac{0.0873}{0.00289}$

5. $\dfrac{(61.3)^2(8.1)}{5.06}$

6. $\dfrac{(21.7)(4.13)^2}{7.09}$

7. $\sqrt[5]{0.0713}$

8. $\dfrac{4}{\sqrt[3]{0.317}}$

9. $\sqrt[3]{\dfrac{(43.7)(8.14)}{0.0368}}$

10. $\sqrt[3]{\dfrac{9310}{(1.08)(62.4)^3}}$

11. $\sqrt[3]{\dfrac{(7)(782.6)}{(4)(3.142)}}$

12. $(3.142)\sqrt[3]{\dfrac{(28.91)^2}{(53)(1.02)}}$

13. $\sqrt[7]{\sqrt[4]{(3.1)^2}}$

14. $\sqrt[4]{\sqrt[7]{(3.1)^2}}$

15. $\dfrac{17}{7.1}\sqrt{\dfrac{(28.01)^3}{(5390)(2.03)}}$

16. $\dfrac{(0.9200)^5(7032)(1.367)}{317.2\sqrt{0.0684}}$

17–32. Perform the computations in Exercises 1–16 by using logarithms.

B–4   *Logarithms of Values of Trigonometric Functions*

Because values of trigonometric functions are real numbers, we can find logarithms for any such values that are positive. Table 6 on page 404 is a table of logarithms for $\sin \theta$, $\cos \theta$, $\tan \theta$, and $\cot \theta$ for values of θ, $0° \le \theta \le 90°$, listed at intervals of 10 minutes. Notice that, to save space, Table 6 shows the logarithms increased by 10. For example, $\log_{10} \sin 19°$ (or $L \sin 19°$) is given as 9.5126; this should be interpreted as $9.5126 - 10$.

To help you interpolate in Table 6, differences between successive logarithms are given in the columns headed d and cd. The differences in the cd column apply to both $L \tan$ and $L \cot$. Of course, a difference shown as 21 means either 0.0021 or -0.0021, as the case may be. The tables are read down and from the left for $0° \le \theta \le 45°$, and up and from the right for $45° \le \theta \le 90°$.

Example 1   Find $\log_{10} \cos 32°26'$ and $\log_{10} \sec 32°26'$.

Solution   Since $32°26' < 45°$, we read down and from the left.

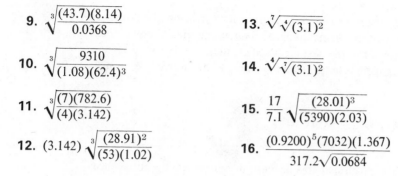

$$y \doteq \tfrac{6}{10}(-0.0008) = -0.00048 \doteq -0.0005.$$

Therefore,

$$\log_{10} \cos 32°26' \doteq 9.9268 - 10 + (-0.0005) = 9.9263 - 10.$$

Since $\sec 32°26' = \dfrac{1}{\cos 32°26'}$,

$$\begin{aligned} \log_{10} \sec 32°26' &= \log_{10} 1 - \log_{10} \cos 32°26' \\ &\doteq (10.0000 - 10) - (9.9263 - 10) \\ &= 0.0737. \end{aligned}$$

Example 2   Find θ if $\log_{10} \sin \theta = 9.2432 - 10$.

Solution

θ	$\log_{10} \sin \theta$
10°10′	9.2468 − 10
n	9.2432 − 10
10°0′	9.2397 − 10

$$10'\begin{bmatrix} \\ y \begin{bmatrix} \\ \end{bmatrix} \end{bmatrix} \begin{bmatrix} 0.0035 \end{bmatrix} 0.0071$$

$$y \doteq 10'\left(\frac{0.0035}{0.0071}\right) = 10'\left(\tfrac{35}{71}\right) \doteq 5';$$

$$\theta = n \doteq 10°0' + 5' = 10°5'.$$

Exercises B–4

Use Table 6 to find $\log_{10} x$.

A **1.** $x = \sin 39°40'$

2. $x = \tan 67°20'$

3. $x = \cos 13°17'$

4. $x = \cot 39°42'$

5. $x = \sec 59°23'$

6. $x = \csc 28°48'$

7. $x = \sin 24'$

8. $x = \cot 89°7'$

9. $x = \csc 75°18'$

10. $x = \sec 70°3'$

Use Table 6 to find y.

11. $L \sin y = 9.7139 - 10$

12. $L \cos y = 9.8241 - 10$

13. $L \tan y = 10.2098 - 10$

14. $L \cot y = 9.8533 - 10$

15. $L \cos y = 9.8790 - 10$

16. $L \sin y = 9.9690 - 10$

17. $L \cot y = 0.8300$

18. $L \tan y = 0.0220$

19. $L \sec y = 0.1100$

20. $L \csc y = 0.2370$

B–5   *Computations Involving Values of Trigonometric Functions*

Logarithms provide a rapid means of making certain computations involving values of trigonometric functions.

Example 1   Solve the right triangle in which $a = 23.1$ and $b = 43.7$.

Solution   We make a sketch. By inspection, $\tan A = \dfrac{a}{b} = \dfrac{23.1}{43.7}$.

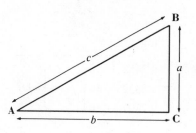

Therefore,

$$\log_{10} \tan A = \log_{10} 23.1 - \log_{10} 43.7$$
$$\doteq 1.3636 - 1.6405$$
$$\doteq (11.3636 - 10) - 1.6405,$$
$$\log_{10} \tan A \doteq 9.7231 - 10.$$

From Table 6, $A \doteq 27°52'$.

Then $B = 90° - A \doteq 90° - 27°52' = 62°8'$.

To find c, we note that $c = \dfrac{a}{\sin A}$,

so that $\log_{10} c = \log_{10} a - \log_{10} \sin A$, or

$$\log_{10} c = \log_{10} 23.1 - \log_{10} \sin 27°52'$$
$$\doteq 1.3636 - (9.6697 - 10)$$
$$= (11.3636 - 10) - (9.6697 - 10)$$
$$= 1.6939.$$

Therefore, $c = \text{antilog}_{10} 1.6939 \doteq 49.42$.

Then $A \doteq 27°52'$, $B \doteq 62°8'$, $c \doteq 49.42$.

Example 2   In triangle **ABC**, $b = 6500$, $A = 34°$, and $B = 14°$. Find a.

Solution   We make a sketch. Using the Law of Sines, we have

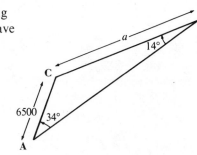

$$\frac{a}{\sin A} = \frac{b}{\sin B},$$

from which we obtain

$$a = \frac{b \sin A}{\sin B}.$$

Then $\log_{10} a = \log_{10} b + \log_{10} \sin A - \log_{10} \sin B$, or

$$\log_{10} a = \log_{10} 6500 + \log_{10} \sin 34° - \log_{10} \sin 14°.$$

From Tables 5 and 6:

$$
\begin{aligned}
\log_{10} 6500 &\doteq 3.8129 \\
\log_{10} \sin 34° &\doteq \underline{9.7476 - 10} \\
&\quad\ 13.5605 - 10 \\
\log_{10} \sin 14° &\doteq \underline{9.3837 - 10} \\
&\quad\ 4.1768
\end{aligned}
$$

Therefore, $\log_{10} a \doteq 4.1768$, and $a \doteq 15{,}020$.

Exercises B–5

Use logarithms to solve the following right triangles. In each case, make a sketch.

A **1.** $b = 82.1$, $A = 28°32'$

2. $a = 3.02$, $A = 10°12'$

3. $a = 8.03$, $c = 17$

4. $a = 7.202$, $c = 25.1$

5. $a = 5.03$, $b = 12.07$

6. $a = 27.93$, $b = 43.25$

Solve the following oblique triangles, using logarithms as convenient. In each case, make a sketch.

B **7.** $C = 76°$, $B = 29°$, $a = 5.02$

8. $A = 41°$, $C = 77°$, $b = 18.3$

9. $c = 80$, $A = 25°30'$, $B = 70°50'$

10. $b = 150$, $c = 85.5$, $B = 110°$

Appendix C

Spherical Trigonometry

C–1　Geometry of the Sphere

Spherical trigonometry is used in air and marine navigation—although for this purpose its functions have largely been taken over by charts and tables—and it has applications to geodetic problems in which the curvature of the earth must be taken into account. Developed in ancient times for studying the "celestial sphere," it is still useful in astronomy when the more distant stars are considered as lying on a spherical background or when a nearby spherical body such as the moon or Mars is being studied.

A plane section of a sphere S is a circle. If the plane passes through the center O of S, then the circle is called a **great circle**. Since three non-collinear points determine a plane, it follows that if A and B are distinct points on S, and A and B are not endpoints of a diameter of S (that is, A, B, and O are not collinear), then on S there is a unique great circle through A and B.

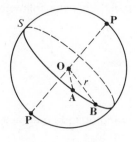

The line through the center O of S perpendicular to the plane determining the great circle through A and B intersects S in two points, P and P'. These are called the **poles** of the great circle.

An arc $\overset{\frown}{\mathbf{AB}}$ of a great circle on S could be measured, as in Chapter 1 of this book, using the radius r of the circle (and of S) as a unit. The ancient astronomers, however, measuring arcs on the celestial sphere by means of their crude sextants, thought of these arcs in terms of central angles measured from the point of view of the observer. For this reason, in spherical trigonometry arcs of circles are measured in terms of degrees, minutes, and seconds, with the usual 360° in a circle.

The measure of an angle between two great circles on S passing through the points $\mathbf{A}$ and $\mathbf{C}$, and $\mathbf{B}$ and $\mathbf{C}$, respectively, is taken to be the measure of the corresponding dihedral angle formed by the planes on which these great circles lie. Alternatively, the angle may be thought of as the corresponding angle between the tangents to the circles at the point $\mathbf{C}$.

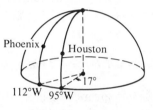

For example, the longitude of Houston is about 95° W, and that of Phoenix is about 112° W. Accordingly, the **meridian circles**, or great circles containing the north and south poles of the earth, passing through these cities intersect each other at an angle of approximately $112° - 95° = 17°$. Further, the meridian circles cut off an arc of about 17° on the equator.

For studying spherical trigonometry it is convenient, although certainly not necessary, to obtain a small sphere on which marks can be made and erased, and a hemispherical cap that fits on the sphere. The cap should have a small hole in its center, and its edge should be divided into degrees. By means of the cap you can draw a great circle on the sphere to serve, for example, as a prime-meridian circle in a representation of the earth. Through the hole in the cap you can mark a point $\mathbf{P}$ on the meridian circle to denote one of the poles of the earth, and then without moving the cap draw an equatorial circle perpendicular to the meridian circle. Being given the longitude and latitude of any point $\mathbf{A}$ on the surface of the earth, you can use the degree scale on the edge of the cap to locate the point $\mathbf{A}_0$ on the equator having the same longitude as $\mathbf{A}$, and then, drawing the meridian circle of $\mathbf{A}$ (the great circle through $\mathbf{A}_0$ and $\mathbf{P}$), you can locate $\mathbf{A}$ by measuring off the latitude of $\mathbf{A}$ from the equator on this meridian circle.

Having thus located two points $\mathbf{A}$ and $\mathbf{B}$ on the surface of the earth, you can read off the great-circle distance $\overset{\frown}{\mathbf{AB}}$ in degrees by means of the degree scale on the edge of the cap. The degree distance can then be converted into *nautical miles* (naut. mi.) if desired, since a **nautical mile** is one minute of arc on a great circle of the earth's surface.

If a sphere and a cap are not readily available, you might obtain a globe on which appears a map of the earth's surface. On this you can find cities, mountains, etc., when given their longitude and latitude, and you can use a tape together with the scale on the equator to determine an approximation to the great-circle distance between two given points.

Exercises C–1

Either on a sphere such as is described in the text or on a globe showing a map of the earth's surface, locate the following pairs of points, and, by measuring, determine the great-circle distance between them (a) in degrees, to the nearest degree, (b) in nautical miles, to the nearest 60 naut. mi.

1. Tallahassee, 84° W., 30° N.; Salem, 123° W., 45°N.
2. Juneau, 134° W., 58° N.; Boston, 71° W., 42° N.
3. Honolulu, 158° W., 21° N.; Chicago, 88° W., 42° N.
4. Mombasa, 40° E., 4° S.; Luang Prabang, 102° E., 20° N.
5. Austin, 98° W., 30° N.; Salt Lake City, 112° W., 41° N.
6. Mt. Everest, 87° E., 28° N.; Mt. Whitney, 118° W., 37° N.

C–2 *Spherical Right Triangles*

The union of three great-circle arcs $\overset{\frown}{AB}$, $\overset{\frown}{BC}$, $\overset{\frown}{CA}$ on the sphere S, meeting at vertices **A**, **B**, **C**, is called a **spherical triangle**. In spherical trigonometry attention is restricted to spherical triangles in which each side and each angle is less than 180°. The triangle then lies on a hemisphere.

The angles of a spherical triangle are usually designated by the same letters A, B, C as the vertices, and the opposite sides by corresponding lowercase letters a, b, c.

On a sphere S with center **O** and radius r, let **ABC** be a **right spherical triangle** with right angle at **C**. Through **B**, draw plane **BDE** perpendicular to **OA**, as

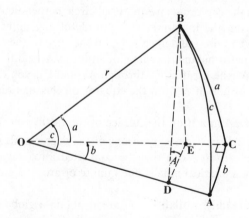

shown. Then angles **ODB**, **ODE**, **OEB**, and **BED** are right angles.

Since $\overline{OD} = r \cos c$, $\overline{OD} = \overline{OE} \cos b$, and $\overline{OE} = r \cos a$, we have

$$\cos c = \cos a \cos b.$$

This relation is called the **Pythagorean Theorem** in spherical trigonometry, since it expresses the length of the hypotenuse in terms of the lengths of the other two sides.

Example   If $a = 30°$, $b = 45°$, $C = 90°$, find c.

Solution   By the Pythagorean Theorem,

$$
\begin{aligned}
c &= \text{Cos}^{-1}(\cos a \cos b) \\
&= \text{Cos}^{-1}(\cos 30° \cos 45°) \\
&= \text{Cos}^{-1}\left(\frac{\sqrt{3}}{2} \cdot \frac{1}{\sqrt{2}}\right) = \text{Cos}^{-1}\frac{\sqrt{6}}{4} \\
&\doteq \text{Cos}^{-1} 0.612 \\
&\doteq 52°15'.
\end{aligned}
$$

Since $\overline{EB} = \overline{DB} \sin A$, $\overline{EB} = r \sin a$, and $\overline{DB} = r \sin c$, we have

$$
\sin A = \frac{\sin a}{\sin c}.
$$

This relation is called the **sine formula** in spherical trigonometry, since it bears a striking similarity to the formula for the sine of an angle in plane trigonometry.

Since $\overline{DE} = \overline{OE} \sin b$, $\overline{OE} = r \cos a$, and $\overline{EB} = r \sin a$, we have

$$
\tan A = \frac{\overline{EB}}{\overline{DE}} = \frac{r \sin a}{r \cos a \sin b},
$$

or

$$
\tan A = \frac{\tan a}{\sin b}.
$$

This relation is called the **tangent formula** in spherical trigonometry, since it is quite similar to the formula for the tangent of an angle in plane trigonometry.

We now have the following formulas:

(1) $\cos c = \cos a \cos b$,	(6) $\tan b = \tan c \cos A$,
(2) $\sin a = \sin c \sin A$,	(7) $\tan a = \tan c \cos B$,
(3) $\sin b = \sin c \sin B$,	(8) $\cos A = \cos a \sin B$,
(4) $\tan a = \sin b \tan A$,	(9) $\cos B = \cos b \sin A$,
(5) $\tan b = \sin a \tan B$,	(10) $\cos c = \cot A \cot B$.

Formulas (1), (2), and (4) are equivalent to the ones we have already derived, and (3) and (5) are obtained from (2) and (4), respectively, by interchanging the roles of A and B, and of a and b. The remaining formulas can be obtained from the first five; thus, from formulas (2) and (4) we have $\cos a = \dfrac{\sin c}{\sin b} \cos A$, and from this and (1) we obtain (6). Proofs of (8) and (10) are left as exercises, and (7) and (9) are obtained from (6) and (8), respectively, by interchanging the roles of A and B, and of a and b.

These ten formulas can be used in solving right spherical triangles ($C = 90°$) when any two additional parts are given. The two parts might, for example, be the angles A and B. In this case there is a unique solution provided $90° < A + B < 270°$ and $|A - B| < 90°$, but no solution otherwise. There are also ambiguous cases. Thus if a and A are given, with $a < A < 90°$ or $90° < A < a$, then there are two solutions; and if A and c are given, with $A = c = 90°$, then there are infinitely many solutions.

Exercises C–2

Solve the right spherical triangle ($C = 90°$) when given the following parts.

A **1.** $a = 115°24'$, $b = 64°17'$

 2. $b = 97°56'$, $c = 92°10'$

 3. $a = 35°35'$, $B = 78°2'$

 4. $c = 44°48'$, $B = 110°27'$

 5. $a = 37°40'$, $A = 37°40'$

 6. $A = 25°52'$, $B = 75°14'$

 7. Draw a figure showing that if a and A are given, $a < A < 90°$, then there are two right spherical triangles ($C = 90°$) containing these parts and together forming a **lune** (portion of a sphere between two great semicircles).

 8. Explain why there are infinitely many spherical triangles with $A = c = C = 90°$.

Find two solutions for the right spherical triangle ($C = 90°$) when given the following parts.

 9. $a = 37°18'$, $A = 73°22'$

 10. $a = 150°$, $A = 120°$

 11. $a = 10°27'$, $A = 50°50'$

 12. $a = 90°$, $c = 90°$

13. Show that in any right spherical triangle ($C = 90°$), $\cos A = \cos a \sin B$.

14. Show that in any right spherical triangle ($C = 90°$), $\cos c = \cot A \cot B$.

C–3 *Napier's Rules*

The formulas (1)–(10) in Section C-2 can be expressed in compact form by means of a mnemonic device discovered by the Scottish mathematician John Napier (1550–1617). First we relabel the parts of the spherical right triangle with **circular parts**, as indicated, excluding the right angle. Fixing attention on any one of the five circular parts, which we shall call the **middle part**, we see that there are then two **adjacent parts** and two **opposite parts**. Thus if b is taken to be the middle part, then a and co-A ($90° - A$) are the adjacent parts, and co-c and co-B are the opposite parts. Further, of any three parts—say, two known and the other to be determined—one can always be considered as the middle part, with the other two adjacent to it or else with the other two opposite it.

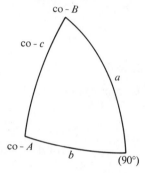

We now have **Napier's rules**:

1. The sine of any middle part is equal to the product of the tangents of its adjacent parts.

2. The sine of any middle part is equal to the product of the cosines of its opposite parts.

For example,

$$\sin a = \tan b \tan (90° - B) = \tan b \cot B,$$

and

$$\sin a = \cos (90° - c) \cos (90° - A) = \sin c \sin A.$$

Exercises C–3

A **1.** Show that if co-A is taken as the middle part, then Napier's Rules are equivalent to two of the ten formulas on page 385.

2. Repeat Exercise 1 with co-c in place of co-A.

3. Repeat Exercise 1 with co-B in place of co-A.

C–4   *Oblique Spherical Triangles*

There are also formulas for solving oblique spherical triangles. Thus, applying

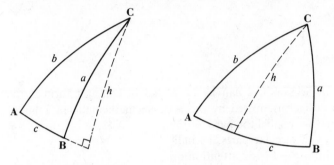

the sine formula to the figures above, we have $\sin A = \dfrac{\sin h}{\sin b}$, and $\sin B = \dfrac{\sin h}{\sin a}$, with analogous formulas involving A, a, C, c. From these we obtain the **Law of Sines**:

$$\frac{\sin a}{\sin A} = \frac{\sin b}{\sin B} = \frac{\sin c}{\sin C}.$$

Similarly, applying the Pythagorean Theorem of Section C-2 to the same figures, and simplifying, we obtain the **Law of Cosines**:

$$\cos a = \cos b \cos c + \sin b \sin c \cos A,$$

with analogous formulas for $\cos b$ and $\cos c$.

Exercises C–4

Use the Law of Sines or the Law of Cosines or both to solve the spherical triangle when given the following parts.

A **1.** $a = 80°40'$, $b = 40°40'$, $c = 121°12'$ **2.** $a = 108°34'$, $b = 82°21'$, $C = 28°22'$

B **3.** Use the Law of Sines to show that $\dfrac{\sin a - \sin b}{\sin a + \sin b} = \dfrac{\sin A - \sin B}{\sin A + \sin B}$, in any spherical triangle.

   4. Use the result in Exercise 3 and any identities to show that the **Law of Tangents** for spherical triangles holds:

$$\frac{\tan \frac{1}{2}(a - b)}{\tan \frac{1}{2}(a + b)} = \frac{\tan \frac{1}{2}(A - B)}{\tan \frac{1}{2}(A + B)}.$$

C–5 *Polar Triangles*

The notion of the **polar triangle A′B′C′** of a given spherical triangle **ABC** is quite useful in spherical trigonometry. The side a of spherical triangle **ABC** has two poles, and we take as **A′** the one of these that lies on the same side of a as **A**. The vertices **B′** and **C′** analogously are the poles of b and c that lie on the same side of b and c as **B** and **C**, respectively. The sides of **A′B′C′** are denoted a', b', c'.

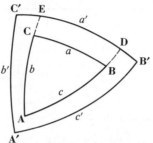

Since **A′** is 90° from each point of a, and **B′** is 90° from each point of b, and since **C** is on both a and b, it follows that **C** is 90° from the great circle $\widehat{A'B'}$, or c'. Further, since **C** and **C′** are on the same side of c, they are on the same side of c'. Analogous statements can be made about **A** and **B**. Hence **ABC** is the polar triangle of **A′B′C′**, and the polar relationship between **ABC** and **A′B′C′** is a reciprocal one.

Since **B′** is 90° from each point on b, and **C′** is 90° from each point on c, in the figure above we have $\widehat{B'E} = 90°$ and $\widehat{DC'} = 90°$. Hence

$$90° + 90° = 180° = \widehat{B'E} + \widehat{DC'} = \widehat{B'C'} + \widehat{DE} = a' + A.$$

Hence, we have the following result:

 Any angle of a spherical triangle is the supplement of the corresponding side of its polar triangle.

To illustrate the usefulness of this last result, let us write the Law of Cosines for **A′B′C′**:

$$\cos a' = \cos b' \cos c' + \sin b' \sin c' \cos A'. \tag{1}$$

Letting $a' = 180° - A$, $b' = 180° - B$, $c' = 180° - C$, $A' = 180° - a$ in (1) yields a new formula, the **dual** of the Law of Cosines:

$$\cos A = -\cos B \cos C + \sin B \sin C \cos a.$$

Exercises C–5

A 1. Solve the spherical triangle **ABC** when given $A = 38°40'$, $B = 72°50'$, $C = 124°32'$.

2. Determine the dual of the Law of Sines and explain why this law might be said to be **self-dual**.

Appendix D

Graphs of Pure Waves

The graph of any function defined by an equation of the form

$$y = a \cos (bx + c) \quad \text{or} \quad y = a \sin (bx + c)$$

where $a, b, c \in \mathcal{R}$ and $a, b \neq 0$, is called a **pure wave.** If the graphs of f and g are pure waves with the same period, we can show that the graph of $f + g$ will also be a pure wave having this same period. For example, the figure below shows the graph of $h(x) = f(x) + g(x) = \cos x + \sin x$, which was constructed in the example on page 93.

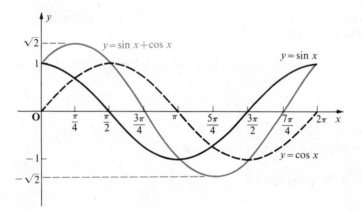

Notice that the graph appears to be a cosine wave with amplitude $\sqrt{2}$ and period 2π which lags a standard cosine wave by $\frac{\pi}{4}$. That is, it seems to be the graph of

$$\left\{ (x, y) \colon \quad y = \sqrt{2} \cos \left(x - \frac{\pi}{4} \right) \right\},$$

and hence a pure wave.

In general, we can show that *any* equation of the form

$$y = A \cos (bx + c_1) + B \sin (bx + c_2), \tag{1}$$

where A and B represent real numbers, $0 \le c_1 < 2\pi, 0 \le c_2 < 2\pi$, is equivalent either to $y = 0$ or to an equation of the form

$$y = C \cos (bx + c_3) \quad (C \ne 0), \tag{2}$$

for a unique value $c_3, 0 \le c_3 < \pi$.

We can prove this statement as follows. Beginning with (1), we write

$$\begin{aligned} y &= A[\cos bx \cos c_1 - \sin bx \sin c_1] + B[\sin bx \cos c_2 + \cos bx \sin c_2] \\ &= A \cos bx \cos c_1 - A \sin bx \sin c_1 + B \sin bx \cos c_2 + B \cos bx \sin c_2 \\ &= [A \cos c_1 + B \sin c_1] \cos bx - [A \sin c_1 - B \cos c_2] \sin bx. \end{aligned}$$

Now let us abbreviate the constant expressions in the brackets by replacing them with the symbols P and Q, respectively, so that (1) is equivalent to

$$y = P \cos bx - Q \sin bx, \tag{3}$$

where

$$P = (A \cos c_1 + B \sin c_2) \quad \text{and} \quad Q = (A \sin c_1 - B \cos c_2). \tag{4}$$

From (4) we note that

$$P^2 + Q^2 = A^2 + B^2 + 2AB \sin (c_2 - c_1).$$

If $A^2 + B^2 + 2AB \sin (c_2 - c_1) = 0$, then $P^2 + Q^2 = 0$ and hence $P = Q = 0$. Thus (3) and, consequently, (1) are equivalent to $y = 0$. If, on the other hand, $A^2 + B^2 + 2AB \sin (c_2 - c_1) \ne 0$, then $P^2 + Q^2 \ne 0$, and we can write (3) as

$$y = \pm \sqrt{P^2 + Q^2} \left(\frac{P}{\pm \sqrt{P^2 + Q^2}} \cos bx - \frac{Q}{\pm \sqrt{P^2 + Q^2}} \sin bx \right). \tag{5}$$

Now for each choice of sign before the radicals,

$$(u, v) = \left(\frac{P}{\pm \sqrt{P^2 + Q^2}}, \frac{Q}{\pm \sqrt{P^2 + Q^2}} \right)$$

is a unique point on the unit circle with center at the origin in the uv-plane (Why?). Therefore we can write

$$\left(\frac{P}{\pm \sqrt{P^2 + Q^2}}, \frac{Q}{\pm \sqrt{P^2 + Q^2}} \right) = (\cos c_3, \sin c_3)$$

Moreover, we can choose the sign before the radical in such a way that the point is in the first or second quadrant and $0 \leq c_3 < \pi$.

Choosing the sign as above, and setting

$$C = \pm \sqrt{P^2 + Q^2}, \tag{6}$$

we now write (5) as

$$y = C(\cos bx \cos c_3 - \sin bx \sin c_3)$$
$$= C \cos (bx + c_3).$$

Thus we have written (1) either in the form $y = 0$ or in the form (2), as desired.

Example Find an equation of the form $y = C \cos (bx + c)$ equivalent to the equation $y = 4 \cos 2x + 3 \sin 2x$.

Solution Comparing $y = 4 \cos 2x + 3 \sin 2x$ with (1), above, we have $A = 4$, $B = 3$, $c_1 = 0$, and $c_2 = 0$. From Equation (4), $P = 4 \cos 0 + 3 \sin 0 = 4$, and $Q = 4 \sin 0 - 3 \cos 0 = -3$. Further, from Equation (6), $C = \pm \sqrt{4^2 + (-3)^2} = \pm 5$.

Then $(u, v) = (\cos c_3, \sin c_3) = \left(\dfrac{4}{\pm 5}, \dfrac{-3}{\pm 5} \right)$. We choose -5 in the denominator so that (u, v) will be in the second quadrant.

Then $\cos c_3 = -\dfrac{4}{5}$, and using Table 1, page 391,

$$c_3 \doteq 3.14 - \left(0.41 \cdot \frac{\pi}{2} \right) \doteq 3.14 - 0.64 = 2.50.$$

Therefore, we have $y \doteq -5 \cos (2x + 2.50)$.

Exercises

Find an equation of the form $y = C \cos (bx + c), 0 \leq c < \pi$, equivalent to the given equation, and sketch its graph. State the amplitude, period, and phase shift of each wave.

A **1.** $y = 3 \cos x + 4 \sin x$ **4.** $y = 4 \cos x + 3 \sin x$

   2. $y = -4 \cos x + 3 \sin x$ **5.** $y = \sqrt{3} \cos 2x + \sin 2x$

   3. $y = 3 \cos x - 4 \sin x$ **6.** $y = \cos 2x + \sqrt{3} \sin 2x$

Table 1   Values of $\cos\left(m \cdot \dfrac{\pi}{2}\right)$ and $\sin\left(m \cdot \dfrac{\pi}{2}\right)$

m	$\cos\left(m \cdot \dfrac{\pi}{2}\right)$	$\sin\left(m \cdot \dfrac{\pi}{2}\right)$	
0.00	1.000	0.000	1.00
0.01	1.000	0.016	0.99
0.02	1.000	0.031	0.98
0.03	0.999	0.048	0.97
0.04	0.998	0.063	0.96
0.05	0.997	0.078	0.95
0.06	0.996	0.094	0.94
0.07	0.994	0.110	0.93
0.08	0.992	0.125	0.92
0.09	0.990	0.141	0.91
0.10	0.988	0.156	0.90
0.11	0.985	0.172	0.89
0.12	0.982	0.187	0.88
0.13	0.979	0.203	0.87
0.14	0.976	0.218	0.86
0.15	0.972	0.233	0.85
0.16	0.969	0.249	0.84
0.17	0.965	0.264	0.83
0.18	0.960	0.279	0.82
0.19	0.956	0.294	0.81
0.20	0.951	0.309	0.80
0.21	0.946	0.324	0.79
0.22	0.941	0.339	0.78
0.23	0.935	0.353	0.77
0.24	0.930	0.368	0.76
0.25	0.924	0.383	0.75
0.26	0.918	0.397	0.74
0.27	0.911	0.412	0.73
0.28	0.905	0.426	0.72
0.29	0.898	0.440	0.71
0.30	0.891	0.454	0.70
0.31	0.884	0.468	0.69
0.32	0.876	0.482	0.68
0.33	0.869	0.495	0.67
0.34	0.861	0.509	0.66
0.35	0.853	0.523	0.65
0.36	0.844	0.536	0.64
0.37	0.836	0.549	0.63
0.38	0.827	0.562	0.62
0.39	0.818	0.575	0.61
0.40	0.809	0.588	0.60
0.41	0.800	0.600	0.59
0.42	0.790	0.613	0.58
0.43	0.780	0.625	0.57
0.44	0.771	0.637	0.56
0.45	0.760	0.649	0.55
0.46	0.750	0.661	0.54
0.47	0.740	0.673	0.53
0.48	0.729	0.685	0.52
0.49	0.718	0.696	0.51
0.50	0.707	0.707	0.50
	$\sin\left(n \cdot \dfrac{\pi}{2}\right)$	$\cos\left(n \cdot \dfrac{\pi}{2}\right)$	n

Table 2 Values of Trigonometric Functions for Angles in Degrees

m (θ) Degrees	Radians	sin θ	csc θ	tan θ	cot θ	sec θ	cos θ		
0° 00'	.0000	.0000	Undefined	.0000	Undefined	1.000	1.0000	1.5708	90° 00'
10'	.0029	.0029	343.8	.0029	343.8	1.000	1.0000	1.5679	50'
20'	.0058	.0058	171.9	.0058	171.9	1.000	1.0000	1.5650	40'
30'	.0087	.0087	114.6	.0087	114.6	1.000	1.0000	1.5621	30'
40'	.0116	.0116	85.95	.0116	85.94	1.000	.9999	1.5592	20'
50'	.0145	.0145	68.76	.0145	68.75	1.000	.9999	1.5563	10'
1° 00'	.0175	.0175	57.30	.0175	57.29	1.000	.9998	1.5533	89° 00'
10'	.0204	.0204	49.11	.0204	49.10	1.000	.9998	1.5504	50'
20'	.0233	.0233	42.98	.0233	42.96	1.000	.9997	1.5475	40'
30'	.0262	.0262	38.20	.0262	38.19	1.000	.9997	1.5446	30'
40'	.0291	.0291	34.38	.0291	34.37	1.000	.9996	1.5417	20'
50'	.0320	.0320	31.26	.0320	31.24	1.001	.9995	1.5388	10'
2° 00'	.0349	.0349	28.65	.0349	28.64	1.001	.9994	1.5359	88° 00'
10'	.0378	.0378	26.45	.0378	26.43	1.001	.9993	1.5330	50'
20'	.0407	.0407	24.56	.0407	24.54	1.001	.9992	1.5301	40'
30'	.0436	.0436	22.93	.0437	22.90	1.001	.9990	1.5272	30'
40'	.0465	.0465	21.49	.0466	21.47	1.001	.9989	1.5243	20'
50'	.0495	.0494	20.23	.0495	20.21	1.001	.9988	1.5213	10'
3° 00'	.0524	.0523	19.11	.0524	19.08	1.001	.9986	1.5184	87° 00'
10'	.0553	.0552	18.10	.0553	18.07	1.002	.9985	1.5155	50'
20'	.0582	.0581	17.20	.0582	17.17	1.002	.9983	1.5126	40'
30'	.0611	.0610	16.38	.0612	16.35	1.002	.9981	1.5097	30'
40'	.0640	.0640	15.64	.0641	15.60	1.002	.9980	1.5068	20'
50'	.0669	.0669	14.96	.0670	14.92	1.002	.9978	1.5039	10'
4° 00'	.0698	.0698	14.34	.0699	14.30	1.002	.9976	1.5010	86° 00'
10'	.0727	.0727	13.76	.0729	13.73	1.003	.9974	1.4981	50'
20'	.0756	.0756	13.23	.0758	13.20	1.003	.9971	1.4952	40'
30'	.0785	.0785	12.75	.0787	12.71	1.003	.9969	1.4923	30'
40'	.0814	.0814	12.29	.0816	12.25	1.003	.9967	1.4893	20'
50'	.0844	.0843	11.87	.0846	11.83	1.004	.9964	1.4864	10'
5° 00'	.0873	.0872	11.47	.0875	11.43	1.004	.9962	1.4835	85° 00'
10'	.0902	.0901	11.10	.0904	11.06	1.004	.9959	1.4806	50'
20'	.0931	.0929	10.76	.0934	10.71	1.004	.9957	1.4777	40'
30'	.0960	.0958	10.43	.0963	10.39	1.005	.9954	1.4748	30'
40'	.0989	.0987	10.13	.0992	10.08	1.005	.9951	1.4719	20'
50'	.1018	.1016	9.839	.1022	9.788	1.005	.9948	1.4690	10'
6° 00'	.1047	.1045	9.567	.1051	9.514	1.006	.9945	1.4661	84° 00'
10'	.1076	.1074	9.309	.1080	9.255	1.006	.9942	1.4632	50'
20'	.1105	.1103	9.065	.1110	9.010	1.006	.9939	1.4603	40'
30'	.1134	.1132	8.834	.1139	8.777	1.006	.9936	1.4573	30'
40'	.1164	.1161	8.614	.1169	8.556	1.007	.9932	1.4544	20'
50'	.1193	.1190	8.405	.1198	8.345	1.007	.9929	1.4515	10'
7° 00'	.1222	.1219	8.206	.1228	8.144	1.008	.9925	1.4486	83° 00'
10'	.1251	.1248	8.016	.1257	7.953	1.008	.9922	1.4457	50'
20'	.1280	.1276	7.834	.1287	7.770	1.008	.9918	1.4428	40'
30'	.1309	.1305	7.661	.1317	7.596	1.009	.9914	1.4399	30'
40'	.1338	.1334	7.496	.1346	7.429	1.009	.9911	1.4370	20'
50'	.1367	.1363	7.337	.1376	7.269	1.009	.9907	1.4341	10'
8° 00'	.1396	.1392	7.185	.1405	7.115	1.010	.9903	1.4312	82° 00'
10'	.1425	.1421	7.040	.1435	6.968	1.010	.9899	1.4283	50'
20'	.1454	.1449	6.900	.1465	6.827	1.011	.9894	1.4254	40'
30'	.1484	.1478	6.765	.1495	6.691	1.011	.9890	1.4224	30'
40'	.1513	.1507	6.636	.1524	6.561	1.012	.9886	1.4195	20'
50'	.1542	.1536	6.512	.1554	6.435	1.012	.9881	1.4166	10'
9° 00'	.1571	.1564	6.392	.1584	6.314	1.012	.9877	1.4137	81° 00'
		cos θ	sec θ	cot θ	tan θ	csc θ	sin θ	Radians	Degrees m (θ)

Table 2 Values of Trigonometric Functions for Angles in Degrees

m (θ) Degrees	Radians	sin θ	csc θ	tan θ	cot θ	sec θ	cos θ		
9° 00′	.1571	.1564	6.392	.1584	6.314	1.012	.9877	1.4137	81° 00′
10′	.1600	.1593	6.277	.1614	6.197	1.013	.9872	1.4108	50′
20′	.1629	.1622	6.166	.1644	6.084	1.013	.9868	1.4079	40′
30′	.1658	.1650	6.059	.1673	5.976	1.014	.9863	1.4050	30′
40′	.1687	.1679	5.955	.1703	5.871	1.014	.9858	1.4021	20′
50′	.1716	.1708	5.855	.1733	5.769	1.015	.9853	1.3992	10′
10° 00′	.1745	.1736	5.759	.1763	5.671	1.015	.9848	1.3963	80° 00′
10′	.1774	.1765	5.665	.1793	5.576	1.016	.9843	1.3934	50′
20′	.1804	.1794	5.575	.1823	5.485	1.016	.9838	1.3904	40′
30′	.1833	.1822	5.487	.1853	5.396	1.017	.9833	1.3875	30′
40′	.1862	.1851	5.403	.1883	5.309	1.018	.9827	1.3846	20′
50′	.1891	.1880	5.320	.1914	5.226	1.018	.9822	1.3817	10′
11° 00′	.1920	.1908	5.241	.1944	5.145	1.019	.9816	1.3788	79° 00′
10′	.1949	.1937	5.164	.1974	5.066	1.019	.9811	1.3759	50′
20′	.1978	.1965	5.089	.2004	4.989	1.020	.9805	1.3730	40′
30′	.2007	.1994	5.016	.2035	4.915	1.020	.9799	1.3701	30′
40′	.2036	.2022	4.945	.2065	4.843	1.021	.9793	1.3672	20′
50′	.2065	.2051	4.876	.2095	4.773	1.022	.9787	1.3643	10′
12° 00′	.2094	.2079	4.810	.2126	4.705	1.022	.9781	1.3614	78° 00′
10′	.2123	.2108	4.745	.2156	4.638	1.023	.9775	1.3584	50′
20′	.2153	.2136	4.682	.2186	4.574	1.024	.9769	1.3555	40′
30′	.2182	.2164	4.620	.2217	4.511	1.024	.9763	1.3526	30′
40′	.2211	.2193	4.560	.2247	4.449	1.025	.9757	1.3497	20′
50′	.2240	.2221	4.502	.2278	4.390	1.026	.9750	1.3468	10′
13° 00′	.2269	.2250	4.445	.2309	4.331	1.026	.9744	1.3439	77° 00′
10′	.2298	.2278	4.390	.2339	4.275	1.027	.9737	1.3410	50′
20′	.2327	.2306	4.336	.2370	4.219	1.028	.9730	1.3381	40′
30′	.2356	.2334	4.284	.2401	4.165	1.028	.9724	1.3352	30′
40′	.2385	.2363	4.232	.2432	4.113	1.029	.9717	1.3323	20′
50′	.2414	.2391	4.182	.2462	4.061	1.030	.9710	1.3294	10′
14° 00′	.2443	.2419	4.134	.2493	4.011	1.031	.9703	1.3265	76° 00′
10′	.2473	.2447	4.086	.2524	3.962	1.031	.9696	1.3235	50′
20′	.2502	.2476	4.039	.2555	3.914	1.032	.9689	1.3206	40′
30′	.2531	.2504	3.994	.2586	3.867	1.033	.9681	1.3177	30′
40′	.2560	.2532	3.950	.2617	3.821	1.034	.9674	1.3148	20′
50′	.2589	.2560	3.906	.2648	3.776	1.034	.9667	1.3119	10′
15° 00′	.2618	.2588	3.864	.2679	3.732	1.035	.9659	1.3090	75° 00′
10′	.2647	.2616	3.822	.2711	3.689	1.036	.9652	1.3061	50′
20′	.2676	.2644	3.782	.2742	3.647	1.037	.9644	1.3032	40′
30′	.2705	.2672	3.742	.2773	3.606	1.038	.9636	1.3003	30′
40′	.2734	.2700	3.703	.2805	3.566	1.039	.9628	1.2974	20′
50′	.2763	.2728	3.665	.2836	3.526	1.039	.9621	1.2945	10′
16° 00′	.2793	.2756	3.628	.2867	3.487	1.040	.9613	1.2915	74° 00′
10′	.2822	.2784	3.592	.2899	3.450	1.041	.9605	1.2886	50′
20′	.2851	.2812	3.556	.2931	3.412	1.042	.9596	1.2857	40′
30′	.2880	.2840	3.521	.2962	3.376	1.043	.9588	1.2828	30′
40′	.2909	.2868	3.487	.2994	3.340	1.044	.9580	1.2799	20′
50′	.2938	.2896	3.453	.3026	3.305	1.045	.9572	1.2770	10′
17° 00′	.2967	.2924	3.420	.3057	3.271	1.046	.9563	1.2741	73° 00′
10′	.2996	.2952	3.388	.3089	3.237	1.047	.9555	1.2712	50′
20′	.3025	.2979	3.357	.3121	3.204	1.048	.9546	1.2683	40′
30′	.3054	.3007	3.326	.3153	3.172	1.049	.9537	1.2654	30′
40′	.3083	.3035	3.295	.3185	3.140	1.049	.9528	1.2625	20′
50′	.3113	.3062	3.265	.3217	3.108	1.050	.9520	1.2595	10′
18° 00′	.3142	.3090	3.236	.3249	3.078	1.051	.9511	1.2566	72° 00′
		cos θ	sec θ	cot θ	tan θ	csc θ	sin θ	Radians	Degrees m (θ)

Table 2 Values of Trigonometric Functions for Angles in Degrees

m (θ) Degrees	Radians	sin θ	csc θ	tan θ	cot θ	sec θ	cos θ		
18° 00′	.3142	.3090	3.236	.3249	3.078	1.051	.9511	1.2566	72° 00′
10′	.3171	.3118	3.207	.3281	3.047	1.052	.9502	1.2537	50′
20′	.3200	.3145	3.179	.3314	3.018	1.053	.9492	1.2508	40′
30′	.3229	.3173	3.152	.3346	2.989	1.054	.9483	1.2479	30′
40′	.3258	.3201	3.124	.3378	2.960	1.056	.9474	1.2450	20′
50′	.3287	.3228	3.098	.3411	2.932	1.057	.9465	1.2421	10′
19° 00′	.3316	.3256	3.072	.3443	2.904	1.058	.9455	1.2392	71° 00′
10′	.3345	.3283	3.046	.3476	2.877	1.059	.9446	1.2363	50′
20′	.3374	.3311	3.021	.3508	2.850	1.060	.9436	1.2334	40′
30′	.3403	.3338	2.996	.3541	2.824	1.061	.9426	1.2305	30′
40′	.3432	.3365	2.971	.3574	2.798	1.062	.9417	1.2275	20′
50′	.3462	.3393	2.947	.3607	2.773	1.063	.9407	1.2246	10′
20° 00′	.3491	.3420	2.924	.3640	2.747	1.064	.9397	1.2217	70° 00′
10′	.3520	.3448	2.901	.3673	2.723	1.065	.9387	1.2188	50′
20′	.3549	.3475	2.878	.3706	2.699	1.066	.9377	1.2159	40′
30′	.3578	.3502	2.855	.3739	2.675	1.068	.9367	1.2130	30′
40′	.3607	.3529	2.833	.3772	2.651	1.069	.9356	1.2101	20′
50′	.3636	.3557	2.812	.3805	2.628	1.070	.9346	1.2072	10′
21° 00′	.3665	.3584	2.790	.3839	2.605	1.071	.9336	1.2043	69° 00′
10′	.3694	.3611	2.769	.3872	2.583	1.072	.9325	1.2014	50′
20′	.3723	.3638	2.749	.3906	2.560	1.074	.9315	1.1985	40′
30′	.3752	.3665	2.729	.3939	2.539	1.075	.9304	1.1956	30′
40′	.3782	.3692	2.709	.3973	2.517	1.076	.9293	1.1926	20′
50′	.3811	.3719	2.689	.4006	2.496	1.077	.9283	1.1897	10′
22° 00′	.3840	.3746	2.669	.4040	2.475	1.079	.9272	1.1868	68° 00′
10′	.3869	.3773	2.650	.4074	2.455	1.080	.9261	1.1839	50′
20′	.3898	.3800	2.632	.4108	2.434	1.081	.9250	1.1810	40′
30′	.3927	.3827	2.613	.4142	2.414	1.082	.9239	1.1781	30′
40′	.3956	.3854	2.595	.4176	2.394	1.084	.9228	1.1752	20′
50′	.3985	.3881	2.577	.4210	2.375	1.085	.9216	1.1723	10′
23° 00′	.4014	.3907	2.559	.4245	2.356	1.086	.9205	1.1694	67° 00′
10′	.4043	.3934	2.542	.4279	2.337	1.088	.9194	1.1665	50′
20′	.4072	.3961	2.525	.4314	2.318	1.089	.9182	1.1636	40′
30′	.4102	.3987	2.508	.4348	2.300	1.090	.9171	1.1606	30′
40′	.4131	.4014	2.491	.4383	2.282	1.092	.9159	1.1577	20′
50′	.4160	.4041	2.475	.4417	2.264	1.093	.9147	1.1548	10′
24° 00′	.4189	.4067	2.459	.4452	2.246	1.095	.9135	1.1519	66° 00′
10′	.4218	.4094	2.443	.4487	2.229	1.096	.9124	1.1490	50′
20′	.4247	.4120	2.427	.4522	2.211	1.097	.9112	1.1461	40′
30′	.4276	.4147	2.411	.4557	2.194	1.099	.9100	1.1432	30′
40′	.4305	.4173	2.396	.4592	2.177	1.100	.9088	1.1403	20′
50′	.4334	.4200	2.381	.4628	2.161	1.102	.9075	1.1374	10′
25° 00′	.4363	.4226	2.366	.4663	2.145	1.103	.9063	1.1345	65° 00′
10′	.4392	.4253	2.352	.4699	2.128	1.105	.9051	1.1316	50′
20′	.4422	.4279	2.337	.4734	2.112	1.106	.9038	1.1286	40′
30′	.4451	.4305	2.323	.4770	2.097	1.108	.9026	1.1257	30′
40′	.4480	.4331	2.309	.4806	2.081	1.109	.9013	1.1228	20′
50′	.4509	.4358	2.295	.4841	2.066	1.111	.9001	1.1199	10′
26° 00′	.4538	.4384	2.281	.4877	2.050	1.113	.8988	1.1170	64° 00′
10′	.4567	.4410	2.268	.4913	2.035	1.114	.8975	1.1141	50′
20′	.4596	.4436	2.254	.4950	2.020	1.116	.8962	1.1112	40′
30′	.4625	.4462	2.241	.4986	2.006	1.117	.8949	1.1083	30′
40′	.4654	.4488	2.228	.5022	1.991	1.119	.8936	1.1054	20′
50′	.4683	.4514	2.215	.5059	1.977	1.121	.8923	1.1025	10′
27° 00′	.4712	.4540	2.203	.5095	1.963	1.122	.8910	1.0996	63° 00′
		cos θ	sec θ	cot θ	tan θ	csc θ	sin θ	Radians	Degrees m (θ)

Table 2   Values of Trigonometric Functions for Angles in Degrees

m (θ) Degrees	Radians	sin θ	csc θ	tan θ	cot θ	sec θ	cos θ		
27° 00′	.4712	.4540	2.203	.5095	1.963	1.122	.8910	1.0996	63° 00′
10′	.4741	.4566	2.190	.5132	1.949	1.124	.8897	1.0966	50′
20′	.4771	.4592	2.178	.5169	1.935	1.126	.8884	1.0937	40′
30′	.4800	.4617	2.166	.5206	1.921	1.127	.8870	1.0908	30′
40′	.4829	.4643	2.154	.5243	1.907	1.129	.8857	1.0879	20′
50′	.4858	.4669	2.142	.5280	1.894	1.131	.8843	1.0850	10′
28° 00′	.4887	.4695	2.130	.5317	1.881	1.133	.8829	1.0821	62° 00′
10′	.4916	.4720	2.118	.5354	1.868	1.134	.8816	1.0792	50′
20′	.4945	.4746	2.107	.5392	1.855	1.136	.8802	1.0763	40′
30′	.4974	.4772	2.096	.5430	1.842	1.138	.8788	1.0734	30′
40′	.5003	.4797	2.085	.5467	1.829	1.140	.8774	1.0705	20′
50′	.5032	.4823	2.074	.5505	1.816	1.142	.8760	1.0676	10′
29° 00′	.5061	.4848	2.063	.5543	1.804	1.143	.8746	1.0647	61° 00′
10′	.5091	.4874	2.052	.5581	1.792	1.145	.8732	1.0617	50′
20′	.5120	.4899	2.041	.5619	1.780	1.147	.8718	1.0588	40′
30′	.5149	.4924	2.031	.5658	1.767	1.149	.8704	1.0559	30′
40′	.5178	.4950	2.020	.5696	1.756	1.151	.8689	1.0530	20′
50′	.5207	.4975	2.010	.5735	1.744	1.153	.8675	1.0501	10′
30° 00′	.5236	.5000	2.000	.5774	1.732	1.155	.8660	1.0472	60° 00′
10′	.5265	.5025	1.990	.5812	1.720	1.157	.8646	1.0443	50′
20′	.5294	.5050	1.980	.5851	1.709	1.159	.8631	1.0414	40′
30′	.5323	.5075	1.970	.5890	1.698	1.161	.8616	1.0385	30′
40′	.5352	.5100	1.961	.5930	1.686	1.163	.8601	1.0356	20′
50′	.5381	.5125	1.951	.5969	1.675	1.165	.8587	1.0327	10′
31° 00′	.5411	.5150	1.942	.6009	1.664	1.167	.8572	1.0297	59° 00′
10′	.5440	.5175	1.932	.6048	1.653	1.169	.8557	1.0268	50′
20′	.5469	.5200	1.923	.6088	1.643	1.171	.8542	1.0239	40′
30′	.5498	.5225	1.914	.6128	1.632	1.173	.8526	1.0210	30′
40′	.5527	.5250	1.905	.6168	1.621	1.175	.8511	1.0181	20′
50′	.5556	.5275	1.896	.6208	1.611	1.177	.8496	1.0152	10′
32° 00′	.5585	.5299	1.887	.6249	1.600	1.179	.8480	1.0123	58° 00′
10′	.5614	.5324	1.878	.6289	1.590	1.181	.8465	1.0094	50′
20′	.5643	.5348	1.870	.6330	1.580	1.184	.8450	1.0065	40′
30′	.5672	.5373	1.861	.6371	1.570	1.186	.8434	1.0036	30′
40′	.5701	.5398	1.853	.6412	1.560	1.188	.8418	1.0007	20′
50′	.5730	.5422	1.844	.6453	1.550	1.190	.8403	.9977	10′
33° 00′	.5760	.5446	1.836	.6494	1.540	1.192	.8387	.9948	57° 00′
10′	.5789	.5471	1.828	.6536	1.530	1.195	.8371	.9919	50′
20′	.5818	.5495	1.820	.6577	1.520	1.197	.8355	.9890	40′
30′	.5847	.5519	1.812	.6619	1.511	1.199	.8339	.9861	30′
40′	.5876	.5544	1.804	.6661	1.501	1.202	.8323	.9832	20′
50′	.5905	.5568	1.796	.6703	1.492	1.204	.8307	.9803	10′
34° 00′	.5934	.5592	1.788	.6745	1.483	1.206	.8290	.9774	56° 00′
10′	.5963	.5616	1.781	.6787	1.473	1.209	.8274	.9745	50′
20′	.5992	.5640	1.773	.6830	1.464	1.211	.8258	.9716	40′
30′	.6021	.5664	1.766	.6873	1.455	1.213	.8241	.9687	30′
40′	.6050	.5688	1.758	.6916	1.446	1.216	.8225	.9657	20′
50′	.6080	.5712	1.751	.6959	1.437	1.218	.8208	.9628	10′
35° 00′	.6109	.5736	1.743	.7002	1.428	1.221	.8192	.9599	55° 00′
10′	.6138	.5760	1.736	.7046	1.419	1.223	.8175	.9570	50′
20′	.6167	.5783	1.729	.7089	1.411	1.226	.8158	.9541	40′
30′	.6196	.5807	1.722	.7133	1.402	1.228	.8141	.9512	30′
40′	.6225	.5831	1.715	.7177	1.393	1.231	.8124	.9483	20′
50′	.6254	.5854	1.708	.7221	1.385	1.233	.8107	.9454	10′
36° 00′	.6283	.5878	1.701	.7265	1.376	1.236	.8090	.9425	54° 00′
		cos θ	sec θ	cot θ	tan θ	csc θ	sin θ	Radians	Degrees m (θ)

Table 2   Values of Trigonometric Functions for Angles in Degrees

m (θ) Degrees	Radians	sin θ	csc θ	tan θ	cot θ	sec θ	cos θ		
36° 00′	.6283	.5878	1.701	.7265	1.376	1.236	.8090	.9425	54° 00′
10′	.6312	.5901	1.695	.7310	1.368	1.239	.8073	.9396	50′
20′	.6341	.5925	1.688	.7355	1.360	1.241	.8056	.9367	40′
30′	.6370	.5948	1.681	.7400	1.351	1.244	.8039	.9338	30′
40′	.6400	.5972	1.675	.7445	1.343	1.247	.8021	.9308	20′
50′	.6429	.5995	1.668	.7490	1.335	1.249	.8004	.9279	10′
37° 00′	.6458	.6018	1.662	.7536	1.327	1.252	.7986	.9250	53° 00′
10′	.6487	.6041	1.655	.7581	1.319	1.255	.7969	.9221	50′
20′	.6516	.6065	1.649	.7627	1.311	1.258	.7951	.9192	40′
30′	.6545	.6088	1.643	.7673	1.303	1.260	.7934	.9163	30′
40′	.6574	.6111	1.636	.7720	1.295	1.263	.7916	.9134	20′
50′	.6603	.6134	1.630	.7766	1.288	1.266	.7898	.9105	10′
38° 00′	.6632	.6157	1.624	.7813	1.280	1.269	.7880	.9076	52° 00′
10′	.6661	.6180	1.618	.7860	1.272	1.272	.7862	.9047	50′
20′	.6690	.6202	1.612	.7907	1.265	1.275	.7844	.9018	40′
30′	.6720	.6225	1.606	.7954	1.257	1.278	.7826	.8988	30′
40′	.6749	.6248	1.601	‘.8002	1.250	1.281	.7808	.8959	20′
50′	.6778	.6271	1.595	.8050	1.242	1.284	.7790	.8930	10′
39° 00′	.6807	.6293	1.589	.8098	1.235	1.287	.7771	.8901	51° 00′
10′	.6836	.6316	1.583	.8146	1.228	1.290	.7753	.8872	50′
20′	.6865	.6338	1.578	.8195	1.220	1.293	.7735	.8843	40′
30′	.6894	.6361	1.572	.8243	1.213	1.296	.7716	.8814	30′
40′	.6923	.6383	1.567	.8292	1.206	1.299	.7698	.8785	20′
50′	.6952	.6406	1.561	.8342	1.199	1.302	.7679	.8756	10′
40° 00′	.6981	.6428	1.556	.8391	1.192	1.305	.7660	.8727	50° 00′
10′	.7010	.6450	1.550	.8441	1.185	1.309	.7642	.8698	50′
20′	.7039	.6472	1.545	.8491	1.178	1.312	.7623	.8668	40′
30′	.7069	.6494	1.540	.8541	1.171	1.315	.7604	.8639	30′
40′	.7098	.6517	1.535	.8591	1.164	1.318	.7585	.8610	20′
50′	.7127	.6539	1.529	.8642	1.157	1.322	.7566	.8581	10′
41° 00′	.7156	.6561	1.524	.8693	1.150	1.325	.7547	.8552	49° 00′
10′	.7185	.6583	1.519	.8744	1.144	1.328	.7528	.8523	50′
20′	.7214	.6604	1.514	.8796	1.137	1.332	.7509	.8494	40′
30′	.7243	.6626	1.509	.8847	1.130	1.335	.7490	.8465	30′
40′	.7272	.6648	1.504	.8899	1.124	1.339	.7470	.8436	20′
50′	.7301	.6670	1.499	.8952	1.117	1.342	.7451	.8407	10′
42° 00′	.7330	.6691	1.494	.9004	1.111	1.346	.7431	.8378	48° 00′
10′	.7359	.6713	1.490	.9057	1.104	1.349	.7412	.8348	50′
20′	.7389	.6734	1.485	.9110	1.098	1.353	.7392	.8319	40′
30′	.7418	.6756	1.480	.9163	1.091	1.356	.7373	.8290	30′
40′	.7447	.6777	1.476	.9217	1.085	1.360	.7353	.8261	20′
50′	.7476	.6799	1.471	.9271	1.079	1.364	.7333	.8232	10′
43° 00′	.7505	.6820	1.466	.9325	1.072	1.367	.7314	.8203	47° 00′
10′	.7534	.6841	1.462	.9380	1.066	1.371	.7294	.8174	50′
20′	.7563	.6862	1.457	.9435	1.060	1.375	.7274	.8145	40′
30′	.7592	.6884	1.453	.9490	1.054	1.379	.7254	.8116	30′
40′	.7621	.6905	1.448	.9545	1.048	1.382	.7234	.8087	20′
50′	.7650	.6926	1.444	.9601	1.042	1.386	.7214	.8058	10′
44° 00′	.7679	.6947	1.440	.9657	1.036	1.390	.7193	.8029	46° 00′
10′	.7709	.6967	1.435	.9713	1.030	1.394	.7173	.7999	50′
20′	.7738	.6988	1.431	.9770	1.024	1.398	.7153	.7970	40′
30′	.7767	.7009	1.427	.9827	1.018	1.402	.7133	.7941	30′
40′	.7796	.7030	1.423	.9884	1.012	1.406	.7112	.7912	20′
50′	.7825	.7050	1.418	.9942	1.006	1.410	.7092	.7883	10′
45° 00′	.7854	.7071	1.414	1.000	1.000	1.414	.7071	.7854	45° 00′
		cos θ	sec θ	cot θ	tan θ	csc θ	sin θ	Radians	Degrees m (θ)

Table 3 Values of Trigonometric Functions for Angles in Radians

$m^R(\theta)$	$m^\circ(\theta)$	$\sin\theta$	$\csc\theta$	$\tan\theta$	$\cot\theta$	$\sec\theta$	$\cos\theta$
0.00	0° 00′	0.0000	Undefined	0.0000	Undefined	1.000	1.000
.01	0° 34′	.0100	100.0	.0100	100.0	1.000	1.000
.02	1° 09′	.0200	50.00	.0200	49.99	1.000	0.9998
.03	1° 43′	.0300	33.34	.0300	33.32	1.000	0.9996
.04	2° 18′	.0400	25.01	.0400	24.99	1.001	0.9992
0.05	2° 52′	0.0500	20.01	0.0500	19.98	1.001	0.9988
.06	3° 26′	.0600	16.68	.0601	16.65	1.002	.9982
.07	4° 01′	.0699	14.30	.0701	14.26	1.002	.9976
.08	4° 35′	.0799	12.51	.0802	12.47	1.003	.9968
.09	5° 09′	.0899	11.13	.0902	11.08	1.004	.9960
0.10	5° 44′	0.0998	10.02	0.1003	9.967	1.005	0.9950
.11	6° 18′	.1098	9.109	.1104	9.054	1.006	.9940
.12	6° 53′	.1197	8.353	.1206	8.293	1.007	.9928
.13	7° 27′	.1296	7.714	.1307	7.649	1.009	.9916
.14	8° 01′	.1395	7.166	.1409	7.096	1.010	.9902
0.15	8° 36′	0.1494	6.692	0.1511	6.617	1.011	0.9888
.16	9° 10′	.1593	6.277	.1614	6.197	1.013	.9872
.17	9° 44′	.1692	5.911	.1717	5.826	1.015	.9856
.18	10° 19′	.1790	5.586	.1820	5.495	1.016	.9838
.19	10° 53′	.1889	5.295	.1923	5.200	1.018	.9820
0.20	11° 28′	0.1987	5.033	0.2027	4.933	1.020	0.9801
.21	12° 02′	.2085	4.797	.2131	4.692	1.022	.9780
.22	12° 36′	.2182	4.582	.2236	4.472	1.025	.9759
.23	13° 11′	.2280	4.386	.2341	4.271	1.027	.9737
.24	13° 45′	.2377	4.207	.2447	4.086	1.030	.9713
0.25	14° 19′	0.2474	4.042	0.2553	3.916	1.032	0.9689
.26	14° 54′	.2571	3.890	.2660	3.759	1.035	.9664
.27	15° 28′	.2667	3.749	.2768	3.613	1.038	.9638
.28	16° 03′	.2764	3.619	.2876	3.478	1.041	.9611
.29	16° 37′	.2860	3.497	.2984	3.351	1.044	.9582
0.30	17° 11′	0.2955	3.384	0.3093	3.233	1.047	0.9553
.31	17° 46′	.3051	3.278	.3203	3.122	1.050	.9523
.32	18° 20′	.3146	3.179	.3314	3.018	1.053	.9492
.33	18° 55′	.3240	3.086	.3425	2.920	1.057	.9460
.34	19° 29′	.3335	2.999	.3537	2.827	1.061	.9428
0.35	20° 03′	0.3429	2.916	0.3650	2.740	1.065	0.9394
.36	20° 38′	.3523	2.839	.3764	2.657	1.068	.9359
.37	21° 12′	.3616	2.765	.3879	2.578	1.073	.9323
.38	21° 46′	.3709	2.696	.3994	2.504	1.077	.9287
.39	22° 21′	.3802	2.630	.4111	2.433	1.081	.9249
0.40	22° 55′	0.3894	2.568	0.4228	2.365	1.086	0.9211
.41	23° 30′	.3986	2.509	.4346	2.301	1.090	.9171
.42	24° 04′	.4078	2.452	.4466	2.239	1.095	.9131
.43	24° 38′	.4169	2.399	.4586	2.180	1.100	.9090
.44	25° 13′	.4259	2.348	.4708	2.124	1.105	.9048
0.45	25° 47′	0.4350	2.299	0.4831	2.070	1.111	0.9004
.46	26° 21′	.4439	2.253	.4954	2.018	1.116	.8961
.47	26° 56′	.4529	2.208	.5080	1.969	1.122	.8916
.48	27° 30′	.4618	2.166	.5206	1.921	1.127	.8870
.49	28° 05′	.4706	2.125	.5334	1.875	1.133	.8823

Table 3 Values of Trigonometric Functions for Angles in Radians

$m^R(\theta)$	$m°(\theta)$	$\sin\theta$	$\csc\theta$	$\tan\theta$	$\cot\theta$	$\sec\theta$	$\cos\theta$
0.50	28° 39′	0.4794	2.086	0.5463	1.830	1.139	0.8776
.51	29° 13′	.4882	2.048	.5594	1.788	1.146	.8727
.52	29° 48′	.4969	2.013	.5726	1.747	1.152	.8678
.53	30° 22′	.5055	1.978	.5859	1.707	1.159	.8628
.54	30° 56′	.5141	1.945	.5994	1.668	1.166	.8577
0.55	31° 31′	0.5227	1.913	0.6131	1.631	1.173	0.8525
.56	32° 05′	.5312	1.883	.6269	1.595	1.180	.8473
.57	32° 40′	.5396	1.853	.6410	1.560	1.188	.8419
.58	33° 14′	.5480	1.825	.6552	1.526	1.196	.8365
.59	33° 48′	.5564	1.797	.6696	1.494	1.203	.8309
0.60	34° 23′	0.5646	1.771	0.6841	1.462	1.212	0.8253
.61	34° 57′	.5729	1.746	.6989	1.431	1.220	.8196
.62	35° 31′	.5810	1.721	.7139	1.401	1.229	.8139
.63	36° 06′	.5891	1.697	.7291	1.372	1.238	.8080
.64	36° 40′	.5972	1.674	.7445	1.343	1.247	.8021
0.65	37° 15′	0.6052	1.652	0.7602	1.315	1.256	0.7961
.66	37° 49′	.6131	1.631	.7761	1.288	1.266	.7900
.67	38° 23′	.6210	1.610	.7923	1.262	1.276	.7838
.68	38° 58′	.6288	1.590	.8087	1.237	1.286	.7776
.69	39° 32′	.6365	1.571	.8253	1.212	1.297	.7712
0.70	40° 06′	0.6442	1.552	0.8423	1.187	1.307	0.7648
.71	40° 41′	.6518	1.534	.8595	1.163	1.319	.7584
.72	41° 15′	.6594	1.517	.8771	1.140	1.330	.7518
.73	41° 50′	.6669	1.500	.8949	1.117	1.342	.7452
.74	42° 24′	.6743	1.483	.9131	1.095	1.354	.7385
0.75	42° 58′	0.6816	1.467	0.9316	1.073	1.367	0.7317
.76	43° 33′	.6889	1.452	.9505	1.052	1.380	.7248
.77	44° 07′	.6961	1.437	.9697	1.031	1.393	.7179
.78	44° 41′	.7033	1.422	.9893	1.011	1.407	.7109
.79	45° 16′	.7104	1.408	1.009	.9908	1.421	.7038
0.80	45° 50′	0.7174	1.394	1.030	0.9712	1.435	0.6967
.81	46° 25′	.7243	1.381	1.050	.9520	1.450	.6895
.82	46° 59′	.7311	1.368	1.072	.9331	1.466	.6822
.83	47° 33′	.7379	1.355	1.093	.9146	1.482	.6749
.84	48° 08′	.7446	1.343	1.116	.8964	1.498	.6675
0.85	48° 42′	0.7513	1.331	1.138	0.8785	1.515	0.6600
.86	49° 17′	.7578	1.320	1.162	.8609	1.533	.6524
.87	49° 51′	.7643	1.308	1.185	.8437	1.551	.6448
.88	50° 25′	.7707	1.297	1.210	.8267	1.569	.6372
.89	51° 00′	.7771	1.287	1.235	.8100	1.589	.6294
0.90	51° 34′	0.7833	1.277	1.260	0.7936	1.609	0.6216
.91	52° 08′	.7895	1.267	1.286	.7774	1.629	.6137
.92	52° 43′	.7956	1.257	1.313′	.7615	1.651	.6058
.93	53° 17′	.8016	1.247	1.341	.7458	1.673	.5978
.94	53° 52′	.8076	1.238	1.369	.7303	1.696	.5898
0.95	54° 26′	0.8134	1.229	1.398	0.7151	1.719	0.5817
.96	55° 00′	.8192	1.221	1.428	.7001	1.744	.5735
.97	55° 35′	.8249	1.212	1.459	.6853	1.769	.5653
.98	56° 09′	.8305	1.204	1.491	.6707	1.795	.5570
.99	56° 43′	.8360	1.196	1.524	.6563	1.823	.5487

Table 3   Values of Trigonometric Functions for Angles in Radians

$m^R(\theta)$	$m^°(\theta)$	$\sin\theta$	$\csc\theta$	$\tan\theta$	$\cot\theta$	$\sec\theta$	$\cos\theta$
1.00	57° 18′	0.8415	1.188	1.557	0.6421	1.851	0.5403
1.01	57° 52′	.8468	1.181	1.592	.6281	1.880	.5319
1.02	58° 27′	.8521	1.174	1.628	.6142	1.911	.5234
1.03	59° 01′	.8573	1.166	1.665	.6005	1.942	.5148
1.04	59° 35′	.8624	1.160	1.704	.5870	1.975	.5062
1.05	60° 10′	0.8674	1.153	1.743	0.5736	2.010	0.4976
1.06	60° 44′	.8724	1.146	1.784	.5604	2.046	.4889
1.07	61° 18′	.8772	1.140	1.827	.5473	2.083	.4801
1.08	61° 53′	.8820	1.134	1.871	.5344	2.122	.4713
1.09	62° 27′	.8866	1.128	1.917	.5216	2.162	.4625
1.10	63° 02′	0.8912	1.122	1.965	0.5090	2.205	0.4536
1.11	63° 36′	.8957	1.116	2.014	.4964	2.249	.4447
1.12	64° 10′	.9001	1.111	2.066	.4840	2.295	.4357
1.13	64° 45′	.9044	1.106	2.120	.4718	2.344	.4267
1.14	65° 19′	.9086	1.101	2.176	.4596	2.395	.4176
1.15	65° 53′	0.9128	1.096	2.234	0.4475	2.448	0.4085
1.16	66° 28′	.9168	1.091	2.296	.4356	2.504	.3993
1.17	67° 02′	.9208	1.086	2.360	.4237	2.563	.3902
1.18	67° 37′	.9246	1.082	2.428	.4120	2.625	.3809
1.19	68° 11′	.9284	1.077	2.498	.4003	2.691	3717
1.20	68° 45′	0.9320	1.073	2.572	0.3888	2.760	0.3624
1.21	69° 20′	.9356	1.069	2.650	.3773	2.833	.3530
1.22	69° 54′	.9391	1.065	2.733	.3659	2.910	.3436
1.23	70° 28′	.9425	1.061	2.820	.3546	2.992	.3342
1.24	71° 03′	.9458	1.057	2.912	.3434	3.079	.3248
1.25	71° 37′	0.9490	1.054	3.010	0.3323	3.171	0.3153
1.26	72° 12′	.9521	1.050	3.113	.3212	3.270	.3058
1.27	72° 46′	.9551	1.047	3.224	.3102	3.375	.2963
1.28	73° 20′	.9580	1.044	3.341	.2993	3.488	.2867
1.29	73° 55′	.9608	1.041	3.467	.2884	3.609	.2771
1.30	74° 29′	0.9636	1.038	3.602	0.2776	3.738	0.2675
1.31	75° 03′	.9662	1.035	3.747	.2669	3.878	.2579
1.32	75° 38′	.9687	1.032	3.903	.2562	4.029	.2482
1.33	76° 12′	.9711	1.030	4.072	.2456	4.193	.2385
1.34	76° 47′	.9735	1.027	4.256	.2350	4.372	.2288
1.35	77° 21′	0.9757	1.025	4.455	0.2245	4.566	0.2190
1.36	77° 55′	.9779	1.023	4.673	.2140	4.779	.2092
1.37	78° 30′	.9799	1.021	4.913	.2035	5.014	.1994
1.38	79° 04′	.9819	1.018	5.177	.1931	5.273	.1896
1.39	79° 39′	.9837	1.017	5.471	.1828	5.561	.1798
1.40	80° 13′	0.9854	1.015	5.798	0.1725	5.883	0.1700
1.41	80° 47′	.9871	1.013	6.165	.1622	6.246	.1601
1.42	81° 22′	.9887	1.011	6.581	.1519	6.657	.1502
1.43	81° 56′	.9901	1.010	7.055	.1417	7.126	.1403
1.44	82° 30′	.9915	1.009	7.602	.1315	7.667	.1304
1.45	83° 05′	0.9927	1.007	8.238	0.1214	8.299	0.1205
1.46	83° 39′	.9939	1.006	8.989	.1113	9.044	.1106
1.47	84° 14′	.9949	1.005	9.887	.1011	9.938	.1006
1.48	84° 48′	.9959	1.004	10.98	.0911	11.03	.0907
1.49	85° 22′	.9967	1.003	12.35	.0810	12.39	.0807

Table 3   Values of Trigonometric Functions for Angles in Radians

$m^R(\theta)$	$m^\circ(\theta)$	$\sin\theta$	$\csc\theta$	$\tan\theta$	$\cot\theta$	$\sec\theta$	$\cos\theta$
1.50	85° 57′	0.9975	1.003	14.10	0.0709	14.14	0.0707
1.51	86° 31′	.9982	1.002	16.43	.0609	16.46	.0608
1.52	87° 05′	.9987	1.001	19.67	.0508	19.70	.0508
1.53	87° 40′	.9992	1.001	24.50	.0408	24.52	.0408
1.54	88° 14′	.9995	1.000	32.46	.0308	32.48	.0308
1.55	88° 49′	0.9998	1.000	48.08	0.0208	48.09	0.0208
1.56	89° 23′	.9999	1.000	92.62	.0108	92.63	.0108
1.57	89° 57′	1.000	1.000	1256	.0008	1256	.0008

Table 4   Squares and Square Roots

N	N^2	$\sqrt{N}$	$\sqrt{10N}$	N	N^2	$\sqrt{N}$	$\sqrt{10N}$
1.0	1.00	1.000	3.162	5.5	30.25	2.345	7.416
1.1	1.21	1.049	3.317	5.6	31.36	2.366	7.483
1.2	1.44	1.095	3.464	5.7	32.49	2.387	7.550
1.3	1.69	1.140	3.606	5.8	33.64	2.408	7.616
1.4	1.96	1.183	3.742	5.9	34.81	2.429	7.681
1.5	2.25	1.225	3.873	6.0	36.00	2.449	7.746
1.6	2.56	1.265	4.000	6.1	37.21	2.470	7.810
1.7	2.89	1.304	4.123	6.2	38.44	2.490	7.874
1.8	3.24	1.342	4.243	6.3	39.69	2.510	7.937
1.9	3.61	1.378	4.359	6.4	40.96	2.530	8.000
2.0	4.00	1.414	4.472	6.5	42.25	2.550	8.062
2.1	4.41	1.449	4.583	6.6	43.56	2.569	8.124
2.2	4.84	1.483	4.690	6.7	44.89	2.588	8.185
2.3	5.29	1.517	4.796	6.8	46.24	2.608	8.246
2.4	5.76	1.549	4.899	6.9	47.61	2.627	8.307
2.5	6.25	1.581	5.000	7.0	49.00	2.646	8.367
2.6	6.76	1.612	5.099	7.1	50.41	2.665	8.426
2.7	7.29	1.643	5.196	7.2	51.84	2.683	8.485
2.8	7.84	1.673	5.292	7.3	53.29	2.702	8.544
2.9	8.41	1.703	5.385	7.4	54.76	2.720	8.602
3.0	9.00	1.732	5.477	7.5	56.25	2.739	8.660
3.1	9.61	1.761	5.568	7.6	57.76	2.757	8.718
3.2	10.24	1.789	5.657	7.7	59.29	2.775	8.775
3.3	10.89	1.817	5.745	7.8	60.84	2.793	8.832
3.4	11.56	1.844	5.831	7.9	62.41	2.811	8.888
3.5	12.25	1.871	5.916	8.0	64.00	2.828	8.944
3.6	12.96	1.897	6.000	8.1	65.61	2.846	9.000
3.7	13.69	1.924	6.083	8.2	67.24	2.864	9.055
3.8	14.44	1.949	6.164	8.3	68.89	2.881	9.110
3.9	15.21	1.975	6.245	8.4	70.56	2.898	9.165
4.0	16.00	2.000	6.325	8.5	72.25	2.915	9.220
4.1	16.81	2.025	6.403	8.6	73.96	2.933	9.274
4.2	17.64	2.049	6.481	8.7	75.69	2.950	9.327
4.3	18.49	2.074	6.557	8.8	77.44	2.966	9.381
4.4	19.36	2.098	6.633	8.9	79.21	2.983	9.434
4.5	20.25	2.121	6.708	9.0	81.00	3.000	9.487
4.6	21.16	2.145	6.782	9.1	82.81	3.017	9.539
4.7	22.09	2.168	6.856	9.2	84.64	3.033	9.592
4.8	23.04	2.191	6.928	9.3	86.49	3.050	9.644
4.9	24.01	2.214	7.000	9.4	88.36	3.066	9.695
5.0	25.00	2.236	7.071	9.5	90.25	3.082	9.747
5.1	26.01	2.258	7.141	9.6	92.16	3.098	9.798
5.2	27.04	2.280	7.211	9.7	94.09	3.114	9.849
5.3	28.09	2.302	7.280	9.8	96.04	3.130	9.899
5.4	29.16	2.324	7.348	9.9	98.01	3.146	9.950
5.5	30.25	2.345	7.416	10	100.00	3.162	10.000

Table 5 Common Logarithms of Numbers*

N	0	1	2	3	4	5	6	7	8	9
10	0000	0043	0086	0128	0170	0212	0253	0294	0334	0374
11	0414	0453	0492	0531	0569	0607	0645	0682	0719	0755
12	0792	0828	0864	0899	0934	0969	1004	1038	1072	1106
13	1139	1173	1206	1239	1271	1303	1335	1367	1399	1430
14	1461	1492	1523	1553	1584	1614	1644	1673	1703	1732
15	1761	1790	1818	1847	1875	1903	1931	1959	1987	2014
16	2041	2068	2095	2122	2148	2175	2201	2227	2253	2279
17	2304	2330	2355	2380	2405	2430	2455	2480	2504	2529
18	2553	2577	2601	2625	2648	2672	2695	2718	2742	2765
19	2788	2810	2833	2856	2878	2900	2923	2945	2967	2989
20	3010	3032	3054	3075	3096	3118	3139	3160	3181	3201
21	3222	3243	3263	3284	3304	3324	3345	3365	3385	3404
22	3424	3444	3464	3483	3502	3522	3541	3560	3579	3598
23	3617	3636	3655	3674	3692	3711	3729	3747	3766	3784
24	3802	3820	3838	3856	3874	3892	3909	3927	3945	3962
25	3979	3997	4014	4031	4048	4065	4082	4099	4116	4133
26	4150	4166	4183	4200	4216	4232	4249	4265	4281	4298
27	4314	4330	4346	4362	4378	4393	4409	4425	4440	4456
28	4472	4487	4502	4518	4533	4548	4564	4579	4594	4609
29	4624	4639	4654	4669	4683	4698	4713	4728	4742	4757
30	4771	4786	4800	4814	4829	4843	4857	4871	4886	4900
31	4914	4928	4942	4955	4969	4983	4997	5011	5024	5038
32	5051	5065	5079	5092	5105	5119	5132	5145	5159	5172
33	5185	5198	5211	5224	5237	5250	5263	5276	5289	5302
34	5315	5328	5340	5353	5366	5378	5391	5403	5416	5428
35	5441	5453	5465	5478	5490	5502	5514	5527	5539	5551
36	5563	5575	5587	5599	5611	5623	5635	5647	5658	5670
37	5682	5694	5705	5717	5729	5740	5752	5763	5775	5786
38	5798	5809	5821	5832	5843	5855	5866	5877	5888	5899
39	5911	5922	5933	5944	5955	5966	5977	5988	5999	6010
40	6021	6031	6042	6053	6064	6075	6085	6096	6107	6117
41	6128	6138	6149	6160	6170	6180	6191	6201	6212	6222
42	6232	6243	6253	6263	6274	6284	6294	6304	6314	6325
43	6335	6345	6355	6365	6375	6385	6395	6405	6415	6425
44	6435	6444	6454	6464	6474	6484	6493	6503	6513	6522
45	6532	6542	6551	6561	6571	6580	6590	6599	6609	6618
46	6628	6637	6646	6656	6665	6675	6684	6693	6702	6712
47	6721	6730	6739	6749	6758	6767	6776	6785	6794	6803
48	6812	6821	6830	6839	6848	6857	6866	6875	6884	6893
49	6902	6911	6920	6928	6937	6946	6955	6964	6972	6981
50	6990	6998	7007	7016	7024	7033	7042	7050	7059	7067
51	7076	7084	7093	7101	7110	7118	7126	7135	7143	7152
52	7160	7168	7177	7185	7193	7202	7210	7218	7226	7235
53	7243	7251	7259	7267	7275	7284	7292	7300	7308	7316
54	7324	7332	7340	7348	7356	7364	7372	7380	7388	7396

*Mantissas; decimal points omitted. Characteristics are found by inspection.

Table 5   Common Logarithms of Numbers

N	0	1	2	3	4	5	6	7	8	9
55	7404	7412	7419	7427	7435	7443	7451	7459	7466	7474
56	7482	7490	7497	7505	7513	7520	7528	7536	7543	7551
57	7559	7566	7574	7582	7589	7597	7604	7612	7619	7627
58	7634	7642	7649	7657	7664	7672	7679	7686	7694	7701
59	7709	7716	7723	7731	7738	7745	7752	7760	7767	7774
60	7782	7789	7796	7803	7810	7818	7825	7832	7839	7846
61	7853	7860	7868	7875	7882	7889	7896	7903	7910	7917
62	7924	7931	7938	7945	7952	7959	7966	7973	7980	7987
63	7993	8000	8007	8014	8021	8028	8035	8041	8048	8055
64	8062	8069	8075	8082	8089	8096	8102	8109	8116	8122
65	8129	8136	8142	8149	8156	8162	8169	8176	8182	8189
66	8195	8202	8209	8215	8222	8228	8235	8241	8248	8254
67	8261	8267	8274	8280	8287	8293	8299	8306	8312	8319
68	8325	8331	8338	8344	8351	8357	8363	8370	8376	8382
69	8388	8395	8401	8407	8414	8420	8426	8432	8439	8445
70	8451	8457	8463	8470	8476	8482	8488	8494	8500	8506
71	8513	8519	8525	8531	8537	8543	8549	8555	8561	8567
72	8573	8579	8585	8591	8597	8603	8609	8615	8621	8627
73	8633	8639	8645	8651	8657	8663	8669	8675	8681	8686
74	8692	8698	8704	8710	8716	8722	8727	8733	8739	8745
75	8751	8756	8762	8768	8774	8779	8785	8791	8797	8802
76	8808	8814	8820	8825	8831	8837	8842	8848	8854	8859
77	8865	8871	8876	8882	8887	8893	8899	8904	8910	8915
78	8921	8927	8932	8938	8943	8949	8954	8960	8965	8971
79	8976	8982	8987	8993	8998	9004	9009	9015	9020	9025
80	9031	9036	9042	9047	9053	9058	9063	9069	9074	9079
81	9085	9090	9096	9101	9106	9112	9117	9122	9128	9133
82	9138	9143	9149	9154	9159	9165	9170	9175	9180	9186
83	9191	9196	9201	9206	9212	9217	9222	9227	9232	9238
84	9243	9248	9253	9258	9263	9269	9274	9279	9284	9289
85	9294	9299	9304	9309	9315	9320	9325	9330	9335	9340
86	9345	9350	9355	9360	9365	9370	9375	9380	9385	9390
87	9395	9400	9405	9410	9415	9420	9425	9430	9435	9440
88	9445	9450	9455	9460	9465	9469	9474	9479	9484	9489
89	9494	9499	9504	9509	9513	9518	9523	9528	9533	9538
90	9542	9547	9552	9557	9562	9566	9571	9576	9581	9586
91	9590	9595	9600	9605	9609	9614	9619	9624	9628	9633
92	9638	9643	9647	9652	9657	9661	9666	9671	9675	9680
93	9685	9689	9694	9699	9703	9708	9713	9717	9722	9727
94	9731	9736	9741	9745	9750	9754	9759	9763	9768	9773
95	9777	9782	9786	9791	9795	9800	9805	9809	9814	9818
96	9823	9827	9832	9836	9841	9845	9850	9854	9859	9863
97	9868	9872	9877	9881	9886	9890	9894	9899	9903	9908
98	9912	9917	9921	9926	9930	9934	9939	9943	9948	9952
99	9956	9961	9965	9969	9974	9978	9983	9987	9991	9996

Table 6 Four-place Logarithms of Values of Trigonometric Functions*

Angle	L Sin	d	L Tan	cd	L Cot	d	L Cos	Angle
0° 0′	——		——		——		10.0000	90° 0′
10′	7.4637	3011	7.4637	3011	12.5363	0	10.0000	50′
20′	7.7648	1760	7.7648	1761	12.2352	0	10.0000	40′
30′	7.9408	1250	7.9409	1249	12.0591	0	10.0000	30′
40′	8.0658	969	8.0658	969	11.9342	0	10.0000	20′
50′	8.1627	792	8.1627	792	11.8373	0	10.0000	10′
1° 0′	8.2419	669	8.2419	670	11.7581	1	9.9999	89° 0′
10′	8.3088	580	8.3089	580	11.6911	0	9.9999	50′
20′	8.3668	511	8.3669	512	11.6331	0	9.9999	40′
30′	8.4179	458	8.4181	457	11.5819	0	9.9999	30′
40′	8.4637	413	8.4638	415	11.5362	1	9.9998	20′
50′	8.5050	378	8.5053	378	11.4947	0	9.9998	10′
2° 0′	8.5428	348	8.5431	348	11.4569	1	9.9997	88° 0′
10′	8.5776	321	8.5779	322	11.4221	0	9.9997	50′
20′	8.6097	300	8.6101	300	11.3899	1	9.9996	40′
30′	8.6397	280	8.6401	281	11.3599	0	9.9996	30′
40′	8.6677	263	8.6682	263	11.3318	1	9.9995	20′
50′	8.6940	248	8.6945	249	11.3055	0	9.9995	10′
3° 0′	8.7188	235	8.7194	235	11.2806	1	9.9994	87° 0′
10′	8.7423	222	8.7429	223	11.2571	1	9.9993	50′
20′	8.7645	212	8.7652	213	11.2348	0	9.9993	40′
30′	8.7857	202	8.7865	202	11.2135	1	9.9992	30′
40′	8.8059	192	8.8067	194	11.1933	1	9.9991	20′
50′	8.8251	185	8.8261	185	11.1739	1	9.9990	10′
4° 0′	8.8436	177	8.8446	178	11.1554	0	9.9989	86° 0′
10′	8.8613	170	8.8624	171	11.1376	1	9.9989	50′
20′	8.8783	163	8.8795	165	11.1205	1	9.9988	40′
30′	8.8946	158	8.8960	158	11.1040	1	9.9987	30′
40′	8.9104	152	8.9118	154	11.0882	1	9.9986	20′
50′	8.9256	147	8.9272	148	11.0728	2	9.9985	10′
5° 0′	8.9403	142	8.9420	143	11.0580	1	9.9983	85° 0′
10′	8.9545	137	8.9563	138	11.0437	1	9.9982	50′
20′	8.9682	134	8.9701	135	11.0299	1	9.9981	40′
30′	8.9816	129	8.9836	130	11.0164	1	9.9980	30′
40′	8.9945	125	8.9966	127	11.0034	2	9.9979	20′
50′	9.0070	122	9.0093	123	10.9907	1	9.9977	10′
6° 0′	9.0192	119	9.0216	120	10.9784	1	9.9976	84° 0′
10′	9.0311	115	9.0336	117	10.9664	2	9.9975	50′
20′	9.0426	113	9.0453	114	10.9547	1	9.9973	40′
30′	9.0539	109	9.0567	111	10.9433	1	9.9972	30′
40′	9.0648	107	9.0678	108	10.9322	2	9.9971	20′
50′	9.0755	104	9.0786	105	10.9214	1	9.9969	10′
7° 0′	9.0859	102	9.0891	104	10.9109	2	9.9968	83° 0′
10′	9.0961	99	9.0995	101	10.9005	2	9.9966	50′
20′	9.1060	97	9.1096	98	10.8904	1	9.9964	40′
30′	9.1157	95	9.1194	97	10.8806	2	9.9963	30′
40′	9.1252	93	9.1291	94	10.8709	2	9.9961	20′
50′	9.1345	91	9.1385	93	10.8615	1	9.9959	10′
8° 0′	9.1436	89	9.1478	91	10.8522	2	9.9958	82° 0′
10′	9.1525	87	9.1569	89	10.8431	2	9.9956	50′
20′	9.1612	85	9.1658	87	10.8342	2	9.9954	40′
30′	9.1697	84	9.1745	86	10.8255	2	9.9952	30′
40′	9.1781	82	9.1831	84	10.8169	2	9.9950	20′
50′	9.1863	80	9.1915	82	10.8085	2	9.9948	10′
9° 0′	9.1943		9.1997		10.8003		9.9946	81° 0′
	L Cos	d	L Cot	cd	L Tan	d	L Sin	Angle

* These tables give the logarithms increased by 10. Hence in each case 10 should be subtracted.

Table 6   Four-place Logarithms of Values of Trigonometric Functions

Angle	L Sin	d	L Tan	cd	L Cot	d	L Cos	Angle
9° 0'	9.1943	79	9.1997	81	10.8003	2	9.9946	81° 0'
10'	9.2022	78	9.2078	80	10.7922	2	9.9944	50'
20'	9.2100	76	9.2158	78	10.7842	2	9.9942	40'
30'	9.2176	75	9.2236	77	10.7764	2	9.9940	30'
40'	9.2251	73	9.2313	76	10.7687	2	9.9938	20'
50'	9.2324	73	9.2389	74	10.7611	2	9.9936	10'
10° 0'	9.2397	71	9.2463	73	10.7537	3	9.9934	80° 0'
10'	9.2468	70	9.2536	73	10.7464	2	9.9931	50'
20'	9.2538	68	9.2609	71	10.7391	2	9.9929	40'
30'	9.2606	68	9.2680	70	10.7320	3	9.9927	30'
40'	9.2674	66	9.2750	69	10.7250	2	9.9924	20'
50'	9.2740	66	9.2819	68	10.7181	3	9.9922	10'
11° 0'	9.2806	64	9.2887	66	10.7113	2	9.9919	79° 0'
10'	9.2870	64	9.2953	67	10.7047	3	9.9917	50'
20'	9.2934	63	9.3020	65	10.6980	2	9.9914	40'
30'	9.2997	61	9.3085	64	10.6915	3	9.9912	30'
40'	9.3058	61	9.3149	63	10.6851	2	9.9909	20'
50'	9.3119	60	9.3212	63	10.6788	3	9.9907	10'
12° 0'	9.3179	59	9.3275	61	10.6725	3	9.9904	78° 0'
10'	9.3238	58	9.3336	61	10.6664	2	9.9901	50'
20'	9.3296	57	9.3397	61	10.6603	3	9.9899	40'
30'	9.3353	57	9.3458	59	10.6542	3	9.9896	30'
40'	9.3410	56	9.3517	59	10.6483	3	9.9893	20'
50'	9.3466	55	9.3576	58	10.6424	3	9.9890	10'
13° 0'	9.3521	54	9.3634	57	10.6366	3	9.9887	77° 0'
10'	9.3575	54	9.3691	57	10.6309	3	9.9884	50'
20'	9.3629	53	9.3748	56	10.6252	3	9.9881	40'
30'	9.3682	52	9.3804	55	10.6196	3	9.9878	30'
40'	9.3734	52	9.3859	55	10.6141	3	9.9875	20'
50'	9.3786	51	9.3914	54	10.6086	3	9.9872	10'
14° 0'	9.3837	50	9.3968	53	10.6032	3	9.9869	76° 0'
10'	9.3887	50	9.4021	53	10.5979	3	9.9866	50'
20'	9.3937	49	9.4074	53	10.5926	4	9.9863	40'
30'	9.3986	49	9.4127	51	10.5873	3	9.9859	30'
40'	9.4035	48	9.4178	52	10.5822	3	9.9856	20'
50'	9.4083	47	9.4230	51	10.5770	4	9.9853	10'
15° 0'	9.4130	47	9.4281	50	10.5719	3	9.9849	75° 0'
10'	9.4177	46	9.4331	50	10.5669	3	9.9846	50'
20'	9.4223	46	9.4381	49	10.5619	4	9.9843	40'
30'	9.4269	45	9.4430	49	10.5570	3	9.9839	30'
40'	9.4314	45	9.4479	48	10.5521	4	9.9836	20'
50'	9.4359	44	9.4527	48	10.5473	4	9.9832	10'
16° 0'	9.4403	44	9.4575	47	10.5425	3	9.9828	74° 0'
10'	9.4447	44	9.4622	47	10.5378	4	9.9825	50'
20'	9.4491	42	9.4669	47	10.5331	4	9.9821	40'
30'	9.4533	43	9.4716	46	10.5284	4	9.9817	30'
40'	9.4576	42	9.4762	46	10.5238	4	9.9814	20'
50'	9.4618	41	9.4808	45	10.5192	4	9.9810	10'
17° 0'	9.4659	41	9.4853	45	10.5147	4	9.9806	73° 0'
10'	9.4700	41	9.4898	45	10.5102	4	9.9802	50'
20'	9.4741	40	9.4943	44	10.5057	4	9.9798	40'
30'	9.4781	40	9.4987	44	10.5013	4	9.9794	30'
40'	9.4821	40	9.5031	44	10.4969	4	9.9790	20'
50'	9.4861	39	9.5075	43	10.4925	4	9.9786	10'
18° 0'	9.4900		9.5118		10.4882		9.9782	72° 0'
	L Cos	d	L Cot	cd	L Tan	d	L Sin	Angle

Table 6 Four-place Logarithms of Values of Trigonometric Functions

Angle	L Sin	d	L Tan	cd	L Cot	d	L Cos	
18° 0'	9.4900	39	9.5118	43	10.4882	4	9.9782	72° 0'
10'	9.4939	38	9.5161	42	10.4839	4	9.9778	50'
20'	9.4977	38	9.5203	42	10.4797	4	9.9774	40'
30'	9.5015	37	9.5245	42	10.4755	4	9.9770	30'
40'	9.5052	38	9.5287	42	10.4713	5	9.9765	20'
50'	9.5090	36	9.5329	41	10.4671	4	9.9761	10'
19° 0'	9.5126	37	9.5370	41	10.4630	4	9.9757	71° 0'
10'	9.5163	36	9.5411	40	10.4589	5	9.9752	50'
20'	9.5199	36	9.5451	40	10.4549	4	9.9748	40'
30'	9.5235	35	9.5491	40	10.4509	5	9.9743	30'
40'	9.5270	36	9.5531	40	10.4469	4	9.9739	20'
50'	9.5306	35	9.5571	40	10.4429	5	9.9734	10'
20° 0'	9.5341	34	9.5611	39	10.4389	4	9.9730	70° 0'
10'	9.5375	34	9.5650	39	10.4350	5	9.9725	50'
20'	9.5409	34	9.5689	38	10.4311	4	9.9721	40'
30'	9.5443	34	9.5727	39	10.4273	5	9.9716	30'
40'	9.5477	33	9.5766	38	10.4234	5	9.9711	20'
50'	9.5510	33	9.5804	38	10.4196	5	9.9706	10'
21° 0'	9.5543	33	9.5842	37	10.4158	4	9.9702	69° 0'
10'	9.5576	33	9.5879	38	10.4121	5	9.9697	50'
20'	9.5609	32	9.5917	37	10.4083	5	9.9692	40'
30'	9.5641	32	9.5954	37	10.4046	5	9.9687	30'
40'	9.5673	31	9.5991	37	10.4009	5	9.9682	20'
50'	9.5704	32	9.6028	36	10.3972	5	9.9677	10'
22° 0'	9.5736	31	9.6064	36	10.3936	5	9.9672	68° 0'
10'	9.5767	31	9.6100	36	10.3900	5	9.9667	50'
20'	9.5798	30	9.6136	36	10.3864	6	9.9661	40'
30'	9.5828	31	9.6172	36	10.3828	5	9.9656	30'
40'	9.5859	30	9.6208	35	10.3792	5	9.9651	20'
50'	9.5889	30	9.6243	36	10.3757	5	9.9646	10'
23° 0'	9.5919	29	9.6279	35	10.3721	6	9.9640	67° 0'
10'	9.5948	30	9.6314	34	10.3686	5	9.9635	50'
20'	9.5978	29	9.6348	35	10.3652	6	9.9629	40'
30'	9.6007	29	9.6383	34	10.3617	5	9.9624	30'
40'	9.6036	29	9.6417	35	10.3583	6	9.9618	20'
50'	9.6065	28	9.6452	34	10.3548	5	9.9613	10'
24° 0'	9.6093	28	9.6486	34	10.3514	6	9.9607	66° 0'
10'	9.6121	28	9.6520	33	10.3480	5	9.9602	50'
20'	9.6149	28	9.6553	34	10.3447	6	9.9596	40'
30'	9.6177	28	9.6587	33	10.3413	6	9.9590	30'
40'	9.6205	27	9.6620	34	10.3380	6	9.9584	20'
50'	9.6232	27	9.6654	33	10.3346	5	9.9579	10'
25° 0'	9.6259	27	9.6687	33	10.3313	6	9.9573	65° 0'
10'	9.6286	27	9.6720	32	10.3280	6	9.9567	50'
20'	9.6313	27	9.6752	33	10.3248	6	9.9561	40'
30'	9.6340	26	9.6785	32	10.3215	6	9.9555	30'
40'	9.6366	26	9.6817	33	10.3183	6	9.9549	20'
50'	9.6392	26	9.6850	32	10.3150	6	9.9543	10'
26° 0'	9.6418	26	9.6882	32	10.3118	7	9.9537	64° 0'
10'	9.6444	26	9.6914	32	10.3086	6	9.9530	50'
20'	9.6470	25	9.6946	31	10.3054	6	9.9524	40'
30'	9.6495	26	9.6977	32	10.3023	6	9.9518	30'
40'	9.6521	25	9.7009	31	10.2991	7	9.9512	20'
50'	9.6546	24	9.7040	32	10.2960	6	9.9505	10'
27° 0'	9.6570		9.7072		10.2928		9.9499	63° 0'
	L Cos	d	L Cot	cd	L Tan	d	L Sin	Angle

Table 6 Four-place Logarithms of Values of Trigonometric Functions

Angle	L Sin	d	L Tan	cd	L Cot	d	L Cos	Angle
27° 0'	9.6570	25	9.7072	31	10.2928	7	9.9499	63° 0'
10'	9.6595	25	9.7103	31	10.2897	6	9.9492	50'
20'	9.6620	24	9.7134	31	10.2866	7	9.9486	40'
30'	9.6644	24	9.7165	31	10.2835	6	9.9479	30'
40'	9.6668	24	9.7196	30	10.2804	7	9.9473	20'
50'	9.6692	24	9.7226	31	10.2774	7	9.9466	10'
28° 0'	9.6716	24	9.7257	30	10.2743	6	9.9459	62° 0'
10'	9.6740	23	9.7287	30	10.2713	7	9.9453	50'
20'	9.6763	24	9.7317	31	10.2683	7	9.9446	40'
30'	9.6787	23	9.7348	30	10.2652	7	9.9439	30'
40'	9.6810	23	9.7378	30	10.2622	7	9.9432	20'
50'	9.6833	23	9.7408	30	10.2592	7	9.9425	10'
29° 0'	9.6856	22	9.7438	29	10.2562	7	9.9418	61° 0'
10'	9.6878	23	9.7467	30	10.2533	7	9.9411	50'
20'	9.6901	22	9.7497	29	10.2503	7	9.9404	40'
30'	9.6923	23	9.7526	30	10.2474	7	9.9397	30'
40'	9.6946	22	9.7556	29	10.2444	7	9.9390	20'
50'	9.6968	22	9.7585	29	10.2415	8	9.9383	10'
30° 0'	9.6990	22	9.7614	30	10.2386	7	9.9375	60° 0'
10'	9.7012	21	9.7644	29	10.2356	7	9.9368	50'
20'	9.7033	22	9.7673	28	10.2327	8	9.9361	40'
30'	9.7055	21	9.7701	29	10.2299	7	9.9353	30'
40'	9.7076	21	9.7730	29	10.2270	8	9.9346	20'
50'	9.7097	21	9.7759	29	10.2241	7	9.9338	10'
31° 0'	9.7118	21	9.7788	28	10.2212	8	9.9331	59° 0'
10'	9.7139	21	9.7816	29	10.2184	8	9.9323	50'
20'	9.7160	21	9.7845	28	10.2155	7	9.9315	40'
30'	9.7181	20	9.7873	29	10.2127	8	9.9308	30'
40'	9.7201	21	9.7902	28	10.2098	8	9.9300	20'
50'	9.7222	20	9.7930	28	10.2070	8	9.9292	10'
32° 0'	9.7242	20	9.7958	28	10.2042	8	9.9284	58° 0'
10'	9.7262	20	9.7986	28	10.2014	8	9.9276	50'
20'	9.7282	20	9.8014	28	10.1986	8	9.9268	40'
30'	9.7302	20	9.8042	28	10.1958	8	9.9260	30'
40'	9.7322	20	9.8070	27	10.1930	8	9.9252	20'
50'	9.7342	19	9.8097	28	10.1903	8	9.9244	10'
33° 0'	9.7361	19	9.8125	28	10.1875	8	9.9236	57° 0'
10'	9.7380	20	9.8153	27	10.1847	9	9.9228	50'
20'	9.7400	19	9.8180	28	10.1820	8	9.9219	40'
30'	9.7419	19	9.8208	27	10.1792	8	9.9211	30'
40'	9.7438	19	9.8235	28	10.1765	9	9.9203	20'
50'	9.7457	19	9.8263	27	10.1737	8	9.9194	10'
34° 0'	9.7476	18	9.8290	27	10.1710	9	9.9186	56° 0'
10'	9.7494	19	9.8317	27	10.1683	8	9.9177	50'
20'	9.7513	18	9.8344	27	10.1656	9	9.9169	40'
30'	9.7531	19	9.8371	27	10.1629	9	9.9160	30'
40'	9.7550	18	9.8398	27	10.1602	9	9.9151	20'
50'	9.7568	18	9.8425	27	10.1575	8	9.9142	10'
35° 0'	9.7586	18	9.8452	27	10.1548	9	9.9134	55° 0'
10'	9.7604	18	9.8479	27	10.1521	9	9.9125	50'
20'	9.7622	18	9.8506	27	10.1494	9	9.9116	40'
30'	9.7640	17	9.8533	27	10.1467	9	9.9107	30'
40'	9.7657	18	9.8559	26	10.1441	9	9.9098	20'
50'	9.7675	17	9.8586	27	10.1414	9	9.9089	10'
36° 0'	9.7692		9.8613		10.1387		9.9080	54° 0'
	L Cos	d	L Cot	cd	L Tan	d	L Sin	Angle

Table 6 Four-place Logarithms of Values of Trigonometric Functions

Angle	L Sin	d	L Tan	cd	L Cot	d	L Cos	
36° 0'	9.7692	18	9.8613	26	10.1387	10	9.9080	54° 0'
10'	9.7710	17	9.8639	27	10.1361	9	9.9070	50'
20'	9.7727	17	9.8666	26	10.1334	9	9.9061	40'
30'	9.7744	17	9.8692	26	10.1308	10	9.9052	30'
40'	9.7761	17	9.8718	27	10.1282	9	9.9042	20'
50'	9.7778	17	9.8745	26	10.1255	10	9.9033	10'
37° 0'	9.7795	16	9.8771	26	10.1229	9	9.9023	53° 0'
10'	9.7811	17	9.8797	27	10.1203	10	9.9014	50'
20'	9.7828	16	9.8824	26	10.1176	9	9.9004	40'
30'	9.7844	17	9.8850	26	10.1150	10	9.8995	30'
40'	9.7861	16	9.8876	26	10.1124	10	9.8985	20'
50'	9.7877	16	9.8902	26	10.1098	10	9.8975	10'
38° 0'	9.7893	17	9.8928	26	10.1072	10	9.8965	52° 0'
10'	9.7910	16	9.8954	26	10.1046	10	9.8955	50'
20'	9.7926	15	9.8980	26	10.1020	10	9.8945	40'
30'	9.7941	16	9.9006	26	10.0994	10	9.8935	30'
40'	9.7957	16	9.9032	26	10.0968	10	9.8925	20'
50'	9.7973	16	9.9058	26	10.0942	10	9.8915	10'
39° 0'	9.7989	15	9.9084	26	10.0916	10	9.8905	51° 0'
10'	9.8004	16	9.9110	25	10.0890	11	9.8895	50'
20'	9.8020	15	9.9135	26	10.0865	10	9.8884	40'
30'	9.8035	15	9.9161	26	10.0839	10	9.8874	30'
40'	9.8050	16	9.9187	25	10.0813	11	9.8864	20'
50'	9.8066	15	9.9212	26	10.0788	10	9.8853	10'
40° 0'	9.8081	15	9.9238	26	10.0762	11	9.8843	50° 0'
10'	9.8096	15	9.9264	25	10.0736	11	9.8832	50'
20'	9.8111	14	9.9289	26	10.0711	11	9.8821	40'
30'	9.8125	15	9.9315	26	10.0685	10	9.8810	30'
40'	9.8140	15	9.9341	25	10.0659	11	9.8800	20'
50'	9.8155	14	9.9366	26	10.0634	11	9.8789	10'
41° 0'	9.8169	15	9.9392	25	10.0608	11	9.8778	49° 0'
10'	9.8184	14	9.9417	26	10.0583	11	9.8767	50'
20'	9.8198	15	9.9443	25	10.0557	11	9.8756	40'
30'	9.8213	14	9.9468	26	10.0532	12	9.8745	30'
40'	9.8227	14	9.9494	25	10.0506	11	9.8733	20'
50'	9.8241	14	9.9519	25	10.0481	11	9.8722	10'
42° 0'	9.8255	14	9.9544	26	10.0456	12	9.8711	48° 0'
10'	9.8269	14	9.9570	25	10.0430	11	9.8699	50'
20'	9.8283	14	9.9595	26	10.0405	12	9.8688	40'
30'	9.8297	14	9.9621	25	10.0379	11	9.8676	30'
40'	9.8311	13	9.9646	25	10.0354	12	9.8665	20'
50'	9.8324	14	9.9671	26	10.0329	12	9.8653	10'
43° 0'	9.8338	13	9.9697	25	10.0303	12	9.8641	47° 0'
10'	9.8351	14	9.9722	25	10.0278	11	9.8629	50'
20'	9.8365	13	9.9747	25	10.0253	12	9.8618	40'
30'	9.8378	13	9.9772	26	10.0228	12	9.8606	30'
40'	9.8391	14	9.9798	25	10.0202	12	9.8594	20'
50'	9.8405	13	9.9823	25	10.0177	13	9.8582	10'
44° 0'	9.8418	13	9.9848	26	10.0152	12	9.8569	46° 0'
10'	9.8431	13	9.9874	25	10.0126	12	9.8557	50'
20'	9.8444	13	9.9899	25	10.0101	13	9.8545	40'
30'	9.8457	12	9.9924	25	10.0076	12	9.8532	30'
40'	9.8469	13	9.9949	26	10.0051	13	9.8520	20'
50'	9.8482	13	9.9975	25	10.0025	12	9.8507	10'
45° 0'	9.8495		10.0000		10.0000		9.8495	45° 0'
	L Cos	d	L Cot	cd	L Tan	d	L Sin	Angle

Summary of Formulas

Distance between Two Points, $A(u_1, v_1)$ and $B(u_2, v_2)$

$$d(\overline{AB}) = \sqrt{(u_2 - u_1)^2 + (v_2 - v_1)^2}$$

16

Basic Identities Involving Circular Functions

66

Periodic Motion

Rotational velocity of a point **P** traveling with *uniform circular motion* is given by

$$\omega = \frac{2\pi}{T},$$

where T is the time required to complete one revolution.

95

Simple harmonic motion of a particle moving back and forth between the endpoints of a line segment is described by an equation of the form

$$y = a \cos (\omega t + b) \quad \text{or} \quad y = a \sin (\omega t + b)$$

100

Reduction Formulas for Trigonometric Functions

148

Basic Identities for Trigonometric Functions

152

Solution of Triangles

Law of Cosines: $c^2 = a^2 + b^2 - 2ab \cos C$

170

Law of Sines: $\dfrac{\sin A}{a} = \dfrac{\sin B}{b} = \dfrac{\sin C}{c}$

174

Area of $\triangle ABC = \frac{1}{2}bc \sin A = \dfrac{b^2 \sin A \sin C}{2 \sin B} = bc \sin \dfrac{A}{2} \cos \dfrac{A}{2}$

173, 176

Law of Tangents (for $\triangle ABC$):

$$\frac{a - b}{a + b} = \frac{\tan \left(\dfrac{A - B}{2} \right)}{\tan \left(\dfrac{A + B}{2} \right)}$$

176

Heron's Formula for area of $\triangle ABC$:

$$\text{Area} = \sqrt{s(s - a)(s - b)(s - c)}, \text{ where } s = \frac{a + b + c}{2}$$

176

Operations with Vectors

For $\mathbf{u} = (x_1, y_1)$, $\mathbf{v} = (x_2, y_2)$, and $r, s \in \mathcal{R}$:

$$\|\mathbf{u}\| = \sqrt{x_1^2 + y_1^2} \quad \text{(norm of } \mathbf{u}\text{)}$$ **186**

$$\cos \theta = \frac{x_1}{\|\mathbf{u}\|}, \quad \sin \theta = \frac{y_1}{\|\mathbf{u}\|} \quad \text{(direction angle } \theta \text{ of } \mathbf{u} \neq 0\text{)}$$ **186**

$$-\mathbf{u} = (-x_1, -y_1) \quad \text{(negative of a vector)}$$ **187**

$$\mathbf{u} + \mathbf{v} = (x_1 + x_2, y_1 + y_2) \quad \text{(sum of vectors)}$$ **188**

$$r\mathbf{u} = (rx_1, ry_1) \quad \text{(product of a scalar and vector)}$$ **188**

$$\mathbf{u} - \mathbf{v} = (x_1 - x_2, y_1 - y_2) \quad \text{(difference of vectors)}$$ **189**

If $\mathbf{a} = (x_3, y_3) = r\mathbf{u} + s\mathbf{v}$ ($\mathbf{a}$ is a linear combination of $\mathbf{u}$ and $\mathbf{v}$), then

$$r = \frac{x_3 y_2 - x_2 y_3}{x_1 y_2 - x_2 y_1} \quad \text{and} \quad s = \frac{x_1 y_3 - x_3 y_1}{x_1 y_2 - x_2 y_1}.$$ **193**

$$\mathbf{u} \cdot \mathbf{v} = x_1 x_2 + y_1 y_2 \quad \text{(inner, dot, or scalar, product of } \mathbf{u} \text{ and } \mathbf{v}\text{)}$$ **198**

$$\cos \alpha = \frac{\mathbf{u} \cdot \mathbf{v}}{\|\mathbf{u}\| \, \|\mathbf{v}\|} \quad \text{(angle } \alpha \text{ between vectors } \mathbf{u} \neq 0 \text{ and } \mathbf{v} \neq 0\text{)}$$ **199**

$$\mathbf{u} \cdot \mathbf{v} = 0 \text{ if and only if } \mathbf{u} \text{ and } \mathbf{v} \text{ are orthogonal (perpendicular)}$$ **200**

$$\mathbf{u} \cdot \mathbf{v} = \pm \|\mathbf{u}\| \, \|\mathbf{v}\| \text{ if and only if } \mathbf{u} \text{ and } \mathbf{v} \text{ are collinear}$$ **200**

$$\mathbf{a} = \frac{\mathbf{u} \cdot \mathbf{a}}{\|\mathbf{u}\|^2} \mathbf{u} + \frac{\mathbf{v} \cdot \mathbf{a}}{\|\mathbf{v}\|^2} \mathbf{v} \quad \text{(linear combination of orthogonal vectors } \mathbf{u} \text{ and } \mathbf{v}\text{)}$$ **202**

Polar Coordinates

Conversion from rectangular to polar coordinates:

$$x = \rho \cos \theta, \quad y = \rho \sin \theta$$ **219**

Conversion from polar to rectangular coordinates:

$$\rho = \pm\sqrt{x^2 + y^2}$$

$$\theta = \text{Tan}^{-1} \frac{y}{x} \text{ for } x \text{ and } \rho \text{ of the same sign,}$$

$$\theta = \text{Tan}^{-1} \frac{y}{x} + \pi^R \text{ for } x \text{ and } \rho \text{ of opposite signs}$$

$$\sin \theta = \frac{y}{\pm\sqrt{x^2 + y^2}} \quad \text{and} \quad \cos \theta = \frac{x}{\pm\sqrt{x^2 + y^2}}$$ **222**

Polar Coordinates (continued)

Distance between two points, (ρ_1, θ_1) and (ρ_2, θ_2):

$$d = \sqrt{\rho_1^2 + \rho_2^2 - 2\rho_1\rho_2 \cos (\theta_1 - \theta_2)}$$ **224**

Operations with Complex Numbers

For $z = (x, y)$, $z_1 = (x_1, y_1)$, $z_2 = (x_2, y_2)$:

$$z_1 + z_2 = (x_1 + x_2, y_1 + y_2) \quad \text{(sum of complex numbers)}$$ **240**

$$z_1 z_2 = (x_1 x_2 - y_1 y_2, x_1 y_2 + y_1 x_2) \quad \text{(product of complex numbers)}$$ **240**

$$-z = (-x, -y) \quad \text{(negative of a complex number)}$$ **241**

$$z^{-1} = \left(\frac{x}{x^2 + y^2}, \frac{-y}{x^2 + y^2} \right) \quad \text{(multiplicative inverse)}$$ **243**

$$z_1 - z_2 = z_1 + (-z_2) \quad \text{(difference of complex numbers)}$$ **243**

$$\frac{z_1}{z_2} = z_1 z_2^{-1}, z_2 \neq (0, 0) \quad \text{(quotient of complex numbers)}$$ **243**

$$\bar{z} = (x, -y) \quad \text{(conjugate)}$$ **244**

$$z = x + yi \quad \text{(standard form; } x \text{ is real part, } y \text{ is imaginary part)}$$ **246**

$$|z| = \sqrt{x^2 + y^2} \quad \text{(absolute value, or modulus)}$$ **249**

If $z_1 = \rho_1(\cos \theta_1 + i \sin \theta_1)$, $z_2 = \rho_2(\cos \theta_2 + i \sin \theta_2)$, then

$$z_1 z_2 = \rho_1 \rho_2 [\cos (\theta_1 + \theta_2) + i \sin (\theta_1 + \theta_2)]$$ **255**

and

$$\frac{z_1}{z_2} = \frac{\rho_1}{\rho_2} [\cos (\theta_1 - \theta_2) + i \sin (\theta_1 - \theta_2)].$$ **257**

De Moivre's Theorem and its extension to negative integers:

If $z = \rho(\cos \theta + i \sin \theta) \in C$, then

$$z^n = \rho^n(\cos n\theta + i \sin n\theta), \quad n \in J$$ **259**

Each nth root of $z = \rho(\cos \theta + i \sin \theta)$, $n \in N$, can be written in the form

$$\rho^{\frac{1}{n}} \left[\cos \left(\frac{\theta + k360°}{n} \right) + i \sin \left(\frac{\theta + k360°}{n} \right) \right], k = 0, 1, \ldots, n - 1, \ldots$$ **261**

2 × 2 Matrices

For $A = \begin{bmatrix} a_1 & b_1 \\ c_1 & d_1 \end{bmatrix}$, $B = \begin{bmatrix} a_2 & b_2 \\ c_2 & d_2 \end{bmatrix}$, and $r \in \mathfrak{R}$:

$$-A = \begin{bmatrix} -a_1 & -b_1 \\ -c_1 & -d_1 \end{bmatrix} \quad \text{(negative of } A) \qquad \textbf{272}$$

$$A + B = \begin{bmatrix} a_1 + a_2 & b_1 + b_2 \\ c_1 + c_2 & d_1 + d_2 \end{bmatrix} \quad \text{(sum of matrices)} \qquad \textbf{273}$$

$$r \begin{bmatrix} a & b \\ c & a \end{bmatrix} = \begin{bmatrix} ra & rb \\ rc & rd \end{bmatrix} \quad \text{(product of scalar and matrix)} \qquad \textbf{273}$$

$$A - B = A + (-B) \quad \text{(difference of matrices)} \qquad \textbf{274}$$

$$AB = \begin{bmatrix} a_1a_2 + b_1c_2 & a_1b_2 + b_1d_2 \\ c_1a_2 + d_1c_2 & c_1b_2 + d_1d_2 \end{bmatrix} \quad \text{(product of matrices)} \qquad \textbf{277}$$

$$\delta(A) = a_1d_1 - b_1c_1 \quad \text{(the determinant of } A) \qquad \textbf{283}$$

$$A^{-1} = \frac{1}{\delta(A)} \begin{bmatrix} d_1 & -b_1 \\ -c_1 & a_1 \end{bmatrix} \quad \text{(multiplicative inverse)} \qquad \textbf{283}$$

We identify the complex number $a + bi$ with the matrix sum

$$aI + bJ = \begin{bmatrix} a & 0 \\ 0 & a \end{bmatrix} + \begin{bmatrix} 0 & b \\ -b & 0 \end{bmatrix} = \begin{bmatrix} a & b \\ -b & a \end{bmatrix} \qquad \textbf{288}$$

Transformations

Rotation of the plane:

$$x' = x \cos \theta - y \sin \theta \quad \text{and} \quad y' = x \sin \theta + y \cos \theta \qquad \textbf{298}$$

$$\begin{bmatrix} \cos \theta & -\sin \theta \\ \sin \theta & \cos \theta \end{bmatrix} \quad \text{(matrix of the transformation)} \qquad \textbf{299}$$

Rotation of axes:

$$x' = x \cos \theta + y \sin \theta \quad \text{and} \quad y' = -x \sin \theta + y \cos \theta \qquad \textbf{300}$$

$$\begin{bmatrix} \cos \theta & \sin \theta \\ -\sin \theta & \cos \theta \end{bmatrix} \quad \text{(matrix of the transformation)} \qquad \textbf{300}$$

Series

The sum of a finite geometric series $\sum_{i=1}^{n} ar^{i-1}$ $(r \neq 1)$:

$$S_n = \frac{a - ar^n}{1 - r}$$ **316**

The sum of an infinite geometric series $\sum_{i=1}^{\infty} ar^{i-1}$ $(|r| < 1)$:

$$S_\infty = \lim_{n \to \infty} \sum_{i=1}^{n} ar^{i-1} = \frac{a}{1 - r}$$ **317**

Harmonic series: $\sum_{i=1}^{\infty} \frac{1}{i} = 1 + \frac{1}{2} + \frac{1}{3} + \cdots + \frac{1}{n} + \cdots$ **320**

Alternating harmonic series:

$$\sum_{i=1}^{\infty} (-1)^{i-1} \left(\frac{1}{i}\right) = 1 - \frac{1}{2} + \frac{1}{3} - \frac{1}{4} + \cdots + (-1)^{n-1}\frac{1}{n} + \cdots$$ **320**

The infinite-series representation of e^x:

$$e^x = 1 + x + \frac{x^2}{2!} + \frac{x^3}{3!} + \cdots + \frac{x^r}{r!} + \cdots$$ **326**

Infinite-series representations for **cos x** and **sin x**:

$$\cos x = 1 - \frac{x^2}{2!} + \frac{x^4}{4!} + \cdots + (-1)^{n+1} \frac{x^{2n-2}}{(2n - 2)!} + \cdots$$

and

$$\sin x = x - \frac{x^3}{3!} + \frac{x^5}{5!} - \cdots + (-1)^{n+1} \frac{x^{2n-1}}{(2n - 1)!} + \cdots$$ **330**

Absolute value of a complex number (p. 249): If $z = (x, y) \in C$, then the absolute value of z is $|z| = \sqrt{x^2 + y^2}$; also called the **modulus** of the complex number.

Absolute value of a real number (p. 362): If $x \in \Re$, then the absolute value of x, $|x|$, is the nonnegative member of the pair x and $-x$.

Alternating harmonic series (p. 320): The convergent series

$$1 - \tfrac{1}{2} + \tfrac{1}{3} - \tfrac{1}{4} + \cdots + (-1)^{n--1} \frac{1}{n} + \cdots .$$

Amplitude of a complex number (p. 250): The direction angle of the vector (x, y) corresponding to the complex number $x + yi$. Also called the **argument**.

Amplitude of a wave (pp. 35, 79): One-half the vertical distance between the maximum and minimum points on a sine wave.

Angle (pp. 143, 144): The union of two rays (**sides**) with a common endpoint (**vertex**) together with a measure of the rotation involved in going from the initial to the terminal side of the angle.

Arccos: *See* Cos^{-1}.

Arcsin: *See* Sin^{-1}.

Argand plane (p. 249): The coordinate plane consisting of points representing complex numbers. Also called the **complex plane**.

Argument of a complex number: *See* Amplitude of a complex number.

Basis vectors (p. 193): Noncollinear vectors which can generate every vector in a vector space.

Bearing (p. 206): A direction angle measured clockwise from a ray directed to the north.

Binomial series (p. 323): An expanded representation of a power whose base is a binomial.

Bound vector (p. 186): A vector whose initial point is at the origin.

Cartesian product (p. 362): For two sets A and B, the set $A \times B$ of all ordered pairs (a, b), where $a \in A$ and $b \in B$.

Circular function (p. 5): A periodic function defined by means of a unit circle.

Closed interval (p. 361): An interval containing both of its endpoints.

Collinear vectors (p. 187): Geometric vectors lying on the same line.

Complex number (p. 240): An ordered pair (x, y) of real numbers. An alternative representation is $x + yi$.

Complex plane: *See* Argand plane.

Components of a vector (p. 194): If a vector **v** is the sum of noncollinear vectors **u** and **w**, then **u** and **w** are **vector components** of **v**. The norms $\|\mathbf{u}\|$ and $\|\mathbf{w}\|$ are then **scalar components** of **v**.

Composition of functions (p. 367): The **composition** $f \circ g$ of two functions f and g is the function whose rule of correspondence is $(f \circ g)(x) = f[g(x)]$.

Conjugate of a complex number (p. 244): The **conjugate** of $z = (x, y)$ is $\bar{z} = (x, -y)$. In standard form, the conjugate of $x + yi$ is $x - yi$.

Convergent sequence (p. 308): A sequence which has a limit.

Convergent series (p. 314): An infinite series for which the corresponding sequence of partial sums is convergent.

cosecant function (p. 56): $\{(x, y): y = \csc x = \dfrac{1}{\sin x}, \sin x \neq 0\}$

Csc (p. 117): The cosecant function with domain restricted to $-\dfrac{\pi}{2} \leq x \leq \dfrac{\pi}{2}, x \neq 0$.

Csc^{-1} (p. 117): The principal inverse cosecant function.

cosh (p. 333): The hyperbolic cosine function.

Cosh^{-1} (p. 334): The inverse hyperbolic cosine function.

cosine function (p. 6): The set of ordered pairs (x, u) where x is the length of arc on the unit circle from $(1, 0)$ to $\mathbf{P}(u, v)$, and u is the first component of $\mathbf{P}$.

Cos (p. 111): The cosine function with domain restricted to $0 \leq x \leq \pi$.

cos^{-1} (p. 110): The inverse relation of cos, read "the inverse cosine."

Cos^{-1} (p. 111): The inverse function of Cos, read "the principal inverse cosine."

cotangent function (p. 57): $\left\{(x, y): y = \cot x = \dfrac{\cos x}{\sin x}, \sin x \neq 0\right\}$.

Cot (p. 117): The cotangent function with domain restricted to $0 < x < \pi$.

Cot^{-1} (p. 117): The principal inverse cotangent function.

coth (p. 333): The hyperbolic cotangent function.

csch (p. 333): The hyperbolic cosecant function.

Cycle of a wave (pp. 35, 79): Any segment of a wave over a single fundamental period of the wave.

Degree (p. 144): The measure of a central angle of a circle whose intercepted arc is equal in length to $\frac{1}{360}$ of the circumference of the circle. A unit of angle measure.

De Moivre's Theorem (p. 259): If $z = \rho(\cos \theta + i \sin \theta) \in C$, and $n \in N$, then $z^n = \rho^n(\cos n\theta + i \sin n\theta)$.

Determinant of a matrix (p. 283): The determinant of the matrix $A = \begin{bmatrix} a & b \\ c & d \end{bmatrix}$ is the real number $\delta(A) = ad - bc$.

Direction angle of a vector (p. 186): If $\mathbf{v} = (x, y)$, $\|\mathbf{v}\| \neq 0$, the **direction angle** θ of $\mathbf{v}$ is given by

$$\cos \theta = \frac{x}{\|\mathbf{v}\|}, \quad \sin \theta = \frac{y}{\|\mathbf{v}\|}, \quad 0° \leq \theta < 360°.$$

Distance between two points (p. 16): For points $P(u_1, v_1)$ and $Q(u_2, v_2)$, $d(\overline{PQ}) = \sqrt{(u_2 - u_1)^2 + (v_2 - v_1)^2}$.

Divergent sequence (p. 308): A sequence which has no limit.

Divergent series (p. 314): An infinite series for which the corresponding sequence of partial sums has no limit.

Dot product of vectors: *See* Inner product of vectors.

Equivalent open sentences (p. 359): Open sentences having the same solution set.

Equivalent vectors (p. 204): Two free vectors having the same magnitude and direction.

Even function (p. 17): A function f in which for every x in its domain, $-x$ also is in the domain, and $f(-x) = f(x)$.

Free vector (p. 204): Any directed line segment in space.

Frequency of a wave (p. 101): The number of cycles of the wave completed in a unit of time.

Function (p. 363): A set of ordered pairs in which no two ordered pairs have the same first component and different second components.

Fundamental period (p. 2): The least positive period of a periodic function.

Geometric sequence (p. 315): A sequence in which the first term is not 0 and each term after the first term is the product of a constant r and the preceding term. Also called a **geometric progression**.

Geometric series (p. 316): A series whose terms are a geometric sequence.

Geometric vector (p. 186): Any directed line segment.

Harmonic motion: *See* Simple harmonic motion.

Harmonic series (p. 320): The divergent series $1 + \frac{1}{2} + \frac{1}{3} + \cdots + \frac{1}{n} + \cdots$.

Hyperbolic function (p. 333): One of a set of functions defined in terms of powers of e.

Identity (p. 23): An equation which contains one or more variables and which is true for all *permissable* values of the variables, that is, for all values of the variables except those which cause any expression in the equation to be undefined.

Identity matrix (p. 278): The (multiplicative) **identity matrix** is $\begin{bmatrix} 1 & 0 \\ 0 & 1 \end{bmatrix}$.

Image of a vector (p. 292): If a transformation maps a set of vectors A into a set of vectors B, each vector in B is an **image** of a vector in A.

Imaginary axis (p. 249): The y-axis in the Argand plane.

Imaginary part of a complex number (p. 246): The **imaginary part** of the complex number (x, y), or $x + yi$, is y.

Infinite sequence: *See* Sequence.

Infinite series: *See* Series.

Inner product of vectors (p. 198): If $\mathbf{u} = (x_1, y_1)$ and $\mathbf{v} = (x_2, y_2)$, the inner product of $\mathbf{u}$ and $\mathbf{v}$ is $\mathbf{u} \cdot \mathbf{v} = x_1x_2 + y_1y_2$. Also called the **scalar product**, or **dot product**, of $\mathbf{u}$ and $\mathbf{v}$.

Interval (p. 361): An interval of real numbers is the set of all real numbers between two real numbers called the **endpoints** of the interval. An interval may include one or both endpoints, or neither.

Interval of convergence (p. 320): The set of all values of x for which a power series formed from a sequence of the form $\{a_{n-1}x^{n-1}\}$ converges.

Inverse of a complex number (p. 243): The (multiplicative) inverse of the nonzero complex number $z = (x, y)$ is the complex number $\left(\dfrac{x}{x^2 + y^2}, \dfrac{-y}{x^2 + y^2} \right)$.

Inverse of a matrix (p. 283): The (multiplicative) **inverse** of a matrix $A = \begin{bmatrix} a & b \\ c & d \end{bmatrix}$ in which $ad - bc \neq 0$ is the matrix $A^{-1} = \left(\dfrac{1}{ad - bc} \right) \begin{bmatrix} d & -b \\ -c & a \end{bmatrix}$.

Inverse function (p. 110): An inverse relation that is a function.

Inverse relation (p. 109): A relation R^{-1} obtained by interchanging the components in every ordered pair in a given relation R.

Invertible matrix (p. 283): A matrix having a multiplicative inverse. Also called a **nonsingular matrix**.

Lag of a wave: *See* Phase shift.

Law of Cosines (p. 170): In a triangle, the square of the length of any side equals the sum of the squares of the lengths of the other two sides decreased by twice the product of the lengths of these two sides and the cosine of the included angle.

Law of Sines (p. 174): The sine of an angle of a triangle is proportional to the length of the opposite side.

Lead of a wave: *See* Phase shift.

Limit of a sequence (p. 308): If for every positive real number d (no matter how small) there is a natural number m such that for all natural numbers $n \geq m$, the difference $|L - s_n| < d$, then L is called the **limit** of the sequence $\{s_n\}$.

Limit of a series (p. 314): The limit of the corresponding sequence of partial sums. Also called the **sum** of the series.

Linear combination of two vectors (p. 192): For vectors **u** and **v**, the sum $\mathbf{a} = r\mathbf{u} + s\mathbf{v}$, where $r, s \in \Re$, is called a **linear combination** of **u** and **v**.

Linear interpolation (p. 154): A process for approximating the value of a function $f(c)$, where $a < c < b$ and $f(a)$ and $f(b)$ are known, which uses the segment with endpoints $(a, f(a))$ and $(b, f(b))$ to approximate the graph of f over the interval with endpoints a and b.

Magnitude of a vector (p. 186): The length of a geometric vector; equal to the **norm** of the corresponding vector.

Mapping of the plane: *See* Transformation of the plane.

Matrix (p. 272): A rectangular array of numbers.

Matrix of a transformation (p. 292): A matrix defining a function which maps each vector in the plane into another vector in the plane.

Measure of an angle (p. 144): A number assigned to an angle corresponding to the amount of rotation associated with the angle.

Minute (p. 153): In angle measure, one-sixtieth of a degree.

Modulus of a complex number: *See* Absolute value of a complex number.

Negative of a complex number (p. 241): If the complex number $z = (x, y)$, the **negative** of z is the complex number $-z = (-x, -y)$.

Negative of a matrix (p. 272): If $A = \begin{bmatrix} a & b \\ c & d \end{bmatrix}$, the **negative** of A is the matrix $-A = \begin{bmatrix} -a & -b \\ -c & -d \end{bmatrix}$.

Negative of a vector (p. 187): If $\mathbf{v} = (x, y)$, the **negative** of **v** is $-\mathbf{v} = (-x, -y)$.

Nonsingular matrix (p. 283): A matrix which has a multiplicative inverse.

Norm of a vector (p. 186): The **norm** of $\mathbf{v} = (x, y)$ is $\|\mathbf{v}\| = \sqrt{x^2 + y^2}$.

Odd function (p. 19): A function f in which for every x in its domain, $-x$ also is in the domain, and $f(-x) = -f(x)$.

Open interval (p. 361): An interval of real numbers that contains neither of its endpoints.

Open sentence in one variable (p. 359): A sentence which contains a variable.

Order of a matrix (p. 274): The number of rows and columns in a matrix. A matrix of order $m \times n$ has m rows and n columns.

Orthogonal vectors (p. 193): Vectors whose direction angles differ by 90°.

Period of a function: *See* Periodic function.

Periodic function (p. 2): A nonconstant function f having the property that for some nonzero number p and for every x in its domain, $x + p$ and $x - p$ are also in the domain and $f(x + p) = f(x)$. The number p is called a **period** of f, and if f has a least positive period, that period is called the **fundamental period** of f.

Phase shift (p. 88): The graph of $y = \sin(x - c)$ is said to **lead** (that is, to come before, as we view it from left to right) the graph of $y = \sin x$ if $c < 0$, and to **lag** (come after) if $c > 0$. The constant c is called the **phase shift**.

Polar axis (p. 216): The ray used as a reference for locating points in a polar coordinate system.

Polar coordinate system (p. 216): A coordinate system of the plane consisting of a fixed ray (the **polar axis**), in which the location of each point (ρ, θ) is determined by its directed distance, ρ, from the endpoint (the **pole**) of the fixed ray, and an angle, θ, determined by the polar axis, the pole, and the point.

Polar coordinates of a point (p. 216): The ordered pair (ρ, θ) paired with the point in a polar coordinate system.

Polar form of a complex number (p. 255): The **polar form** of the complex number $z = (x, y)$ is $z = \rho(\cos\theta + i\sin\theta)$, where $|\rho| = \sqrt{x^2 + y^2}$, $\sin\theta = \dfrac{y}{\rho}$, $\cos\theta = \dfrac{x}{\rho}$.

Pole (p. 216): The endpoint of the reference ray in a polar coordinate system.

Power series (p. 319): A series formed from a sequence of the form $\{a_{n-1}x^{n-1}\}$, where the a's are constants.

Pre-image of a vector (p. 292): If a transformation maps a set of vectors A into a set of vectors B, each vector in A is a **pre-image** of a vector in B.

Projection of a vector (p. 200): The vector component $\mathbf{a}_u$ of a vector $\mathbf{a}$ parallel to the vector $\mathbf{u}$.

Pure imaginary number (p. 246): A complex number of the form $(0, y)$, or yi ($y \neq 0$).

Quadrantal angle (p. 147): An angle in standard position which has its terminal side on a coordinate axis.

Radian (p. 144): The measure of a central angle of a circle whose intercepted arc is equal in length to the radius of the circle. A unit of angle measure.

Ratio Test (p. 321): If the sequence of ratios $\left\{\dfrac{a_{n+1}}{a_n}\right\}$ converges to L and if $|L| < 1$, then the series $\sum\limits_{i=1}^{\infty} a_i$ converges. If $|L| > 1$, the series diverges, and if $|L| = 1$, the test fails.

Real axis (p. 249): The x-axis in the Argand plane.

Real part of a complex number (p. 246): The **real part** of the complex number (x, y), or $x + yi$, is x.

Reduction identity (p. 30): An identity used to express any value of a periodic function in terms of a function value in the first quadrant.

Reference angle (p. 150): The positive acute angle α between the x-axis and the terminal side of any angle θ.

Relation (p. 363): Any set of ordered pairs.

Resolution of a vector (p. 194): An expression of a vector as a linear combination of two vectors.

Resultant of vectors (p. 188): The sum of two geometric vectors.

Rotational velocity (p. 95): The ratio of the arc length traveled by a point (or a ray) on a unit circle to the time elapsed.

Scalar (p. 185): A real number.

Scalar product of two vectors: *See* Inner product of vectors.

secant function (p. 56): $\left\{(x, y): y = \sec x = \dfrac{1}{\cos x}, \cos x \neq 0\right\}$.

Sec (p. 117): The secant function with domain restricted to $0 \le x \le \pi, x \neq \dfrac{\pi}{2}$.

Sec^{-1} (p. 117): The principal inverse secant function.

sech (p. 333): The hyperbolic secant function.

Second (p. 153): One-sixtieth of a minute.

Sequence (p. 307): A function, denoted $\{a_n\}$, whose domain is the set N of natural numbers. The members of the range are called the **terms** of the sequence. Also called an **infinite sequence**.

Sequence of partial sums (p. 311): The sequence $\left\{\displaystyle\sum_{i=1}^{n} a_i\right\}$ for a sequence $\{a_n\}$. Also denoted $\{A_n\}$.

Series (p. 311): The expression $a_1 + a_2 + a_3 + \cdots + a_n + \cdots$ with a corresponding sequence $\{a_n\}$. Also called an **infinite series**.

Sigma notation (p. 312): The notation $\displaystyle\sum_{i=1}^{n} a_i$ which represents the sum $a_1 + a_2 + a_3 + \cdots + a_n$. Also called **summation notation**.

Simple harmonic motion (p. 100): The movement of a particle back and forth between the endpoints of a segment in accord with an equation of the form $y = a \cos(\omega t + b)$ or $y = a \sin(\omega t + b)$.

sine function (p. 6): The set of ordered pairs (x, v), where x is the length of arc on the unit circle from $(1, 0)$ to $P(u, v)$, and v is the second component of P.

Sin (p. 112): The sin function with domain restricted to $-\dfrac{\pi}{2} \le x \le \dfrac{\pi}{2}$.

Sin^{-1} (p. 113): The inverse function of Sin, read "the principal inverse sine."

Sine wave (pp. 35, 79): The graph of a function defined by an equation of the form $y = a \sin b(x - c) + d$ or $y = a \cos b(x - c) + d$, where $a, b, c, d \in \Re$ and $a, b \neq 0$.

Singular matrix (p. 283): A matrix which has no multiplicative inverse.

sinh (p. 333): The hyperbolic sine function.

sinh^{-1} (p. 334): The inverse hyperbolic sine function.

Solution set of an open sentence (p. 359): The subset of the replacement set for which the accompanying open sentence becomes a true statement. Also called the **truth set**.

Standard form of a complex number (p. 246): $x + yi$, with $x, y \in \Re$.

Standard position for an angle (p. 145): An angle whose vertex is at the origin and whose initial side coincides with the positive x-axis is said to be in **standard position**.

Standard position for a vector (p. 186): A vector with initial point at the origin is said to be in standard position.

Summation notation: *See* Sigma notation.

tangent function (p. 49): $\left\{ (x, y) \colon y = \tan x = \dfrac{\sin x}{\cos x}, \cos x \neq 0 \right\}.$

Tan (p. 117): The tangent function with domain restricted to $-\dfrac{\pi}{2} < x < \dfrac{\pi}{2}.$

Tan^{-1} (p. 117): The principal inverse tangent function.

tanh (p. 333): The hyperbolic tangent function.

tanh^{-1} (p. 334): The inverse hyperbolic tangent function.

Transformation of the plane (p. 292): A function that maps each vector $\begin{bmatrix} x \\ y \end{bmatrix}$ in the plane into a vector $\begin{bmatrix} x' \\ y' \end{bmatrix}$ in the plane. Also called a **mapping of the plane**.

Trigonometric function (p. 148): A function with a set of angles as domain and a set of real numbers as range.

Uniform circular motion (p. 95): If a point moves around a circle at a constant speed, it is traveling with **uniform circular motion**.

Unit circle (p. 5): The circle with radius 1 and center at the origin.

Unit vector (p. 193): A vector whose norm is 1.

Variable (p. 359): A symbol which may represent any element of a specified set. The members of the set are called the values of the variable.

Zero complex number (p. 241): $(0, 0)$, or $0 + 0i$.

Zero matrix (p. 272): A matrix all of whose entries are zeros.

Zero vector (p. 187): The vector $(0, 0) = \mathbf{0}$. Geometrically, the origin.

Index

Absolute value
  of complex numbers, 249
  of real numbers, 362
Addition
  of angles, 146
  axioms of, 239, 358
  of complex numbers, 239–241
  of functions, 92, 366
  of matrices, 273
  of ordinates for graphing, 92–93
  of vectors, 188
Addition properties
  of cos, 15–19
  of sin, 27–30
Additive identity and inverse elements
  for complex numbers, 241
  for matrices, 273
  for real numbers, 358
  for vectors, 187
Algebraic identity, 23
Alternating harmonic series, 320
Ambiguous case, 177–179
Amplitude
  of a complex number, 250
  of a function or wave, 35, 79
Angle(s), 143
  of depression, 169
  difference of, 146
  dihedral, 383
  direction, 186, 204
  of elevation, 169
  measure of, 144–145
  negative, 146
  quadrant of terminal side, 147
  quadrantal, 147
  reference, 150
  rotation of, 144–146
  sides, 144–145
  standard position, 145
  sum of, 146

Antilogarithm, 374
Applications
  computer, 46, 74, 105, 181, 304, 343
  Environmental Exploration, 139
  Exploring the Universe, 267
  Synthesis and Analysis of Waves, 340
  Waves and the World We Live In, 76
  World Maps, 234
Arccos x, *See* $\mathrm{Cos}^{-1} x$
Arc length
  of Cos^{-1} and Sin^{-1}, 122–125
  in terms of time, 95–98
Arcsin x, *See* $\mathrm{Sin}^{-1} x$
Area of a triangle, 173–176
ARISTARCHUS OF SAMOS, 268
Argand plane, 249
Argument of a complex number, 250
Associative properties
  of complex numbers, 240–242
  of a field, 239
  of matrices, 273–274, 278
  of real numbers, 358
  of vectors, 190
Asymptotes of circular functions, 51, 61–62
Axiom(s)
  of a field, 239–242
  for real numbers, 358
Axis
  imaginary, 249
  polar, 216
  real, 249
  reflection in an, 296

Basic identities, 66
Basis vectors, 192–197
Bearing, 206
Binary operations, 239, 357
Binomial series, 323–325
Bound vector, 186

Cartesian coordinates
  conversion from polar, 219
  conversion to polar, 222
Cartesian product, 362
Centangle, 147
Centrifugal force, 213
Characteristic of a logarithm, 373
Characteristic equation, 286
Characteristic polynomial, 286
Characteristic roots, 286
Checking solutions, 129
Circle
  in angle measurement, 144–146
  in polar coordinates, 220–222, 225
  uniform circular motion, 95–98
  unit, 5
Circuit, 101
Circular functions, 5–11, 49–58
  basic identities, 66
  graphs, 79–92
  reciprocal, 56–58
Circular parts of a spherical triangle, 382
Cis θ, 255
Closure properties
  of complex numbers, 240–241
  of a field, 239
  of matrices, 273
  of real numbers, 358
  of vectors, 190
Collinear vectors, 187, 200
Common ratio of a geometric sequence, 316
Commutative properties
  of complex numbers, 240–242
  of a field, 239
  of matrices, 273–274, 277–280
  of real numbers, 358
  of vectors, 190
Commutative group, 190, 273
Compass rose, 206
Completeness Axiom, 358
Complex numbers, 239–266, 287–290
  addition of, 239–241
  equality of, 240
  field axioms for, 239
  graphical representation of, 249–253

matrix representation of, 287–289
multiplicative identity, 242–243
multiplicative inverse, 242–243
polar form, 254–257
product of, 239–241, 250–252, 255
quotients of, 242–244, 256–257
roots of, 261–264
standard form, 246
and vectors, 249–253
Complex plane, 249
Components of a vector, 194, 201
  scalar, 194
Composition of functions, 119–125, 367–368
Comprehensive Test, 345–355
Computer investigations, 46–47, 74–75, 105,
    181–183, 304–305, 343–344
Conjugate of a complex number, 244
Convergent infinite series, 314
Convergent sequence, 308–309
Coordinate systems
  Cartesian, 363
  polar, 216–230
Cos^{-1}
  as circular function, 111–112, 119–125
  as trigonometric function, 161–162
Cosecant, 56, 62–63, 68
  definition of, 56
  geometric interpretation of, 68
  graph, 62
Cosh, 333
Cosh^{-1}, 334
Cosine function
  addition properties of, 15–19
  basic identities, 66
  change by quadrants, 12
  definition of, 6
  double-angle formulas, 152
  even function, 17
  geometric interpretation, 7
  graph of, 32–35
  graphs of families of functions involving,
    79–91
  half-angle formulas, 152
  inverse of, *See* Cos^{-1}
  period, 7

reduction identities, 30
series for, 330
sign by quadrant, 7
for special values of *x*, 10–12
for 2*x*, 38
using tables, 40–43, 153–157
for $\frac{x}{2}$, 39
Cosines, Law of, 170–173
  in spherical trigonometry, 388
    dual of, 389
Cot^{-1}, 117–120, 123, 162
Cotangent, 57, 62–63, 68
  definition of, 57
  geometric interpretation, 68
  graph, 62
Coth, 333
Csc^{-1}, 117–120, 123, 162
Csch, 333
Cumulative review
  Chapters 1–3, 106–107
  Chapters 4–6, 232–233
  Chapters 7–9, 338–339
Current, alternating, 101
Cycle of a function or wave, 35, 79

Decimals, 318, 359
Degree measure, 144
De Moivre's theorem, 259
Depression, angle of, 169
Determinant, 283
Difference
  of angles, 146
  of functions, 366
  of vectors, 189
Dihedral angle, 383
Directed line segment, 186, 204
Direction of vectors, 185–187, 204
  opposite, 187
Direction angle of vectors, 186
Displacement in harmonic motion, 100

Distance
  between two points, 16, 199
  on the number line, 362
Distributive axiom, 239, 273, 278, 358
Divergent infinite series, 314
Divergent sequence, 308
Division
  of complex numbers, 242–244, 256–257
  of functions, 366
Domain, 363
Dot product, 198
Double-angle formulas, 152
Dual of the Law of Cosines, 389
Dummy symbol, 313

e, 326
Eigenvalues, 286
Elements of a set, 356
Elevation, angle of, 169
Endpoints of an interval, 361–362
Entries in a matrix, 272
Environmental Exploration, 139–141
Equality
  axioms for the real numbers, 358
  of complex numbers, 240
  of matrices, 272
  of vectors, 187
Equations
  characteristic, 286
  checking solutions, 129
  general solution, 127
  graphs of polar, 224–229
  particular solution, 127
  quadratic, 127–136, 360
  transformations on, 359–360
  trigonometric, 161–163
Equivalent open sentences, 359, 361
Equivalent vectors, 204
ERATOSTHENES, 269
EULER, LEONHARD, 332
Euler's equations, 332
Even functions, 17
Exploring the Universe, 267

Factorials, 324
Families of functions, graphs, 79–92
Field, 239–243, 287, 357
    ordered, 357
Forces, 211–213
FOURIER, JEAN BAPTISTE JOSEPH, 341
Fourier analysis, 341–342
Four-leaved rose, 226
Free vectors, 204–211
Frequency, 101
Function(s)
    amplitude of a, 35, 79
    circular, 5–11
    composition of, 367–368
    cycle of a, 35, 79
    definition, notation, 363–364
    difference of, 366
    even, 17
    hyperbolic, 332–334
    inverse circular, 109–125
    inverse trigonometric, 161–163
    odd, 19
    periodic, 1–3
    product of, 366
    quotient of, 366
    reciprocal, 56–63, 119–120
    sum of, 92, 366
    trigonometric, 148–151
Fundamental period, 2

General solution, 127
Geometric progression, 315
Geometric sequence, 315
Geometric series, 316–317
Geometric vector, 186–191, 200
Governor for an engine, 215
Graphs
    of complex numbers, 249–253
    of cos and sin, 32–36
    of Cos^{-1} and Sin^{-1}, 111, 113
    of cot, csc, sec, 60–63
    of Cot^{-1}, Csc^{-1}, Sec^{-1}, 118

of families of functions, using amplitude,
    period, cycle, and phase shift, 79–91
to illustrate identities, 36, 54
in the plane, 363–367
polar, 219–229
of sums of functions, 92–93
of tan, 51–53
of Tan^{-1}, 118
wave, 35
Graphing by addition of ordinates, 92–93
Great circles, 382
    poles of, 382
Ground speed, 208
Groups, commutative, 190, 273

Half-angle identities, 152
Half-angle law, 173
Half-open interval, 361
Harmonic motion, 100–103
Harmonic series, 320
Heading, 206
Heron's formula, 176
HIPPARCHUS, 268
Hyperbolic functions, 332–334

Identities
    algebraic, 23
    definition of, 23
    list of basic, 66
    procedures for deriving and verifying,
        23–25, 64–70
    reduction, 30
    trigonometric, 152
Identity elements
    See Additive identity and inverse elements
    and Multiplicative identity and inverse
        elements
Identity matrix, 278
Images, 292
Imaginary axis, 249
Imaginary number, pure, 246
Inclined planes, problems involving, 211–216

Index in summation notation, 312
Inequalities, 361
Infinite sequences, 307–310
Infinite series, 311–334
  convergent, 314
  divergent, 314
Initial point, 186
Initial side, 144
Inner product of vectors, 198–203
Integers, 3, 357
Interpolation, linear, 154–157, 374
Intersection of sets, 357
Interval
  closed, 361
  of convergence, 321
  open, 361
  half-open, 361
  graph of, 362
"Into" mapping, 293
Inverse circular functions, 109–125
Inverse elements
  See Additive identity and inverse elements
  and Multiplicative identity and inverse
    elements
Inverse relations, 109–110
Inverse trigonometric functions, 161–163
Invertible matrices, 283
Irrational numbers, 359
Isomorphism, 246

Lag, 88
Latitude, 235, 383
Law(s)
  of cosines, 170–173, 198, 208, 388
  half-angle, 173
  of sines, 174–176, 208, 388
  of tangents, 176, 388
Lead, 88
Length of a line segment, 16
Limit
  of a sequence, 308
  of a series, 314
Linear combination, 192

Linear interpolation, 154–157, 374
Logarithms
  to base 10, 369–370
  computations using, 376
  of trigonometric functions, 378–381
  use in problem solving, 175
  use of tables, 372–375
Longitude, 383

Magnification, 293, 296
Magnitude, 186
Mantissa, 373
Mapping of the plane, 292
Maps, 234–237
Matrices, 271–305
  for complex numbers, 287–289
  computer investigations, 304–305
  determinants of, 283
  equal, 272
  identity, 278
  inverse, 282–284
  negative, 272
  operations with, 271–284
  order of, 274
  products of, 277–280
  properties of, 273
  of rotation, 299–300
  transformation, 292–296
  for vectors, 291–296
  zero, 272
Measuring circle, 145
Member of a set, 356
Meridian circles, 383
Minute of angle measure, 153
Modulus of a complex number, 249
Motion
  simple harmonic, 100–103
  uniform circular, 95–98
Multiplication
  axioms for, 239, 358
  of complex numbers, 239–241, 250–252, 255

of functions, 366
of matrices, 273, 277–280
Multiplicative identity and inverse elements
  for complex numbers, 242–243
  for matrices, 282–284
  for real numbers, 358

NAPIER, JOHN, 387
Napier's rules, 387
Natural numbers, 308, 357
Nautical mile, 383
Navigational applications, 204–211
Negative, 146, 187, 241, 272
Nonsingular matrix, 283
Norm, 186
  unit, 193
Notation
  factorial, 324
  scientific, 372
  set-builder, 356, 364
  summation, 312
nth term of a sequence, 308
Number line
  distance on the, 362
  for measuring arcs, 5–7, 10–11
Numbers
  axioms for the real, 358
  irrational, 359
  natural, 308, 357
  rational, 357
  real, 3, 239, 287, 357–359
  See also Complex numbers

Objectives, chapter, 1, 49, 79, 109, 143, 185,
  239, 271, 307
Oblique spherical triangles, 388
Odd function, 19
One-to-one correspondence, 308
"Onto" mapping, 293

Open interval, 361
Open sentences
  involving circular functions, 127–136
  equivalent, 359, 361
  inequalities and absolute value, 361–362
  transformations of, 359, 361
  See also Equations
Opposite directions, 187
Opposite parts of a spherical triangle, 387
Order of a matrix, 274
Order axioms, 358
Ordered fields, 357
Ordered pairs, 186, 240, 362
Ordinates, graphing by addition of, 92–93
Origin, reflection in the, 296
Orthogonal vectors, 193, 200

Parallelogram law, 188
Partial sums, sequence of, 311
Particular solution, 127
Period of a function, 2, 84
Periodic functions, 1–3
Periodic motion, 95–103
Phase shift, 88, 100–103
Plane
  complex, 249
  graphing in the, 362–368
  mapping of the, 292
  rotations of the, 296, 298–299
  transformations of the, 292–296, 299–301
Point rotating about a circle, 95
Points
  distance between, 16
  initial, 186
Polar axis, 216
Polar coordinates, 216–230
  conversion from Cartesian, 219
  conversion to Cartesian, 222
Polar form for complex numbers, 254–257
Polar graphs, 219–229
Polar representation of complex numbers,
  254–265

Polar triangles, 389
Pole
  of a great circle, 382
  in polar plane, 216, 218
Power series, 319
Pre-images, 292
Principal inverse functions, 110–111
Product, *See* Multiplication
Progression, geometric, 315
Projections, 234–237
Proper subset, 357
Protractor, 143
Pure imaginary number, 246
PYTHAGORAS, 340
Pythagorean identity, 7, 159, 167, 170, 385

Quadrantal angle, 147
Quadrantal values of cos and sin, 10–12
Quadratic equations, 360
Quotient, *See* Division

Radian measure, 144
Range, 363
Ratio, common, 316
Ratio test, 320–321
Rational numbers, 357
Real axis, 249
Real numbers, 3, 239, 287, 357–359
  axioms for the, 358
Real part of a complex number, 246
Reciprocal functions, 56–63, 119–120
Reduction identities, 29–30, 66, 148
Reference angles, 150
Reflection
  in an axis, 296
  in the line $y = x$, 111, 296
  in the line $y = -x$, 296
  in the origin, 296
Reflexive property of equality, 358
Relations, 109–110, 363
  inverse, 109–110
Resolving vectors, 194

Resultant of vectors, 188
Right triangles, *See* Triangles
Roots
  of complex numbers, 261–264
  of negative numbers, 246
Rotation(s)
  of angle, 145
  of axes, 300–301
  of the plane, 296, 298–299
Rotational velocity, 95–98

Scalar, 185
Scalar components of a vector, 194
Scalar product, 198
Scientific notation, 372
Sec^{-1}, 117–120, 123, 162
Secant, 56
  definition of, 56
  geometric interpretation, 68
  graph, 60–62
Sech, 333
Second of angle measure, 153
Self-dual law, 389
Sentences, open
  See Open sentences
Sequences, 307
  convergent, 308
  divergent, 308
  geometric, 315
  infinite, 307
  limit of, 308
  of partial sums, 311
Series, 311–334
  alternating harmonic, 320
  binomial, 323–325
  convergent infinite, 314
  for cos x, 330
  divergent infinite, 314
  geometric, 316
  harmonic, 320
  limit of, 314
  power, 319
  for sin x, 330

Set(s), 356–359
  intersection of, 357
  null, 357
  operations with, 357
  of ordered pairs, 363–364
  solution, 127, 359
  truth, 359
  union of, 357
  universal, 357
  well-defined, 356
Sextants, 383
Shearing, 294, 296
Shrinking, 296
Sides of an angle, 144
Sigma notation, 312
Significant figures, 168
Simple harmonic motion, 100–103
Sin^{-1}, 112–114, 119–125, 162
Sine function
  addition properties of, 27–30
  basic identities, 66
  change by quadrants, 12
  definition of, 6
  double-angle formulas, 152
  geometric interpretation, 7
  graph, 32–35
  graphs of families of functions
    involving, 79–91
  half-angle formulas, 152
  inverse of, *See* Sin^{-1}
  odd function, 19
  period, 7
  reduction identities, 30
  series for, 330
  sign by quadrant, 7
  for special values of x, 10–12
  for $2x$, 38
  using tables, 40–43, 153–157
  for $\frac{x}{2}$, 39
Sine formula in spherical trigonometry, 385
Sine waves, 35, 79–91
Sines, Law of, 174–176
  dual of, 389
  in spherical trigonometry, 388

Singular matrix, 283
Sinh, 333
Sinh^{-1}, 334
Slope of a line, 154
Solution of triangles, 164–179, 181–183
Solution sets
    See Open sentences
Spanning, 193
Speed, rotational, 95–97
Spheres, 382–384
Spherical triangles
  oblique, 388
  right, 384–385
Spherical trigonometry, 382–389
  Law of Cosines, 388
  Law of Sines, 388
  Law of Tangents, 388
  Pythagorean theorem, 384–385
  sine formula, 385
  tangent formula, 385
Standard form of complex numbers, 245–247
Standard position, 145, 186
Stretching, 295–296
Subsets, 356
Subsets of $\Re$, 357, 359
Subtraction
  of complex numbers, 242–244
  of matrices, 274
Sum, *see* Addition
Summaries, chapter, 44, 72, 104, 137, 179,
    230, 265, 302, 335
Summation notation, 312
Symbols, list of, x
Symmetric property of equality, 358
Synthesis and Analysis of Waves, 340

Tables
  common logarithms of numbers, 402
  $\cos\left(m \cdot \frac{\pi}{2}\right)$ and $\sin\left(m \cdot \frac{\pi}{2}\right)$, 391
  logarithms of trigonometric functions, 404
  squares and square roots, 401
  trigonometric functions (degrees), 392
  trigonometric functions (radians), 397

Tables, use of
  for circular functions, 40–43
  for logarithmic functions, 372–375
  for trigonometric functions, 153–157
Tan^{-1}, 117–120, 123, 162
Tangent formula in spherical trigonometry,
  385
Tangent function, 49–53, 64–68, 152
  addition formulas, 64–65
  definition of, 49
  double-angle formula, 152
  geometric interpretation, 68
  graph, 51–52
  half-angle formula, 152
  period, 52
  reduction formulas, 66
  of $2x$, 65
  of $\frac{x}{2}$, 65
Tangents, Law of, 176
  in spherical trigonometry, 388
Tanh, 333
Tanh^{-1}, 334
Telescopes, 140, 267
Term of a sequence, 307
Terminal point, 186
Terminal side, 144, 158–160
Tests, chapter, 45, 73, 104, 138, 180, 232,
  266, 303, 337
Test, comprehensive, 345–355
Transformation
  of open sentences, 359, 361
  of the plane, 292–296, 298–301
Transformation matrices, 291–296, 299–300
Transitive property of equality, 358
Translation
  of sine waves, 81, 86
  of vectors, 204
Triangles
  area of, 173–176
  polar, 389
  right, 164–169, 380–381
  solution of, 164–179, 181–183
  spherical, 384–386
Trichotomy property, 358

Trigonometric equations, 161–163
Trigonometric functions, 148–151
  computations involving, 380–381
  geometric properties, 167
  inverse, 161–163
  logarithms of, 404
  in terms of point on terminal side,
    158–161
  reduction formulas, 148
  using tables for, 153–157
Trigonometric identities, 152
True course, 208
Truth set, 359
  See also Open sentences
Tuning fork, 100, 341

Uniform circular motion, 95–98
Union of sets, 357
Unit circle, 5–11
Unit norm, 193
Unit vector, 193, 195
Universal set, 357

Variable, 359
Vector(s), 185–216, 249–253, 291–296
  addition, 188
  angle between, 198
  applications to forces, 211–216
  applications to navigation, 204–209
  basis, 192–197
  binary operations on, 188
  bound, 186
  collinear, 187, 200
  and complex numbers, 249–253
  components, 194, 201
  difference of, 189
  direction angle of, 186, 194
  equal, 187
  equivalent, 204
  free, 204–211
  geometric representation, 186–191
  inner product, 198–203

matrix representation of, 291–296
negative, 187
norm, 186, 194
notation, 185
orthogonal, 193, 200
properties of, 185–203
product with a scalar, 188
projection, 200–201
resultant, 188
standard position, 186
sum of, 188
unit, 193, 195
zero, 187
Vector spaces, 190, 273–274, 291
Velocity, rotational, 95–98
Voltage, 101

Wave graph, 35, 390
Waves
    amplitude of, 35, 79
    cycle of, 35, 79
    electromagnetic, 76–77
    frequency of, 101
    sine, 35, 79–91
    translation of sine, 81, 86
Waves and the World We Live In, 76–77
Weight, 211
World Maps, 234

Zero complex number, 241
Zero matrix, 272
Zero vector, 187

Credits

page 76   W. B. Finch
      77   Communications Satellite Corporation
     139   United States Naval Department
     140   National Aeronautics and Space Administration
     141   National Aeronautics and Space Administration
     267   National Aeronautics and Space Administration
268–269   National Aeronautics and Space Administration
     341   Jeff Albertson/Stock, Boston

BCDEFGHIJ–FL–8543210/79

Answers To Odd-Numbered Exercises

Chapter 1   The Cosine and Sine Functions

Exercises 1–1, pages 3–5

1. (a) 4 (b) 3 (c) 5   **3.** (a) 4 (b) 1 (c) -1 **5.** (a) 8 (b) 2 (c) 0   **7.** (a), (b), (d), (f), (g)   **9.** fundamental period $= 1$ **11.** fundamental period $= 2$

Exercises 1–2, pages 8–9

1. $\dfrac{5\pi}{2} = \dfrac{\pi}{2} + 2\pi,\, k = 1$ **3.** $-\dfrac{5\pi}{4} = \dfrac{3\pi}{4} + (-2\pi),\, k = -1$ **5.** $-\dfrac{9\pi}{4} = \dfrac{7\pi}{4} + (-4\pi),\, k = -2$

7. $5\pi = \pi + 4\pi,\, k = 2$ **9.** $2107\pi = \pi + 2106\pi,\, k = 1053$ **11.** $\sin \dfrac{\pi}{2}$ **13.** $\sin \dfrac{3\pi}{2}$ **15.** $\sin \dfrac{5\pi}{3}$

17. $\cos 0$ **19.** $\cos 0.125\pi$ **21.** $\sin \pi$ **23.** $\dfrac{\sqrt{2}}{2}$ **25.** $\frac{1}{2}$ **27.** $-\dfrac{\sqrt{3}}{2}$ **29.** $\cos 0 = 1,\, \sin 0 = 0$;

$\cos \dfrac{\pi}{2} = 0,\, \sin \dfrac{\pi}{2} = 1;\, \cos \pi = -1,\, \sin \pi = 0;\, \cos \dfrac{3\pi}{2} = 0,\, \sin \dfrac{3\pi}{2} = -1$ **31.** 2π **33.** π

Exercises 1–3, pages 13–14

1.

x	$\cos x$	$\sin x$
0	1	0
$\dfrac{\pi}{6}$	$\dfrac{\sqrt{3}}{2} \doteq 0.87$	$\dfrac{1}{2} = 0.5$
$\dfrac{\pi}{4}$	$\dfrac{\sqrt{2}}{2} \doteq 0.71$	$\dfrac{\sqrt{2}}{2} \doteq 0.71$
$\dfrac{\pi}{3}$	$\dfrac{1}{2} = 0.5$	$\dfrac{\sqrt{3}}{2} \doteq 0.87$
$\dfrac{\pi}{2}$	0	1
π	-1	0
$\dfrac{3\pi}{2}$	0	-1

3.

x	$\cos x$	$\sin x$
$\dfrac{\pi}{4}$	$\dfrac{\sqrt{2}}{2} \doteq 0.71$	$\dfrac{\sqrt{2}}{2} \doteq 0.71$
$\dfrac{3\pi}{4}$	$-\dfrac{\sqrt{2}}{2} \doteq -0.71$	$\dfrac{\sqrt{2}}{2} \doteq 0.71$
$\dfrac{5\pi}{4}$	$-\dfrac{\sqrt{2}}{2} \doteq -0.71$	$-\dfrac{\sqrt{2}}{2} \doteq -0.71$
$\dfrac{7\pi}{4}$	$\dfrac{\sqrt{2}}{2} \doteq 0.71$	$-\dfrac{\sqrt{2}}{2} \doteq -0.71$

5. $P_1\left(\dfrac{\sqrt{2}}{2}, \dfrac{\sqrt{2}}{2}\right),\, P_3\left(-\dfrac{\sqrt{2}}{2}, -\dfrac{\sqrt{2}}{2}\right),\, P_4\left(-\dfrac{\sqrt{2}}{2}, \dfrac{\sqrt{2}}{2}\right)$ **7.** $P_1\left(\dfrac{\sqrt{3}}{2}, \dfrac{1}{2}\right),\, P_2\left(-\dfrac{\sqrt{3}}{2}, \dfrac{1}{2}\right),$

$P_3\left(-\dfrac{\sqrt{3}}{2}, -\dfrac{1}{2}\right)$ **9.** 0   **11.** $\dfrac{\sqrt{2}}{2}$ **13.** 0   **15.** 0   **17.** $0, \pi, 2\pi$ **19.** $\dfrac{5\pi}{6}, \dfrac{7\pi}{6}$ **21.** $\dfrac{3\pi}{2}$

23. $\dfrac{\pi}{4}$ **25.** $0, \pi$ **27.** $\{x: 0 \le x \le \pi\}$ **33.** (a) $\dfrac{\pi}{4}, \dfrac{3\pi}{4}, \dfrac{5\pi}{4}, \dfrac{7\pi}{4}$ (b) $\dfrac{\pi}{4}, \dfrac{3\pi}{4}, \dfrac{5\pi}{4}, \dfrac{7\pi}{4}$

(c) $\dfrac{\pi}{6}, \dfrac{5\pi}{6}, \dfrac{7\pi}{6}, \dfrac{11\pi}{6}$

Exercises 1–4, pages 20–23

1. -0.26 **3.** -0.97 **5.** 0.87 **7.** 0.87 **9.** 0 **11.** $\frac{63}{65}$ **13.** $-\dfrac{\sqrt{2}}{10}$ **15.** 0.12 **17.** 0.99

19.

x	$\cos x$	$\sin x$
0	1	0
$\dfrac{\pi}{6}$	$\dfrac{\sqrt{3}}{2} \doteq 0.87$	$\dfrac{1}{2} = 0.50$
$\dfrac{\pi}{4}$	$\dfrac{\sqrt{2}}{2} \doteq 0.71$	$\dfrac{\sqrt{2}}{2} \doteq 0.71$
$\dfrac{\pi}{3}$	$\dfrac{1}{2} = 0.5$	$\dfrac{\sqrt{3}}{2} \doteq 0.87$

x	$\cos x$	$\sin x$
$\dfrac{\pi}{2}$	0	1
$-\dfrac{\pi}{6}$	$\dfrac{\sqrt{3}}{2} \doteq 0.87$	$-\dfrac{1}{2} = -0.50$
$-\dfrac{\pi}{4}$	$\dfrac{\sqrt{2}}{2} \doteq 0.71$	$-\dfrac{\sqrt{2}}{2} \doteq -0.71$
$-\dfrac{\pi}{2}$	0	-1

21. $\dfrac{\pi}{4}, \dfrac{5\pi}{4}$ **23.** $\dfrac{3\pi}{4}, \dfrac{7\pi}{4}$ **25.** $\frac{1}{2}$

Exercises 1–5, pages 26–27

1. $\cos\left(x - \dfrac{\pi}{2}\right) = \sin x$ **3.** $\cos(x - \pi) = -\cos x$ **5.** $\cos(2\pi - x) = \cos x$ **7.** (a) (2), (i)

(b) (12), (ii) (c) (5), (iii) (d) (6), (iii) (e) (9), (ii) (f) (1), (i) (g) (10), (i) (h) (3), (i) **21.** 0 **23.** 0

Exercises 1–6, pages 30–31

1. $\sin\dfrac{\pi}{6}$ **3.** $-\sin\dfrac{\pi}{3}$ **5.** $-\cos\dfrac{\pi}{3}$ **7.** $\sin\dfrac{\pi}{4}$ **9.** $-\cos\dfrac{\pi}{13}$ **11.** $\sin\dfrac{\pi}{4}$ **13.** $\sin\dfrac{5\pi}{12} = \dfrac{\sqrt{2} + \sqrt{6}}{4}$,

$\sin\dfrac{2\pi}{3} = \dfrac{\sqrt{3}}{2}$, $\sin\dfrac{11\pi}{12} = \dfrac{-\sqrt{2} + \sqrt{6}}{4}$ **15.** $\sin\dfrac{7\pi}{4} = -\dfrac{\sqrt{2}}{2}$, $\sin 2\pi = 0$, $\sin\dfrac{9\pi}{4} = \dfrac{\sqrt{2}}{2}$

17. $\frac{33}{65}$, II **19.** $-\frac{99}{65}$ **21.** $\frac{27}{65}$ **23.** $-\frac{63}{65}$, III or IV **25.** $\frac{27}{65}$ **27.** $\frac{99}{65}$ **29.** $\frac{16}{65}$, II **31.** $\frac{112}{65}$

33. $\frac{112}{65}$ **35.**

x	$\cos x$	$\sin x$
$\dfrac{\pi}{12}$	$\dfrac{\sqrt{2} + \sqrt{6}}{4} \doteq 0.97$	$\dfrac{\sqrt{6} - \sqrt{2}}{4} \doteq 0.26$
$\dfrac{5\pi}{12}$	$\dfrac{\sqrt{6} - \sqrt{2}}{4} \doteq 0.26$	$\dfrac{\sqrt{2} + \sqrt{6}}{4} \doteq 0.97$

37. π **39.** $\dfrac{\pi}{4}$

Exercises 1–7, pages 36–37

7. $\left(-\dfrac{5\pi}{6}, -\dfrac{1}{2}\right), \left(-\dfrac{\pi}{6}, -\dfrac{1}{2}\right), \left(\dfrac{7\pi}{6}, -\dfrac{1}{2}\right), \left(\dfrac{11\pi}{6}, -\dfrac{1}{2}\right)$ **9.** $(-2\pi, 0), (-\pi, 0), (0, 0), (\pi, 0),$

$(2\pi, 0)$ **11.** $\left(-\dfrac{7\pi}{6}, -\dfrac{\sqrt{3}}{2}\right), \left(-\dfrac{5\pi}{6}, -\dfrac{\sqrt{3}}{2}\right), \left(\dfrac{5\pi}{6}, -\dfrac{\sqrt{3}}{2}\right), \left(\dfrac{7\pi}{6}, -\dfrac{\sqrt{3}}{2}\right)$ **13.** $\left(-\dfrac{3\pi}{2}, 1\right),$

$\left(-\dfrac{\pi}{2}; -1\right), \left(\dfrac{\pi}{2}, 1\right), \left(\dfrac{3\pi}{2}, -1\right)$ **17.** (a) $\left\{-\dfrac{11\pi}{6}, -\dfrac{7\pi}{6}, -\dfrac{5\pi}{6}, -\dfrac{\pi}{6}, \dfrac{\pi}{6}, \dfrac{5\pi}{6}, \dfrac{7\pi}{6}, \dfrac{11\pi}{6}\right\}$

(b) $\left\{-\dfrac{7\pi}{4}, -\dfrac{5\pi}{4}, -\dfrac{3\pi}{4}, -\dfrac{\pi}{4}, \dfrac{\pi}{4}, \dfrac{3\pi}{4}, \dfrac{5\pi}{4}, \dfrac{7\pi}{4}\right\}$ (c) $\left\{-\dfrac{7\pi}{4}, -\dfrac{5\pi}{4}, -\dfrac{3\pi}{4}, -\dfrac{\pi}{4}, \dfrac{\pi}{4}, \dfrac{3\pi}{4}, \dfrac{5\pi}{4}, \dfrac{7\pi}{4}\right\}$

Exercises 1–8, pages 39–40

1.

x	0	$\dfrac{\pi}{6}$	$\dfrac{\pi}{4}$	$\dfrac{3\pi}{4}$	$\dfrac{5\pi}{6}$	π
$\dfrac{x}{2}$	0	$\dfrac{\pi}{12}$	$\dfrac{\pi}{8}$	$\dfrac{3\pi}{8}$	$\dfrac{5\pi}{12}$	$\dfrac{\pi}{2}$
$\cos\dfrac{x}{2}$	1	$\sqrt{\dfrac{1}{2}\left(1+\dfrac{\sqrt{3}}{2}\right)}$ $\doteq 0.96$	$\sqrt{\dfrac{1}{2}\left(1+\dfrac{\sqrt{2}}{2}\right)}$ $\doteq 0.92$	$\sqrt{\dfrac{1}{2}\left(1-\dfrac{\sqrt{2}}{2}\right)}$ $\doteq 0.39$	$\sqrt{\dfrac{1}{2}\left(1-\dfrac{\sqrt{3}}{2}\right)}$ $\doteq 0.26$	0
$\sin\dfrac{x}{2}$	0	$\sqrt{\dfrac{1}{2}\left(1-\dfrac{\sqrt{3}}{2}\right)}$ $\doteq 0.26$	$\sqrt{\dfrac{1}{2}\left(1-\dfrac{\sqrt{2}}{2}\right)}$ $\doteq 0.39$	$\sqrt{\dfrac{1}{2}\left(1+\dfrac{\sqrt{2}}{2}\right)}$ $\doteq 0.92$	$\sqrt{\dfrac{1}{2}\left(1+\dfrac{\sqrt{3}}{2}\right)}$ $\doteq 0.96$	1

3. (a) $-\dfrac{3}{5}$ (b) $-\dfrac{24}{25}$ (c) $\dfrac{2}{\sqrt{5}}$ (d) $-\dfrac{7}{25}$ (e) $\dfrac{1}{\sqrt{5}}$ **5.**

x	Quadrant			
	I	II	III	IV
$\dfrac{x}{2}$	I	I	II	II

Exercises 1–9, pages 42–43

1. $\sin x = 0.876$, $\cos x = 0.482$ **3.** $\sin x = 0.426$, $\cos x = 0.905$ **5.** $\sin x = 0.368$, $\cos x =$
-0.930 **7.** $\sin x = -0.661$, $\cos x = -0.750$ **9.** $\sin x = 0.339$, $\cos x = -0.941$ **11.** $\sin x =$
0.368, $\cos x = -0.930$ **13.** $\dfrac{0.21\pi}{2}$ **15.** $\dfrac{0.66\pi}{2}$ **17.** $\dfrac{3.79\pi}{2}$ **19.** $\dfrac{1.34\pi}{2}$

Chapter Test, page 45

1. $f(2p), f(0)$ **3.**

x	$\cos x$	$\sin x$
$\dfrac{2\pi}{3}$	$-\dfrac{1}{2}$	$\dfrac{\sqrt{3}}{2}$
$\dfrac{3\pi}{4}$	$-\dfrac{\sqrt{2}}{2}$	$\dfrac{\sqrt{2}}{2}$
$\dfrac{5\pi}{6}$	$-\dfrac{\sqrt{3}}{2}$	$\dfrac{1}{2}$

5. $\cos\left(\dfrac{\pi}{4} + x\right) = \dfrac{\sqrt{2}}{2}(\cos x - \sin x)$

9. 1.39π

Chapter 2   Four More Circular Functions

Exercises 2–1, pages 53–54

1. 1   **3.** $-\sqrt{3}$ **5.** $-\sqrt{3}$ **7.** 1   **9.** $\pm\frac{5}{12}$ **11.** $\pm\frac{5}{12}$ **19.** $\left(-\dfrac{\pi}{4}, -1\right)$ **21.** (a) $\sin x = \cos x = \dfrac{\sqrt{2}}{2}$ (b) $\sin x = -\dfrac{\sqrt{2}}{2}$, $\cos x = \dfrac{\sqrt{2}}{2}$ (c) $\sin x = \dfrac{\sqrt{3}}{2}$, $\cos x = \frac{1}{2}$ (d) $\sin x = -\frac{1}{2}$, $\cos x = \dfrac{\sqrt{3}}{2}$ **23.** (a) $x = \dfrac{\pi}{3}, \dfrac{4\pi}{3}$ (b) $x = -\dfrac{\pi}{3}, \dfrac{2\pi}{3}, \dfrac{5\pi}{3}$ (c) $-\dfrac{\pi}{3}, \dfrac{\pi}{3}, \dfrac{2\pi}{3}, \dfrac{4\pi}{3}, \dfrac{5\pi}{3}$

Exercises 2–2, pages 59–60

1.

x	$\sec x$	$\csc x$	$\cot x$
0	$\dfrac{1}{\cos 0} = 1$	$\dfrac{1}{\sin 0}$ undef.	$\dfrac{\cos 0}{\sin 0}$ undef.
$\dfrac{\pi}{6}$	$\dfrac{1}{\cos\frac{\pi}{6}} = \dfrac{2}{\sqrt{3}}$	$\dfrac{1}{\sin\frac{\pi}{6}} = 2$	$\dfrac{\cos\frac{\pi}{6}}{\sin\frac{\pi}{6}} = \sqrt{3}$
$\dfrac{\pi}{4}$	$\dfrac{1}{\cos\frac{\pi}{4}} = \sqrt{2}$	$\dfrac{1}{\sin\frac{\pi}{4}} = \sqrt{2}$	$\dfrac{\cos\frac{\pi}{4}}{\sin\frac{\pi}{4}} = 1$
$\dfrac{\pi}{3}$	$\dfrac{1}{\cos\frac{\pi}{3}} = 2$	$\dfrac{1}{\sin\frac{\pi}{3}} = \dfrac{2}{\sqrt{3}}$	$\dfrac{\cos\frac{\pi}{3}}{\sin\frac{\pi}{3}} = \dfrac{1}{\sqrt{3}}$
$\dfrac{\pi}{2}$	$\dfrac{1}{\cos\frac{\pi}{2}}$ undef.	$\dfrac{1}{\sin\frac{\pi}{2}} = 1$	$\dfrac{\cos\frac{\pi}{2}}{\sin\frac{\pi}{2}} = 0$

3. -2 **5.** -1 **7.** $\dfrac{1}{\sqrt{3}}$ **9.** -2 **11.** 1 **25.** $x = -\dfrac{3\pi}{4}, \dfrac{3\pi}{4}, \dfrac{5\pi}{4}$ **27.** $x = \dfrac{\pi}{2}$ **29.** $x = -\dfrac{5\pi}{6},$ $\dfrac{\pi}{6}, \dfrac{7\pi}{6}$

Exercises 2–3, page 63

3. $x = 0, x = \pi, x = 2\pi$ **5.** $x = 0, x = \pi, x = 2\pi$ **11.** (a) all $x \neq k\pi, k \in J$ (b) all $x \neq k\left(\dfrac{\pi}{2}\right), k \in J$

Exercises 2–5, pages 71–72

13. (a) 1 (b) $\sin x$ (c) 1 (d) 1 (e) $\cos x$ (f) 1 (g) $\sin x$ (h) $\tan x$ (i) $\cos x$ (j) $\tan x$
(k) 1 (l) 1 (m) $\cos x$

Chapter Test, page 73

1. $-\frac{4}{3}$ **5.** $\dfrac{2 \sin x}{\sin x \cot x + \cos x} = \tan x$

Chapter 3   *Applications of Circular Functions*

Exercises 3–1, pages 82–83

11. $\{y: 1 \le y \le 5\}$ **13.** $\{y: 1 \le y \le 2\}$ **15.** $\mathcal{R}$ **17.** 3 **19.** -5

Exercises 3–2, page 88

21. Any value of the form $\dfrac{\pi}{2} + 2k\pi, k \in J$

Exercises 3–3, page 92

1. amp. $= 2$, per. $= 2\pi$, phase shift $= -\dfrac{\pi}{4}$ **3.** amp. $= 1$, per. $= \dfrac{\pi}{2}$, phase shift $= \dfrac{\pi}{8}$ **5.** amp. not defined, per. $= \dfrac{\pi}{3}$, phase shift $= \dfrac{\pi}{6}$ **7.** amp. not defined, per. $= 8\pi$, phase shift $= -\dfrac{\pi}{2}$ **9.** amp. not defined, period $= \dfrac{\pi}{2}$, phase shift $= -\dfrac{\pi}{6}$ **11.** amp. $= 1$, per. $= 4$, phase shift $= -1$

13. $a = -1$, $c =$ any number of the form $(2k + 1)\dfrac{\pi}{2}, k \in J$ **15.** $x = (k + 1)\dfrac{\pi}{4}$ for $0 \le k \le 8$

Exercises 3–4, page 94

21. For example, $a = 5$, $c \doteq 0.41\left(\dfrac{\pi}{2}\right)$

Exercises 3–5, pages 98–100

1. π **3.** 3π **5.** $\dfrac{10\pi}{3}$ **7.** $\omega = 3\pi/\text{sec.}$; speed $= 15\pi$ in./sec.   **9.** π in.; $\omega = -\dfrac{\pi}{30}\Big/\text{min.}$

11. (a) $(0, 6)$ (b) $(0, -6)$ **13.** $\frac{12}{5}$; $\left(3 \cos \frac{6\pi}{5}, 3 \sin \frac{6\pi}{5}\right)$ **15.** 2; $\left(-\frac{3}{2}, \frac{3\sqrt{3}}{2}\right)$; 2π units

17. $u = 5 \cos\left(\omega t + \frac{\pi}{6}\right)$, $v = 5 \sin\left(\omega t + \frac{\pi}{6}\right)$

Exercises 3–6, page 103

1. -120 volts   **3.** 115 volts   **5.** $y = 3 \cos t$ **7.** $\pm a\omega$; 0; $t = \dfrac{2k\pi - b}{\omega}$; $t = \dfrac{(2k + 1)\pi - b}{\omega}$;

$t = \dfrac{(2k + 1)\dfrac{\pi}{2} - b}{\omega}$

Chapter Test, pages 104–105

7. $y = a \cos(\omega t + b)$, $y = a \sin(\omega t + b)$

Cumulative Review · Chapters 1–3, pages 106–107

1. $-\dfrac{\sqrt{35}}{6}$ **3.** 0 **5.** $2 \cos^2 x$ **11.** $-\frac{4}{3}$ **13.** $\cos x = -\frac{3}{5}$, $\sin x = \frac{4}{5}$, $\tan x = -\frac{4}{3}$, $\sec x = -\frac{5}{3}$,

$\cot x = -\frac{3}{4}$ **15.** $\csc x$ **17.** $\sec x$ **27.** 8π **29.** $\dfrac{9\pi}{2}$

Chapter 4   Inverses of Circular Functions

Exercises 4–1, pages 115–117

1. $y = 0$

3. $y = \dfrac{\pi}{4}$

5. $y = \dfrac{\pi}{3}$

7. $y = \dfrac{\pi}{6}$

9. $\dfrac{\pi}{3}$

11. $\dfrac{\pi}{3}$

13. 0.175π

15. 0.295π

17. 0.800

19. $\dfrac{\sqrt{2}}{2}$

21. $\dfrac{\pi}{6}$

23.

x	$\text{Cos}^{-1} x$	$\cos(\text{Cos}^{-1} x)$	$\text{Sin}^{-1} x$	$\sin(\text{Sin}^{-1} x)$
-1	π	-1	$-\dfrac{\pi}{2}$	-1
$-\dfrac{\sqrt{3}}{2}$	$\dfrac{5\pi}{6}$	$-\dfrac{\sqrt{3}}{2}$	$-\dfrac{\pi}{3}$	$-\dfrac{\sqrt{3}}{2}$
$-\dfrac{1}{2}$	$\dfrac{2\pi}{3}$	$-\dfrac{1}{2}$	$-\dfrac{\pi}{6}$	$-\dfrac{1}{2}$
0	$\dfrac{\pi}{2}$	0	0	0
$\dfrac{1}{2}$	$\dfrac{\pi}{3}$	$\dfrac{1}{2}$	$\dfrac{\pi}{6}$	$\dfrac{1}{2}$
$\dfrac{\sqrt{3}}{2}$	$\dfrac{\pi}{6}$	$\dfrac{\sqrt{3}}{2}$	$\dfrac{\pi}{3}$	$\dfrac{\sqrt{3}}{2}$
1	0	1	$\dfrac{\pi}{2}$	1

25. $\text{Cos}^{-1} x + \text{Sin}^{-1} x = \dfrac{\pi}{2}$ for each of the given values; $\text{Cos}^{-1} x + \text{Sin}^{-1} x = \dfrac{\pi}{2}$, $-1 \le x \le 1$

27. (a)

x	$\sin x$	$\text{Sin}^{-1}(\sin x)$
$-\dfrac{\pi}{2}$	-1	$-\dfrac{\pi}{2}$
0	0	0
$\dfrac{\pi}{2}$	1	$\dfrac{\pi}{2}$
π	0	0
$\dfrac{3\pi}{2}$	-1	$-\dfrac{\pi}{2}$
2π	0	0
$\dfrac{5\pi}{2}$	1	$\dfrac{\pi}{2}$
3π	0	0
$\dfrac{7\pi}{2}$	-1	$-\dfrac{\pi}{2}$

(c) yes; 2π

(d) $-\dfrac{\pi}{2} \le x \le \dfrac{\pi}{2}$

(e) $-\dfrac{\pi}{2} \le x \le \dfrac{\pi}{2}$; $-\dfrac{\pi}{2} \le x \le \dfrac{\pi}{2}$

Exercises 4–2, pages 120–122

1. $y = \dfrac{\pi}{3}$ **3.** $y = \dfrac{2\pi}{3}$ **5.** $y = \dfrac{\pi}{2}$ **7.** $\dfrac{\pi}{4}$ **9.** $\dfrac{\pi}{4}$ **11.** $-\dfrac{\pi}{3}$ **13.** $\dfrac{\pi}{6}$ **15.** 1 **17.** 1 **19.** $\sqrt{3}$

21. $\dfrac{\sqrt{3}}{2}$ **25.** $\text{Cot}(\text{Cot}^{-1} x) = x$, $x \in \Re$; $\text{Cot}^{-1}(\text{Cot } x) = x$, $0 < x < \pi$; $\text{Sec}(\text{Sec}^{-1} x) = x$, $|x| \ge 1$; $\text{Sec}^{-1}(\text{Sec } x) = x$, $0 \le x \le \pi$, $x \ne \dfrac{\pi}{2}$; $\text{Csc}(\text{Csc}^{-1} x) = x$, $|x| \ge 1$; $\text{Csc}^{-1}(\text{Csc } x) = x$, $-\dfrac{\pi}{2} \le x \le \dfrac{\pi}{2}$, $x \ne 0$

27. yes; π

Exercises 4–3, pages 126–127

1. $\dfrac{2\sqrt{2}}{3}$ **3.** $\dfrac{\sqrt{3}}{2}$ **5.** $\dfrac{\pi}{2}$ **7.** $\dfrac{\pi}{2}$ **9.** $\dfrac{1}{\sqrt{3}}$ **11.** $\dfrac{2}{\sqrt{3}}$ **13.** $\frac{5}{3}$ **15.** $\text{Arcsin}\left(-\dfrac{\sqrt{3}}{2}\right)$, Arcsin 0,

Arcsin $\frac{1}{2}$ **17.** Arccos 1, Arctan 1, Arcsin 1 **19.** $\dfrac{\sqrt{3}}{2}$ **21.** $\dfrac{\sqrt{6} + \sqrt{2}}{4}$ **23.** $\frac{24}{25}$ **25.** $-(2 + \sqrt{3})$

27. 1 **29. (a)** any real x such that $|x| < \dfrac{\pi}{2}$ **(b)** any real x such that $|x| > \dfrac{\pi}{2}$ **35. (a)** $\sqrt{\dfrac{1 - x}{2}}$

(b) $\sqrt{\dfrac{1 + \sqrt{1 - x^2}}{2}}$

Exercises 4–4, page 131

1. $\left\{\dfrac{\pi}{2}\right\}$ 3. $\left\{\dfrac{2\pi}{3}, \dfrac{4\pi}{3}\right\}$ 5. $\left\{\dfrac{\pi}{4}, \dfrac{3\pi}{4}, \dfrac{5\pi}{4}, \dfrac{7\pi}{4}\right\}$ 7. $\left\{0, \dfrac{\pi}{3}, \dfrac{2\pi}{3}, \pi, \dfrac{4\pi}{3}, \dfrac{5\pi}{3}\right\}$ 9. $\left\{\dfrac{2\pi}{3}, \pi, \dfrac{4\pi}{3}\right\}$

11. $\left\{\dfrac{3\pi}{4}, \dfrac{7\pi}{4}\right\}$ 13. $\left\{\dfrac{\pi}{6}, \dfrac{5\pi}{6}, \dfrac{7\pi}{6}, \dfrac{11\pi}{6}\right\}$ 15. $\left\{\dfrac{\pi}{2}, \dfrac{3\pi}{4}, \dfrac{3\pi}{2}, \dfrac{7\pi}{4}\right\}$ 17. $\left\{\dfrac{\pi}{8}, \dfrac{\pi}{4}, \dfrac{3\pi}{8}, \dfrac{5\pi}{8}, \dfrac{3\pi}{4}, \dfrac{7\pi}{8},\right.$

$\left. \dfrac{9\pi}{8}, \dfrac{5\pi}{4}, \dfrac{11\pi}{8}, \dfrac{13\pi}{8}, \dfrac{7\pi}{4}, \dfrac{15\pi}{8}\right\}$ 19. $\left\{\dfrac{2\pi}{3}, \dfrac{4\pi}{3}\right\}$ 21. $\{0\}$ 23. $\left\{x: x = \dfrac{\pi}{2} + k\pi, \dfrac{\pi}{3} + k\pi, \dfrac{2\pi}{3} + k\pi,\right.$

$\left. k \in J\right\}$ 25. $\left\{x: x = (2k + 1)\dfrac{\pi}{2}, k \in J\right\}$

Exercises 4–5, page 136

1. $\left\{0, \dfrac{\pi}{3}, \pi, \dfrac{5\pi}{3}\right\}$ 3. $\left\{0, \dfrac{\pi}{6}, \dfrac{5\pi}{6}, \pi\right\}$ 5. $\left\{0, \dfrac{\pi}{4}, \pi, \dfrac{5\pi}{4}\right\}$ 7. $\left\{\pi, \dfrac{7\pi}{6}, \dfrac{11\pi}{6}\right\}$ 9. $\left\{\dfrac{\pi}{2}\right\}$

11. $\left\{\dfrac{\pi}{6}, \dfrac{\pi}{2}, \dfrac{5\pi}{6}, \dfrac{3\pi}{2}\right\}$ 13. $\left\{0, \dfrac{\pi}{4}, \pi, \dfrac{5\pi}{4}\right\}$ 15. $\left\{\dfrac{\pi}{2}, \dfrac{3\pi}{2}\right\}$ 17. $x = \dfrac{1}{\sqrt{3}}$

19. $x = 0$ 21. $\left\{x: x = \dfrac{5\pi}{8} + k\pi \text{ or } x = \dfrac{7\pi}{8} + k\pi, k \in J\right\}$ 23. $\left\{x: x = (2k + 1)\dfrac{\pi}{2}, k \in J\right\}$

25. $\left\{x: x \doteq 1.41\dfrac{\pi}{2} + 2k\pi, 2.59\dfrac{\pi}{2} + 2k\pi, k \in J\right\}$ 27. $\left\{x: x = k\pi, \dfrac{\pi}{3} + 2k\pi, \dfrac{5\pi}{3} + 2k\pi, k \in J\right\}$

Chapter Test, page 138

1. $y = -\dfrac{\pi}{6}$ 3. 1 5. $\dfrac{2\pi}{3}$ 7. $\frac{4}{5}$ 9. $\left\{x: x = k\pi \text{ or } x = \dfrac{\pi}{4} + k\pi, k \in J\right\}$ 11. $\left\{\dfrac{2\pi}{3}, \dfrac{4\pi}{3}\right\}$

Chapter 5   Trigonometric Functions

Exercises 5–1, page 147

1. $45°$ 3. $120°$ 5. $720°$ 7. $648°$ 9. $\dfrac{\pi}{4}^R$ 11. $\dfrac{2\pi}{3}^R$ 13. $\dfrac{7\pi}{6}^R$ 15. $-\dfrac{5\pi}{6}^R$ 17. 25^C

19. $\frac{80}{9}^C$ 21. (a) $162°$ (b) $\dfrac{9\pi}{10}^R$ 23. (a) $936°$ (b) $\dfrac{26\pi}{5}^R$

Exercises 5–2, page 151

1.

$m^R(\theta)$	$m^\circ(\theta)$	$\cos\theta$	$\sin\theta$	$\tan\theta$
0	0	1	0	0
$\dfrac{\pi}{6}$	30	$\dfrac{\sqrt{3}}{2}$	$\dfrac{1}{2}$	$\dfrac{1}{\sqrt{3}}$
$\dfrac{\pi}{4}$	45	$\dfrac{\sqrt{2}}{2}$	$\dfrac{\sqrt{2}}{2}$	1
$\dfrac{\pi}{3}$	60	$\dfrac{1}{2}$	$\dfrac{\sqrt{3}}{2}$	$\sqrt{3}$
$\dfrac{\pi}{2}$	90	0	1	undef.
$\dfrac{2\pi}{3}$	120	$-\dfrac{1}{2}$	$\dfrac{\sqrt{3}}{2}$	$-\sqrt{3}$
$\dfrac{3\pi}{4}$	135	$-\dfrac{\sqrt{2}}{2}$	$\dfrac{\sqrt{2}}{2}$	-1
$\dfrac{5\pi}{6}$	150	$-\dfrac{\sqrt{3}}{2}$	$\dfrac{1}{2}$	$-\dfrac{1}{\sqrt{3}}$

3. $-\tan 30^\circ$ **5.** $\cos 80^\circ$ **7.** $-\sin 45^\circ$ **9.** $-\tan 60^\circ$ **11.** $-\cos 60^\circ$ **13.** $-\dfrac{\sqrt{3}}{2}$ **15.** $-\dfrac{\sqrt{3}}{2}$

17. $\dfrac{1}{\sqrt{3}}$ **19.** $-\dfrac{\sqrt{3}}{2}$

Exercises 5–4, pages 157–158

1. 0.5200   **3.** 1.090   **5.** 1.038   **7.** 0.9119   **9.** 0.8267   **11.** 0.9168   **13.** 1.860   **15.** 3.954
17. $36^\circ 20'$ **19.** $72^\circ 46'$ **21.** $33^\circ 5'$ **23.** $18^\circ 00'$ **25.** 0.63^R **27.** 1.27^R **29.** 0.58^R **31.** 0.31^R
33. -0.2588 **35.** 0.6249   **37.** -1.836 **39.** less than   **41.** either 0° or 90° **43.** less than

Exercises 5–5, page 161

1. $\cos\theta = -\dfrac{\sqrt{2}}{2}$, $\sin\theta = \dfrac{\sqrt{2}}{2}$, $\tan\theta = -1$, $\theta = 135^\circ$ **3.** $\cos\theta = \frac{3}{5}$, $\sin\theta = \frac{4}{5}$, $\tan\theta = \frac{4}{3}$,
$\theta \doteq 53^\circ 08'$ **5.** $\cos\theta = 1$, $\sin\theta = 0$, $\tan\theta = 0$, $\theta = 0^\circ$ **7.** $\cos\theta = \dfrac{\sqrt{10}}{10}$, $\sin\theta = -\dfrac{3\sqrt{10}}{10}$,
$\tan\theta = -3$, $\theta \doteq 288^\circ 26'$ **9.** $\cos\theta = \frac{1}{2}$, $\sin\theta = -\dfrac{\sqrt{3}}{2}$, $\tan\theta = -\sqrt{3}$, $\theta = 300^\circ$ **11.** $(-1, \sqrt{3})$
13. $(-2\sqrt{3}, -2)$ **15.** $(0, 5)$ **17.** $(2.298, -1.9284)$ **19.** $\cos\theta = -\dfrac{\sqrt{2}}{2}$, $\sin\theta = -\dfrac{\sqrt{2}}{2}$
21. $\cos\theta = 0$, $\sin\theta = 1$ **23.** $\cos\theta = \frac{1}{2}$, $\sin\theta = \dfrac{\sqrt{3}}{2}$

Exercises 5–6, pages 163–164

1. Domain = $\{x: |x| \leq 1, x \in \Re\}$, Range = $\left\{y: |y| \leq \dfrac{\pi}{2}, y \in \Re\right\}$ **3.** Domain = $\Re$, Range = $\left\{y: |y| < \dfrac{\pi}{2}, y \in \Re\right\}$ **5.** Domain = $\{x: |x| \geq 1, x \in \Re\}$, Range = $\left\{y: |y| < \dfrac{\pi}{2}, y \neq 0, y \in \Re\right\}$

7. 45° **9.** $\dfrac{\sqrt{3}}{2}$ **11.** 90° **13.** $\{0°, 120°, 180°, 300°\}$ **15.** $\{30°, 90°, 150°\}$ **17.** $\{60°, 120°, 240°, 300°\}$

19. $\{0°, 45°, 90°, 180°, 225°, 270°\}$ **21.** $\cos = \frac{1}{2}$, $\sin = \dfrac{\sqrt{3}}{2}$, $\tan = \sqrt{3}$ **23.** $\cos = \dfrac{\sqrt{3}}{2}$, $\sin = \frac{1}{2}$, $\tan = \dfrac{1}{\sqrt{3}}$ **25.** 1 **27.** $\dfrac{3}{\sqrt{10}}$

Exercises 5–7, pages 168–169

1. $a = 5$, $B \doteq 67°23'$, $A \doteq 22°37'$ **3.** $B = 54°$, $a \doteq 7.64$, $b \doteq 10.52$ **5.** $A = 25°45'$, $a \doteq 8.69$, $b \doteq 18.01$ **7.** $b \doteq 17.32$, $A = 30°$, $B = 60°$ **9.** 46° **11.** 10 in. **17.** $\dfrac{1}{\sqrt{1 - x^2}}$ **19.** $\dfrac{\sqrt{1 - x^2}}{x}$

21. $\dfrac{1}{\sqrt{2 - x^2}}$ **23.** 294 ft., 49 ft. **25.** 3760 ft.

Exercises 5–8, pages 172–173

1. 2.5 **3.** 5.3 **5.** 8.5 **7.** 92°50' **9.** 47°30' **11.** 51.4 mi. **13.** 17.8 cm., 7.3 cm.
15. 811.3 m.

Exercises 5–9, pages 175–176

1. 60 **3.** 169.0 **5.** 218.8 **7.** 4.9 **9.** 23°30' **11.** 6°10' **13.** 4.9 mi., 11.3 mi. **15.** 9.3 ft.

Exercises 5–10, page 179

1. $B \doteq 35°50'$, $A \doteq 102°10'$, $a \doteq 11.68$ **3.** $C \doteq 47°31'$, $A \doteq 97°27'$, $a \doteq 12.10$; or $C \doteq 132°29'$, $A \doteq 12°31'$, $a \doteq 2.64$ **5.** $B \doteq 59°56'$, $C \doteq 33°4'$, $c \doteq 8.19$ **7.** 3.13×10^7 mi. or 1.33×10^8 mi.

Chapter Test, page 180

1. (a) $\dfrac{12\pi^R}{5}$ (b) $-25°$ **3.** (a) $\frac{1}{2}$ (b) $\dfrac{2}{\sqrt{3}}$ **5.** 0.8454 **7.** $\{0°, 180°\}$ **9.** 13 **11.** (a) none
(b) 2 (c) none or one

Chapter 6   Vectors

Exercises 6–1, pages 190–191

1. $\|\mathbf{u}\| = \sqrt{10}$, $\|\mathbf{v}\| = 2\sqrt{10}$ **3.** $\|\mathbf{u}\| = 10$, $\|\mathbf{v}\| = 5$ **5.** $\|\mathbf{u}\| = \sqrt{17}$, $\|\mathbf{v}\| = \sqrt{17}$ **7.** (2, 2)
9. $(-3, 0)$ **11.** $(-4\sqrt{2}, -4\sqrt{2})$ **13.** $(-2, 10)$ **15.** $(-11, 16)$ **17.** (8, 12) **19.** $(-4, 7)$
21. $(-5, -8)$ **23.** $(4, -1)$ **25.** $(2, -3)$ **27.** $(-1, 4)$

Exercises 6–2, pages 196–197

1. (a) $1\mathbf{i} + 3\mathbf{j}$ (b) $-23\mathbf{i} + (-4)\mathbf{j}$ **3.** (a) $4\mathbf{i} + 8\mathbf{j}$ (b) $-12\mathbf{i} + 16\mathbf{j}$ **5.** (a) $10\frac{1}{3}\mathbf{i} + 1\frac{1}{3}\mathbf{j}$
(b) $19\mathbf{i} + 6\mathbf{j}$ **7.** (a) $5\sqrt{2}\left(-\dfrac{1}{\sqrt{2}}, \dfrac{1}{\sqrt{2}}\right)$ (b) $135°$ **9.** (a) $5\sqrt{2}\left(\dfrac{7}{5\sqrt{2}}, \dfrac{1}{5\sqrt{2}}\right)$ (b) $8°$

11. (a) $\sqrt{6}\left(\dfrac{1}{\sqrt{2}}, \dfrac{1}{\sqrt{2}}\right)$ (b) $45°$ **13.** $\left(\dfrac{1}{\sqrt{2}}, -\dfrac{1}{\sqrt{2}}\right)$ **15.** $\left(\dfrac{1}{2}, \dfrac{3}{2\sqrt{3}}\right)$ **17.** $(\cos 45°, \sin 45°)$,

or $\left(\dfrac{1}{\sqrt{2}}, \dfrac{1}{\sqrt{2}}\right)$ **19.** $0\mathbf{i} + 7\mathbf{j}$ **21.** $-9.397\mathbf{i} + 3.420\mathbf{j}$ **23.** $\left(\dfrac{\sqrt{3}-1}{2}\right)\mathbf{k} - \left(\dfrac{\sqrt{3}+1}{2}\right)\mathbf{m}$

25. $\left(\dfrac{3+\sqrt{3}}{2}\right)\mathbf{k} - \left(\dfrac{1-3\sqrt{3}}{2}\right)\mathbf{m}$ **27.** $\mathbf{k} - \mathbf{m}$

Exercises 6–3, page 203

1. 1 **3.** 0 **5.** 29 **7.** 26 **9.** $75°$ **11.** $45°$ **13.** $150°$ **15.** $\sqrt{3}\,\mathbf{u} - \mathbf{v}$ **17.** $\dfrac{\sqrt{3}}{2}\mathbf{u} + \dfrac{1}{2}\mathbf{v}$
19. $\left(\dfrac{1-\sqrt{3}}{2}\right)\mathbf{u} + \left(\dfrac{1+\sqrt{3}}{2}\right)\mathbf{v}$

Exercises 6–4, pages 209–211

1. 136 mi., $98°$ **3.** $94°$, 226 mph **5.** $79°$, 204 mph **7.** 7 knots **9.** 45 naut. mi., $191°$
11. $65°$, 1:14 P.M.

Exercises 6–5, pages 215–216

1. 433 lb., 250 lb. **3.** 14 lb. **5.** 86 lb., 105 lb. **7.** 34 lb., $327°$ **9.** 502 lb., 576 lb.

Exercises 6–6, pages 223–224

1. $(-3, 0)$ **3.** $(1, \sqrt{3})$ **5.** $(\sqrt{3}, 1)$ **7.** $(-1, \sqrt{3})$ **9.** $\left(3\sqrt{2}, \dfrac{\pi}{4}^{R}\right)$ **11.** $\left(1, \dfrac{11\pi}{6}^{R}\right)$
13. $\left(5, \dfrac{4\pi}{3}^{R}\right)$ **15.** $(5, 53°10')$ **17.** $\rho \cos\theta = 4$ **19.** $\rho \sin\theta = 2$ **21.** $\rho(\cos\theta + \sin\theta) = 0$,
or $\theta = 135°$ **23.** $\rho^2 = 16$ **31.** $x^2 + y^2 = 36$ **33.** $y = -x$ **35.** $(x^2 + y^2)^3 = 16y^2$
37. $\{(4, 90°)\}$ **39.** $\{(3, 120°)\}$

Chapter Test, page 232

1. (a) $\sqrt{26}$ (b) $(5, -29)$ **3.** (a) $2\sqrt{10}\left(-\dfrac{1}{\sqrt{10}}, \dfrac{3}{\sqrt{10}}\right)$ (b) $\cos\theta = -\dfrac{1}{\sqrt{10}}$, $\sin\theta = \dfrac{3}{\sqrt{10}}$

5. 69.9 mi., $\tan\theta = \dfrac{-4}{4 + \sqrt{3}}$ **7.** For example, $(-4, 255°)$, $(4, 435°)$, $(-4, 615°)$

Cumulative Review · Chapters 4–6, pages 232–233

1. $\dfrac{4\pi}{3}, \dfrac{5\pi}{3}$ **3.** $\dfrac{2\pi}{3}, \dfrac{5\pi}{3}$ **5.** $-\dfrac{\pi}{2}$ **7.** $\dfrac{4}{5}$ **9.** $x = \dfrac{\pi}{2}, \dfrac{3\pi}{2}$ or $\dfrac{3\pi}{4}, \dfrac{7\pi}{4}$ **11.** $210°$ **13.** (a) 0.2679

(b) 0.5000 **15.** $\sin\theta = -\dfrac{5}{\sqrt{29}}, \cos\theta = \dfrac{2}{\sqrt{29}}$ **17.** $A = 36°, a \doteq 87, c \doteq 148$ **19.** 16.67

21. (a) 7 **(b)** $(-1, 35)$ **23.** $5(\frac{4}{5}, -\frac{3}{5})$ **25.** $x = -12$ **27.** $75°$ **29.** normal component $\doteq$ 138 lb., parallel component $= 80$ lb.

Chapter 7   Complex Numbers

Exercises 7–1, page 242

1. (a) $(4, 8)$ **(b)** $(-9, 20)$ **3.** (a) $(9, 9)$ **(b)** $(12, 44)$ **5.** (a) $(3\frac{1}{2}, 2\frac{1}{2})$ **(b)** $(0, 6\frac{1}{6})$ **7.** (a) $(0, 2)$
(b) $(-2, 2)$ **9.** (a) $(-1, 0)$ **(b)** $(0, -1)$ **11.** (a) $(1, -2\sqrt{6})$ **(b)** $(-3\sqrt{3}, -7\sqrt{2})$

Exercises 7–2, page 245

1. $(-4, 0); (4, 0)$ **3.** $(-12, 0); (\frac{4}{3}, 0)$ **5.** $(0, 8); (0, 2)$ **7.** (a) $(-3, -1)$ **(b)** $(\frac{4}{25}, -\frac{3}{25})$
(c) $(4, -3)$ **(d)** $(\frac{2}{5}, \frac{1}{5})$ **9.** (a) $(-3, -4)$ **(b)** $(\frac{1}{17}, -\frac{4}{17})$ **(c)** $(1, -4)$ **(d)** $(-\frac{2}{17}, \frac{8}{17})$
11. (a) $(8, 0)$ **(b)** $(\frac{1}{4}, 0)$ **(c)** $(4, 0)$ **(d)** $(3, 0)$ **13.** $(\frac{11}{5}, \frac{7}{5})$ **15.** $\left(\dfrac{2}{7}, \dfrac{3\sqrt{6}}{14}\right)$ **17.** $(2\sqrt{3}, -\sqrt{2})$

Exercises 7–3, pages 248–249

1. (a) $8 + 5i$ **(b)** $-2 - i$ **(c)** $9 + 19i$ **(d)** $\frac{21}{34} + \frac{1}{34}i$ **3.** (a) $17 - 3i$ **(b)** $-3 + 5i$ **(c)** $74 - 18i$
(d) $\frac{33}{58} + \frac{19}{58}i$ **5.** (a) $6 + 3i$ **(b)** $-6 + 3i$ **(c)** $18i$ **(d)** $\frac{1}{2}i$ **7.** (a) $(\sqrt{3} - 1)i$ **(b)** $(\sqrt{3} + 1)i$
(c) $\sqrt{3}$ **(d)** $-\sqrt{3}$ **9.** (c) **11.** (c) **13.** (c) **15.** (c) **17.** $-2i$ **19.** $21 - 20i$ **21.** $18i$
23. -9 **25.** $(a^2 - b^2) + 2abi$ **27.** $x = 3$ **29.** $x = 5$ **31.** $x = \dfrac{\pi}{3}$ **33.** $x = \dfrac{2\pi}{3}$
35. $x = 0, \dfrac{\pi}{2}, \pi, \dfrac{3\pi}{2}$

Exercises 7–4, page 254

13. $-i$ **15.** -1 **17.** 1 **19.** i **21.** $9 + 5i$ **23.** $6 + 12i$ **25.** -4 **27.** $\frac{3}{5} + \frac{1}{5}i$ **29.** i

Exercises 7–5, pages 257–258

1. $\dfrac{\sqrt{3}}{2} + \frac{1}{2}i$ **3.** $0 + i$ **5.** $2\sqrt{2} - 2\sqrt{2}\,i$ **7.** $\cos 60° + i\sin 60°$ **9.** $2(\cos 300° + i\sin 300°)$
11. $\sqrt{2}\,(\cos 45° + i\sin 45°)$ **13.** $6(\cos 90° + i\sin 90°)$ **15.** $3\sqrt{5}\,(\cos 333°30' + i\sin 333°30')$
17. (a) $6i$ **(b)** $\dfrac{\sqrt{3}}{3} + \frac{1}{3}i$ **19.** (a) -50 **(b)** $1 + \sqrt{3}\,i$ **21.** (a) $4(\cos 0° + i\sin 0°)$
(b) $2(\cos 90° + i\sin 90°)$ **23.** (a) $15\sqrt{2}\,(\cos 225° + i\sin 225°)$ **(b)** $\dfrac{3\sqrt{2}}{10}(\cos 315° + i\sin 315°)$

Exercises 7–6, pages 260–261

1. $32 + 32\sqrt{3}\,i$ **3.** $\dfrac{1}{2000} + \dfrac{\sqrt{3}}{2000}i$ **5.** -8 **7.** $-\frac{81}{4}$ **9.** $\frac{1}{9}i$ **11.** $64 + 64i$ **13.** -4

Exercises 7–7, page 264

1. $1, -\dfrac{1}{2} + \dfrac{\sqrt{3}}{2}\,i, -\dfrac{1}{2} - \dfrac{\sqrt{3}}{2}\,i$ **3.** $\sqrt{3} + i, -1 + \sqrt{3}\,i, -\sqrt{3} - i, 1 - \sqrt{3}\,i$ **5.** $1.98 + 0.31i$, $0.31 + 1.98i$, $-1.78 + 0.91i$, $-1.41 - 1.41i$, $0.91 - 1.78i$ **7.** $\{\cos 0° + i\sin 0°, \cos 72° + i\sin 72°, \cos 144° + i\sin 144°, \cos 216° + i\sin 216°, \cos 288° + i\sin 288°\}$ **9.** $\{2(\cos 80° + i\sin 80°), 2(\cos 200° + i\sin 200°), 2(\cos 320° + i\sin 320°)\}$ **13.** $0; 0$ **15.** $\{\sqrt[8]{8}\,(\cos 33.75° + i\sin 33.75°), \sqrt[8]{8}\,(\cos 303.75° + i\sin 303.75°), \sqrt[8]{8}\,(\cos 213.75° + i\sin 213.75°), \sqrt[8]{8}\,(\cos 123.75° + i\sin 123.75°)\}$

Chapter Test, page 266

1. (a) $(6, 2)$ (b) $(13, 18)$ **3.** $x = -2$ **5.** $-10 + 11i$ **7.** (a) $2\sqrt{2}\,(\cos 15° + i\sin 15°)$ (b) $\dfrac{\sqrt{2}}{2}\,(\cos 75° + i\sin 75°)$ **9.** $\{\cos 15° + i\sin 15°, \cos 105° + i\sin 105°, \cos 195° + i\sin 195°, \cos 285° + i\sin 285°\}$

Chapter 8   Matrices

Exercises 8–1, pages 275–276

1. $\begin{bmatrix} 1 & 3 \\ 1 & -3 \end{bmatrix}$ **3.** $\begin{bmatrix} 3 & -1 \\ 11 & 3 \end{bmatrix}$ **5.** $\begin{bmatrix} 3 & 9 \\ 3 & -9 \end{bmatrix}$ **7.** $8\begin{bmatrix} 1 & 0 \\ 0 & 1 \end{bmatrix}$ **9.** $3\begin{bmatrix} 2 & 7 \\ -5 & 0 \end{bmatrix}$ **11.** $\dfrac{1}{12}\begin{bmatrix} -96 & 4 \\ 12 & 9 \end{bmatrix}$

13. $X = \begin{bmatrix} 3 & 0 \\ 0 & 3 \end{bmatrix}$ **15.** $X = \begin{bmatrix} -\frac{3}{2} & -\frac{1}{2} \\ \frac{1}{2} & -\frac{11}{2} \end{bmatrix}$ **17.** $X = \begin{bmatrix} 3 & -\frac{5}{2} \\ -\frac{3}{2} & 2 \end{bmatrix}$ **19.** $X = \begin{bmatrix} -1 & 1 \\ 1 & -1 \end{bmatrix}$

Exercises 8–2, page 281

1. $\begin{bmatrix} 0 & 11 \\ -4 & -15 \end{bmatrix}$ **3.** $\begin{bmatrix} 1 & 3 \\ -1 & 2 \end{bmatrix}$ **5.** $\begin{bmatrix} 9 & 18 \\ 7 & 1 \end{bmatrix}$ **7.** $\begin{bmatrix} 13 & -21 \\ 8 & -13 \end{bmatrix}$ **9.** $\begin{bmatrix} 1 & 1 \\ -8 & 8 \end{bmatrix}$ **11.** $\begin{bmatrix} -3 & -3 \\ -72 & 32 \end{bmatrix}$

13. $x_1 = 4, x_2 = 1$ **15.** $x_1 = -2, x_2 = -1$ **17.** $x_1 = 2, x_2 = 6$ **25.** $c = a^2$

Exercises 8–3, pages 284–287

1. $\begin{bmatrix} \frac{3}{5} & -\frac{1}{5} \\ \frac{2}{5} & \frac{1}{5} \end{bmatrix}$ **3.** no inverse **5.** $\begin{bmatrix} \frac{\sqrt{3}}{2} & \frac{1}{2} \\ -\frac{1}{2} & \frac{\sqrt{3}}{2} \end{bmatrix}$ **7.** $\begin{bmatrix} -\frac{6}{5} & \frac{12}{5} \\ \frac{12}{5} & -\frac{9}{5} \end{bmatrix}$ **9.** $x = 0, y = -4$ **11.** $x = 3$, $y = -2$ **13.** $x = 5, y = 14$ **25.** $x^2 - 7x + 8 = 0; \dfrac{7 \pm \sqrt{17}}{2}$

Exercises 8–4, page 290

1. $\begin{bmatrix} 7 & -1 \\ 1 & 7 \end{bmatrix}, 7 - i$ **3.** $\begin{bmatrix} 5 & -3 \\ 3 & 5 \end{bmatrix}, 5 - 3i$ **5.** $\begin{bmatrix} 6 & -8 \\ 8 & 6 \end{bmatrix}, 6 - 8i$ **7.** $\begin{bmatrix} 0 & 2 \\ -2 & 0 \end{bmatrix}, 2i$

9. $6\left(\cos \dfrac{\pi}{2} + i\sin \dfrac{\pi}{2}\right), 0 + 6i$ **11.** $4(\cos 30° + i\sin 30°), 2\sqrt{3} + 2i$ **17.** $2 - i$ **19.** $\sqrt{2} + \sqrt{2}\,i$

Exercises 8–5, pages 296–298

1. magnification   **3.** reflection in the origin and magnification   **5.** reflection in the x-axis and stretching   **7.** reflection in the line $y = x$ and in the y-axis   **9.** magnification   **11.** reflection in the origin   **13.** shrinking and reflection in the x-axis   **15.** reflection in the line $y = -x$ **17.** reflection in the origin   **19.** reflection in the origin   **21.** reflection in the y-axis   **23.** reflection in the x-axis   **25.** $\begin{bmatrix} 1 & 0 \\ 0 & -1 \end{bmatrix}$ **27.** $\begin{bmatrix} -1 & 0 \\ 0 & 1 \end{bmatrix}$ **29.** $\begin{bmatrix} \frac{1}{2} & 0 \\ 0 & 1 \end{bmatrix}$

Exercises 8–6, pages 301–302

1. $(0, 0), \left(\frac{3}{2}, \frac{\sqrt{3}}{2}\right), (1, 3\sqrt{3})$ **3.** $(0, 0), (1, \sqrt{3}), (1 - \sqrt{3}, 1 + \sqrt{3}), (-\sqrt{3}, 1)$ **5.** $(-1, -1), (0, -2), (1, -1)$ **7.** $(0, 0), \left(\frac{3}{2}, -\frac{\sqrt{3}}{2}\right), (5, \sqrt{3})$ **9.** $(0, 0), (1, -\sqrt{3}), (1 + \sqrt{3}, 1 - \sqrt{3}), (\sqrt{3}, 1)$ **11.** $(-1, 1), (-2, 0), (-1, -1)$ **13.** $\begin{bmatrix} 0 & -1 \\ 1 & 0 \end{bmatrix}$ **15.** $\begin{bmatrix} -\dfrac{27\sqrt{2}}{34} & -\dfrac{11\sqrt{2}}{34} \\ \dfrac{11\sqrt{2}}{4} & -\dfrac{27\sqrt{2}}{34} \end{bmatrix}$

Chapter Test, page 303

1. $\begin{bmatrix} 2 & 8 \\ -6 & -8 \end{bmatrix}$ **3.** $\begin{bmatrix} 0 & 5 \\ 0 & -1 \end{bmatrix}$ **5.** $x_1 = 3, x_2 = -11$ **7.** magnification and reflection in the origin   **9.** reflection in the y-axis

Chapter 9   Infinite Series and Circular Functions

Exercises 9–1, page 311

1. 3, 6, 9, 12   **3.** $3, \frac{5}{3}, \frac{7}{5}, \frac{9}{7}$ **5.** $\frac{1}{2}, \frac{1}{4}, \frac{1}{8}, \frac{1}{16}$ **7.** $i, -1, -i, 1$ **9.** 1   **11.** 0   **13.** 0   **15.** 2   **17.** 1   **19.** 1

Exercises 9–2, pages 314–315

1. $2, \frac{7}{2}, \frac{29}{6}, \frac{73}{12}$ **3.** $-1, -\frac{1}{2}, -\frac{5}{6}, -\frac{7}{12}$ **5.** $2, 3, 3\frac{2}{3}, 4\frac{1}{6}$ **7.** 1, 3, 7, 15   **9.** 1, 5, 32, 288   **11.** $1, -2, 5, -10$ **13.** 55   **15.** $\frac{422}{243}$ **17.** $\frac{709}{420}$

Exercises 9–3, pages 318–319

1. $\frac{4}{27}$ **3.** $\frac{40}{27}$ **5.** $\frac{364}{9}$ **7.** 24   **9.** 54   **11.** $\frac{2}{9}$ **13.** $\frac{91}{333}$ **15.** $\frac{86}{37}$ **17.** $\frac{247}{300}$

Exercises 9–4, page 323

1. $\{x: |x| < 1\}$ **3.** $\{x: |x| < 1\}$ **5.** $\{x: |x| < 1\}$ **7.** $\{x: |x| < 2\}$ **9.** $\mathcal{R}$ **11.** (a) $\frac{3}{2} + \frac{5}{12}x + \frac{7}{36}x^2 + \frac{9}{80}x^3$ (b) $\frac{1}{2} + \frac{7}{24}x + \frac{13}{72}x^2 + \frac{521}{4320}x^3$

Exercises 9–5, pages 326–327

1. $n(n - 1)$ **3.** $\frac{n + 2}{n + 4}$ **5.** $(2n + 2)(2n + 1)$ **7.** $1 + 8x + 28x^2 + 56x^3$ **9.** $1 - \frac{10}{x} + \frac{45}{x^2} - \frac{120}{x^3}$

11. 1.01   **13.** 0.82   **15.** $\{x: -3 < x < -1\}$ **17.** $\{x: 1 < x < 3\}$ **19.** 2.7183

21. $1 - x + \dfrac{x^2}{2!} - \dfrac{x^3}{3!} + \cdots + \dfrac{(-1)^r x^r}{r!} + \cdots$

Exercises 9–6, pages 331–332

1. 0.10   **3.** 0.54   **5.** 0.48   **7.** 0.87   **9.** $\sin \dfrac{x}{2} = \dfrac{x}{2} - \dfrac{x^3}{2^3(3!)} + \cdots + (-1)^{n+1} \dfrac{x^{2n-1}}{2^{2n-1}(2n-1)!}$

11. $\sin 2x = 2x - \dfrac{2^3 x^3}{3!} + \cdots + (-1)^{n+1} \dfrac{2^{2n-1} x^{2n-1}}{(2n-1)!}$

Exercises 9–7, page 335

9. 1.543   **11.** -0.521

Chapter Test, page 337

1. $\frac{1}{3}$ **3.** (a) $\frac{43}{30}$ (b) $\frac{3}{4}$ **5.** (a) $6, \frac{15}{2}, \frac{63}{8}$ (b) 8   **7.** 1.02   **9.** $0 + i$

Cumulative Review · Chapters 7–9, pages 338–339

1. $(2, -3)$ **3.** $(-14, 32)$ **5.** $\left(-\frac{17}{10}, \frac{2}{5}\right)$ **7.** $-\frac{1}{10} - \frac{7}{10}i$ **9.** $\cos 240° + i \sin 240°$

11. $\frac{5}{2}(\cos 60° + i \sin 60°)$ **13.** $\begin{bmatrix} 1 & 14 \\ 2 & 4 \end{bmatrix}$ **15.** $\begin{bmatrix} -5 & -7 \\ 6 & 11 \end{bmatrix}$ **17.** $\begin{bmatrix} -\frac{1}{2} & -1 \\ \frac{1}{2} & 2 \end{bmatrix}$ **19.** $\begin{bmatrix} 7 & 11 \\ -11 & 7 \end{bmatrix}$,

$7 + 11i$ **21.** magnification and reflection in the y-axis   **23.** $(0, 0), (-\sqrt{3}, 1), (-1, -\sqrt{3})$

25. $\frac{5}{6}, \frac{8}{7}, \frac{11}{8}, \frac{14}{9}$ **27.** $1, \frac{5}{2}, \frac{43}{10}, \frac{63}{10}$ **29.** $n^3 - n$ **31.** 0.39

Comprehensive Test   pages 345–355

Chapter 1

1. (b)   **3.** (a)   **5.** (c)   **7.** (b)   **9.** (d)

Chapter 2

1. (a)   **3.** (b)   **5.** (b)   **7.** (c)   **9.** (c)

Chapter 3

1. (c)   **3.** (b)   **5.** (a)   **7.** (a)

Chapter 4

1. (b)   **3.** (d)   **5.** (b)   **7.** (b)

Chapter 5

1. (b)   **3.** (d)   **5.** (a)   **7.** (c)   **9.** (b)

Chapter 6

1. (a)   **3.** (c)   **5.** (c)   **7.** (c)

Chapter 7

1. (b)   **3.** (d)   **5.** (b)   **7.** (b)

Chapter 8

1. (c)   **3.** (b)   **5.** (d)   **7.** (d)

Chapter 9

1. (b)   **3.** (a)   **5.** (c)   **7.** (b)

Appendix B   Using Logarithms

Exercises B–1, pages 371–372

1. 1   **3.** 0   **5.** -2 **7.** $\log_{10} 235 + \log_{10} 172$ **9.** $18 \log_{10} 28$ **11.** $\log_{10} 81.7 - \log_{10} 23.9$
13. $\log_{10} 21.2 + 2 \log_{10} 7.6 - \log_{10} 1.15$ **15.** $\log_{10} 21.3 + \frac{1}{6} \log_{10} 5 - \log_{10} 6.1 - 2 \log_{10} 8.7$
17. $\log_{10} 8.3 + 1$ **19.** $\log_{10} 6.75 - 1$ **21.** $\log_{10} 8.231 + 2$

Exercises B–2, page 375

1. 0.9652   **3.** 1.7782   **5.** $8.1461 - 10$ **7.** 5.8573   **9.** 0.3377   **11.** $8.1881 - 10$ **13.** 25.4
15. 0.487   **17.** 0.0751   **19.** 4.007   **21.** 0.8366   **23.** 399,600

Exercises B–3, pages 377–378

17. 21,650   **19.** 3.526   **21.** 6016   **23.** 0.5896   **25.** 21.30   **27.** 7.582   **29.** 1.084   **31.** 3.393

Exercises B–4, page 379

1. $9.8050 - 10$ **3.** $9.9882 - 10$ **5.** 0.2930   **7.** $7.8352 - 10$ **9.** 0.0145   **11.** $31°10'$
13. $58°20'$ **15.** $40°49'$ **17.** $8°25'$ **19.** $39°5'$

Exercises B–5, page 381

1. $a \doteq 44.6, c \doteq 93.4, B = 61°28'$ **3.** $A \doteq 28°11', B \doteq 61°49', b \doteq 14.98$ **5.** $A \doteq 22°37',$
$B \doteq 67°23', c \doteq 13.08$ **7.** $A = 75°, b \doteq 2.52, c \doteq 5.043$ **9.** $C = 83°40', a \doteq 34.66, b \doteq 76.03$

Appendix C   Spherical Trigonometry

Exercises C–1, page 384

1. (a) $34°$ **(b)** 2040 naut. mi.   **3. (a)** $63°$ **(b)** 3780 naut. mi.   **5. (a)** $15°$ **(b)** 900 naut. mi.

Exercises C–2, pages 386–387

1. $c \doteq 100°43', A \doteq 113°9', B \doteq 66°29'$ **3.** $b \doteq 70°, c \doteq 73°51', A \doteq 37°17'$ **5.** $c = 90°,$
$b = 90°, B = 90°$ **9.** $c \doteq 39°14', b \doteq 13°9', B \doteq 21°5',$ or $c \doteq 140°46', b \doteq 166°51', B \doteq 158°55'$
11. $c \doteq 13°32', b \doteq 8°38', B \doteq 39°58',$ or $c \doteq 166°28', b \doteq 171°22', B \doteq 140°2'$

Exercises C–4, page 388

1. $A \doteq 5°20', B \doteq 3°31', C \doteq 175°23'$

Exercises C–5, page 389

1. $a \doteq 38°48', b \doteq 106°39', c \doteq 124°18'$

Appendix D   Graphs of Pure Waves

1. $y = -5 \cos (x + 2.21)$ **3.** $y = 5 \cos (x + 0.93)$ **5.** $y = -2 \cos \left(2x + \frac{5\pi}{6} \right)$